Historical Geology

A SERIES OF BOOKS IN Geology

EDITORS: James Gilluly, A. O. Woodford

Drawing by Chas. Addams; © 1963 The New Yorker Magazine, Inc.

A. O. WOODFORD

Pomona College, Claremont, California

Historical Geology

W. H. FREEMAN AND COMPANY

 San Francisco and London

PREFACE

THE BULK of man's knowledge about the history of the earth has grown so great that not all can be told, or even mentioned, in only a few hundred pages. Some type of selection must be practiced. Three types have been used by writers of textbooks: (1) a writer may make a condensed summary of the whole range of earth history, covering the whole globe and all of geologic time; (2) or—more commonly—he may treat in considerable detail the geologic history of one region, such as North America or Britain; (3) or he may concentrate on what he considers the major discoveries of historical geology, excluding everything that does not bear in one way or another on the understanding of these discoveries. The present book is the result of an attempt to use the third method. I am glad to acknowledge that in this choice I am following the practice of the great teacher from whom I first learned about geologic history, Professor John C. Merriam, whose lectures at the University of California I heard in 1915. I am still trying to use Merriam's method; but I have discarded some of his topics and have added others, some of which involve fields of study that did not exist in his time.

Among recent general works, I have found especially useful Bernhard Kummel's *History of the Earth* (W. H. Freeman & Co., San Francisco, 1961) and P. B. King's *The Evolution of North America* (Princeton University Press, 1959). I have used, as the source for Chapter 7 and Appendix C, my essay "Correlation by Fossils" in *The Fabric of Geology*, edited by Claude C. Albritton Jr., copyright © 1963 by The Geological Society of America, Inc.; this material is used here with the permission of the Society and of Freeman, Cooper & Company of San Francisco, the publishers of *The Fabric of Geology*.

In collecting material and putting it together, I have been aided by my daughter, Marjorie W. Bray. Many photographs have been provided by J. S. Shelton and the American Museum of Natural History. One or more chapters have been critically read by C. C. Albritton Jr., R. M. Alf, C. A. Anderson, A. K. Baird, W. Charles Bell, G. J. Bellemin, J. H. Callomon, Sherwin Carlquist, Ivan Colburn, R. R. Compton, Allan Cox, W. H. Freeman, James Gilluly, David L. Jones, T. H. McCulloh, D. B. McIntyre, M. C. McKenna, R. E. MacMillen, M. A. Murphy, W. L. Quaide, J. F. Richmond, J. S. Shelton, L. T. Silver, George I. Smith, Patsy J. Smith, R. H. Tedford, W. D. Thornbury, J. W. Wells, W. P. Woodring, and D. H. Zenger. D. O. Doehring, H. L. James, M. L. Natland, C. A. Nelson, A. R. Palmer, and Bobb Schaefer reviewed, and suggested modifications in, smaller sections of the manuscript. Most of these readers have not seen the chapters in their present form, and they have not given blanket approval to the contents. In particular, J. H. Callomon would put less trust in quantitative stratigraphic paleontology (Chap. 7), even though he himself has made a notable contribution to that subject; James Gilluly would be more restrained in endorsing radiometric ages (Chap. 8); and W. Charles Bell would be less optimistic about the possibility of precise time correlations.

A friend of Lewis Carroll (*Life and Letters*, p. 301) advised a young man who was going out to be a judge in India: "Give your *decisions* boldly and clearly; they will probably be *right*. But do *not* give your *reasons;* they will probably be *wrong*." In this book I give reasons. If you find a reason, or anything else, that is wrong, let me or my publisher know. We are both interested.

A. O. WOODFORD
Pomona College, Claremont, California

March 10, 1965

CONTENTS

CHAPTER 1

Rocks and
Their Structures

THE READER of this book is presumed to have been introduced to the elements of physical geology. He knows that a *mineral* is a natural, homogeneous, solid substance with a fairly definite chemical composition and a characteristic crystal structure. He knows that most *rocks* are aggregates of minerals and that rocks are classified, according to their origin, as *sedimentary, igneous,* and *metamorphic.* He knows that sedimentary rocks occur in thin layers, called *strata,* and contain remains of ancient plants and animals, called *fossils.*

With such knowledge, the reader is at least partially prepared to study the history of the earth's thin outer crust and the closely related history of the life that has developed on that crust—the topics that will be the subject matter of this book. The evidence of this history is found chiefly in the stratified rocks and is derived especially from the fossils contained in those rocks.

1-1. *Introduction*

Historical geology puts man in a new perspective, for it makes the whole story of human affairs seem almost instantaneously brief. Pharaoh and Caesar become practically contemporaneous with Einstein and Churchill if we compare the time that separated the earlier men from the later with the many millions of years that separated the first trilobites from the dinosaurs or the dinosaurs from the elephants. Human history may not be the end—or even the climax—of the succession of events.

The geologic history of life involves fascinating changes of the type called evolutionary—successive adaptations of different kinds of animals and plants to the various environments available to living things. The dinosaurs were for a long time the great hay-burners; then they disappeared. After a considerable time large elephants developed, and by this time there was a different kind of hay to burn. There is ebb and flow in the history of life.

That history will be our principal concern, but it will be intimately intertwined with the physical history of the continents and of the seas that have repeatedly encroached on them. Each continent has its own sedimentary history, more or less fragmentary and largely a record of intermittent marine invasions; that is, each continent has its own series of sedimentary deposits, and for most continents these deposits are mostly marine.

A prime purpose of any general geologic history is to discover, by comparison of the evidence from different continents, to what extent the physical and biological history of one continent can be correlated with that of others. Marine fossils, changing from the bottom to the top of the successions of stratified rocks, will prove to be the chief means of correlation between continents at most levels. We shall also find significance in the similarities and differences, on different continents, of land plants and such land animals as dinosaurs and horses. The study of land animals, in fact, furnishes the principal clues to past intercontinental connections and separations.

Generalizations about rocks, fossils, and geologic history may seem mere words, distant from the lives of men. They become significant, however, and have a tremendous impact upon one's philosophy of life, once their origins and implications are understood. Such understanding will be the goal of this and succeeding chapters. The greatest of the conclusions are very human statements, part of our cultural inheritance, and they can best be understood as steps in human history— that is, as they first became apparent to men.

Historical geology has two bases, physical geology and biology. The present chapter, on rocks and their structures, restates some of the elements of physical geology, with emphasis on their basic importance for historical geology and some hints as to the way they will be applied. The second chapter will treat some of the elements of biology in similar fashion.

1-2. Structures in Stratified Rocks

In the year 1669 Nicolaus Steno, a Danish physician who served the Duke of Florence, published a little book that contained some simple laws on which the most far-reaching conclusions of geology are based. Steno, whose primary interest was in the anatomy of modern vertebrate animals, had dissected the head of a large shark brought in by Italian fishermen. He noted that the teeth of the modern shark (Fig. 1-1) were similar in shape, material, and structure to the even larger "tongue-stones" from the island of Malta, which had been puzzling the curious for 1,700 years or more. The tongue-stones had come from soft rocks, exposed in Maltese cliffs. Could it be that they were the teeth of sharks that had lived in an ancient sea? And how could such a speculation be tested?

In no time at all, Steno was considering a more general problem, that of a "solid [such as a tongue-stone] contained within another solid" (such as a mass of sandstone). More precisely, "given something possessed of a certain shape, and produced according to the laws of nature, to find in the substance itself evidence disclosing the place and manner of its production." Such evidence is called circumstantial, both in law and in common usage. Even if a crime is unwitnessed, a person may be convicted of it by circumstantial evidence. In lawsuits such evidence involves the fallible memories of human beings and is commonly considered less than perfect. Steno's problem was the reliability of the circumstantial evidence provided by nature.

We must consider whether, in the light of all that is known today, circumstantial evidence accumulated from the observation of nature is a trustworthy basis for the history of the long past. We must take account, in particular, of coincidence, the chance resemblance of things produced in different ways. Let us begin, not with nature, but with an example from human cultural history. Take the play called *Hamlet*. How were its many editions produced? By reproducing the words of one intelligent and purposeful man, perhaps named Shakespeare? By reproducing the work of a group of persons? Originally by

 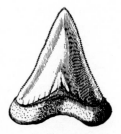

Fig. 1-1. *Shark's teeth. (From Nicolaus Steno, 1667.)*

printing the words of one person, or one group, with later modifications and chance duplications by other persons or groups? The extension of these possibilities, further and further, leads theorists to consider the possibility that *Hamlet* might be duplicated by a battalion of monkeys pounding typewriter keys at random. This is a very long chance— indeed, barely conceivable. Somewhat more plausible is the hypothesis that the play might be duplicated by a single deranged human being who made conventional words out of letters but put the words together at random. Still more plausible, perhaps, is the hypothesis that a particular copy of *Hamlet* might have been written, independently and rather recently, by an intelligent person who duplicated, by chance, the original *Hamlet*. There are other possibilities, and varying degrees of probability may be attached to them. But most people take the common-sense view that all copies of *Hamlet* have as their ultimate source the manuscript of a single gifted playwright who lived in Elizabethan time. It is equally probable, geologists feel, that the tongue-stones are sharks' teeth, though the probability is more difficult to express accurately.

Our alphabet contains twenty-six letters. If our battalion of monkeys is given typewriters with twenty-six keys, the first letter struck by the first monkey has one chance in twenty-six of being the same as the first letter in *Hamlet*. The chance that the second letter will also be the same as that in *Hamlet* is 1/26 of 1/26 ($1/26^2$ or $1/676$), and so on. The probability (or lack of probability) that a tongue-stone is a chance imitation of a shark tooth is harder to calculate. We may formalize the elements of the comparison by listing the characteristics of a tongue-stone and those of a tooth taken right out of a shark: (1) chemical composition: both calcium phosphate; (2) general shape: both almost triangular; (3) base: both rough and irregular; (4) other margins: wavy or saw-toothed in both; (5) outer layer: thin, shiny, and microscopically laminated in both; etc., etc. Taking the first point, we have, in-

stead of twenty-six letters, several score mineral compositions. For the second point, we must consider many possible general shapes, perhaps about fifty, all represented by substances found in nature. As point after point is considered, the odds pile up against chance resemblance. Some comparisons of details, however, would bring out the fact that the tongue-stone and the tooth of a present-day shark are not absolutely identical—certainly not in size, and not even entirely in shape. (Not all the teeth from the same shark are alike.) In general, the differences between tongue-stones and the teeth of some modern sharks are such as one might expect if the tongue-stones had gone through many editions, with many minor changes, to produce the teeth of the modern shark.

Today practicing geologists have enough knowledge and common sense to recognize, on sight, shark teeth found in rocks. They think that they see shark teeth, and that is all there is to it; but they owe their proficiency to the patient study of the facts about tongue-stones and sharks' teeth by Steno and his successors.

Steno not only was familiar with the fossil tongue-stones from Malta; he also knew about other fossils, found in Italy, which he considered closely related to modern shellfish. (Fossil representatives of all types of animals having preservable hard parts are known today.) He was especially concerned, however, with another aspect of the problem of fossils: how sharks' teeth, seashells, and other remains of marine life have come to be present in rocks far from the present ocean and high above its level. This is, indeed, a difficult question. Marine fossils have been found in most parts of all continents except the main central part of Africa (and ice-covered Antarctica). They even occur in the rocks that make up the crests of some of the highest mountains. The first part of Steno's solution was a simple one: "Nature and Scripture agree in this, that all things were covered with water." He went on to try to explain how the sediments that contain the fossils happen to be arranged in strata, the order in which the strata formed, and what happened to them during the gradual shrinking and lowering of the supposed deep primeval ocean. In the course of this interpretation he formulated the laws that bear his name.

1-3. *Steno's Laws for the Interpretation of Strata*

Steno's laws, and especially the assumption behind them, are fundamental: they must always be at the back of one's mind when one interprets the types of rocks that he dealt with. Steno's assumption was the uniformity of nature, in the past as at present. Nature's laws, he assumed, have not changed during all the time of the earth's existence. We may therefore establish rules for the interpretation of strata by observing the layers of sediment as they are formed today. Sedimentary beds are forming now in lowlands and in the sea. Steno's observations of strata being formed in Italian valleys and along Italian shores led

him to three simple conclusions, which he stated as laws.

The **Law of Superposition** states that in a series of beds, as originally deposited, the upper are the younger, for each bed must have been formed by deposition upon a relatively firm and solid substratum. This law is the principal basis for our notions of relative age in geology. It is illustrated by the horizontal strata exposed in the walls of the Grand Canyon (Fig. 1-2). All the beds below any stratum must have been in existence before that particular stratum was deposited.

The **Law of Original Horizontality** states that, when strata are first formed, their upper (and usually also their lower) surfaces are approximately horizontal (Figs. 1-2 and 1-3). Strata that are now inclined to the horizon (Fig. 1-4) must therefore have been tilted after their formation.

The **Law of Original Continuity** states that a sedimentary bed, at the time of its formation, is a continuous sheet that either thins to a feather edge or extends to a barrier that forms

Fig. 1-2. *Horizontal strata in the Grand Canyon, Arizona. (Photograph by J. Carkhoff, U.S. Geological Survey.)*

Fig. 1-3. *View northeast across the upper Arno Valley, at Il Tasso, 25 miles southeast of Florence, Italy. Edges of horizontal strata exposed in foreground; inclined strata in the distant Pratomagno range. (Photograph by Augusto Azzaroli, University of Florence.)*

a margin of the basin of deposition. Therefore there cannot have been, originally, an exposed edge of the entire bed, from top to bottom. If the edges of strata are seen exposed, they must have been exposed by breakage and dislocation or by wear. By this law we know that the edges of the strata seen in Figures 1-2 and 1-3 must have been exposed by wear (erosion) or by the breaking of the strata and the displacement of their continuations out of our sight.

Using these three laws, Steno worked out the geologic history of the region around Florence. He formalized his conclusions by drawing vertical *structure sections* (Fig. 1-5), of which the first (numbered 20) apparently represents the present structure across the Arno Valley of north-central Italy, in which Florence lies. Sections 21, 22, etc., show earlier stages, back to the primary set of horizontal strata figured in section 25. In order to explain the present inclined state of some of these early strata, Steno imagined the formation of

Fig. 1-4. *Lignite (intermediate between peat and coal) in inclined dark strata, overlain (just below tree) by pale horizontal strata. West side of upper Arno Valley, Italy. (Photograph by Augusto Azzaroli, University of Florence.)*

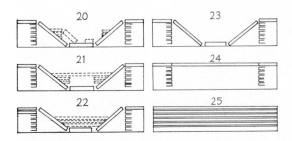

Fig. 1-5. *Geological history of Tuscany.* (*From Nicolaus Steno, 1669.*)

a great subterranean cavity (section 24) and then the collapse of its roof (section 23), forming a first Arno Valley. Then this valley was partially filled by the strata marked by dashes in section 22. Then a smaller cavity formed (section 21), and its roof caved in to produce the present state (section 20). Note that there are two, and only two, sets of strata, and two periods of cavity formation, roof collapse, and

consequent tilting of strata. The whole history, according to Steno, involved six episodes in two series, each consisting of successive deposition, cavern formation, and roof collapse. The results of this hypothetical history fit the observable present surface conditions fairly well, as one can see in part by studying Figure 1-3, but it is hard to believe in the great caverns. Even the greatest known caverns, such as those near Carlsbad in New Mexico, are not nearly as big as the Arno Valley, and the thousands of wells that have been drilled for oil all over the world rarely penetrate cavities of any size at all. We must try again for a satisfactory explanation of tilted strata. But Steno was the first to show clearly that a problem exists. He was also practically the first to subdivide a succession of stratified rocks in a systematic way or to give an account of the stratigraphic history of a region. He was the first stratigrapher.

Fig. 1-6. *Section through the coal beds and other strata in Somerset, south of Bristol, England.* (*From John Strachey, Philos. Trans. Roy. Soc. London, 1719.*)

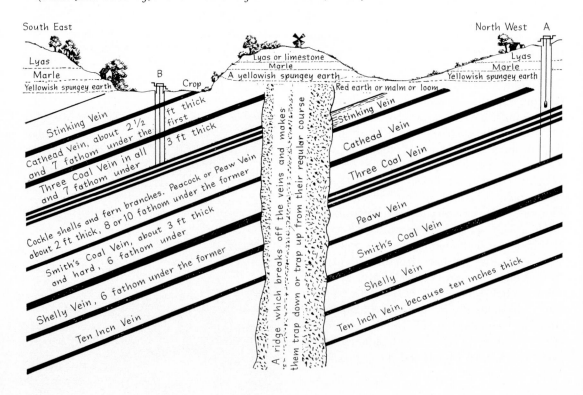

1-4. *Sedimentary Structures*

a. *Strachey's Observations on Dipping and Faulted Beds*

Steno's little book made a big stir for a short time. It was annotated by Sir Isaac Newton, and a translation was published in London. Then it was generally forgotten until rediscovered more than a hundred years later. In the meantime, the problems of the sedimentary rocks were attacked by coal miners, especially in England and Scotland. In 1719, when coal mining and the Industrial Revolution were just beginning, John Strachey reported to the Royal Society of London the character, succession, and downslope to the southeast of the parallel beds of coal near Bristol in the west of England (Fig. 1-6). The coal beds are separated by layers of non-inflammable material, and are interrupted and offset by nearly vertical slip zones, called "ridges" by the Bristol miners. The amount of the apparent vertical offset along a slip can be measured as the depth by which miners, such as those working northwest from shaft B of Figure 1-6, must descend, beyond the "ridge," to find again the coal bed in which they had been working.

Strachey showed that careful attention to geological structure may be useful to men. The essential first step is the description of the position of a stratum that is no longer horizontal but still possesses a plane upper surface. Strachey's method of description was clumsy and has been replaced by the angles of strike and dip (Fig. 1-7). The **strike** of the plane is the bearing (angle with the north-south direction) of any horizontal line in the plane. The **dip** of the plane is the angle that the plane makes with the horizontal. This angle is measured in a vertical plane perpendicular to the strike line. The elevations and exact geographic positions of three points in a plane make possible the determination of both strike and dip. These three points may be intersections of a contact with contour lines, as shown in Figure 1-7.

Similarly, planes or thin zones of broken rock along which movement has occurred—Strachey's ridges, now generally called *faults*—also have strike and dip. In Figure 1-5 the dip of the fault is nearly vertical (90° to the horizontal), a fairly common case, but in general the dip of a fault may have any value from 0° to 90°.

The first problem attacked by Strachey was that of the fault, illustrated by Figure 1-6 and already discussed. A second problem, equally important both practically and in geologic theory, involved changes in the strike or dip of beds, or in both. Strachey concluded that, in the Bristol district, such changes occur at faults (ridges); but this connection between faulting and change of dip or strike is not necessary or universal.

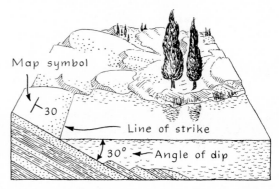

Fig. 1-7. *Above: strike and dip (from Gilluly, Waters, and Woodford,* Principles of Geology, *W. H. Freeman & Co., 1959); below: determination of strike and dip of a plane from locations and elevations of three points on the plane.*

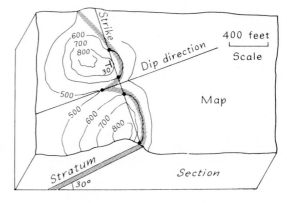

b. Hutton's Observations

Sixty or seventy years after Strachey's time, James Hutton and James Hall of Edinburgh took advantage of the continuously exposed rocks in cliffs on Scotland's east coast to follow individual beds through changes of dip. By 1795 they had shown that in these cliffs the changes of dip express *folds* in the strata. In the single cliff represented by Figure 1-8 a number of beds can be traced through an upfold and a downfold, practically without faulting. We now call upfolds *anticlines* and downfolds *synclines*. The folds of Figure 1-8 are rather small. A single upfold or downfold may, however, be miles across and many miles long.

The exposed portions of strata, whether horizontal, tilted, or folded, are subject to erosion by streams and waves. Folded strata, for example, may be eroded down to a fairly smooth surface and then overlain by newer strata. The newer beds are then *unconformable* on the older, and the surface of contact is an *unconformity*. A great Scottish unconform-

ity was recognized in several places by Hutton, who showed one such locality in an illustration reproduced as our Figure 1-9. Note the evidence of truncated folds in the nearly vertical beds beneath the unconformity. Hutton saw that an unconformity, especially an angular unconformity like that of the figure (or of Fig. 1-6, top) is a notable feature in a series of strata. The unconformable contact between adjacent beds represents a long history of varied events. The lower beds, after accumulation in what might be called the zone of deposition, were folded and brought into a zone of erosion, probably by uplift. Erosion was probably slow and may have been complex, possibly due in part to streams, in part to lake or ocean waves. The present contact between the two bodies of rock, across the eroded edges of the inclined strata, merely marks the last in a long series of stages in the erosion of a landscape now lost. On this final erosion surface sedimentation was re-established, and horizontal beds were deposited above the unconformity.

Fig. 1-8. *Folded strata on seacoast southeast of Edinburgh, Scotland. (Redrawn from James Hutton,* Theory of the Earth, *1795.)*

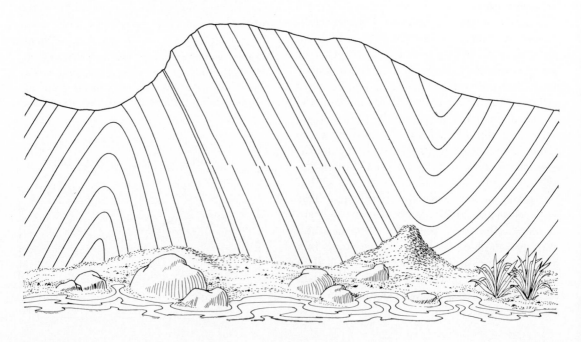

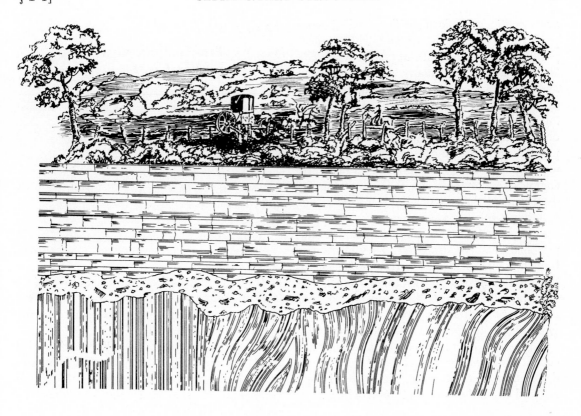

Fig. 1-9. *Unconformity at Jedburgh, Scotland. (Redrawn from James Hutton,* op. cit.*)*

A different interpretation of Steno's observations of the strata around Florence now becomes possible. In the Florence area exposures of strata such as those shown in Figure 1-3 are far from being continuous. That figure does not show strata bent into folds, and apparently Steno saw no exposures of complete folds. Later study, however, suggests that the oldest rocks near Florence have been folded somewhat, though not exactly in the manner noted in Scotland.

The introduction of the concepts of folding and unconformity raised new questions. What forces produced the folds? How did they operate? How rapidly? How continuously? When the tops of the upfolds were planed off by erosion, as the first step toward the development of an unconformity, what happened to the debris? Hutton worked out tentative answers to some of these questions. He concluded that elevation and the accompanying deformation are caused by expansion under the influence of heat. Erosion is constantly at work tearing down the high places; at the same time the transported products of erosion gradually fill up the low places. At any one place, erosion of protruding land is succeeded by deposition on a subsiding sea floor. After the seaway fills with sediment, said Hutton, the spot is again raised into the zone of erosion by expansion under the influence of heat, with accompanying folding or faulting, or with both.

Since Hutton's day, the observation of folded and faulted marine strata and of unconformities has led invariably to inferences of this general type; but today two qualifications are necessary. For one thing, no geologist now has the confidence that Hutton had in the ultimate transformation of every part of every continent to deep sea floor and of every part of every ocean to dry land. The physical problems connected with any such wholesale transformation, particularly of land to *deep* sea or vice versa, are discussed at length in textbooks of physical geology under the heading *isostasy*. The second qualification has to do with the effectiveness of heat-induced expansion as the cause of the folding and faulting of great masses of sedimentary strata. The complex sets of folds and the faults of great displacement that are now known were rather certainly formed in some other way or ways.

Folds, faults, and unconformities are the principal *geologic structures*. They are therefore the chief elements in *structural geology*, though the recognition of these elements is only the initial stage in the unraveling of that complex subject. Folds, faults, and other deformational structures of the rocks, including the broadest of uplifts or depressions, are called *structural* or *tectonic* features. If the deformational structures are deep-seated, they are said to be the results of *diastrophism*.

1-5. *Silicate and Carbonate Rocks*

The earth's solid crust is composed chiefly of the chemical elements listed in Table 1-1. Two rarer elements, carbon (C) and phosphorus (P), are important for historical geology, especially because they are constituents

TABLE 1-1

Principal Elements of the Earth's Crust

ELEMENT	SYMBOL	PERCENTAGE BY WEIGHT
Oxygen	O	46
Silicon	Si	28
Aluminum	Al	8
Iron	Fe	5
Calcium	Ca	4
Sodium	Na	3
Potassium	K	3
Magnesium	Mg	2

of the hard parts of organisms. Sulphur (S) is compounded with metals, making sulphides, in many ores. Hydrogen (H) unites with oxygen to form water (H_2O).

A compound of oxygen with another element is called an oxide. The very common mineral quartz is silicon dioxide (SiO_2). A compound of silicon, oxygen, and one or more other elements is called a silicate. Most common minerals are silicates. A compound of carbon, oxygen, and one or more other elements is called a carbonate. The mineral calcite is calcium carbonate ($CaCO_3$), the essential constituent of most seashells and of an important sedimentary rock, limestone. A compound of phosphorus, oxygen, and one or

TABLE 1-2

Principal Rock-forming Minerals

Quartz	SiO_2	Light-colored, glassy
Feldspars		
Orthoclase	K Al silicate	White or pink
Plagioclase	Na Ca Al silicate	White
Micas		Split into thin, elastic plates
Muscovite	K Al silicate	White
Biotite	K Fe Mg Al silicate	Black, dark-brown, or dark-green
Hornblende	Fe Mg Ca Al silicate	Black or dark-green; splits into well-defined prisms
Pyroxene	Fe Mg Ca Al silicate	Black or dark-green; splits into plates or rough prisms
Chlorite	Mg Fe Al silicate	Green; splits into flexible plates
Clay minerals	Hydrous Al silicates	Earthy
Calcite	$CaCO_3$	White; splits into diamond-shaped bits
Dolomite	$CaMg(CO_3)_2$	White; splits into diamond-shaped bits

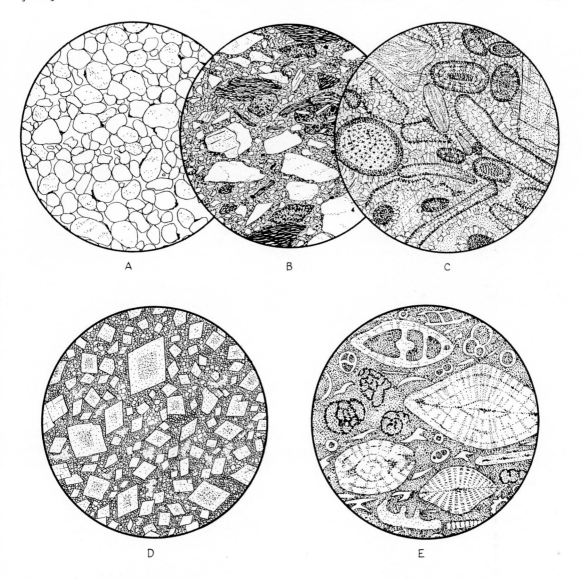

Fig. 1-10. *Sedimentary rock textures in thin section. (From Williams, Turner, and Gilbert,* Petrography, *W. H. Freeman & Co., 1954.)*

A. *Uncemented quartz sandstone (Ordovician; Beloit, Wis.). Diameter 2.5 mm.*

B. *Graywacke (Ordovician; Newfoundland). Diameter 1.5 mm. Grains mostly quartz (clear), rock fragments (dark), and feldspar (with cleavage cracks); matrix: fine sand, silt, and clay.*

C. *Limestone (Jurassic; Bath, England) composed primarily of oolites (radial and concentric structures, upper right) and shell fragments (rounded, club-like, fibrous, or with cracks in rhombic pattern); matrix: crystalline calcite, largely as bladed rims surrounding each oolite and shell fragment. Diameter 2.5 mm.*

D. *Dolomitic limestone (Ordovician; New York). Diameter 1 mm. Microcrystalline calcite of uneven grain size containing rhomb-shaped crystals of dolomite.*

E. *Foraminiferal limestone (Eocene; Italy). Foraminifers in matrix of microcrystalline calcite (densely stippled). Diameter 3 mm.*

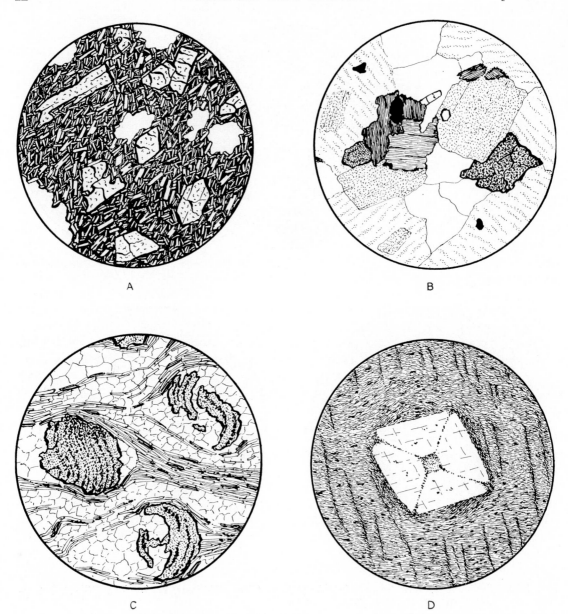

Fig. 1-11. *Igneous and metamorphic textures in thin section. (From Williams, Turner, and Gilbert, op. cit.)*

A. *Hemicrystalline: basalt (Parícutin, Mexico). Diameter 2.5 mm. Large crystals, small crystals, and dark glass.*

B. *Coarse crystalline: biotite granite (Conway, N.H.). Diameter 3 mm. Clear quartz, lightly stippled feldspar, dark biotite, etc.*

C. *Banded crystalline: garnet-mica-quartz schist (Scotland). Diameter 5 mm. Garnet in eyes, about which the mica layers curve.*

D. *Large new crystal in contact-metamorphosed slate (Bavaria). Diameter (of circle) 3 mm.*

more other elements is called a phosphate. Bones are calcium phosphate.

Most rocks are composed of silicate minerals and from the chemical point of view are called *silicate rocks*. Great sheets of sediments, however, and the resulting rocks, are made up of calcium and magnesium carbonates and are therefore called *carbonate rocks*. The principal rock-forming minerals are listed in Table 1-2.

1-6. *Sedimentary, Igneous, and Metamorphic Rocks*

When classified according to *manner of origin*, rocks are divided into three groups, sedimentary, igneous, and metamorphic.

a. Sedimentary Rocks

The strata that Steno saw were shown by him and his successors to be **sedimentary rocks**, analogous to the sediments forming in valleys, in lakes, and offshore in the ocean today. An example (Fig. 1-10) is sandstone, a rock made up of sand grains, either uncemented and loosely coherent (A) or cemented together (B). Since the grains are fragments of pre-existing rocks, the texture is called **clastic.** If the fragments are mostly made up of quartz (A) or of quartz and silicate minerals such as feldspars and micas (B), the rock is **silicoclastic.** If the fragments are mostly calcite or dolomite, both of which contain calcium and lack silicon, the rock is **calciclastic** (C). Some other sedimentary rocks, instead of being composed mostly of clastic grains, are made up mostly of closely interlocking, newly formed crystals; their texture is **crystalline;** an example is the dolomitic limestone (D). Still other sedimentary rocks are mostly **organic** (E), being composed of the fossil remains of organisms.

Sedimentary rocks may be subdivided, according to *place of origin*, into **marine** rocks, deposited in the sea, and **continental,** or nonmarine, rocks, deposited elsewhere. Continental deposits are **lacustrine,** deposited in lakes; **alluvial** (noun, **alluvium**), deposited along rivers and other streams; **glacial,** deposited by glaciers; **eolian,** deposited by the wind; etc. Among the many original structures in sedimentary rocks, *cross-bedding* (cross stratification) is especially useful because the inclined (cross) beds have original dips in the general direction of flow of the current.

b. Igneous Rocks

Igneous rocks are those thought (and sometimes proved) to have solidified from hot melts. The most certainly igneous rocks are those that have solidified as surface lavas in historic times—for example, lava flows from Vesuvius. Numerous more ancient rocks are so similar to those erupted from Vesuvius and other active volcanoes that they too are considered volcanic and therefore igneous. Some of these rocks are composed chiefly of small interlocking crystals, such as those of the fine-grained, dark-colored rock called basalt (Fig. 1-11A). Others, especially the high-silica obsidian, are made up entirely or almost entirely of glass. Still others are clastic rocks made up of crystals of feldspar or other minerals common in lavas, plus bits of volcanic rock such as basalt; such rocks are called *tuffs* and are often practically identical with ash discharged explosively from active volcanoes. Some rocks of volcanic texture and composition have a different mode of occurrence, first emphasized by Hutton and his friends in Edinburgh, who found exposed, on the outskirts of their city, continuous thin dikes of basalt (Fig. 1-12) that cut across stratified rocks, as if filling fissures. The dikes have thin borders of hard, recrystallized sandstone that Hutton explained as the result of baking by the hot liquid that filled the cracks. In contrast to an *extrusive* lava flow, such crack fillings are called *intrusive* igneous rocks. Hutton considered it probable that hot liquid rock, or *magma*, had forced its way into the cracks from some deep-seated source, and that the dikes were not just lava that had dropped into open cracks from above; and all later observers have agreed with him. Intrusive rocks of volcanic texture are included with the other products of volcanoes in the great group of **volcanic rocks.**

Even commoner than basalt are the light-colored, coarser-grained crystalline rocks called *granite* (Fig. 1-11B) and *granodiorite* —quartz-feldspar rocks whose minor differences in composition are given in the list of common rocks at the end of this chapter. Most

Fig. 1-12. *Nearly vertical dike in nearly horizontal gravels, northwestern Arizona, 10 miles southeast of Boulder Dam. (Photograph by J. S. Shelton.)*

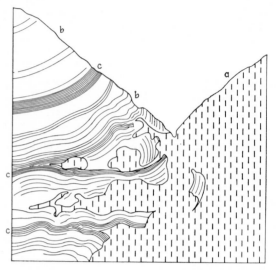

Fig. 1-13. *Granite contact in Glen Tilt, Scotland:* a, *granite;* b, *limestone;* c, *blue argillaceous schist. (After Charles Lyell,* Principles of Geology, *1833.)*

occurrences of these rocks, in Scotland and elsewhere, are large bodies underlying the other rocks of the area. But, thought Hutton, if granite, too, is igneous, solidified from the molten state, somewhere it probably filled fissures and is preserved as dikes. Finally he found what he sought at Glen Tilt in the Highlands north of Edinburgh, where, in the course of a mile, no less than six large dikes of red granite traverse black micaceous rock and white limestone, producing a vivid contrast by the difference in colors. Their relations are represented by a famous Lyell drawing (Fig. 1-13). The placing of granite and granodiorite in the igneous genetic group is based upon such circumstantial evidence, fortified by the recent slow crystallization in the laboratory of slightly hydrous melts of granitic composition under confining pressures as high as those produced by several miles of overlying rock. The circumstantial evidence is essential, as will appear below.

All granites, granodiorites, and other coarse-grained crystalline rocks that can be shown to be igneous are grouped together in the second great subdivision of the igneous rocks, the deep-seated **plutonic rocks**, or **plutonites**.

Some masses of granite or granodiorite, however, have ambiguous relations with the surrounding rocks, as we shall see in the following section.

c. Metamorphic Rocks

A third group of rocks, the **metamorphic,** was proposed in 1833 by Hutton's follower Charles Lyell, in the greatest of geologic textbooks, his *Principles of Geology*:

"If we examine gneiss, which consists of the same materials as granite, or mica-schist which is a binary compound of quartz and mica . . . we find that it is made up of a succession of beds, the planes of which are, to a certain extent, parallel to each other. . . . As in [ordinary sedimentary] series we meet with limestone alternating again and again with micaceous or argillaceous sand, so we find . . . gneiss and mica-schist alternating with pure and impure granular limestones.

"*Passage of gneiss into granite*—If, then, reasoning from the principle that like effects have like causes, we attribute the stratification of gneiss, mica-schist, and other associated rocks, to sedimentary deposition from a fluid, we encounter this difficulty, that there is often a transition from gneiss, one of the stratified series, into granite, which, as we have shown, is of igneous origin. Gneiss is composed of the same ingredients as granite, and its texture is equally crystalline. It sometimes occurs in thick beds, and in these the rock is often quite undistinguishable, in hand specimens, from granite; yet the lines of stratification are still evident. These lines imply deposition from water, while the passage into granite would lead us to infer an igneous origin. In what manner can we reconcile these apparently conflicting views? The Huttonian hypothesis offers, we think, the only satisfactory solution of this problem. According to that theory, the materials of gneiss were originally deposited from water in the usual form of aqueous strata, but these strata were subsequently altered by their proximity to granite, and to other plutonic masses in a state of fusion, until they assumed a granitiform texture. The reader will be prepared, by what we have said of granite [compare Fig. 1-13], to conclude that when voluminous masses of melted rock have been for ages in an incandescent state, in contact with sedimentary deposits, they must produce some alteration in their texture, and this alteration may admit of every intermediate gradation between that resulting from perfect fusion, and the slightest modification which heat can produce."

A sedimentary rock recrystallized without fusion was called metamorphic by Lyell. An example is represented in Figure 1-11C. Later writers extended the term "metamorphic rocks" to include all rocks, originally igneous or sedimentary or even previously metamorphosed, that have been partially or completely recrystallized at higher than ordinary temperatures but without fusion. Some gneisses, for example, have the composition of plutonic rocks and are also intrusive into other metamorphic rocks; the best explanation seems to be that these gneisses are metamorphosed plutonic rocks. That is to say, not all gneisses, by any means, can be stated positively to be recrystallized sediments.

We must also distinguish between *contact metamorphism*, which occurs close to granitic or other intrusions, and *regional metamorphism*. A contact metamorphic zone may be only a few feet wide and even around a large granitic mass is rarely more than a few miles thick. Well-formed new crystals may make up only part of the metamorphic rock (Fig. 1-11D). Such zones are not very important, in themselves, as elements of the earth's crust. Regional metamorphism, on the other hand, transforms belts at least scores of miles wide and hundreds of miles long into very fine-grained lustrous *slates*, coarser-grained *schists* (Fig. 1-11C), and *gneisses*. The schists and gneisses are almost always associated with plutonic rocks. They may, as in the Sierra Nevada and the eastern Appalachians, grade successively into slates and unmetamorphosed sedimentary rocks. Regionally metamorphosed rocks are important in historical geology, especially for the trouble they cause: in regionally metamorphosed belts, most fossils have been destroyed, and the relations between strata are obscured.

1-7. Chemical Changes During Weathering and Metamorphism

A few chemical changes in rocks must be considered even in historical geology. These are the changes that occur in weathering, which is the decay of exposed rocks at the earth's surface, and in metamorphism, which goes on deep beneath the surface and is chemically more or less the opposite of weathering. In weathering, complex silicates, such as feldspar and hornblende, go to pieces. The sodium and potassium, as well as much of the calcium and magnesium, dissolve out and are carried away by ground water. The residue is likely to be a black or yellow or red clay, made up of one or more aluminum-silicate clay minerals colored black by organic matter or yellow-red by iron. In metamorphism, the clay minerals may be transformed back into more complex silicates—feldspar, hornblende, and two kinds of platy minerals, chlorite and micas. At a depth of five miles or so and at temperatures of 200 or 300 degrees centigrade, chlorite, an iron-magnesium-aluminum silicate, may form, making a chlorite-bearing schist. At somewhat higher temperatures the chlorite may acquire some potassium and change to biotite, the rock becoming a biotite-bearing schist. The schist may then remain unchanged during its rise to the surface region and during exposure by erosion. Oftentimes, however, the rise through a zone where chlorite is the more stable mineral results in a partial or complete change back to chlorite. Every one of these changes is significant in one way or another in connection with some aspect of geologic history.

1.8. *Evidence in Rocks of the Temperatures and Pressures of Their Formation*

The conditions of formation of the sedimentary, volcanic, plutonic, and metamorphic rocks are now somewhat better known than in Lyell's day. Laboratory experiments, in particular, have shown the temperatures and pressures at which the various minerals of the rocks may form.

Sediments can be seen forming at ordinary temperatures and pressures. The ascertainable temperatures range from those close to the freezing point of water ($0°C$), beneath glaciers or in deep or polar oceans, to some 35–40°C (95–104° Fahrenheit) in hot climates. In this range of temperatures quartz is stable, but feldspars and many other silicates, if water is available, tend to change slowly to clay minerals (hydrous aluminum silicates) or, under certain tropical or subtropical conditions, to laterite minerals (aluminum and iron hydroxides). The commonest new minerals formed during or immediately after sedimentation are (1) clay minerals, found especially in clay and shale, but also in many sandstones; (2) the calcite of limestone; (3) the dolomite of dolomite rock; and (4) the amorphous opal and fine-grained crystalline quartz that make up cherts.

Volcanic rocks form at high temperatures and ordinary pressures. The temperatures of crystallization are commonly 900–1,000°C as shown both by direct measurement on lava flows and by the presence of high-temperature forms of silica, especially quartz crystals of the hexagonal variety, and of feldspar.

Plutonic rocks such as granite crystallize at about 600°C, as shown by the presence of low-temperature forms of quartz and feldspar. No doubt the relatively low temperature is made possible by the presence of water in the melts.

The lowest temperature of metamorphism, that at which clay minerals begin to change to the micas of lustrous slates, may be about 150°. This conclusion seems to follow from the temperatures found in certain wells more than 20,000 feet deep, where shales are changing into slightly slaty rocks containing very small scales of apparently new-formed micaceous minerals. These same minerals can also be made in the laboratory at nearly the same temperatures.

But some metamorphic rocks probably formed at the same temperatures as granite and similar plutonites, for they contain the plutonic minerals. One wonders if some granites, especially those with faint traces of banding, may not also be metamorphic—that is, may have recrystallized without fusion. Lyell knew, as we have seen (p. 15), that some granites and gneisses have the same mineral composition and grade into each other.

Clearly, metamorphism and deep-seated melting (plutonism) are closely related phenomena. Both indicate high pressures as well as high temperatures—conditions that are possible only several miles below the earth's surface. If rocks now exposed in New England and the Sierra Nevada are the products of sedimentation followed by metamorphism and plutonism, then the original sedimentary rocks not only were deeply buried, probably in part melted, and recrystallized, but were also then elevated into the zone of erosion, where the thick cover of overlying rocks, whose insulating capacity had made possible the high temperatures and whose weight had produced the high pressures under which they had been formed, was eroded away. In all regions of widespread plutonism and metamorphism, extensive folding or faulting (Fig. 1-14), or both, have also occurred. The deformation of belts of sedimentary rocks; their recrystallization by, and the invasion of, plutonites; the uplift of the crystalline terrains and their exposure by erosion—all these make sequences of events that are perhaps the grandest features of geologic history. The evidence is

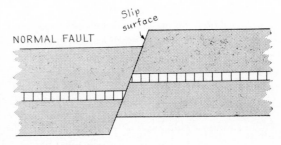

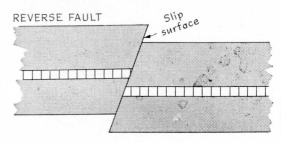

Fig. 1-14. *Normal and reverse faults.*

commonly recorded beneath a far-reaching unconformity. In some cases we can date rather closely the time of plutonic and metamorphic activity, demonstrate that the rocks so formed were rather quickly exposed by erosion, and even gain some insight into the complex processes that produced these results.

COMMON ROCKS AND STRUCTURAL FEATURES

Rocks
  Igneous (silicate rocks).
    Volcanic (mostly fine-crystalline or clastic; grains mostly too small to identify with naked eye, though some little crystals are usually distinguishable).
      Non-clastic, mostly crystalline.
        Basalt—dark-gray to black; calcium-sodium feldspar plus pyroxene; low in silica; commonest volcanic rock. An intrusive variant is called *dolerite*.
        Andesite—gray (or oxidized brown); sodium-calcium feldspar plus lesser amount of hornblende, biotite, or pyroxene; medium high in silica.
        Rhyolite—light-colored; quartz, feldspar, biotite, and glass; granitic composition.

Clastic.

Tuff—consolidated volcanic ash, composed of sand-size or finer grains.

Volcanic breccia—composed of angular blocks of volcanic rock.

Volcanic conglomerate—composed of rounded blocks of volcanic rock (possibly much younger than the volcanic episode, perhaps derived by erosion from volcanic breccia).

Plutonic (crystalline; grains easily distinguished with naked eye). These rocks are all *plutonites;* those containing quartz are *quartz plutonites.*

Granite—light-gray or pink; potassium feldspar, less sodium-calcium feldspar, quartz, biotite, muscovite, etc.; high in silicon; very common.

Granodiorite—light-gray; sodium-calcium feldspar, less potassium feldspar, quartz, biotite, etc.; high in silicon; very common.

Granite and granodiorite pegmatites—very coarse-grained, light-colored dike rocks of granitic or granodioritic composition; some crystals inches or even feet across.

Gabbro—dark-colored; calcium-sodium feldspar and pyroxene; basaltic composition.

Serpentine—green; high in magnesium, low in silicon; hydrated.

Sedimentary (silicate, carbonate, and other rocks).

Conglomerate—consolidated gravel.

Sandstone—consolidated sand. Varieties: *quartz sandstone; arkose,* mostly quartz and feldspar; *graywacke,* quartz, feldspar, rock fragments, and abundant clayey matrix.

Siltstone—consolidated silt, usually containing some clastic grains visible with lens; commonly with numerous little mica flakes aligned on bedding planes.

Loess—soft massive rock composed of silt grains, almost without mica; wind-deposited.

Shale—rock composed of clay and silt, with more or less mica, splitting into thin sheets on bedding planes.

Clay—soft massive rock composed of clay particles; if hard, *claystone.*

Marl—massive rock, usually soft, composed of clay and calcium carbonate.

Limestone—calcium carbonate rock (mineral calcite) with crystalline, organic, or clastic texture.

Dolomite (rock)—mostly dolomite (mineral), a calcium-magnesium carbonate; crystalline.

Chert—fine-grained silica rock, made up of microcrystalline quartz or amorphous opal.

Evaporites: rock salt (sodium chloride), *gypsum* (hydrous calcium sulphate), *anhydrite* (anhydrous calcium sulphate), etc.; crystalline.

Metamorphic (silicate, carbonate, and other rocks).

Gneiss—crystalline, coarse-grained; made up of bands easily visible at arm's length.

Schist—crystalline, medium- to fine-grained; finer-banded.

Slate—hemicrystalline, very fine-grained; splits into thin lustrous sheets.

Also many kinds of unbanded rocks, including:

Crystalline limestone, or *marble*—calcium carbonate.

Quartzite—crystalline; a high-silicon rock composed almost entirely of quartz.

Greenstone—fine-crystalline; meta-volcanic rock colored dull-green by chlorite.

Post-deformational rock structures (results of deformation).
  Folds.
    Anticlines—upfolds.
    Synclines—downfolds.
  Faults (see Fig. 1-14).
    Normal fault—hanging wall down.
    Reverse fault—hanging wall up.
    Flat thrust fault—slip surface nearly horizontal; commonly older rocks faulted
      onto younger rocks.
    Strike slip fault—slip surface nearly vertical; relative movement nearly horizontal;
      displacements of tens, even hundreds, of miles in Scotland, California, and
      New Zealand; significance for historical geology not yet evaluated.
Descriptive terms for stratified rocks.
  Dip and *strike*—see Fig. 1-7.
  Thickness—measured perpendicular to bedding.
Major structural features, so large and flat that they are recognized only in broad views.
  Platforms—high-standing, rather flat-topped masses, continental or sub-continental in
    extent.
  Geosynclines—long and moderately broad depressions that have been partially or
    completely filled with sediments many thousands of feet thick.
  Basins—equidimensional depressed structures, developed in platforms or in geo-
    synclines; tens or hundreds of miles across; considered as depressed structures,
    structural basins; after being filled with sediments, also *sedimentary basins*
    (which may be further deformed).

REFERENCES

1. James Gilluly, A. C. Waters, and A. O. Woodford:
   Principles of Geology, 2nd ed. (Freeman, San Francisco, 1959)

2. K. F. Mather and S. L. Mason: *A Source Book in
   Geology* (McGraw-Hill, New York, 1939)

3. Nicolaus Steno: *De solido intra solidum naturaliter
   contento dissertationis prodromus* (Florence, 1669),
   translated by John G. Winter (University of Michigan Studies; The Macmillan Co., New York, 1916)

4. Charles Lyell: *Principles of Geology,* 3 vols. (Murray, London, 1830, 1833)

CHAPTER 2

Ancient Life

A LONG record of life is preserved in the rocks. In the upper strata are found the remains of many close relatives of plants and animals living today. In the lower strata are whole groups of plants and animals that seem strange to us. Careful study of these strange fossils has, however, revealed indications of relationships to modern forms. As a result, unified animal and plant classifications have been set up. Botanists and paleobotanists have developed a single classification that includes all plants, living and extinct, and zoologists and paleozoologists (commonly called paleontologists) have made a similar synthesis for living and extinct animals.* The study of the often fragmentary fossil remains of both plants and animals is still, however, a special discipline, called **paleontology**, one division of which, called **paleobotany**, deals with plants, and another, called **paleozoology**, deals with animals. A group of fossil plants from a single locality or from a single level in the rocks is called a **fossil flora**, and a group of animal remains, similarly limited, is called a **fossil fauna**.

2-1. *The Geologic Column and Time Scale*

The sedimentary rocks of a region make a local geologic column. By Steno's first law the column is also an age succession, with the oldest strata at the bottom and the youngest at

* See Appendix A and Appendix B.

the top. In Chapter 3 we shall take up the standard geologic column, worked out in Europe, and in Chapters 5, 6, and 7 we shall see that worldwide time correlations between local columns are possible by means of fossil faunas (and fossil floras). For the present, the rock systems of the standard column and the units of geologic time derived from it (Table 2-1) must be taken on faith.

Fossils are at least locally abundant in all systems from the Cambrian to the Pleistocene, inclusive. Fossils are very rare in Precambrian rocks.

2-2. *Living and Non-living Things*

A dog that has been dead a week is easily distinguished from one that is still alive, and a block of freshly quarried granite is very different from either. And yet, of some things, very small or long dead, it is hard to say whether they have ever been alive. The sub-microscopic viruses that cause colds and other diseases, for example, grow somewhat as living things do but are put together simply and geometrically, like the rows and layers of atoms in the crystals of granite. And the fossils in the rocks vary from unmistakable bones, teeth, and shells to traces so vague that they, too, become matters of doubt and disputation.

One characteristic of living things is a special kind of growth. At first the individuals are very small; commonly, as they grow, they become more complex as well as larger; finally

TABLE **2-1**

The Geologic Column and the Units of Geologic Time*

STANDARD GEOLOGIC COLUMN	UNITS OF GEOLOGIC TIME
Cenozoic Systems	Cenozoic Era
Pleistocene System	Pleistocene Period
Neogene System ⎫ Tertiary	Neogene Period
Paleogene System ⎭	Paleogene Period
Mesozoic Systems	Mesozoic Era
Cretaceous System	Cretaceous Period
Jurassic System	Jurassic Period
Triassic System	Triassic Period
Paleozoic Systems	Paleozoic Era
Permian System	Permian Period
Carboniferous System	Carboniferous Period
Pennsylvanian	
Mississippian	
Devonian System	Devonian Period
Silurian System	Silurian Period
Ordovician System	Ordovician Period
Cambrian System	Cambrian Period
Precambrian rocks	Precambrian time

*See Chaps. 3 and 7 for discussions of the geologic column and geologic time.

they reproduce, and in their progeny the process of growth and differentiation is repeated. Thus generation succeeds generation.

Consider first the fine structure of almost any ordinary plant or animal. A thin slice of any part, studied under the microscope, is seen to be composed of a multitude of **cells**, each separated from neighboring cells by a wall or boundary region that is denser, or stains a different shade, or is otherwise distinguishable (Fig. 2-1). Internally, cells are complex; in particular, during the division that results in increase of the number of cells, nuclear material condenses and nuclear strands called **chromosomes** are formed. The chromosomes can be seen as bundles of dark strands in some of the cells of Figure 2-1. They contain the carriers of the code for growth and heredity that are called **genes.** Cells are varied in shape, some being equidimensional, others being plates or long fibers. Similar cells are grouped into tissues: membranes, fibrous masses, spongy masses, rigid frameworks, or protective envelopes. The sacs, fibers, spongy masses, and other tissues are assembled into

Fig. 2-1. *Sections of plant and animal tissues, showing cell walls and internal structures. In cells undergoing division, the nucleus takes the form of thread-like bodies called chromosomes. (Reproduced from Ref. 2.)*
LEFT. *Section of part of the growing tip of an onion root.*
RIGHT. *A piece of salamander skin.*

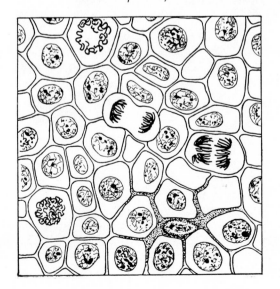 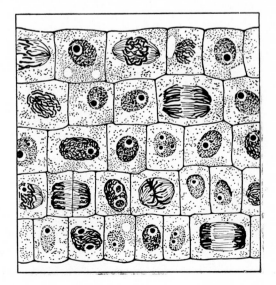

organs that have special functions, such as movement, the absorption of food, and reproduction. The living thing is an **organism,** adapted to survival in certain surroundings and capable of reproduction. Its substance, while it is living and after death, is called **organic.** Organic remains found in the rocks are called **fossils** if they show any organic structure (see § 1-1); and even traces of such structures, preserved in the rocks after all organic substances have disappeared, are also called fossils.

2-3. *Plants and Animals*

Systematists commonly divide organisms into two groups, the plant and animal kingdoms. A large organism, such as a dog or a

Fig. 2-2. *Marine Neogene diatoms, greatly enlarged* (A, Coscinodiscus argus; B, Sceptroneis caducea); *Recent foraminifers* (C, Planulina limbata, *1 mm across;* D, Quinqueloculina); *and* (E) *Paleogene radiolarians, greatly enlarged, from Barbados, West Indies.* (*From K. E. Lohman, Patsy J. Smith, Ruth Todd, and W. R. Riedel, U.S. Geological Survey.*)

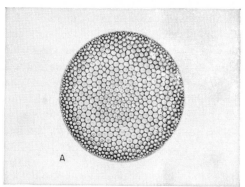
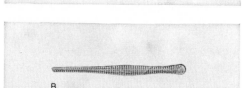

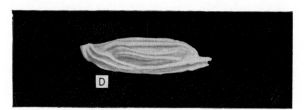
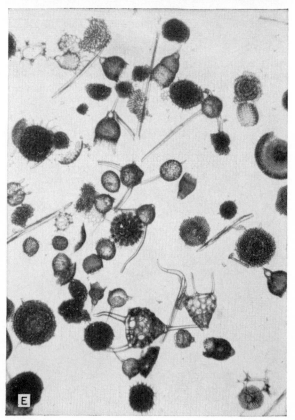

tree, is assigned without difficulty: a dog moves, for one thing, but a tree is stationary; and further study shows that the muscles, nerves, lungs, and other tissues and organs of a dog's body are very unlike the tubes and fibers of a tree. Smaller organisms also are usually placed in one kingdom or the other without uncertainty: an oyster, for example, is an animal despite its stationary position in a shell cemented to a substratum, for it has a muscle, like a dog's, which it can contract to close its shell, a digestive tract somewhat similar to a dog's, and a dependence on food similar to that of more mobile animals.

The distinction between plants and animals becomes difficult only among the one-celled organisms (Fig. 2-2). (Sometimes an attempt is made to avoid the difficulty by putting most one-celled organisms into a third kingdom, the Protista, which must then be distinguished from both plants and animals.) In this book, the one-celled diatoms (Fig. 2-2AB), which have tiny external skeletons, like lacy little siliceous pillboxes, are considered plants, the foraminifers (Fig. 2-2CD) and the radiolarians (Fig. 2-2E) one-celled animals. The best distinction, here and elsewhere, seems to be a biochemical one. Diatoms are like trees and other many-celled plants in one respect, a fundamental one: they manufacture carbohydrates (compounds of carbon, hydrogen, and oxygen), much like the wood of higher plants, from carbon dioxide and water, using sunlight as the source of energy and minute amounts of a green pigment, chlorophyll, as the synthesizing agent. Animals cannot use such simple materials directly; they eat plants. Living foraminifers and radiolarians, even at first glance, seem more like animals because they are somewhat mobile: for example, they send out temporary filaments to which food particles adhere. What is more important is that they contain no chlorophyll and so must get their energy from carbohydrates or other fuel that has been synthesized by plants. The solar energy absorbed by plants and preserved in carbohydrates is partially or completely released as heat energy when animals transform

the carbohydrates into new organic substances or decompose them back to water and carbon dioxide. Plants may therefore be defined as fuel-makers, animals as fuel-users. Even this definition breaks down for the fungi—the mushrooms and their allies—which are obviously closely related to simple green plants but do not contain chlorophyll.

2-4. *The Animal Phyla and Their Representation Among Fossils*

The main divisions of the animal kingdom are called **phyla.** The principal animal phyla, in the order of increasing complexity of the animals, are the following:

Protozoa (protozoans): one-celled animals; examples: foraminifers, radiolarians.
Porifera: sponges.
Coelenterata (coelenterates): corals and the like.
Platyhelminthes: flatworms.
Nematoda (nematodes): roundworms.
Annelida (annelids): segmented worms.
Bryozoa (bryozoans): moss-animals.
Brachiopoda (brachiopods): lampshells.
Arthropoda (arthropods): insects, spiders, crabs, shrimps, trilobites, etc.
Mollusca (mollusks): snails, clams, nautiloids, ammonoids, etc.
Echinodermata (echinoderms): starfish, crinoids (sea-lilies), sea-urchins, etc.
Chordata (chordates): mostly vertebrates; also non-vertebrate animals with notochord, including graptolites.

Some of these phyla have many representatives (species) with hard parts that are preserved as fossils in the rocks. Other phyla are practically unknown as fossils. An estimate of the relative abundance of the living and fossil species, phylum by phylum, is shown in Figure 2-3; the estimates are rough, of course, and indicate some ignorance as well as much knowledge.

The nine invertebrate phyla extensively represented in the fossil record are listed along with some important subdivisions in Table 2-2. Three of the subdivisions are wholly extinct, and a fourth has only one set of living representatives. These four groups are the graptolites, which were perhaps primitive relatives of the vertebrates; the trilobites (Fig. 2-16), classified among the arthropods; the nautiloids (Fig. 2-20), a group of mollusks that includes the living *Nautilus;* and the ammonoids (Figs. 2-8B and 2-22), which have shells similar to those of nautiloids. Graptolites and trilobites are exclusively Paleozoic, nautiloids mostly Paleozoic, and ammonoids upper Paleozoic and Mesozoic. These four groups are given special attention in the present chapter, and ammonoids are a principal subject of Chapter 7. These and other groups of paleontological importance are described systematically in Appendix B.

2-5. *Preservation of Fossils*

Plant and animal tissues are sometimes preserved unchanged. In the youngest deposits (Pleistocene System of the Cenozoic), such preservation is the rule for seashells and not uncommon for the trunks and branches of trees. Even Pleistocene mammoths (hairy elephants) have been preserved entire in the deep freeze of northern Siberia; when dogs can get at the thawed flesh, they eat it greedily.

Many shells that are much older than Pleistocene also appear to be composed of un-

Fig. 2-3. *Relative numbers of known species, living and fossil, in the animal phyla. (Adapted from S. W. Muller and Allison Campbell, 1954, for Bernhard Kummel,* History of the Earth, *W. H. Freeman & Co., 1961.)*

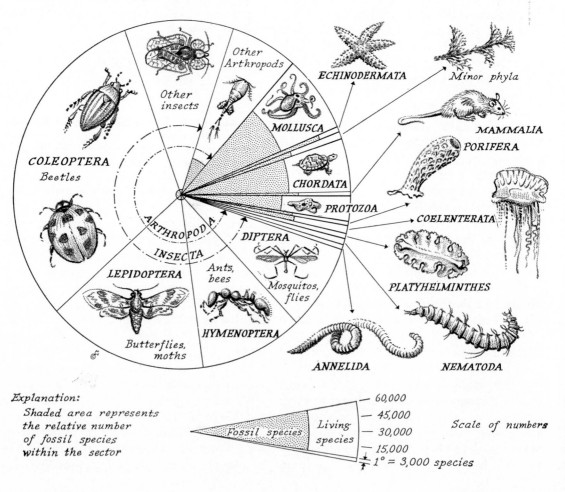

Explanation:
   Shaded area represents
   the relative number
   of fossil species
   within the sector

Fossil species | Living species

— 60,000
— 45,000
— 30,000
— 15,000
1° = 3,000 species

Scale of numbers

TABLE 2-2

Invertebrate Phyla of Greatest Paleontological Interest*

PHYLUM	SUBDIVISION	NOTES
Protozoa		One-celled animals.
	Order Foraminifera	Foraminifers; minute, chambered shells of calcium carbonate or other material.
	Order Radiolaria	Microscopic, rayed shells, usually of silica.
Porifera		Sponges; simplest aggregates of specialized cells.
Coelenterata	Class Anthozoa	Corals; cup-shaped, tentacle-fringed animals, builders of marine limestone reefs.
Bryozoa		Moss-animals; marine.
Brachiopoda		Lampshells; marine.
Mollusca		Shellfish and related animals of sea, land, and fresh water.
	Class Pelecypoda	Clams, oysters, etc.
	Class Gastropoda	Water and land snails.
	Class Cephalopoda	Nautilus, squid, etc.
	Subclass Nautiloidea	Nautiloids; coiled; like nautilus.
	Subclass Ammonoidea	Ammonoids; coiled; partitions of chambered shell crinkled.
Arthropoda		Jointed-legged invertebrates; external skeletons.
	Class Trilobita	Marine Paleozoic arthropods with 3-lobed segments; marine.
	Class Crustacea	Crabs, etc.; marine and fresh-water.
	Class Insecta	Enormously abundant today; fossil record rather scanty.
Echinodermata		Globular or flat, 5-fold symmetry; example, starfish; all marine.
	Classes Cystoidea and Blastoidea	Crinoid-like, arms rudimentary or lacking.
	Class Crinoidea	Sea-lilies; central cups, arms.
	Class Echinoidea	Echinoids: sand-dollars, sea-urchins, and related slow crawlers.
Chordata?	Class Graptolithina	Graptolites; small, branching, colonial; marine; Paleozoic.

* For methods of identification, see Appendix B.

changed original material. Most mollusks secrete shells of calcium carbonate; the shells of many genera consist wholly or partially of the unstable mineral aragonite, which sooner or later dissolves and may be replaced by calcite. Many early Cenozoic shells retain pearly aragonite inner layers, and aragonite has been identified in a few shells as old as late Paleozoic. The calcite portions of such shells may also be original material, but this is harder to prove.

Much more commonly, fossils have undergone partial or complete chemical alteration. Wood and leaves change from the light-colored original carbohydrates to thinner, compressed, black relics, partially changed to elemental carbon by loss of hydrogen and oxygen. Masses of such altered plant material are called lignite if moderately changed, coal if more thoroughly changed. In extreme cases most of the carbon is lost, too, and the plant remains are mere **impressions** in the rocks, still

Fig. 2-4. *Carbonized leaves in Carboniferous rock. (From Bernhard Kummel, op. cit.)*

Fig. 2-5. *Cast and Molds. (From Bernhard Kummel, op. cit.)*
ABOVE. *Inside view of pelecypod cast.*
BELOW. *Molds of ammonites.*

showing the shape and veins of leaves (Fig. 2-4) or regular sets of leaf pits on trunk or branches. Insects and other animals or parts of animals are similarly preserved, as carbonized remains or as impressions.

Some fossils are molds or casts of wood, shells, and other organic substances. A **mold** (Fig. 2-5) is the form left after the solution or removal of the original material. If the substance removed was that of a mud-filled shell, the cavity may have not only an **external mold** but also an **internal mold**. A filled mold is a **cast**, which may be either a natural **replace-**

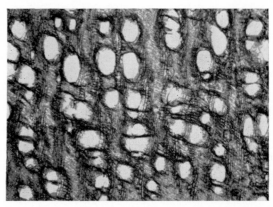

Fig. 2-6. *Petrified wood, perhaps of poplar type: replacement by opal with preservation of wood structure; vessels filled with quartz. Thin section (G. B. Bellemin), × 40.*

ment by a mineral such as quartz or an artifact of plaster or latex.

Some replacements, in which the internal structure of the original material is preserved, must have developed bit by bit rather than by the filling of empty molds. An example is the petrified wood of Figure 2-6, in which the original wood has been replaced by opal, with the preservation of many cell boundaries; the sap-carrying vessels (shown in cross-section) have been filled with clear quartz.

The material of many fossil shells is coarse-grained calcite, the same material, chemically, as the original shells; it is recognized as a replacement by the absence of the original fine structure. Other replaced shells are composed of entirely new material, such as quartz or pyrite (iron sulphide).

Original material or not, many fossil invertebrates and plants are things of beauty, treasured by the collector. Among the finest are crinoids from the upper Paleozoic of Iowa and Indiana and from the Jurassic of Germany (Figs. 2-18 and 2-19). The collector with a microscope need not wait for the rare perfect large specimen. If he lives within a hundred miles of the Atlantic or Gulf coast of the United States, from Maryland to Texas, or anywhere along the Pacific coast, or at many another American locality, he can find slightly consolidated Mesozoic or Cenozoic marine or fresh-water sediments that will yield superb washed concentrates of diatoms (Fig. 2-7), radiolarians, or foraminifers. The diatoms, in particular, are beautiful beyond words.

2-6. Biological Classification

Groups of related organisms that have been named and defined according to established rules are called **taxa**. The primary taxa are the **phyla**. The principal subdivisions of the phyla are called *classes*, of classes *orders*, and of orders *families*. Families are divided into *genera*, and genera into *species*.

The **species** is the fundamental group. The members of a living species are so similar to one another that they form a single inter-breeding assemblage, with fertile offspring. All living human beings belong to one species, *Homo sapiens*, and all living dogs to another, *Canis familiaris*. All domestic horses are examples of *Equus caballus*, and all asses may be included, at least for our purposes, in *Equus asinus*. The mule, progeny of ass and mare, is not fertile, and so horses and asses are considered separate species.

Although a genus, such as *Equus*, usually includes several species, some genera include but one species each, made up of individuals with no known relatives, living or extinct, that are similar enough to be put in the same genus.

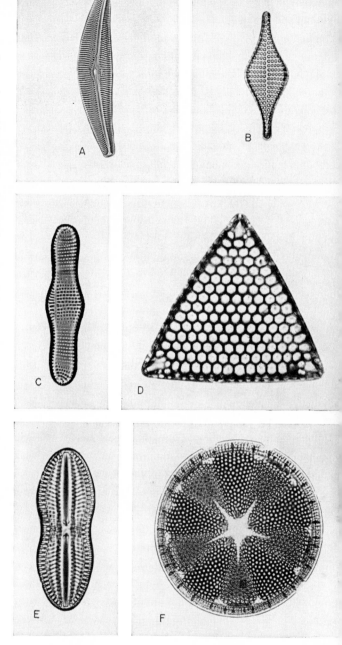

Fig. 2-7. *Diatoms, greatly enlarged. (Courtesy of K. E. Lohman, U.S. Geological Survey.)*
A. Cymbella cistula (*fresh-water, Neogene, Nevada*).
B. Rhaphoneis elegans (*marine, Neogene*).
C. Achnanthes inflata (*fresh-water, Pleistocene, New Mexico*).
D. Triceratium favus (*marine, Cenozoic*).
E. Diploneis prisca (*marine, Neogene*).
F. Actinoptychus heliopelta (*marine, Neogene*).

Every species has a definite place in the general classification. The edible oysters of commerce may be used as examples. They belong in the phylum Mollusca, and their exact position can be shown thus:

Phylum Mollusca (clams, snails, etc.).
    Class Pelecypoda (clams, oysters, and other headless mollusks with bivalved shells).
      Order Isodontidae (a group whose shells typically, but not in oysters, have hinge teeth derived from two ridges).
        Family Ostreidae (the oysters).
          Genus *Ostrea* (the flat oysters).
            Species *Ostrea edulis* (European oyster) or *Ostrea lurida* (native Pacific Coast oyster) or other species.

The names for all ranks are Latin, often of a kind that might have puzzled Cicero or Caesar. International rules have been established to govern their formation. Every day new taxonomic (systematic) terms are published, for species, genera, or higher groups. The roots of the words in valid (taxonomically legal) new terms may be barbaric, but the endings must be passable Latin. *Rooseveltia newyorkensis* would be accepted. The generic name is a noun, and the trivial name (the second part of the species name) is an adjective, as in the hypothetical *Rooseveltia newyorkensis* or the actual *Ostrea edulis,* or is a genitive noun, as in *Equus stenonis* (Steno's horse), or is a noun in apposition, as in *Kosmoceras jason* (§ 7-4.a). The noun has determinable gender (*Rooseveltia* would be feminine), and the adjective must agree: thus *Equus caballus,* masculine, but *Ostrea lurida,* feminine. If a single species of plant or animal, or a taxonomic unit of higher rank, has two or more legally constructed names, both properly defined, the earliest name is chosen, by the Law of Priority. Perfectly legal differences of opinion about nomenclature may, however, still persist; some people, for example, may set off part of the genus *Equus* as the genus *Asinus,* but others may still, if they wish, call the asses *Equus.*

Since two words are used in the name of each species, the system is said to be **binomial.**

The whole system of classification, for both plants and animals, goes back to Carolus Linnaeus, a Swedish biologist (1707–1778), and so is commonly called the **Linnaean system.**

2-7. *Origin of the Idea of Evolution*

Linnaeus and almost all other interested persons of his time thought each species specially created by God. The problem of the classifier, then, was merely to discover differences between species that had existed since the beginning of things. About fifty or sixty years after Linnaeus's principal publications, however, as we shall see in Chapter 3, successive sets of strata in both France and England were found to contain different sets of fossil species. Philosophical persons were greatly agitated. Baron Georges Cuvier (1769–1832), who had found in the rocks near Paris many of the kinds of mollusks and vertebrates that were arousing all the excitement, suggested that all life in the European area, after being extinguished time after time, had been renewed again and again by immigration from somewhere else. Other people came out squarely for universal extinctions followed by new creations. But many of the species at upper levels in the rocks were obviously similar to those at lower levels; oyster-like shells, for example, were succeeded by unmistakable oysters, and strange-looking sea snails by sea snails of more modern aspect. A god who could create the multitude of forms found in a single flora or fauna seemed strangely uninspired and ungodlike in his later activity, for all the new creations were surprisingly similar to the previous ones. Inevitably, someone thought of evolution or discovered that the Greeks had already thought of it. When Charles Darwin, in his *Origin of Species* (1859), not only suggested relationships between successive species but also propounded a mechanism of continuous evolution (natural selection among the endless minor variations that he found to occur), the scientific world accepted the ideas with relief.

2-8. *Species in Paleontology*

In the years that followed, paleontologists described many faunas and floras, made up, in the aggregate, of tens of thousands of species. As some local successions of faunas became better and better known, continuous gradations were found between species in lower strata and other species in higher strata. It was common for many fossil species to be distinguished, each name applying to only a few specimens. In time the number of similar species in some genera became ridiculous. We realize now that each investigator should de-

scribe as few new species as possible, should indicate the range of variation within each described species, and should, if possible, justify the definition of each species on statistical grounds.

One basic procedure is illustrated here. Figure 2-8A represents statistically the sizes (diameters) of specimens of similar-looking ammonites of the genus shown in B. The specimens were collected from a Jurassic bed in England. Diameters increase from left to right. The length of each solid vertical line is proportional to the number of specimens in a size group. The first line stands for two speci-

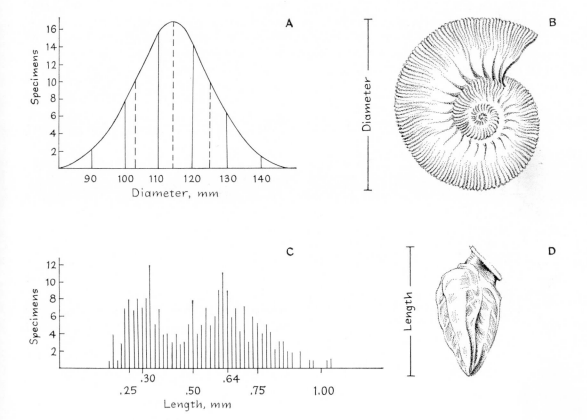

Fig. 2-8. *Size distribution in species or supposed species.*
A. *Diameters of 48 specimens of the ammonite* Kosmoceras, *from an 8-inch layer in Oxford Clay (Jurassic), Peterborough, England. (Data from Roland Brinkmann, 1929.)*
B. *A Kosmoceras specimen from Peterborough, about one-half natural size.*
C. *Lengths of 237 specimens of the foraminifer* Bolivina bicostata *in a sample of Pacific Ocean mud, taken at a water depth of 260 feet off El Salvador. (After Patsy J. Smith, 1963.)*
D. *A specimen of* Bolivina bicostata, × 50.

mens with diameters between 85 and 95 mm, the second line for eight specimens with diameters between 95 and 105 mm, etc. The vertical lines are enveloped by a bell-shaped symmetrical curve, the **normal curve,** based on the measurements. First the **mean** (average) diameter was calculated. It proved to be 114 mm. A broken vertical line was then drawn to mark this value, which is the **mode** at the apex of the curve, which in this case is also its center. Points on the curve were calculated according to statistical rules, which made 68 percent of the area beneath the curve lie between the diameters 103 and 125 mm, each of which is 11 mm from the mean. This value, 11 mm, is the **standard deviation,** a measure of the sample's variability in size that can be used to estimate the variability of the fossil population from which the sample was drawn. Normal distribution of sizes or other characteristics, conforming to a curve such as that of Figure 2-8A, is considered evidence in favor of the idea that the sample represents a single species.

Not every collection of similar-looking biological specimens has normal size distribution. A more complex distribution is shown in Figure 2-8, which represents (C) the lengths of the members of a group of small foraminifers (exemplified in D) found in a sample of the top half-inch of mud on the floor of the Pacific Ocean off Central America. The height of each vertical line is proportional to the number of specimens having the length indicated at the base of the line. This distribution appears to be bimodal. A smooth curve might be drawn with two apices, one near length 0.30 mm, the other near length 0.64 mm. That is, the little animals seem to fall into two size groups, and so, in spite of their otherwise similar appearance, they may belong to two species. They may, however, so far as this diagram shows, represent two age groups of a single species, or two types of development (sexual and asexual), or two successive populations of a single species now mingled in a half-inch of bottom ooze.

By statistical and other methods the number of species recognized in many groups of animals and plants has now been greatly reduced. Among fossil bears, for example, the 100 or more species that had been described from the European Pleistocene have been reduced to three or four by a well-known Finnish investigator (Fig. 2-9). Under the new arrangement, most specimens are assigned to two species that range through most of the Pleistocene. The reduction from many supposedly distinct species of short stratigraphic range to a few long-ranging species was justified by statistical and other evidence of gradation. Future students of fossil bears may raise some of the subspecies of Figure 2-9 to the rank of species, despite the gradations, but they will base their species, not on single specimens, however complete, but on all known specimens in the population or populations under consideration.

Fig. 2-9. *Stratigraphic ranges of European Pleistocene species and subspecies of bears (genus Ursus). Principal species:* U. arctos (*brown bear) and* U. spelaeus (*cave bear). (From Björn Kurtén, 1957.)*

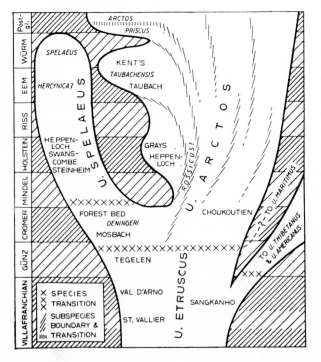

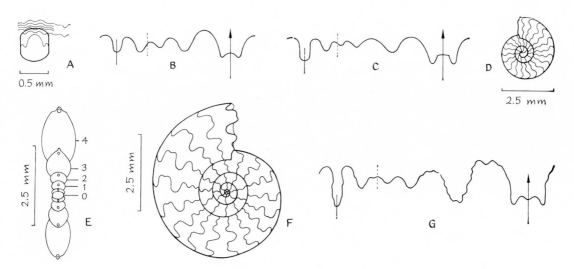

Fig. 2-10. *Development of the Cretaceous ammonite* Oregoniceras. *(After J. P. Smith, 1898.)*
   A. *Embryonic chamber and first six sutures.*
   B, C. *Later, slightly more complicated sutures. The arrow at the periphery points toward the aperture.*
   D. *A denuded shell at the C stage, showing septa.*
   E. *Transverse section through four whorls.*
   F. *Five denuded whorls, showing septa.*
   G. *A rather late, somewhat complicated suture.*

The systematic paleontologist, in the course of his work, makes many measurements and many taxonomic decisions. At the end of a study, he uses statistical diagrams to find out if his sorting has been completed satisfactorily. The more numerous the fossils and the more continuous their distribution through the strata, the more difficult is the sorting and the more necessary the statistical tests.

2-9. Ammonoids and the So-called Biogenetic Law

Between 1860 and 1920 many zoologists and paleontologists asserted that there was a relation between the development of an individual and the development of the group to which it belonged. They tossed about such weighty phrases as "the biogenetic law: ontogeny (the development of an individual) recapitulates phylogeny (the development of the group)." More precisely, in the words of

Alpheus Hyatt, "modifications . . . tend to appear first in the adolescent or adult stages of growth, and then to be inherited in successive descendants at earlier and earlier stages, . . . until they either become embryonic or are crowded out . . . and replaced . . . by characteristics of later origin."

This idea of recapitulation affected every branch of paleontology, but what seemed to be the best examples were found among the ammonoids. Some Upper Carboniferous ammonoids apparently recapitulated in their earliest whorls the characteristic features of earlier ammonoids and even those of the simpler, very early nautiloids. In Upper Cretaceous strata true ammonites, with convoluted adult sutures (compare § B-7.c.2), seemed in their earlier whorls to recapitulate features possessed by their Carboniferous adult ancestors. Some pertinent features of the development of an Upper Cretaceous specimen are shown in Figure 2-10: At A the embryonic chamber and the first six septa are shown as if unrolled, presenting in this short space micro-simulations of the adult septa of a whole series of Paleozoic genera; at B and C later, slightly more complicated but still Paleozoic-like sutures are shown; the whole of the little shell at this stage is represented at D; the first ammonitic (Mesozoic) feature is a marginal keel on the third whorl of the section at E; then the sutures become more and more complicated, as in the last whorl at F, until at G the crenulations are almost as numerous, though not as pronounced, as in the adult (not shown).

No one can deny the validity of the comparisons made by the nineteenth-century paleontologists, though it has since been shown that exactly contrary tendencies were sometimes ignored. But the implications as to lines of descent are not now taken seriously. The tiny genes in the first cell of a new individual contain the whole program for its later development. The genes are similar to the program fed into a computer, telling it what things to do and the order in which to do them. The program for the development of an individual organism may include a favorable variation from the previous norm, and the variation may become part of the distinctiveness of a new species. But only chance would produce a variation of the adult form and also produce at an immature stage the previous adult form. Such chance results did apparently occur in the sutures of Figure 2-10, and the chance resemblances seem to be characteristic of this Cretaceous species.

The whole history of the biogenetic law deserves thoughtful consideration by any scientist. At present we must consider the law unsound. But we must not forget the facts upon which it was based. They may come in handy as future theories develop.

2-10. *Evolution and the Principle of Simplicity*

In this book organic evolution is assumed, for there is now no rival theory that even attempts to explain both the variety of existing life on earth and the record of past life preserved in the rocks. But some implications of evolution, and an important problem, need to be mentioned. We must remember, in our theorizing, that organisms differ endlessly. Plants and animals, for example, make things that are varied chemically as well as physically: skin and bones, wood, urea, citric acid (in the lemon and other citrus fruits), oils, resins, earwax, and a thousand more. At the present time, an apple seed will become a tree that produces a fruit with an acid different from citric acid. Some kinds of brachiopods make calcium phosphate shells; other kinds make calcium carbonate shells. The marvels of inheritance are astounding enough if we consider only the differences in the present world; they tax the imagination almost beyond its capacity when we think of the evolution of these varied organisms, with their multiform development and varied products, from common ancestors. Perhaps we can imagine one ancestor, or pair of ancestors, for the lemon and the apple, a single kind of animal as ancestor for the cow and the sheep, perhaps even one for the clam and the snail. But one single ancestor for the sheep and the apple? Incredulity is natural. Its best antidote is an attempt to explain life as developing from two or more sources. We might start with two creations, one the ancestor of all plants, the other of all animals. Inevitably we should be forced to make these protoypes simple—one-celled. Our two prototypes would be so similar to each other and so different from both sheep and apple that our first objections to the common origin of plants and animals would lose all their force. For simplicity's sake we should then postulate tentatively a single primal kind of living thing.

Such a procedure is a crude example of the use of what has been called the **principle of simplicity.** This principle, first emphasized by the fourteenth-century scholastic philosopher William of Ockham and sometimes called Ockham's Razor, is stated thus: *Entia non sunt multiplicanda praeter necessitatem.* Paraphrases in English might include "Entities should not be increased unnecessarily," "The fewer the concepts, the better," and "Keep your tastes simple."

The principle of simplicity is a rule of convenience. It is not proof. If life spontaneously developed from non-living material once, certainly it might have done so twice or many times. But the principle of simplicity leads us to begin with the hypothesis of a single event, the origin of life. Then, if we should find the world of living things divisible into two great groups of dissimilar organisms, with no problematic species left over, we might, by the same principle of simplicity, assume *two* primal kinds of living things, one for each group. Our actual classification, with its difficulties over one-celled organisms, seems more compatible with a single origin for all life, in a far-off Precambrian time.

2-11. *Life Realms: Land, Fresh Water, and Ocean*

Plants and animals are adjusted to one of two strikingly different habitats, water and air. Take first the water (aquatic habitat). Plants that use sunlight as a source of energy live only in the uppermost, lighted levels of the sea and other bodies of water. Animals, less limited in vertical range, may float at the surface, swim at all levels, or live on the bottom. The floaters, both plant and animal, are collectively called the **plankton,** and the bottom dwellers the **benthos.** The corresponding adjectives are **planktonic** and **benthonic.** Many benthonic animals, cemented to the bottom or otherwise fixed in position, are **sessile.** Swimming animals make up a group with another Greek name, the **nekton,** but this we shall rarely use.

Group after group of animals has a large number of representatives in the ocean and a smaller number in fresh water. Most fresh-water groups have peculiar features of some sort by which they can easily be distinguished from their marine relatives, at least by the specialist in the study of the group. Fresh-water crayfish differ markedly from their ma-

rine relatives, the crabs and lobsters; fresh-water clams, especially those with pearly shells, are strikingly different from their much more varied relatives in the ocean. Some groups of animals, such as the corals, are exclusively marine. In one way or another, the assemblages of aquatic fossils found in the rocks can almost always be recognized as either marine or fresh-water.

It is even easier to distinguish aquatic plants

Fig. 2-11. *Food chain or net of the North Sea herring at successive stages of its growth. Herring dark, its prey and predators light. (From Ref. 3.)*

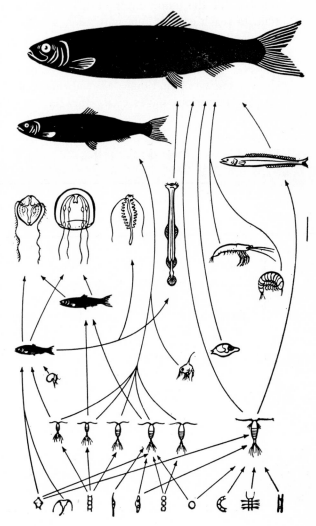

from land plants, or aquatic faunas from groups of animals that walk or crawl on the land or fly through the air. For one thing, almost all sessile animals are aquatic.

2-12. *Ecology*

a. Marine Ecologic Associations

The relation of living things to their environments is called their **ecology.** One of the most obvious relations, especially in the sea, is that of hunter and prey. Near the surface of the ocean, protozoans live on minute floating plants, shrimps and similar animals live on protozoans, small fish live on shrimps and the like, and large fish eat small fish. The numbers of the many kinds of living things tend to reach equilibrium, with each kind as abundant as possible under the environmental conditions. The complexity of the relationships is illustrated by Figure 2-11, which shows, among other things, the herring and its prey at various stages of its growth.

Each aquatic species is adapted to a particular range of temperature, pressure, salinity, roughness, and clarity of water. Bottom-dwelling animals and plants have additional preferences or requirements: rock for attachment, sand in which to dig, etc. They are affected particularly by one environmental condition, the depth of water. Depth determines pressure and light and is a major factor in fixing the temperature. The principal depth zones useful for making biological distinctions, shown in Figure 2-12, are called (1) **littoral,** or intertidal; (2) **sublittoral,** down to a depth of about 600 feet; (3) **bathyal,** between 600 and about 12,000 feet in depth; and (4) **abyssal,** below about 12,000.

At any one depth, especially in shallow water, the benthonic animals (and plants) fall into three groups: one living in the sand or mud or other material of the bottom (Fig. 2-13), one living on or attached to the muddy or rocky or other surface (Fig. 2-14), and one made up of fish, scallops, snails, and other

Fig. 2-12. *Benthonic depth zones.*

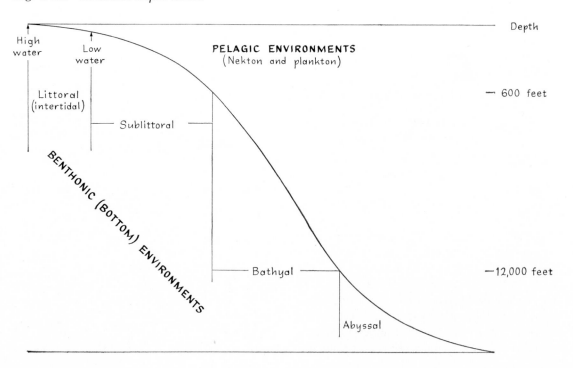

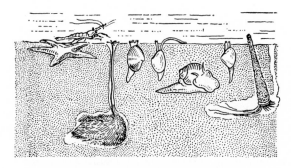

Fig. 2-13. *Sand fauna at about 30-foot depth, off Denmark, showing pelecypods, starfish, and gastropods. (From Ref. 3.)*

animals that hover in seaweed or swim close to the bottom or crawl about on the sea floor.

The many variations in environment result in many ecologic **communities,** or assemblages. Even in one small region, such as the ocean waters off Denmark, seven or eight bottom communities are known. One kind of clam is prevalent in the shallow and in part brackish water close to the mouth of the Baltic Sea; several other pelecypod species are associated in the sand off exposed salt-water beaches; and a third group made up of pelecypod and echinoderm species lives in the mud and sand of protected bays. At somewhat greater depths, from 50 to 300 feet, the sea floor may be covered with brittlestars (rela-

Fig. 2-14. *Marine fauna on stony bottom at 80-foot depth off Denmark, showing pelecypods, corals, algae, brittlestars, etc. (From Ref. 3.)*

tives of the starfish) or made up of the tiny burrows of minute shrimp-like arthropods.

From a slightly different point of view the Danish aquatic communities may be grouped into three **facies,** or aspects, of the general fauna: (1) brackish, (2) littoral marine, and (3) sublittoral marine. These facies are general and are found all over the world, though the particular species of the Danish communities are not so widespread. A fourth general facies—shallow, rocky, some distance from the shore—is the rocky-reef facies, which has two climatically important varieties, the tropical, littoral, coral-reef facies and the deeper-water, temperate, rocky-bank facies, made up of fishing banks at depths, usually, between 100 and 400 feet, with both rocky and sandy bottoms, swarming with shellfish and crabs, with fish swimming in and near communities composed of seaweed and adhering small animals.

b. Present Faunal (and Floral) Provinces

At the present time temperature facies are especially important. There is a single circumpolar shallow marine Arctic facies, but the corresponding temperate and tropical facies are divided by the north-south trending continents and deep oceans into regional units. The principal north temperate faunas are the European, or Eastern Atlantic, the East Coast American, the West Coast American, and the Asiatic. Each of these faunas characterizes a regional marine **faunal province.** Similar faunal (and floral) provinces are distinguished on land.

c. Changes in a Community

Changes are continually occurring in the composition of each local community. One species becomes more common, another more rare. A species may even disappear from a locality or a region—or from all its haunts, becoming extinct. Another species may move in to take its place, as the Lower California sardine did, to some extent, when the California sardine was fished to extinction in the nineteen-fifties.

The spread of the present shallow-water mollusks is determined largely by the rate of movement of the young larvae, which commonly float with the plankton for a short time before settling down to adult stability. In this fashion marine clams and snails may spread slowly, usually only a few feet or a few hundred feet per year. Sometimes, however, they spread much more rapidly. The American slipper-shell, a snail that is practically sessile as an adult, after being introduced into English waters, spread 200 miles along the southeast English coast in twenty-five years, or at the rate of eight miles a year. A chiefly European species of snail, *Littorina littorea*, reached Nova Scotian waters by 1200 or 1300 A.D., for it has been collected from an Indian camp site of that time. It may have been introduced to Nova Scotia by the Norsemen, who established temporary settlements in Newfoundland at about the same time. It moved southward much later, reaching Maine in 1868 and New Haven in 1880. The 360 miles from Maine to New Haven were traversed in twelve years, at thirty miles a year.

Fig. 2-15. *Partial and complete barriers.*

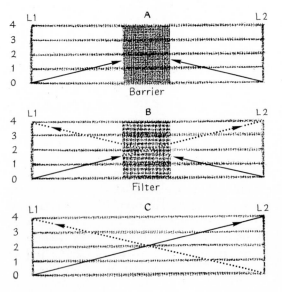

d. Barriers

The shallow-water species do not spread indefinitely. They are stopped by three more or less impenetrable barriers: land, deep water, and unfavorable temperatures. The limiting depth of water varies with the species, but no shallow-water species can endure the conditions at the bottom of the deep ocean. Temperate species cannot stand Arctic temperatures, and Arctic species cannot live in warm water. The American slipper-shell, after being kept on the west side of the Atlantic for ages by temperature and other natural barriers, was transported across the ocean by man.

Barriers to the spread of shallow-water, bottom-dwelling, marine organisms may be classified according to their degrees of completeness, as shown diagrammatically in Figure 2-15, where the arrows indicate the movement of organisms between localities L1 and L2 in successive intervals of time 0–1, 1–2, etc. Deep ocean or land of continental proportions is ordinarily a complete barrier (A), but even such a barrier may be turned by a flank movement or crossed directly by a lucky accident, such as the floating of a natural raft across an ocean. Temperature differences are filter barriers (B), barring some animals and letting others through. Currents moving constantly in one direction may conceivably produce almost completely unidirectional barriers (C); such barriers are not numerous in the present oceans, but they may have been more important at some times in the past (compare § 7-4.a).

The principal barriers affecting planktonic plants and animals are land and unfavorable temperatures. The plankton is spread by currents. The courses of currents in all oceans have been determined by the movements of many thousands of drift bottles. One bottle, launched in 1929 in the Indian Ocean southwest of Australia, was reported later off the southern tip of South America, in the South Atlantic, and again in the Indian Ocean; it came ashore in western Australia in 1935, after circumnavigating the southern world and covering "some 16,800 nautical miles in 2,447 days—a respectable average of about 6.8 miles per day" (Ref. 5). Planktonic organisms, unlike drift bottles, are limited in their migrations by water temperatures. The tropical plankton, for example, is hemmed in by temperature barriers at the north and south, as well as being split by the American and African land barriers (Ref. 3, vol. 1, p. 367).

2-13. *Ecology of Some Important Groups of Fossil Animals*

The roots, trunks, and leaves of palms and other trees, the bones of horses and camels, and the shells of clams and oysters immediately give us hints as to the conditions of deposition of the strata that contain them. But fossils belonging to groups that are extinct or now restricted in occurrence are less informative. We must judge such fossils by their association with the remains of plants and animals of known habitat and by the analogy between their organs or structures and organs or structures of known function.

Such estimates concerning ecology are especially important, for one reason or another, when applied to the trilobites, the graptolites, the crinoids, and two kinds of shell-bearing cephalopod mollusks, the nautiloids and the ammonoids. (The ammonoids are divided into the Mesozoic ammonites and the Paleozoic goniatites; see Appendix B.) As the trilobites, graptolites, and ammonoids include many guide fossils (to be defined later in this chapter), their mobility becomes a characteristic of particular interest.

a. Trilobite Ecology

Trilobites (Fig. 2-16) are known to have lived in the sea, for they are found with other animals that are exclusively marine. The minute larvae (A, magnified 20×), being thin and having broad surfaces, were probably planktonic floaters. The adults had numerous movable legs, which they must have used either for crawling on, or for swimming above, the sea bottom. They had, in fact, two sets of

Fig. 2-16. *Adaptive forms among trilobites. (From* Treatise on Invertebrate Paleontology, *1959, courtesy Geological Society of America and University of Kansas Press.)*
A. Paradoxides? *larva, 1.5 mm across.*
B. Cyclopyge, *35 mm long.*
C. Odontopleura, *50 mm across.*
D. Ceraurus, *60 mm long.*

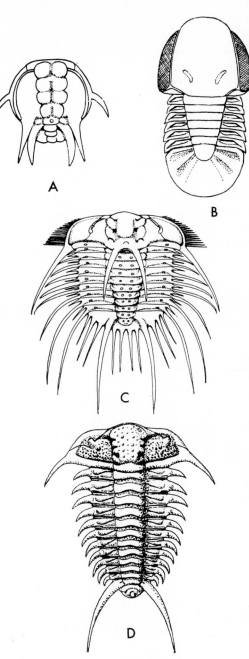

A

B

C

D

leg-like appendages, one set sturdy and per-haps used for crawling, the other set more delicate and perhaps used as gills and for swimming. That some trilobites crawled about on the sea floor is strongly indicated by the trails associated with Cambrian trilobite re-mains in the Grand Canyon region (Fig. 2-17). The shovel-like heads of these trilobites may have been used for digging in the mud; their lack of biting mouth parts may mean that they were also detritus feeders (mud-eaters).

Other trilobites may have been swimmers that never or almost never descended to the sea floor. Among these may well have been some little fellows with big eyes (Fig. 2-16B). These forms resemble somewhat the living crustacean *Cystisoma*, which spends the day at depth but rises to the surface at night. Another small trilobite had a full set of mar-ginal spines (C), which would have helped it float, by the increase of surface area and con-sequently of the surface tension, but would have been a handicap to movement on the sea floor. Still another kind (D) is thought, because of statistical evidence, to have lived far above the sea floor. Of 1,160 specimens found at one locality, 1,110 lay with their con-vex backs down and their legs up. The de-scriber of this occurrence thought these ani-mals must have swum on their backs, but a critic pointed out that dead animals of their shape, falling a great distance through quiet water, would mostly get into this position; back-down would be the favored position, the result of streamlined fall.

Study of all the many trilobite groups has led to the conclusion that most lived on the sea floor, that many swam or floated, and that the larvae of all forms floated about for a short time. The bottom-dwellers may have been limited to particular depths or particular kinds of bottom. The majority of genera are found mostly in shales or fine sandstones, a smaller number chiefly in limestones, almost none in conglomerates, and none in the prob-ably deep-sea radiolarian cherts.

b. Graptolite Ecology

The graptolites (see § B-10) were little co-lonial animals, which are thought from their associations to have been exclusively marine. It is clear that they did not swim. The den-droid graptolites were mostly sessile, with

Fig. 2-17. *Trail of a trilobite, probably* Olenellus, *in the Lower Cambrian of the Grand Canyon, Arizona. (From J. S. Shelton,* Geology Illustrated, *W. H. Freeman & Co.)*

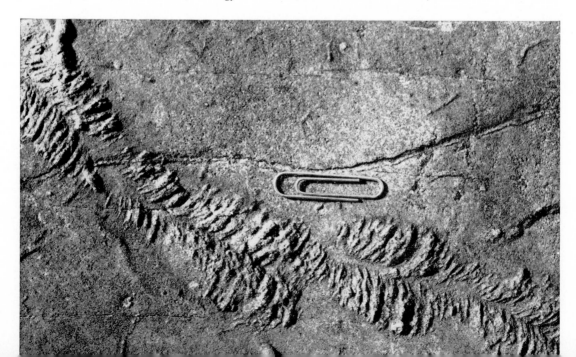

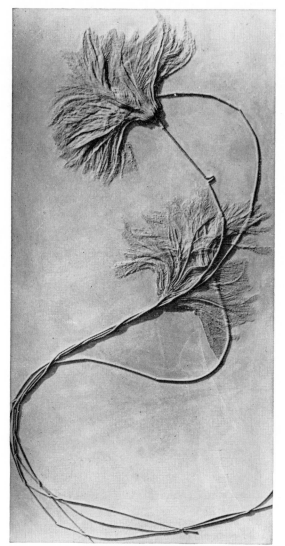

thickened stems and discoidal, branching basal organs. A few dendroids (especially *Dictyonema flabelliforme;* see § B-10) and the whole group of Graptoloidea, including the best guide fossils of the Ordovician and Silurian, were non-sessile. They may have floated free, perhaps suspended from a float made by the colony; or they may have been attached to floating seaweeds; or they may have been attached to seaweeds that were attached to the sea floor. That many graptoloids actually floated about is indicated by the wide distribution, in some cases worldwide, of genera and even species. Graptoloids are found in most kinds of sedimentary rocks, from sandstones to limestones, and are best preserved in certain rare cherts, but they are most abundant in black shales that contain few other fossils. This distribution fits well with the hypothesis of planktonic drifting, the dead animals having fallen onto every sort of sea floor and having been most commonly preserved in facies that lack bottom-dwelling scavengers.

c. Crinoid Ecology

Paleozoic and early Mesozoic crinoids were locally abundant in the shallow seas on the continental platforms. They were commonly attached by long jointed stems to the sea floor or to floats. They occur in communities of many individuals or as masses of skeletal plates. Where the individual specimens are

Fig. 2-18. *Crinoids* (Pentacrinus subangularis) *with long stems and heads 20 inches across, in the Berlin Natural History Museum, from the Lower Jurassic, Holzmaden-Teck, southwestern Germany. (Collected, prepared, and photographed by Dr. Bernhard Hauff.)*

Fig. 2-19. *Group of crinoids* (Pentacrinus subangularis) *on carbonized log 75 inches long, in Senckenburg Museum, Frankfurt-am-Main, from the Lower Jurassic, Holzmaden-Teck, southwestern Germany. (Collected, prepared, and photographed by Dr. Bernhard Hauff.)*

well preserved, they are not as thickly crowded as oysters or mussels; the individuals, commonly all belonging to a single species, have some living space. Groups of *Pentacrinus subangularis* (Figs. 2-18 and 2-19) from Lower Jurassic shale at Holzmaden, in southwestern Germany, are notable for large size (calyces 15–20 inches across), perfect preservation, and haunting beauty. They also seem to be mementos of an inescapable fate. Apparently a group of crinoids became attached to a log that floated lower and lower in the water until finally the accumulated weight of the growing animals carried the mass to the muddy sea floor, where the crinoids fell prostrate (Fig. 2-19), perhaps after death by suffocation. The idea that the Holzmaden logs ultimately became overloaded is based on the observation that the larger the log, the larger, more numerous, and longer-stemmed the crinoids.

d. Nautiloid and Ammonoid Ecology

The chambered nautilus still lives in the East Indies. The genus *Nautilus* is made up of six species, which furnish the best clues to the anatomy and behavior of their extinct relatives, the other nautiloids and the ammonoids. A nautilus is an active, tentacled marine animal that lives many feet below the surface, swimming rapidly backward by expelling quick jets of water from its funnel-shaped hyponome (see § B-7.c.2). It is a carnivore and scavenger, feeding on crabs, lobsters, and other animals at or near the sea bottom. Males are larger than females, and the shells of males have broader apertures. Both the calcium carbonate of the shell and the animal itself are heavier than sea water, but the chambers, other than the living chamber, contain gas, making the mean specific gravity (weight per unit of volume) the same as that of sea water. The animal can rest poised in the water, rise easily to the surface, or sink as easily to the bottom. Animals that die in captivity remain floating after death, in the customary position. Arthur Willey, whose letters from New Guinea

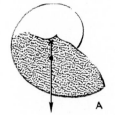 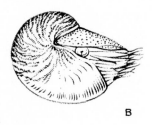

Fig. 2-20. Nautilus pompilius. (*After A. E. Trueman, 1940.*)
A. *Position of calculated equilibrium for shell and animal; centers of buoyancy and gravity marked by cross and dot, respectively.*
B. *Animal in shell, floating at rest.*

in 1897 included the first precise information about the behavior of the living nautilus, emphasized that "there is one thing a *Nautilus* cannot do, namely, turn upside down." This fact is explained by the low center of gravity of the shell with the animal in it (Fig. 2-20A). The normal position in the water is shown in Figure 2-20B, but the animal can use its tentacles to hold itself in a somewhat different position on the sea floor.

Important conclusions concerning ammonite ecology were reached by A. E. Trueman of England, on the basis of comparisons between centers of gravity and of buoyancy. The center of buoyancy is the center of gravity of the water displaced by shell and animal in contrast to the actual center of gravity of the shell and its contents during life. Trueman assumed that Mesozoic ammonites, like the living *Nautilus*, were heavy animals that occupied only the last chamber of the shell, the others being filled with light-weight gas. When he plotted centers of buoyancy and gravity on diagrams (Fig. 2-21), he found that the ammonites fell into two groups. In one the body chamber occupied half a whorl or less, as in *Nautilus;* the centers of gravity being well separated from the centers of buoyancy, the animals could only have been at ease hanging below the buoyant, gas-filled chambers of their coils (A–H). The first two such shells, A and B, were closely coiled, the others loosely coiled or partly uncoiled. No doubt these were primarily swimming animals, like the nautilus, though the little G and H may have just floated and lived on plankton. The members of the other group, I–L, had long body chambers, up to more than one complete turn. All were closely coiled. Their centers of gravity and centers of buoyancy were so close together that the animals could have taken almost any position with ease, but the normal position may have been with the aperture facing half upward, as in the nautilus (Fig. 2-20B). Though these animals could

have crawled about more easily than the nautilus, the evidence indicates that they and most other ammonoids were primarily swimmers. A 2.5-inch shell of the common *Dactylioceras* of the Lower Jurassic (Fig. 2-21I), in which the body chamber takes up a whole whorl, is very thin and weighs only 1/5 ounce; it could not have reduced the animal's mobility very much. If some ammonites spent part of their time on the sea floor, they may have been quick-acting eaters of lively food, or they may have moved slowly and eaten what was lying about.

Fig. 2-21.   *Centers of buoyancy and gravity of ammonites, marked as in Fig. 2-20: A, B, I–L, Jurassic; C–H, Cretaceous. (After A. E. Trueman, 1940.)*

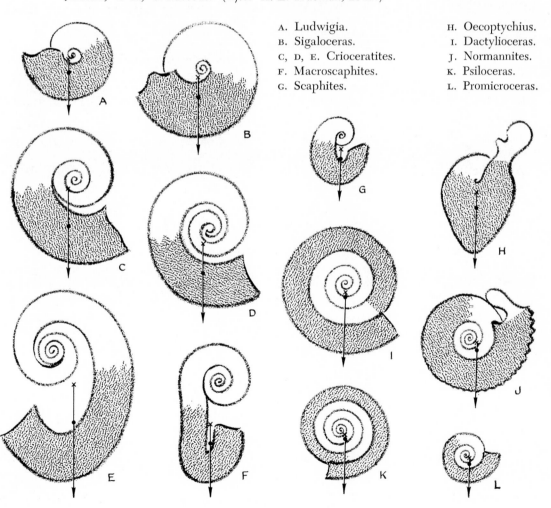

A. Ludwigia.
B. Sigaloceras.
C, D, E. Crioceratites.
F. Macroscaphites.
G. Scaphites.
H. Oecoptychius.
I. Dactylioceras.
J. Normannites.
K. Psiloceras.
L. Promicroceras.

Fig. 2-22. *A late Jurassic perisphinctid ammonite and (at the bottom) the impression of its periphery, from Solnhofen, Bavaria. (From August Rothpletz, 1909.)*

After the deaths of the animals, many ammonite shells may have floated away to more or less distant final resting places, as nautilus shells do today. That such transportation actually occurred is indicated by impressions preserved in the lithographic limestone (Upper Jurassic) at Solnhofen, in southern Germany. This stone hardened from the limy mud of Bahama-like tidal flats. Figure 2-22 shows one of several ammonites found there. The impression of the shell's outer margin, below, indicates that the shell, floating with its gas-filled chambers up and its body chamber down, touched down on its rim as it grounded, fell over on its side when the tide changed, and remained stranded.

In the Mesozoic rocks, many accumulations of ammonite shells are composed wholly of adult specimens. Some such accumulations are in black shales that contain few other fossils. Such assemblages of shells may have been

floated into the places where they are now found after the deaths of the animals. These are called **death assemblages.** They may not represent at all fully the life assemblages of ecologic associates that included the ammonites. In other cases, as in the Solnhofen limestone, a single assemblage may represent both the faunas and the floras of all the life realms —land, air, sea, and fresh water.

Most Paleozoic nautiloids were heavier-shelled than the ammonites and probably lived somewhat different lives. They may have crawled on the bottom, perhaps both competing with the trilobites for food and preying on the trilobites and shellfish.

2-14. *Guide Fossils, Facies Fossils, and Persistent Fossils*

A **guide fossil** is a guide to the relative age of the bed in which it is found; it belongs to a species with wide horizontal distribution and short vertical range in the strata. A **persistent fossil,** on the other hand, has a long vertical range and is therefore useless for close determination of relative age.

A **facies fossil** is limited to a particular environment. In the broad sense of the term, practically all fossils are facies fossils, for most species are limited to one of the three sedimentary realms—marine, fresh-water, and continental. As generally used, however, the term refers to a species, genus, or larger group that is restricted, usually, to a particular environmental belt on the sea floor, such as the shore. Most corals are outstanding examples: all except a few rare kinds of corals are restricted to clear and shallow seas, and the commonest types flourish only in the well-aerated waters of tidally exposed masses of rock in tropical seas. Since the conditions favorable to corals are realized only in narrow belts, coral reefs are sure to be narrow zones in the rocks, bordered by dissimilar rocks containing different fossils.

The best guide fossils are the remains of animals that ranged widely when living, so that their remains became entombed in the various lithologic facies of a set of contemporary sediments, such as shore sands, lagoonal clays, limy deposits, and deep-water oozes. They are shells or other preservable materials with sufficient complexity so that slight changes undergone by the animal in the course of time are reflected by changes in the hard parts, making possible the recognition of many distinct species, each with a short vertical range in the strata. Since planktonic and swimming animals were most likely to fulfill these requirements, it is no surprise to find that the floating graptolites and the swimming ammonites, two groups with delicately complicated hard parts, make the best guide fossils for the Ordovician and Silurian (graptolites) and the Mesozoic (ammonites). Ammonoid precursors of the true ammonites are also valued guides for parts of the late Paleozoic.

2-15. *Climaxes of Invertebrate History*

A survey of the geologic record shows that the general aspect of the shallow-water invertebrate faunas slowly changed. In the Paleozoic, whether the bottom was sandy, muddy, or calcareous, the most abundant animal remains that have been preserved are those of brachiopods, which are accompanied by less persistent or less widespread trilobites, cephalopods, and other types. Coral reefs were fairly numerous, and in the late Paleozoic some were scores of miles long. In some lower Mesozoic (Triassic) rocks the most abundant remains are commonly brachiopod shells, especially in central Europe, but in upper Mesozoic rocks brachiopods become rarer, being replaced partially or completely by ammonites, gastropods, and pelecypods. In Cenozoic rocks practically the only shellfish left are gastropods and pelecypods. During the Mesozoic and Cenozoic, corals and calcareous algae formed tropical reefs, and echinoids built up other shallow-water limy deposits, analogues of late Paleozoic crinoidal limestones.

In somewhat deeper water, the late Paleozoic limestone-builders were fusulinid foraminifers. The corresponding Cretaceous rock is chalk, composed, in part, of the shells of small foraminifers. The corresponding lower Cenozoic rock is limestone made up of foraminifers of a different kind (nummulitic limestone, Fig. 1-10E).

The dominant animals of the early Paleozoic seas were invertebrates, for no vertebrates are found in Cambrian rocks, and vertebrates (fish) are rare in Ordovician and Silurian strata. During the Cambrian the trilobites were the lords of creation, their only rivals being the abundant but sessile brachiopods. During the Ordovician the varied nautiloid mollusks appeared, and some of them were probably rather active. Since the trilobites, at the same time, became smaller, on the average, and also somewhat rarer, the nautiloids were probably the masters of the Ordovician seas. The nautiloids decreased markedly, however, during the Silurian, just as fishes were becoming fairly common. Since then the vertebrates have dominated almost all scenes.

2-16. *Summary*

Fossils, especially invertebrate marine fossils, are the principal sources of information concerning general geological history. They are the guides to the different levels in the geologic column, and by their ecology they indicate the conditions that prevailed at particular places. When we study any one level in the geologic column, a synthesis of local data makes possible regional and even worldwide pictures of the distribution of land and sea, the depths of the sea, and, frequently, some parts of the climatic patterns.

Fossils are prime evidence concerning the evolution of plants and animals to their present state. They furnish the only evidence of great extinct groups of organisms, the study of which may give us hints concerning the future of life as well as knowledge of its past.

▨ | REFERENCES

1. W. H. Matthews III: *Fossils: An Introduction to Prehistoric Life,* 337 pages (Barnes & Noble, New York, 1962)

2. G. G. Simpson, C. S. Pittendrigh, and L. H. Tiffany: *Life: An Introduction to Biology,* 845 pages (Harcourt, Brace, & World, Inc., New York, 1957)

3. J. W. Hedgpeth and H. S. Ladd (editors): *Treatise on Marine Ecology and Paleoecology,* 2 vols., 1,296 + 1,077 pages, Geol. Soc. Amer., Memoir 67 (1957)

4. C. S. Elton: *The Ecology of Invasions by Animals and Plants,* 181 pages (Methuen, London, 1958)

5. Gordon Gaskill: "Bottle Overboard!" READER'S DIGEST, vol. 74, No. 445, pp. 247–252 (May 1959)

CHAPTER 3

The Standard
Geologic Column

A LOCAL geologic column is a formal, summary representation of the sedimentary rocks
of an area in the order of their formation, an
order established by the use of Steno's first
law. The first local geologic columns were
worked out in Europe. A synthesis of these
local columns then established a generalized
geologic column that became the standard for
the world. The local column most valuable in
the synthesis was that of England and Wales.
This area is therefore of first importance. Once
the standard column was set up, it became
the basis for the geologic time scale, in terms
of which geologic history is expressed.

The summary representation of local stratigraphy is achieved by a grouping of the
strata into formations in ways that will be discussed later. The surface distribution of the
formations is then represented on geologic
maps, and the maps are used as the data
from which vertical structure sections may
be derived. In the mapping of a series of formations distinctive fossils (guide fossils) commonly play an important role. The ways in
which formations, fossils, maps, and structure
sections are related can best be illustrated by
the achievements of a pioneer British geologist, William Smith, especially as they are
recorded on the geologic map of England and
Wales that he published in 1815.

It must not be supposed, however, that the
stratigraphic classification of rocks began with
Smith. The first important local arrangement
was made by Steno (§ 1-3) in 1669. In the
middle of the eighteenth century an Italian
(Giovanni Arduino) and a German (J. G.
Lehmann) suggested almost simultaneously a
generally applicable three-fold division. The
three groups of rocks came to be known as
Primitive or Primary (oldest), Secondary, and
Tertiary. Later a fourth and still younger
group, made up of unconsolidated surficial deposits, was added and called Quaternary. This
classification and others proposed before 1800
were both general and hard to apply precisely
at any particular spot. Stratigraphy as a useful
science actually began with Smith and his contemporaries.

3-1. *William Smith's Geologic Map of England and Wales* (1815)

Between 1790 and 1815, soon after ordinary
maps became moderately precise, revolution-
ary methods of geologic mapping were developed independently in France and England.
The **geologic map** was thereby transformed
from a mere record of the places where this
or that rock might be found into a medium
from which the subsurface structure and the

Fig. 3-1. *A lock of the old Somerset Coal Canal near Bath, England. Width and depth each 6 or 7 feet; facing of oolitic limestone. Construction superintended by William Smith about 1798. (Photograph by A. O. Woodford, 1959.)*

boundaries in deducing structure. The discovery was that certain fossils—the guide fossils—make it possible to correlate formations in different areas.

William Smith (1769–1839) was a coal-mine surveyor who turned to canal-building and then to geologic mapping. He superintended the construction of the Somerset Coal Canal near Bath (Fig. 3-1). Bath is in southwestern England, east of Bristol; it was a popular spa in Roman times and again in the eighteenth and the early nineteenth century. As the digging of the canal slowly advanced, Smith found time to collect and study the fossils in the strata traversed. As early as 1799 he gave two friends a table showing the formations near Bath and their characteristic fossils. Smith distinguished his formations primarily by the characteristics of the rocks themselves; for example, one was a soft gray clay, a second a firm red sandstone, a third a hard white limestone. As he expanded his geologic mapping to cover all England, he used all the aids and hints he could find: not only the characteristic fossils, wherever he

geologic column might be inferred. William Smith's geologic map of England and Wales (1815) can be used to explain both the mapping technique and a great new discovery. The technique was the accurate mapping of formation boundaries and the use of these

Fig. 3-2. *Folkestone on the English Channel, looking northeast toward the Chalk cliffs of Dover. The Chalk dips away from the observer; it is underlain by beds of fossiliferous clay and sandstone that crop out in the low cliffs beyond the small Folkestone harbor. (Photograph by Aerofilms & Aero Pictorial Ltd.)*

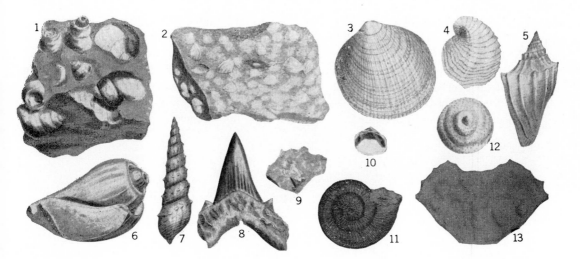

Fig. 3-3. *Two plates from William Smith's* Strata Identified by Organized Fossils *(1816), slightly reduced.*

ABOVE. *London Clay pelecypods (Nos. 2, 3, 4, 10), gastropods (Nos. 5, 6, 7, 12), shark teeth (Nos. 8, 9), ammonite (No. 11), and crab (No. 13). The ammonite* (Ammonites communis) *is an anomaly discussed in the text.*

BELOW. *Lower Chalk* Inoceramus *(Nos. 1, 2), other pelecypods (Nos. 6, 7), gastropods (Nos. 3, 5), ammonite (No. 4), brachiopod (No. 8), and shark teeth (No. 9).*

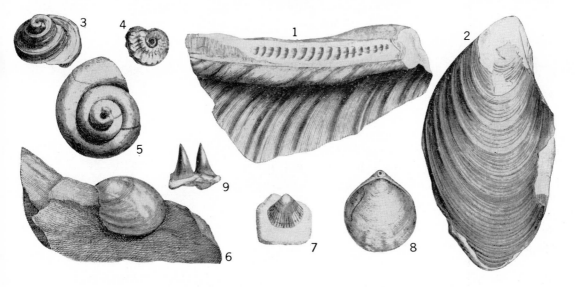

could find them, but also the characteristic types of vegetation on certain rocks. His list of formation names is a guide to his recognition and memory system; among the names are Chalk, London Clay, and Oaktree Marl.

In England, as in France, the white Chalk, a soft but tough limestone, stands out as grass-covered plateaus or as ridges that are easily followed across country. The chalk rock itself crops out in many a valley wall or sea cliff (Fig. 3-2) and has been exposed in numberless canal cuts and other excavations. In dipping sequences the Chalk makes ridges because the rocks below it and above it are easily eroded. The underlying clay, for example, crops out in the low sea cliffs beyond the small harbor in the middle distance of Figure 3-2, in marked contrast to the bold exposures and high cliffs of the overlying Chalk beyond.

The differences between the fossil assemblages discovered by Smith are illustrated by two of the plates he published in 1816 (Fig. 3-3), one representing fossils from the lower part of the Chalk, the other those from the London Clay, which is a formation above the Chalk. The pelecypod genus *Inoceramus* (below, 1 and 2) and the ammonite (below, 4) are not known above the Chalk, except

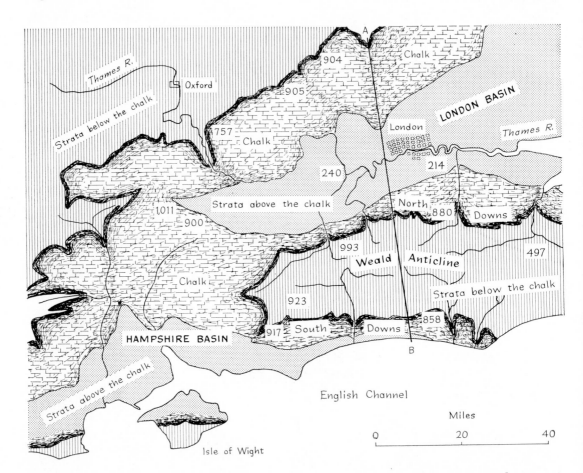

Fig. 3-4. *Simplified geologic map of part of southeastern England; numbers are spot elevations in feet. (After William Smith, 1815.)*

Fig. 3-5. *North-south section, from London to the English Channel, derived from Fig. 3-4. Dips exaggerated.*

for rare occurrences that seem to have been the results of erosion and redeposition in younger strata, and the clams and snails of the upper plate are never found as low as the Chalk. The two fossil assemblages are, in fact, characteristic of their respective formations. An apparent exception, the ammonite (above, 11) represented as a London Clay fossil, was collected in Norfolk, northeast of London and outside what is now considered the area of London Clay outcrops. It is rather certainly an example of redeposition in very young rocks, far above the pre-Chalk level to which this ammonite species is now known to be restricted. It probably came originally from an outcrop in east-central England, whence it was carried by an ice sheet in Pleistocene time. It then became, along with other miscellaneous ice-transported material, part of the Pleistocene boulder-clay in Norfolk, where other redeposited ammonites have been discovered since Smith's time. The boulder-clay was apparently misidentified as London Clay by Smith.

Wherever Smith found the uppermost Chalk exposed, it was overlain by non-fossiliferous "brick-earth," which was commonly succeeded by fossiliferous London Clay. The usual exposure of Chalk, however, showing through the thin soil of the broad Chalk ridges, is not the uppermost bed of the formation but a nearly flat bevel across beds (Fig. 3-2). According to Steno's third law (rediscovered in Smith's time), such an exposure of the edges of strata indicates erosion or faulting. Tilting followed by erosion seems the most probable explanation, especially when one realizes that all the British formations—not just the Chalk—are similarly beveled. It is this exposure of the whole succession of strata, apparently by erosion following deformation, that makes it possible to deduce from the geologic map the structures and relative ages of the formations.

Smith distinguished twenty-two formations that crop out in England and Wales, mostly in long, narrow, parallel strips that run, commonly southwest-northeast, across country (Fig. 3-7). The strips change into a more complicated pattern south of London, making especially fruitful a more detailed consideration of this southeastern part of the country.

A simplified version of the southeastern part of the map Smith published in 1815 is shown in Figure 3-4. The Chalk areas are shown by a conventional limestone pattern, with a dark band at the base to simulate cliff outcrops, the strata above the Chalk (largely London Clay) by a second pattern, and the strata below the Chalk by a third pattern.

The attitude of the Chalk (its strike and dip) varies from one part of the area to another. Northwest of London the dip is southeast, as shown especially by the southeast-pointing V in the basal contact of the Chalk where this contact is crossed by the Thames River. With a modern map we could determine the strike and dip precisely by the three-point method described in § 1-4.a (compare Fig. 1-7), taking one point at the river crossing and the other two high up on the valley sides. But even Smith's map shows the general direction of the dip. The low point on the contact, near the river's edge, is the farthest southeast in any group of points that can be chosen, and so the general direction of dip must be southeast. If we also note the spot elevations on Smith's map—the highest in this vicinity only 757 feet above sea level—and the horizontal scale, we discover that the deep V in the basal contact of the Chalk represents a very slight southeastern dip, perhaps less than 100 feet per mile, which is hardly measurable in degrees.

South of London the base of the Chalk dips gently north, as shown by the north-pointing V's along the Thames tributaries. So London must lie in a flat syncline, a structural basin. Beneath London one might expect to find the London Clay, underlain by the Chalk. Near the English south coast, the base of the Chalk dips gently south, as shown by the south-pointing V's along the little rivers that flow into the Channel from the north. The Chalk ridges immediately south of London, extending east to Dover (Fig. 3-2), are called the North Downs, and those near the south

Fig. 3-6. *Looking west over Steyning, near Brighton, England, 40 miles south of London. South Downs, underlain by Chalk, in middle distance. The wooded escarpment, sloping down to the right, is cut in Chalk. At the extreme right, the Weald lowland is cut on weak strata below the Chalk. (Photograph by Aerofilms & Aero Pictorial Ltd.)*

coast are called the South Downs (Fig. 3-6). Between the two is a lowland called the Weald, where the strata that underlie the Chalk are exposed (Fig. 3-2, foreground; Fig. 3-6, right). This central area, between the north-dipping North Downs and the south-dipping South Downs, must mark the center of an upfold. This structure is called the Weald Anticline. At its west end the Chalk makes a low plateau, bounding the Weald, where the dips must be nearly horizontal, perhaps slightly westward.*

3-2. Structure Sections

One of the advantages of an accurate geologic map is the possibility of deriving from it vertical **structure sections** showing the continuations of outcropping strata beneath the earth's surface. Take, for example, a section

* All the dips discussed here seem to be downstream. This is not the only possible relation. Suggestion: Use the three-point method to show the form of the V made (1) by a horizontal contact crossed by a stream valley and (2) by a contact dipping upstream.

along the line *AB*, marked on Figure 3-4. This section, derived from the map and its explanation, is shown as Figure 3-5. It could also be derived from independent observations on the ground, and such observations would be a prudent check on the accuracy of the map. But the map has this advantage over a few measured sections: structure sections may be constructed from it anywhere, in any direction. Inspection of the map, plus the construction of a few sections, as desired, gives the best idea of the stratigraphy and structure of the whole area.

Structure can be read directly from a geologic map only if the map also gives some idea of the form of the land surface (or has marked on it the dips and strikes of the strata). A geologic map on which no river courses or hills or contour lines or spot elevations are shown can nevertheless be interpreted structurally if one or more structure sections also are furnished. We find such a combination in Figure 3-8 (a revision of Smith's map prepared by William Phillips in 1821) and Figure 3-7 (a diagrammatic northwest-southeast

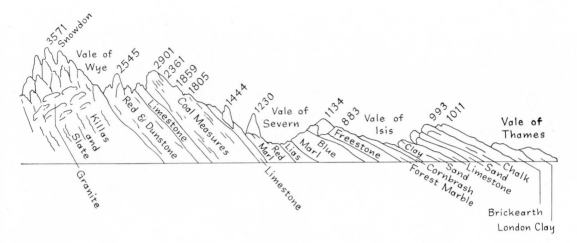

Fig. 3-7. *Structure section from Mt. Snowdon, in northern Wales, to London; numbers are elevations in feet. (Modified slightly from William Smith, 1815.)*

structure section). Here we have the oldest rocks at the northwest end of the section, in Wales, and the youngest in the London Basin. This map and this structure section give sufficient basis for most, but not all, of the standard column.

3-3. *The Standard Geologic Column and Time Scale*

The principal units of the standard column were given in Table 2-1; they are repeated in Table 3-1. Most of the names were proposed

TABLE 3-1

The Geologic Column

MODERN MAIN DIVISIONS	MODERN SUBDIVISIONS (SYSTEMS)		OLD MAIN DIVISIONS (ARDUINO, ABOUT 1760, AND OTHERS)
Cenozoic	Recent Pleistocene		Quaternary (still used)
	Neogene Paleogene		Tertiary (still in common use)
Mesozoic	Cretaceous (Chalk, etc.) Jurassic Triassic		Secondary
Paleozoic	Permian Carboniferous (Coal Measures, etc.) Devonian		
	Silurian Ordovician Cambrian		(Not found in the regions studied)
Precambrian (Pre-Paleozoic)			Primitive (Primary)

Fig. 3-8. *Geological map of England, Wales, and part of Scotland, after W. D. Conybeare and William Phillips, 1822. (From Bernhard Kummel, History of the Earth, W. H. Freeman & Co., 1961.)*

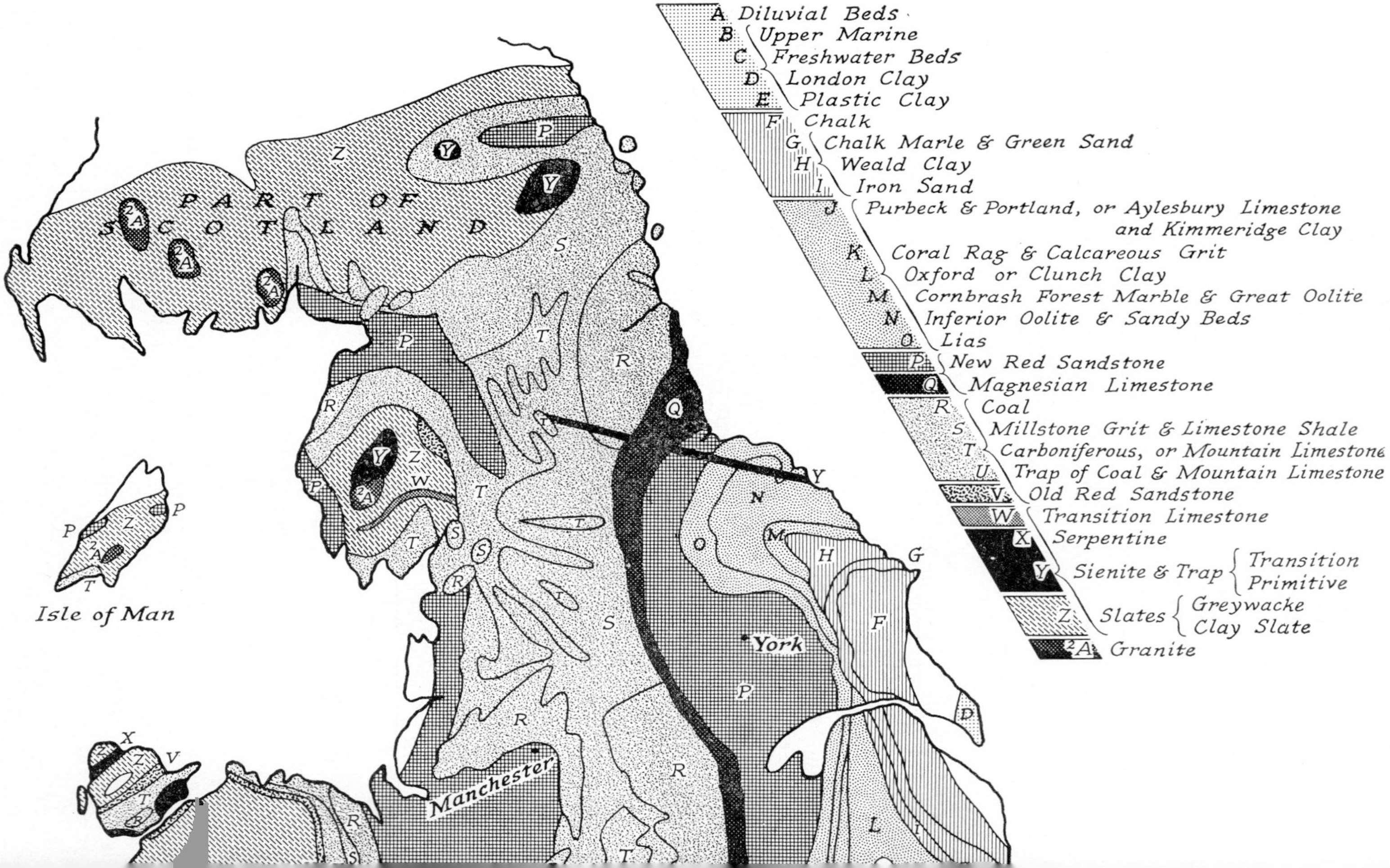

A Diluvial Beds
B Upper Marine
C Freshwater Beds
D London Clay
E Plastic Clay
F Chalk
G Chalk Marle & Green Sand
H Weald Clay
I Iron Sand
J Purbeck & Portland, or Aylesbury Limestone and Kimmeridge Clay
K Coral Rag & Calcareous Grit
L Oxford or Clunch Clay
M Cornbrash Forest Marble & Great Oolite
N Inferior Oolite & Sandy Beds
O Lias
P New Red Sandstone
Q Magnesian Limestone
R Coal
S Millstone Grit & Limestone Shale
T Carboniferous, or Mountain Limestone
U Trap of Coal & Mountain Limestone
V Old Red Sandstone
W Transition Limestone
X Serpentine
Y Sienite & Trap {Transition
Z Slates {Greywacke {Primitive} Clay Slate
Z' A' Granite

and generally accepted between 1822 and 1847. Smith, like most working stratigraphers, was interested chiefly in the local column, the local structure, and the application of his knowledge to farming and other practical pursuits. In his old age, at least, he thought of his column as the standard of reference for the world, but perhaps not as the basis for a time scale and geologic history.

The transition from the use of Table 2-1 or 3-1 as a column to its use as a time scale is nevertheless so easy that we make it almost unconsciously. The Cretaceous Period was the time when the rocks of the Cretaceous System accumulated, and other periods have similar meanings.

A time scale so based may have gaps, especially where the rocks of a system overlie an unconformity. In succeeding chapters we shall study several such gaps with some care, attempt to discover if they are worldwide, and discuss the interesting and satisfying conclusions to which the study leads. Here we can merely state the principal conclusion: no worldwide gaps have yet been demonstrated.

3-4. *British Formations and the Standard Geologic Column*

The way in which the formations established by Smith and his successors came to be grouped into the systems of Table 3-1 is summarized in Tables 3-2, 3-3, and 3-4, which will be explained in the following pages. The object of the discussion is two-fold: first, to show the easy and natural way in which the units of Table 3-1 were established; second, to pro-

TABLE 3-2

From Old Red Sandstone to Chalk

1822 FORMATIONS (FIG. 3-8)	MODERN SYSTEMS (OR SUB-SYSTEMS)	FACIES	GUIDE FOSSILS
Chalk	Upper Cretaceous	Marine	Echinoids, foraminifers, ammonites
Chalk Marl (clay), Green Sand	Lower Cretaceous	Marine	Ammonites
Weald Clay & Iron Sand	Lower Cretaceous	Brackish and fresh-water	Reptiles, plants
Purbeck Beds (marl, shell limestone, etc.) Portland Limestone Kimmeridge Clay	Jurassic	Mostly marine	Ammonites, pelecypods, gastropods
Coral Rag & calcareous grit (mostly limestone)	Jurassic	Marine	Ammonites
Oxford or Clunch Clay	Jurassic	Marine	Ammonites
Cornbrash, Forest Marble, & Great Oolite (limestone)	Jurassic	Marine	Ammonites, etc.
Inferior Oolite (limestone) & sandy beds	Jurassic	Marine	Ammonites
Lias (clay and limestone)	Jurassic	Marine	Ammonites
New Red Sandstone	Triassic & Permian	Continental	Very few (fish, etc.)
Magnesian Limestone, etc.	Permian	Marine & continental	Few (fish, brachiopods, etc.)
Coal Measures Millstone Grit, etc.	Upper Carboniferous (Pennsylvanian)	Mostly swamp and coastal plain	Plants, fresh-water clams, ammonoids
Mountain Limestone	Lower Carboniferous (Mississippian)	Marine	Corals, ammonoids, brachiopods
Old Red Sandstone	Devonian	Continental	Fish (rather rare)

vide sufficient background so that each unit will have a definite meaning.

In general, the formations on which the column is based succeed one another in order from northwest to southeast (Fig. 3-7). The successive formations have positions somewhat similar to those of shingles on a roof, but most are prolonged much farther underground than the shingle analogy suggests.

Smith was most successful in differentiating the rocks in the middle of the column, especially those between coal and Chalk, and so we shall begin with this part of the British section.

a. From Old Red Sandstone (and Coal) to Chalk*

By 1822 Smith and two or three other field geologists had made possible the geologic map of England and Wales reproduced, somewhat simplified, as Figure 3-8. A generalized structure section, Figure 3-7, is taken directly from Smith (1815). The effects of topography on flat contacts are smoothed out in Figure 3-8, and so structure is harder to read from it than from the larger-scale map, Figure 3-4.

The principal area of old rocks is in northern and central Wales. East of Wales the prevailing dip is eastward, as shown, much exaggerated, in Smith's section (Fig. 3-7). Old Red Sandstone (red and dun stone) is overlain by Mountain Limestone, Coal Measures, etc.

Smith began his work, for practical purposes, with a study of the **Coal Measures.** The individual beds of this formation are mostly only a few inches or a few feet thick, but all together their recorded thickness is between 6,000 and 8,000 feet in some of the more or less synclinal coal basins. The rocks include coal beds underlain by clays, interbedded sandstones and shales, and some iron ore. The series is characterized by the presence of coal beds (compare Strachey's section, Fig. 1-5). Because of structural complications—folds, faults, and unconformities—the Coal Measures

*See Table 3-2.

crop out discontinuously. The principal line of coal fields extends almost due north from the east end of the Bristol Channel, through Birmingham in the Midlands, to Newcastle on the northeast English coast, almost at the Scottish border. Most of the rocks west of this line are older than the coal, and most of the rocks to the east are younger than the coal.

Below the Coal Measures Smith found a very coarse sandstone (the **Millstone Grit**) and below the Grit the **Mountain Limestone,** a thick formation that is prominent at the surface in the central county of Derbyshire, where it has been cut by deep river gorges to make a mountainous topography. The Mountain Limestone, Millstone Grit, and Coal Measures, taken together, were called the **Carboniferous** (coal-bearing) **System** by W. D. Conybeare in 1822.

Lying stratigraphically above the Coal Measures is a limestone, at least in part marine and somewhat similar to the Mountain Limestone, but less boldly expressed in the topography and with other distinctive characteristics. Since it is dolomitic, it was early called the **Magnesian Limestone.** In many places it is a limestone conglomerate, and it is interbedded with or overlain by red and blue siltstone, anhydrite and gypsum, and salt. These strata are attributed to what is now called the Permian System (Table 3-2).

The Permo-Carboniferous rocks are bounded below and above by two series of red beds. The lower red formation, the **Old Red Sandstone** (Smith's Red and Dun Stone), underlies the Mountain Limestone and is commonly thousands of feet thick. In the west of England and Wales, especially in southern Wales, these thick red strata are striking features of the landscape, separating the monotonous and complexly folded older rocks of Wales, especially of central and northern Wales, from the gently folded Mountain Limestone, Coal Measures, and younger rocks of southern Wales and central England. The Old Red, for reasons that will be developed later in this chapter, is now considered Devonian.

The **New Red Sandstone** (Smith's **Red**

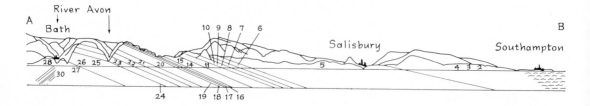

Fig. 3-9. *A structure section by William Smith, 1819.*

ABOVE. *Geologic section along the line Bath-Salisbury-Southampton: 1–4, Cenozoic; 5–28, Mesozoic (mostly Jurassic and Cretaceous); 30, Coal Measures. (Redrawn from Thomas Sheppard,* William Smith: His Maps and Memoirs, *1920.)*

BELOW. *Map of southwestern England, showing the positions of three structure sections: AB, above; CD and EF, Fig. 3-15.*

Marl), perhaps not as striking an element in the landscape as the Old Red, lies on top of the Magnesian Limestone and contains as much so-called marl as sandstone. The marl is a non-calcareous siltstone, much like consolidated loess; it may have been wind-deposited, as loess is. (Compare § 16-2.b.) The colors of the New Red are less uniformly reddish than those of the Old Red. Most of the New Red, for reasons that will be given later in this chapter, is now considered Triassic.

Above the New Red Sandstone, a whole series of formations differentiated by Smith (Lias clay, oolitic limestone, etc.) are now in-

cluded in the **Jurassic System.** These formations, which are not labeled adequately in Figure 3-7, are listed in Table 3-2 and shown diagrammatically in Figure 3-9, units 9–27. They are well exposed in cuestas, like irregular rows of nearly horizontal shingles, whose dip is greatly exaggerated in the figure. Some of these rocks were exposed in the canal banks near Bath where Smith did much of his early work. They contain corals, ammonites, and many other fossils that either are very similar to the hard parts of organisms now living in the sea or can reasonably be considered to be the remains of animals related more remotely to modern marine animals. The sequence is made up of similar rock types, several times repeated, and the fossils throughout belong to the same groups, so that the whole assemblage makes an ideal system of sedimentary rocks. For a time the English called it the Oolitic because so much of the limestone is composed of the sand-sized accretions called oolites (Fig. 1-10C). The French name *Jurassique* (Jurassic in English), proposed for the system in 1829 and now generally accepted, comes from the Jura Mountains of the Swiss-French border (Fig. 3-10), where rocks with similar fossils crop out. In Britain, the Lower Jurassic (Lias) is mostly dark shale; the Middle Jurassic is noted for its white oolitic limestone (units 20 and 22 of Fig. 3-9); and the Upper Jurassic consists of black shale and white limestone. In Britain important iron ores occurred in the Middle Lias; in eastern France extensive and very productive beds of iron ore are at the very top of the Lias.

The uppermost system in the central body of British strata is made up of the three highest units in Table 3-2: two clay and sand units, topped by the Chalk. The Chalk, in particular, extends across England from the Channel to the North Sea (Fig. 3-8). The system was first called **Cretaceous** (English form of the French *Crétacé*, from the Latin word for chalk) in 1822.

b. An Important Unconformity

On the geologic map of Britain (Fig. 3-8) we see that some contacts are discordant with (oblique to) others. One such discordance is at the base of the New Red Sandstone (*P*). In northeasternmost England this contact is parallel to that between the Coal Measures and the Magnesian Limestone, indicating at least apparent conformity between all three formations, but farther south, in the Midlands and northern Wales, the New Red is in discordant contact with almost all the older

rocks, from the Magnesian Limestone down, lying successively on Coal Measures, Millstone Grit, Mountain Limestone, Old Red Sandstone, and even the still older slates of Wales (*Z*). This discordance is a major unconformity. It is also an overlap of a kind that will be discussed further in Chapter 4.

The discordance at the base of the New Red Sandstone is important. For one thing, it affects the thickness of older rocks present beneath the New Red at any particular point. It even determines the presence or absence of individual strata or whole formations. In England this is especially important if one wishes to dig through a covering of younger rocks to find Carboniferous coal or Permian salts.

The lowest beds in the New Red Sandstone do not represent the same stratigraphic level

Fig. 3-10. *Outline map of Europe, showing some places of geological importance.*

Precambrian   Cambrian   Ordovician   Silurian

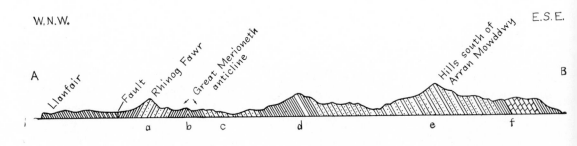

Fig. 3-11. *Geology of northern Wales.*

ABOVE. *Geological map, showing anticlinal Cambrian and Precambrian areas and synclinal Ordovician and Ordovician-Silurian areas. (After A. K. Wells and J. F. Kirkaldy, 1956.)*

BELOW. *Structure section from Harlech southeast: a–d, Cambrian; e–f, Ordovician. (Modified slightly from Adam Sedgwick, 1847.)*

at all localities. In some places the lowest beds are almost certainly Triassic, but elsewhere the sandstones grade into or interfinger with the Magnesian Limestone or the upper Coal Measures. It follows that the principal deformations of the lower Coal Measures and older rocks were pre-Permian. The Magnesian Limestone, with its few marine fossils, has rather restricted distribution; the truly Triassic part of the wholly continental New Red unconformably covers the Magnesian Limestone and broad tracts of older rocks with an overlapping continental deposit. In other words, the Triassic part of the New Red is considerably more extensive than the Paleozoic part. Moreover, the principal discordance in the attitudes of the strata, especially as seen in detail on the ground, is not between the Permian, the highest system of the Paleozoic, and the Triassic, the lowest system of the Mesozoic (Table 3-1), but somewhat lower, within the Paleozoic rocks. We shall find later that systems and other worldwide stratigraphic units must be separated on paleontological rather than structural grounds.

c. Marine Strata below the British Carboniferous[*]

1. THE LOWER PALEOZOIC OF WALES. In southern and eastern Wales and adjoining parts of England the Old Red Sandstone lies unconformably on a steeply dipping complex of older rocks. The basal bed of the Old Red is commonly a conglomerate composed of rounded boulders of a great variety of rocks, especially the pre–Old Red rocks now exposed to the west and north, mostly in Wales. In Wales these older Paleozoic rocks are chiefly the "interminable graywacke" of the

early English geologists: sandstones of the graywacke type interbedded with siltstones, highly folded and without easy and obvious distinctions between major units.

The interminable graywacke was left alone by Smith and his contemporaries, as something that could hardly be reduced to stratigraphic subdivisions. Then, in 1831, Roderick Murchison and his friend Adam Sedgwick attacked the graywacke and associated rocks, Sedgwick in northern Wales and Murchison in southern Wales. These two celebrated English geologists were men of very different origins. Murchison was one of the Duke of Wellington's young officers; after 1815 he was looking for something to do. Geology became his opportunity for new excitement and new glory. Sedgwick, on the other hand, had embraced geology strictly as a livelihood. He was the son of a North Country clergyman and had lived precariously at Cambridge as a tutor of mathematics until 1818, when he was fortunate enough to obtain the university's Woodwardian professorship of geology. The chair had been vacated because the previous holder had married, thereby violating the rules of the foundation. Sedgwick was the Woodwardian professor from 1818 to 1873, and he made this position the leading one of its kind in the world.

Sedgwick was invited to join Murchison when the latter, with "wife and maid, two good grey nags and a little carriage," went to southern Wales in June 1831. Sedgwick, however, was unable to leave Cambridge until August; then he entered northern Wales (Fig. 3-11), accompanied by Charles Darwin, who stayed for two weeks.

Sedgwick had the better area so far as seeing the structure was concerned. He perceived that the rocks in northern Wales consisted of three or four anticlinal folds with synclines be-

[*] See Table 3-3.

TABLE 3-3

Strata below the British Carboniferous

SYSTEM	TYPE AREA	FACIES NAME	FACIES IN TYPE AREA	LITHOLOGY IN TYPE AREA
Devonian	Devonshire	Devon Facies	Marine	Slates, sandstones, etc.
		Old Red Sandstone	Continental	Red sandstone, etc.
Silurian	Southeastern Wales		Marine; shallow & shelly as well as graptolitic & probably deep (graywacke in northern Wales)	Mostly shale (graywacke in north)
Ordovician	Northern Wales		Marine; shallow & shelly as well as graptolitic & probably deep (graywacke in west-central Wales)	Mostly shales, mudstones, tuffs, & lavas (graywacke southwest of type area)
Cambrian	Northern Wales		Marine, at least in part	Shales, mudstones, grits, & conglomerates

tween (Fig. 3-11), although the strata in some places were almost on edge and the local structure was not particularly obvious. He discovered a few fossils in the upper beds and used them in making some distinctions. He called the lower two-thirds of this North Wales section the **Cambrian System** (from the medieval Latin name for Wales) when he and Murchison published their first general report in 1835.

Murchison, at the same time, described the upper part of the South Wales graywacke, just below the Old Red, as the **Silurian System** (from the classical Latin name of an ancient Welsh border tribe, the Silures). Four years later he published his masterpiece, a quarto volume called *The Silurian System*, which contained descriptions of hundreds of fossil species by several specialists and was accompanied by his own fine geologic map. He also recognized the possible equivalence of Sedgwick's Upper Cambrian and his own Lower Silurian; and later he definitely reduced the Cambrian to the lower strata that had yielded few if any fossils in northern Wales.

The value of the tiny carbonaceous graptolites as guide fossils was not recognized by Sedgwick and Murchison. It remained for Charles Lapworth, in 1879, to straighten out some difficulties of correlation by the use of graptolites and to introduce the third major subdivision of the pre–Old Red sequence, the **Ordovician System** (named for another ancient tribe, the Ordovices). This system corresponds to the lower part of Murchison's Silurian and the upper part of Sedgwick's Cambrian (marked Ordovician in Fig. 3-11). There is a moderately extensive unconformity above much of the Welsh Ordovician, with the Silurian overlapping onto the Cambrian (Fig. 3-12). The Ordovician is the most interesting part of the British lower Paleozoic, for it has the greatest variety of rock facies, including not only well-developed limestones at the eastern edge of the area but also, farther northwest, in northern Wales, a complicated volcanic sequence. The volcanic area includes Snowdon, the highest peak in Britain south of the Scottish Highlands, and is sometimes called Snowdonia.

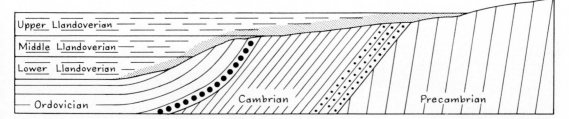

Fig. 3-12. *Diagrammatic section, showing Cambrian, Ordovician, and Lower Silurian conformable in the geosyncline of central Wales, and Silurian overlapping eastward onto the platform. (After A. K. Wells and J. F. Kirkaldy, 1956.)*

The closely folded, steeply dipping Cambrian, Ordovician, and Silurian rocks of Wales, especially those of the graywacke and black shale (graptolitic) facies, are very thick. The Cambrian slates, mudstones, and grits are perhaps 15,000 feet thick. The thickness of the Ordovician is rather hard to measure, but the volcanic accumulations of Snowdonia are surely many thousand feet thick. The Silurian has a shale (altered to slate) facies that is at least 10,000 feet thick in northern Wales.

The geographic distribution of the non-volcanic facies has been worked out most thoroughly for the Silurian. The graywacke facies is at the northwestern end of the outcrop belt, a shelly facies of limestone and shale, with abundant brachiopods, is at the southeast, and the graptolitic black-shale facies is between the other two. An example of this facies distribution for a small part of the Middle Silurian is shown in Figure 3-13. No wonder Murchison, doing pioneer rough mapping, did not recognize that these dissimilar rocks should be correlated, especially as the thinness and gentle dips of the beds in the shelly facies (Fig. 3-14) make a strong contrast to the thickness and steep dips of the sequences in the two other facies.

The brachiopods of the shelly facies indicate shallow-water deposition. The graptolitic shales lack shallow-water fossils and so may have been deposited in deep water. The graywackes and siltstones of the graywacke facies contain abundant evidence of contemporaneous sliding and slumping of the sediments while they were still soft, as though some beds

that had been deposited in shallow water slid down into deeper water and became mingled with a deeper facies. Note in Figure 3-13 the arrows indicating the directions of movement of the sediments. The data for drawing these arrows were furnished, in part, by the slump structures in the graywacke facies: grooves, striations, and other features that indicate the directions in which the slumped masses moved.

2. CALEDONIAN FOLDING. The unconformity commonly present at the top of the Silurian (local base of the Old Red) indicates that the early Paleozoic rocks were folded before the local Old Red was laid down. This deformation is called the **Caledonian folding.** The Caledonian folds in England and Wales, and also in Scotland, are elongated northeast-

Fig. 3-13. *Map of middle Wenlock (Middle Silurian) facies in Wales. (After W. A. Cummins, 1957.)*

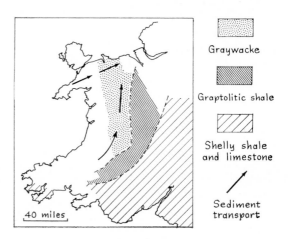

Graywacke

Graptolitic shale

Shelly shale and limestone

Sediment transport

40 miles

Fig. 3-14. *Shelly facies of the Silurian dipping rather gently to the right: Wenlock Edge, Shropshire, western England. (Photograph by Aerofilms & Aero Pictorial Ltd.)*

southwest. There are two main belts of Caledonian folds, one in Wales and England and a second, parallel to the first, two hundred miles to the northwest, in Ireland and Scotland.

3. THE DEVONIAN OF DEVONSHIRE. Marine formations make the best standards for worldwide correlation because the fossils they contain are the most widespread. A marine type section for the system represented by the Old Red Sandstone in most of Britain, north of the Bristol Channel (Fig. 3-15A), was found by Murchison and Sedgwick in Devonshire, an English county south of the Bristol Channel, across from Wales.

The rocks of Devonshire (Fig. 3-15B) are largely slates and sandstones of two series. The upper contains plants, like those of the Coal Measures, and ammonoids (goniatites). After considerable difficulty this series was demonstrated to be Carboniferous, largely Lower Carboniferous. The lower series near its northern margin is interbedded with typi-cal Old Red Sandstone, the rock one might expect to find beneath the Carboniferous. Most of this lower series looks very much like the Silurian and older rocks of Wales, but its locally abundant marine fossils are not those of the Silurian or pre-Silurian systems. For one thing, there are no graptolites; for another, the shelly facies, in part limestone, contains species that are intermediate between those of the Silurian and those of the Mountain Limestone of the Carboniferous. Murchison and Sedgwick suggested in 1838 that these rocks were contemporaneous with the Old Red Sandstone sequences north of the Bristol Channel. Later it was realized that the primitive fishes and other peculiar fossils of the Old Red Sandstone in Scotland and elsewhere were probably the remains of freshwater animals and that their different habitat explains their striking differences from the much more numerous marine fossils in other formations. Thus we have in Devonshire an interfingering of the marine and continental facies of the Devonian System (Fig. 3-15C). We shall consider in Chapter 11 the problems raised by the distribution of these two facies.

d. Permian and Triassic

The British section between the top of the Old Red Sandstone and the Chalk is fairly complete, but the two units between the Coal Measures and the Jurassic made unsatisfactory standards for comparisons with other regions, for the lower is poorly supplied with marine fossils and the upper is entirely non-marine. So the early geologists went to the European continent for standard sequences. These two parts of the standard column are now called Permian and Triassic.

1. THE PERMIAN SYSTEM. The Magnesian Limestone of England contains a few fish, marine reef invertebrates, and other fossils and is accompanied by beds of reddish clay, with more or less rock salt, gypsum, and other evaporites, especially in the subsurface of east-central England. Marine fossils are so rare and of such persistent types that the unit is unsatisfactory as a type member of the standard column. Similar limestones, with the same kinds of fish and invertebrates, and similar salts, in much greater volume, are also found in Germany. The Magnesian Limestone's equivalents in Germany have the same stratigraphic position as in England; that is, they are just above the Coal Measures and below the strata that we shall soon have reason to call Triassic. When the strata just above the Coal Measures are followed east into Russia, their lower divisions become normally marine, with abundant fossils. In 1841 Sir Roderick Murchison, by then Director of the Geological Survey of Great Britain, visited Russia, gained

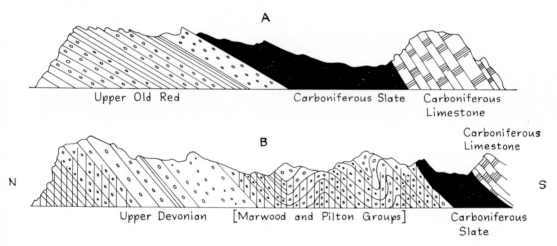

Fig. 3-15. *Old Red Sandstone and Marine Devonian.* (A *and* B *after* J. W. Salter, 1863; C *after* A. K. Wells *and* J. F. Kirkaldy, 1956.) A. *Section* (CD *in Fig.* 3-9) *across Old Red Sandstone and Carboniferous of Pembrokeshire, southwestern Wales.* B. *North-south section* (EF *in Fig.* 3-9) *through the somewhat slaty Upper Devonian and Carboniferous of northern Devonshire. The lower Devonian rocks of the section are reddish and non-fossiliferous.* C. *Correlation and facies diagram: South Wales–North Devon–South Devon.*

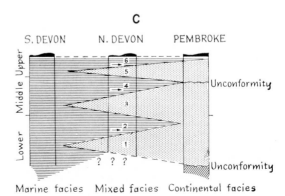

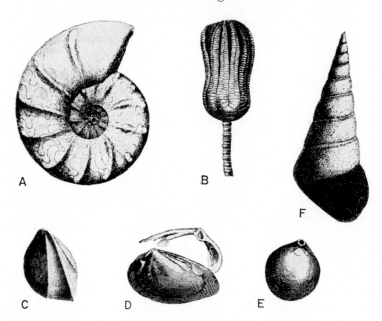

Fig. 3-16. *Fossils of the Muschelkalk facies of the Middle Triassic. (From Roland Brinkmann, Historische Geologie, Enke, Stuttgart, 1959.)*
  A. Ceratites nodosus *(ceratitic ammonite), 120 mm across.*
  B. Encrinus liliiformis *(crinoid), 90 mm long.*
  C. Myophoria vulgaris *(pelecypod), 30 mm long.*
  D. Trigonodus sandbergeri *(pelecypod), 35 mm long.*
  E. Terebratula vulgaris *(brachiopod), 23 mm long.*
  F. Undularia scalata *(gastropod), 70 mm long.*

favor with the Czar, and conducted a grand expedition eastward to Perm and other districts near the Ural Mountains, where the explorers found the stratigraphic positions of the dolomite and part of the red beds occupied by limestones and other rocks containing brachiopods, fusulines, and other marine fossils. In 1845 Murchison and his associates published two great volumes on the results of the expedition. They gave the name **Permian** to the ma-

Fig. 3-17. *Fossils of the Alpine facies of the Triassic. (From Roland Brinkmann, Historische Geologie, Enke, Stuttgart, 1959.)*
  A. Tirolites cassianus [*ceratite-like ammonite; Lower Triassic, Scythian Stage (see Appendix D)], 26 mm across.*
  B. *Suture of* Tirolites cassianus.
  C. Ceratites trinodosus *(ceratitic ammonite; Middle Triassic, Anisian Stage), 44 mm across.*
  D. Ptychites studeri *(ammonite; Middle Triassic, Anisian Stage), 96 mm across.*
  E. Daonella lommeli *(pelecypod; Middle Triassic, Ladinian Stage), 45 mm long.*
  F. Pinacoceras metternichi *(ammonite; Upper Triassic, Norian Stage), 200 mm across.*
  G. Megalodon scutatus *(pelecypod; Upper Triassic, Norian Stage), 68 mm high.*
  H. Terebratula gregaria *(brachiopod; Upper Triassic, Rhaetian Stage), 20 mm long.*

rine (and continental) Russian strata, and this name has become the one used to designate the system everywhere.

2. THE TRIASSIC SYSTEM. In western Germany the rocks just below the Jurassic and above the equivalent of the Magnesian Lime-

stone are mostly red sandstone and siltstone, almost without fossils, just as in England. In the very midst of the thick red-bed section, however, there is a limestone rich in marine brachiopods and other fossils, the Muschelkalk (mussel or shell limestone). The three-fold division into red beds, limestone, and more

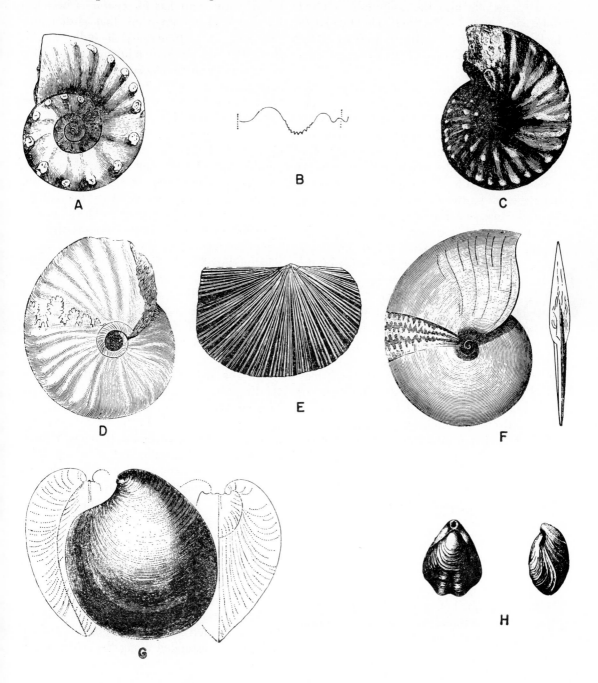

A

B

C

D

E

F

G

H

red beds was the basis for the name **Triassic,** proposed by the German F. A. von Alberti in 1834.

This set of facies, one-third marine, two-thirds lacking marine fossils and containing some land and fresh-water fossils, is called the **Germanic facies** of the Triassic, a term that is used to include also the uniformly red-bed sequence found in England. The Germanic facies is characteristic of the Triassic of northwestern Europe as far south as northern Switzerland.

In the eastern Alps, and especially in the Dolomite Mountains of northeastern Italy (Fig. 3-10), the Triassic shows a contrasting **Alpine facies,** with dolomites thousands of feet thick and containing, as typical fossils, ammonites and flat thin pelecypods assigned to genera restricted to the Triassic or even characteristic of particular parts of the system. Typical Muschelkalk and Alpine Triassic fossils are shown in Figures 3-16 and 3-17; the Alpine ammonites are more varied. The thick calcareous strata of the Alpine facies of the Triassic contain some reef structures (compare § 4-4) that imply deposition of at least some parts of these rocks in shallow water. Great thicknesses of limestone, now transformed into dolomite, may have been built up as the substratum sank. Other parts of the formation lack shallow-water shells and may have been deposited in water hundreds or thousands of feet deep between or beyond reefs. Both the Germanic and the Alpine facies of the Triassic are found in other parts of the world.

3-5. *The Type Cenozoic*[*]

We have now considered the standard column up to and including the Cretaceous. The post-Cretaceous strata have long been called Tertiary and Quaternary (Table 3-1). The **Tertiary** contains a somewhat greater proportion of poorly consolidated sedimentary forma-

* See Table 3-4.

tions than the Mesozoic. Even its marine strata are often describable as sand, clay, and gravel. Many lower and middle Tertiary limestones, however, in the southern Alps, in the Ile de France around Paris, in Persia, in the Himalayas, and elsewhere, are hard rocks, and a middle Tertiary sandstone of the hills north of the Alps has for centuries been cut into blocks of building stone that harden upon standing. The **Quaternary** includes marine shore deposits and loose alluvium, which filled valleys, and also the glacial boulder-clay, loess, and thin rubbly deposits that spread all over Scandinavia and other northern areas, covering Tertiary and older formations alike.

The subdivision of the Tertiary, the principal part of the Cenozoic, on a basis comparable to that now used for the older rocks, was left to the Continental geologists of the middle nineteenth century. They divided the Tertiary into the **Paleogene** (older) and the **Neogene** (newer) **System**—systems that are somewhat synthetic, their type areas being widely distributed. The greater part of the Paleogene is based on a Paris Basin sequence; its missing portions are filled in with bits of section from the London, Belgian, and Hanover (North German) Basins (Fig. 3-10). Most of the Neogene can be found on the southern side of the Po Valley of northern Italy. The Paleogene is well represented in the English column by the locally fossiliferous London Clay and by other sands and clays that overlie the Chalk in the Thames syncline around London. Part of the Neogene is present northeast of London (at *B* in Fig. 3-8). Correlations between strata in Italy or France and strata thought to be of the same age in England are made by molluscan and other fossils (compare Chap. 7). Almost all of the Paleogene mollusks belong to extinct species (compare Fig. 3-3), whereas all but the very lowest Neogene formations contain molluscan faunas composed of species at least half of which are still living.

The great development of the Paleogene was in the sea called the **Tethys,** a greater Mediterranean that extended along the whole south-

TABLE 3-4

Cenozoic Systems

OLD DIVISIONS (STILL USED)	SYSTEMS (NAMES USED IN THIS BOOK)	SUB-SYSTEMS	TYPE AREAS	FACIES IN TYPE AREAS
Quaternary	Pleistocene System (Lyell, 1839)		East coast of Sicily	Shallow marine
	Neogene System (Hoernes, 1853)	Pliocene (Lyell, 1833)	South side of Po Valley, Italy	Shallow to moderately deep marine
		Miocene (Lyell, 1833)	South side of Po Valley, Italy	Shallow marine
Tertiary			Aquitaine Basin of southwestern France	Shallow marine
	Paleogene System (Naumann, 1866)	Oligocene (Beyrich, 1854)	Hanover Basin, Germany	Shallow marine
		Eocene (Lyell, 1833)	Paris Basin, France	Shallow marine
		Paleocene (Schimper, 1874)	Paris Basin, France	Continental (non-marine)
			London Basin, England	Continental and marine
			Belgian Basin	Marine

ern part of Eurasia and included the sites of the present Alps and Himalayas. In this region the top of the Paleogene is marked by the greatest of several unconformities attributable to a folding that, because it was important in the history of the Alps, is called the **Alpine folding.** Elsewhere—for instance, in southwestern France—the beds are all still horizontal, and the boundary between Paleogene and Neogene can be established only with difficulty.

The greater part of the relatively thin and local Quaternary sediments are now called **Pleistocene,** though the youngest sediments of all are set off as **Recent.** The type Pleistocene in eastern Sicily was described by Charles Lyell in 1833, but the present name (meaning most recent) was not proposed by him until 1839. Marine shallow-water Pleistocene sands and clays fringe many shores. Their molluscan fossils are practically all assigned to living species. The continental Pleistocene deposits, on the contrary, sometimes contain the teeth and bones of extinct mammalian species, such as the mastodon and the mammoth.

Perhaps Europe is not the best continent for a Cenozoic type section, but the major divisions set up there have proved fairly satisfactory the world over.

3-6. Correlation with North America

Local columns in North America, like those in Australia, Antarctica, South America, and eastern Asia, are calibrated by comparison with the standard column in Europe. In America several local columns are derived from successions of formations, either undeformed or only slightly deformed, that have been used as continental or regional standards of reference. The section exposed in the Grand Canyon of northern Arizona is especially clear and convincing, both in the succession of the formations and in their individual variations (contemporary facies). It will be the subject of Chapter 5. A second American column, perhaps even more important, is derived from the section in western New York and Pennsylvania, exclusively Paleozoic and one of the best Paleozoic sections in the world. Here, south of the Adirondack pre-Paleozoic rocks, a flat or gently dipping Ordovician-Permian section extends from the Mohawk River valley (base of the section) southwest to the Coal Measures and continental Permian near Pittsburgh. The column derived from the New York–Pennsylvania section will be considered in Chapter 6. But first of all we must stop to summarize, in Chapter 4, the generalizations that can be made about stratigraphic assemblages of the sort that have been described in the present chapter.

EUROPEAN FORMATION NAMES USED IN THE TEXT OF THIS CHAPTER

SYSTEM	FORMATION NAME
Neogene	None
Paleogene	London Clay
Cretaceous	Chalk (with a capital *C* to distinguish it from the substance chalk)
Jurassic	Lias (Lower Jurassic)
Triassic	New Red Sandstone and Muschelkalk
Permian	Magnesian Limestone
Carboniferous	Coal Measures
	Millstone Grit
	Mountain Limestone
Devonian	Old Red Sandstone
Silurian	None
Ordovician	None
Cambrian	None

REFERENCES

Current

1. A. K. Wells and J. F. Kirkaldy: *Outline of Historical Geology*, 3rd ed. (Murby, London, 1951)

Classics

2. William Smith: *A Delineation of the Strata of England and Wales, with Part of Scotland* (London, 1815)

3. William Smith: *Strata Identified by Organized Fossils* (London, 1816–   )

4. W. D. Conybeare and William Phillips: *Outlines of the Geology of England and Wales* (London, 1822)

5. R. I. Murchison: *The Silurian System*, with separate geologic map (London, 1839)

6. R. I. Murchison, Edouard de Verneuil, and Alexander von Keyserling: *The Geology of Russia in Europe and the Ural Mountains* (London, 1845)

CHAPTER 4

Stratigraphic Assemblages

Rocks and fossils (Chaps. 1 and 2) are the geologic raw materials. The standard geologic column (Chap. 3) is the grand generalization that makes historical geology possible. Another preliminary chapter (the present one) is required to set forth the stratigraphic complications and the relations between stratigraphy and structure that give variety and character to the geologic record.

Stratigraphy, a geologic subscience, includes the description of local geologic columns, their subdivision into groups of strata, and the connecting of each local group with strata of similar age in other columns. The process of relating more or less nearly contemporaneous strata to one another is called **correlation.**

Correlations have been made mostly by one or more of three methods: (1) tracing strata of one column into those of another column by surface mapping or along mine galleries (practically limited to coal seams) or by comparison of data from closely spaced wells; (2) recognition and matching, in two areas isolated from each other, of an unusual and distinctive sequence, such as coal measures overlain by red sandstone and evaporites; (3) the use of fossils. The third method is the only one that has proved useful for overseas correlations; it is so important that it deserves special treatment, which it will get in Chapter 7.

The present chapter is limited in scope to regional or even more local correlations, mostly by methods 1 and 2, with emphasis on the hints they give as to ancient geographies and events. Here changes of facies furnish the principal evidence and also provide the practical obstacles in the way of correlation. The changes of facies that we shall consider here are changes in rock type (changes in lithology, in **lithofacies**). We shall leave the problems of variations in the fossil assemblages (**fossil facies, biofacies**) for consideration in Chapter 7.

The geologic environment controls sedimentation, determining the thickness and character of the sedimentary strata. In a structural basin the beds deposited at a particular time may be thick and continuous shales; on an adjacent platform they may be thin and discontinuous limestones; in a region of contemporaneous uplift they may be coarse conglomerate, or nothing at all may be deposited.

Basins and platforms come in various sizes. In this chapter we shall be concerned primarily with the major structural subdivisions of a continent, but we shall also give some attention to smaller units.

4-1. *Present-day Sedimentary Facies*

In order to get some understanding of the rock facies of past times, studies are made of the variety of sediments that are being formed today. These are, obviously, contemporaneous with one another. We take three sets of present-day facies as examples: (1) a strip extending from the mouth of the Mississippi River across Florida to the Puerto Rico trench; (2) the Colorada River delta, the nearby Pacific Coast continental shelf, and the associated trenches or basins; (3) the East Indian deltas, shelf, and trenches.

A section from the mouth of the Mississippi River to the Bahama Banks and the Puerto Rico trench (Fig. 4-1, *ABC*) crosses belts of unlike sediments and one stretch (the Florida peninsula) where little sedimentation is going on today. The sediments brought into the Gulf of Mexico by the Mississippi River and the smaller rivers farther east include some fine sand but are mostly silt and clay—potential shale—made up chiefly of more or less platy aluminum silicates (the clay minerals and the micas). Farther east, just west of the Florida peninsula, the broad, shallow submarine shelf, cut in limestone, is covered locally with sands made up of fragments of shells and calcareous algae. The wide beaches on the east coast of Florida are mostly quartz sand (silicoclastic) at the north but become chiefly calcium carbonate sands (calciclastic) south of Miami. The quartz sand must have moved south from the mouths of Carolina and Georgia rivers, where there is still a little admixed feldspar (perhaps 5 percent). Southward from the river mouths the feldspar gradually disappears, and the quartz is diluted more and more with calcium carbonate grains, from shells and other sources. Out in the Atlantic, the rocky reefs and shallow basins of the Bahamas are nearly pure calcium carbonate, with rolled oolites abundant in and around the basins. The cross-bedded oolitic sands are similar to those that make up Jurassic limestones in England (§ 3-4.a).

The chemical elements that make up these varied sedimentary deposits may all have come from the same sources, deep in the continent. One might, indeed, trace the constituents back, step by step, to the ultimate sources, particularly Precambrian granitic rocks composed mostly of quartz, feldspars, micas, and hornblende. As a result of long weathering, followed by erosion, transportation, and deposition, the chemically complex original rocks have given rise to rocks that are chemically simple: silica sands, aluminum silicate clays (from feldspars and other silicates), and organic, chemically precipitated, and calciclastic limestone derived from the calcium salts carried to the sea in solution by river waters.

The mineralogically simple and nearly chemically pure sediments exemplified by the Mississippi-Bahama section are not the only kinds forming today. Small basins near high lands, in particular, are filled with different materials. Examples in the southwesternmost part of the United States are represented in Figure 4-1, *DEF*, a section across a series of ridges and intervening troughs or trenches. The easternmost basin or trough, at the head of the Gulf of California, is filled by the Upper Neogene–Recent, mostly non-marine delta of the Colorado River, up to 10,000 feet thick. The delta is made up of interbedded silt and fine sand. The sand is about 55 percent quartz, 20 percent volcanic rock fragments, 10 percent carbonates, 10 percent potassium feldspar (orthoclase), and 1 percent plagioclase feldspar (determinations by R. H. Merriam, University of Southern California). The abundance of volcanic fragments and feldspars is evidence that the processes of weathering and geochemical separation have not gone to completion. The Gulf trough is separated from the Pacific Ocean by the highlands of southernmost California and Baja California. In the continental borderland west of the highlands there are many deep, elongated basins. The innermost (Los Angeles) basin is filled with many thousands of feet of sediments and is now an above-water part of the continent. The next basin, which is only partially filled, has only 2,500 feet of sea water in it and the outer ones are about 5,000 feet deep. The basin sedi-

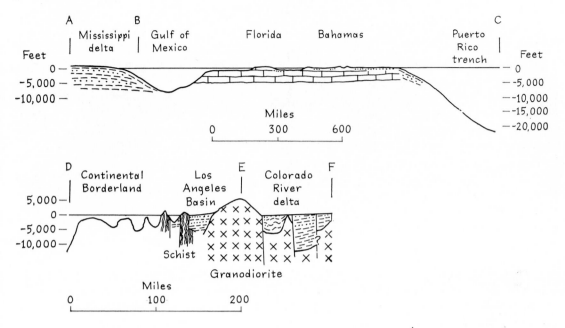

Fig. 4-1. *Depositional facies at the margins of North America, structure sections and map: ABC, Lower Mississippi River–Florida–Puerto Rico Trench; DEF, San Clemente Island–Los Angeles Basin and San Diego–southwestern Arizona.*

ments were derived from the nearby coastal highlands. These highlands are composed chiefly of biotite-rich granodioritic rocks. In this region of high relief, rapid erosion, and short streams, weathering is very incomplete, and the sands deposited in the basins are made up of approximately equal amounts of quartz and feldspar, the latter mostly plagioclase, with noticeable amounts of biotite mica. Fine-grained mica, feldspar, and quartz from the granodioritic rocks are present with the clay minerals in the basin silts. Small contributions to the basin sediments were also derived from the schist ridges between the inner basins. No basin sediments are composed of single pure chemical substances.

In this southwestern region, most sediments are deltaic or other deposits in basins. Deltas are of two kinds: (1) from continental to shal-

low marine; (2) deep-water. The first kind is much commoner and until recently was the only type known. A shallow delta is an embankment built out into a water body at the mouth of a river. If a delta of this type partially fills a deep basin, steep-fronted parts of the deltaic mass may give way and slide or flow into deeper parts of the basin, to be redeposited there.

The basin deposits are best known from core samples, sometimes ten or more feet long, obtained from tubes driven into the basin floors. Many core samples are made up of successive thin layers, each composed of a coarse basal portion—sand with a clay-silt matrix—grading upward into sandy-silty mud. These banded deposits are especially characteristic of the sides or ends of the deep basins, at points where the sea floor, though thou-

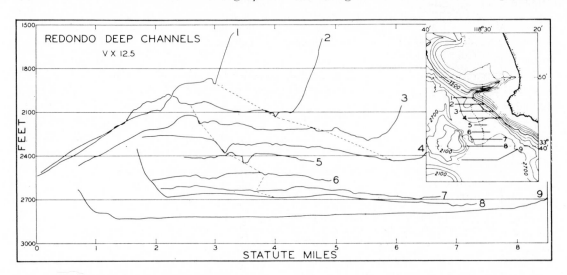

Fig. 4-2. *Map and profiles of the delta at the mouth of Redondo submarine canyon, off the Palos Verdes peninsula near Los Angeles, California. Two channels, cut into the upper part of the delta, are marked by dashed lines connecting notches in the profiles. (From K. O. Emery, The Sea off Southern California, Wiley, New York, 1960.)*

sands of feet below the sea's surface, has the broad convex form of a delta (Fig. 4-2). Apparently the dirty sands and poorly sorted muds were deposited on the submarine deltas from muddy flows (turbidity currents) that originated as slumps in marginal submarine canyons cutting into great masses of previously deposited, poorly consolidated sediments. The muds and sands in the bottom of the Puerto Rico trench may have had a similar origin. No turbidity currents have been discovered at work off California or in the Puerto Rico trench, but they have been demonstrated in the Mediterranean and in the main basin of the western North Atlantic through their effects on the numerous submarine cables in these regions.

The poorly sorted (dirty) sands of the deep basins off California are potential graywackes (see the classification of rocks at the end of Chapter 1 and also below). Graywackes are the commonest sandstones in geosynclinal and basin accumulations. Some examples were given in Chapter 3.

Limestone is very rare in the Recent (and slightly older) marine sediments off the south-western United States, but the silts contain numerous shells of microscopic foraminifers (§ 2-3), and locally, in shallow water, the sands and muds contain the larger shells of mollusks.

Complex sediments of the types found in the Colorado River delta and in the coastal basins are likely to contain mineral grains and rock fragments that give clues to the sources of the materials. The potassium feldspar that is uniformly abundant in the Colorado River delta points to sources far up the river and its tributaries. The plagioclase feldspar dominant in the coarse sediments of the Los Angeles and offshore basins points to local sources. These guides to sources confirm expectations based on the obvious circumstances. The study of some ancient sediments, however, leads to less obvious, sometimes surprising conclusions, as we shall find later, especially in Chapter 13.

In the East Indies (Fig. 4-3), Sumatra, Java, and Borneo are bounded on the north by shallow shelf seas less than 600 feet deep (the Java Sea and more than 200,000 square miles of the southern part of the South China Sea) that probably include troughs kept full of sediment by the discharges of the Mekong and other great southeastern Asiatic rivers. Most of this shelf area was emergent during Pleistocene epochs of lowered sea level and was drained northeast (north of Borneo) and southeast (south of Borneo) by streams whose courses can still be made out from the submarine topography. East of the shelf area, the seas between the islands are deep, especially north and southeast of Celebes; depths in the Banda Sea reach 4,500 feet. The bottoms of these deep tropic seas are largely covered with foraminiferal oozes; volcanic and other islands that rise from the ocean floor are capped or fringed by coral reefs.

The island arc that includes Sumatra and

Java contains many active explosive volcanoes, from which ash has been blown to great distances. The volcano Tambora, on an island east of Java, exploded in 1815 and spread ash over an area with a radius of 250 miles, including the part of the Java Sea that lies inside the dotted line of the map (Fig. 4-3). The 1815 ash-fall was a foot thick in Bali and eight inches thick in eastern Java. The ash had a peculiar composition, high in sodium and potassium; it was recognizable in many deep-water cores taken in the Java Sea in 1930 (Ref. 4), extending through a thickness of eight inches 200 miles northwest of the source and through a thickness of fifteen inches 150 miles northeast of the source.

On the south side of the island arc lies the

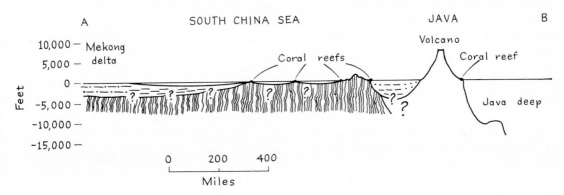

Fig. 4-3. *Depositional facies in the East Indies, with volcanoes marked on map by crosses.*

deepest part of the Indian Ocean, with a depth of 20,000 feet a hundred miles offshore. If turbid flows debouch into the Indian Ocean or into the inner deep basins, such as the Banda Sea, they no doubt deposit potential *volcanic graywacke*, a kind of rock that is common in the mountains that have developed on the sites of ancient geosynclinal accumulations along both sides of North America, as well as in other regions.

In the geologic past associations like those of Figures 4-1 and 4-3 have been common. The typical section might be a composite derived chiefly from Figure 4-3, with the northern (South China Sea) portion occupied in large part by calcareous banks and lagoons of the Bahama type. The geography of almost any past geologic time would also show the continental platforms more widely covered by shallow seas than they are today. The deposits of shallow seas on the platforms are called **epicontinental.** Some epicontinental seas of the past covered the greater parts of some continents, depositing limestone especially, with smaller areas of shale and sandstone. Rarely, shale has predominated.

4-2. *Continental Assemblages Indicating Extreme Climates*

The three sets of predominantly marine sediments just described are good guides to general conditions of sedimentation, but by themselves they are rather poor indicators of climate. It is true that marine animals of one group, the reef-forming corals, do their rock-building only in tropical waters, and that the distribution of biofacies also gives valuable hints concerning climate, as we shall learn in Chapter 7. But the clues to climatic conditions furnished by marine facies assemblages are, in general, somewhat obscure.

The continental sediments formed in a humid temperate or tropical climate are also rather noncommittal. It is not even easy to decide whether a non-fossiliferous sediment of Mississippi-delta type is continental or marine. Two non-marine associations, however, give quite definite indications of particular climatic conditions. These are the arid and the glacial sets of facies. Both are notably represented in the geologic column.

The association of facies that indicates extreme aridity is not now completely represented anywhere in the world. In the rocks this association includes brilliantly red sandstone, commonly coarse, pebbly, and poorly sorted; deep-red or purple clays and shales; pink or glaringly white cross-bedded eolian sandstones; and, in some places, thousands of feet of evaporites: anhydrite, rock salt, and even the very soluble magnesium and potassium sulphates and chlorides. Modern desert sands are gray or pink rather than red. The red color in the rocks may have been produced by post-depositional oxidation of the iron. The centers of modern desert basins are marked only by salt lakes or deposits of rock salt and gypsum. The east bay of the Caspian Sea is depositing some other salts, but nothing forming today even approaches the great and varied salt accumulations of the Permian.

The glacial association includes boulder clay (an unstratified clay, containing rock fragments, that is technically called **till** or, if consolidated into firm rock, **tillite**), outwash sands, and the **varved** (banded) silt-clay sequences deposited in glacier-bounded lakes. The glaciers that deposit till almost always scratch and scour the underlying rock, producing what is called a **glaciated pavement.**

Complete glacial associations, with pavements, are widespread in the Pleistocene of high latitudes and altitudes, and also in the Lower Permian or uppermost Carboniferous of South Africa, India, and other regions. Boulder clays considered tillites, but without the other features of the association, have also been reported at many other levels in the geologic column. Some of these boulder-bearing clays may really be tillites, but some are probably mixtures of fault gouge and fault breccia or the products of arid or submarine mud flows.

4-3. *Rock Facies (Lithofacies)*

A sedimentary formation (compare Chap. 3, second paragraph) is a mappable unit, usually (but not always) belonging to one facies, made up chiefly of one or a few kinds of rock, and formed under more or less uniform conditions. Two contemporaneous formations, such as a shale and a limestone, may also be called two contemporaneous lithofacies or, with a different emphasis, two contemporaneous Pleistocene (or Upper Devonian, or what not) facies.

The clay now being deposited on the outer marine portions of the Mississippi delta is merely the topmost layer of a thick accumulation of similar sediment, perhaps centrally many thousands of feet thick, deposited during

Fig. 4-4. *A cyclic sequence: underclay, coal, and marine shale and limestone in the Upper Carboniferous of western Illinois. (From H. R. Wanless, 1957.)*

a period millions of years long. The section probably thins out considerably in the Gulf of Mexico, so that it has the shape of a lop-sided lens, thickest near the river mouth and with a breadth perhaps 500 times the maximum thickness. At 1,000 or 2,000 feet below its surface the clay has probably had most of the sea water squeezed out of it by compaction, its micaceous grains probably lie nearly horizontal, and a sample would probably split parallel to this horizontal lamination; in depth, in other words, the clay probably becomes a shale. Beyond the Florida peninsula, on the Bahama Banks, another mass of sediments is accumulating, and this mass is a potential limestone formation. In general, a single sedimentary formation has usually formed in one area, under one set of conditions; contemporaneous with it, probably, were other formations, formed in other areas and perhaps under other conditions. Most individual formations are wholly or mostly marine, or wholly or mostly continental.

Closely related sedimentary rocks are frequently interbedded. In particular, sandstone and siltstone in layers from an inch to two or three feet thick make up sequences with aggregate thicknesses of hundreds or even thousands of feet. Such a sequence is usually called one formation. The origin of such a formation—the reason for the rhythmic alternations —is likely to be hard to determine. An explanation in terms of annual or longer climatic rhythms is commonly sought.

More varied facies, sometimes in part marine, in part continental, are also interbedded in layers so thin that their mapping as separate formations becomes impractical. An example is furnished by the coal measures (coal and associated beds) of Illinois. In such a case the mappable unit, the formation, may be made up of a coal and its associated sandstone and other continental beds plus the immediately overlying marine strata (Fig. 4-4). Or a formation may include several such alternations of marine and continental deposits.

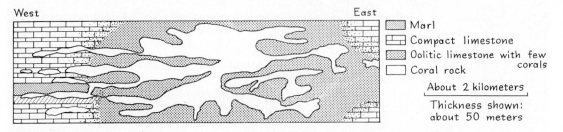

Fig. 4-5. *The reef of Valfin, in the Upper Jurassic north of Geneva, Switzerland.* (*After Emilien Bourgeat, 1888.*)

4-4. *Silicoclastic and Other Sedimentary Rocks*

An important distinction in the classification of sedimentary formations is that between the siliceous clastic rocks, made up of grains that are fragments of durable pre-existing rocks or soils, and rocks that are composed of newly precipitated (crystalline) or calciclastic materials. Examples of the siliceous clastic series are quartz conglomerate, quartz sandstone, graywacke, siltstone, and shale. Examples of new precipitates are cherts and the major portions of many limestones, the limestones being more abundant. The new precipitates, whether inorganic or composing the hard parts of organisms, may soon be broken and thereby become clastic, but the significance of these calciclastic fragments is very different from that of the siliceous grains that are carried long distances by currents.

Most limestones are texturally complex—in part clastic, in part organic, in part crystalline. If limestones are classified primarily by grain size, those whose grains are of sand size— from 1/16 mm to 2 mm—are most commonly clastic **calcarenites** ($CaCO_3$ sandstones, such as the southeast Florida beach sands would become if cemented) or **oolites** (rocks made up of the little accretionary masses also called oolites; see Fig. 1-10C). The clastic grains may be derived from mollusk shells or echinoderm fragments or may even be the slightly battered skeletons of foraminifers. Limestones whose units are mostly larger than 2 mm may be made up of fossils or fragments of fossils

held together by a crystalline cement. Limestones whose grains have dimensions less than 1/16 mm are commonly derived from limy muds, like those of the Bahama platform, composed chiefly of little crystals or fragments of crystals, more or less firmly stuck together.

Many limestones are well stratified, the individual beds being distinguished by differences in grain size or texture that may modify the effects of erosion. In sections exposed along coasts or rivers, beds a few inches or a few feet thick show up in relief. But in some terrains the regularity of the bedding is interrupted suddenly by masses of structureless or complexly varied limestone called **reefs,** frequently containing extensive coral colonies. Some reefs are only a few feet in any dimension; others are hundreds of feet thick, perpendicular to the bedding. The reef rock of Figure 4-5 grades laterally, in both directions, into regularly bedded limestone or dolomite. Great reefs, however, are commonly bounded in at least one direction by coarse, blocky, cross-bedded clastic limestone, containing many coral or algal fragments. This coarse debris is like that which accumulates on the steep seaward sides of the tropical coral reefs of the present oceans.

Siliceous clastic formations indicate the contemporaneous existence of one or more areas affected by erosion. Coarse clastic sedimentary rocks—conglomerates and breccias—give the most evidence concerning the nearness of eroding land masses and the composition of their rocks. Limestones, on the other hand, suggest—but by no means prove—deposition at considerable distances from high land and equally far from the mouths of great rivers. Even clastic limestone or oolite shows that deposition occurred in an area free from the silicate or silica sand and mud that are brought to the sea by rivers.

4-5. *Law of Correlation of Facies (Walther's Law)*

Johannes Walther, a German geologist, pointed out in 1894 that the facies associations, which we see forming side by side today, are commonly found in the rocks both side by side and in vertical succession, and frequently as parts of a single formation. Almost any correlation diagram covering a large region would furnish illustrations of this law. An example from southwestern Iran is shown as Figure 4-6. Section 5 of this figure shows the Asmari Limestone underlain by calcareous shale and overlain by anhydrite and gypsum. **Walther's law** states that the limestone probably passes laterally into these other rocks, and in section 1, at the northwestern edge of the region, we see the stratigraphic position of the Lower Asmari Limestone occupied by calcareous shale and gypsum. Figure 4-6 makes Walther's law specific: the boundaries between contemporaneous facies move lat-

Fig. 4-6. *Changes of facies in the Cenozoic rocks of southwestern Iran: section a few thousand feet thick and a few hundred miles long. (After A. N. Thomas, 18th International Geological Congress, 1950.)*

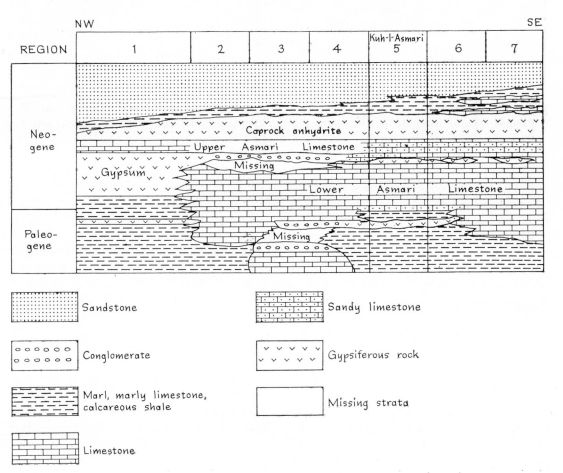

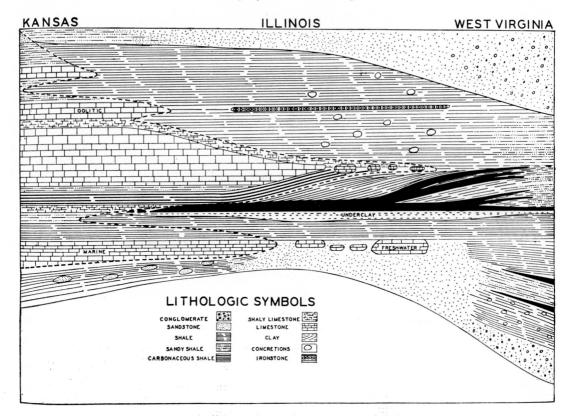

KANSAS ILLINOIS WEST VIRGINIA

OOLITIC

UNDERCLAY

MARINE

FRESH-WATER

LITHOLOGIC SYMBOLS

CONGLOMERATE		SHALY LIMESTONE	
SANDSTONE		LIMESTONE	
SHALE		CLAY	
SANDY SHALE		CONCRETIONS	
CARBONACEOUS SHALE		IRONSTONE	

Fig. 4-7. *Facies changes in a Pennsylvanian coal cycle (cyclothem) between Kansas and West Virginia. Marine strata to the left of the dashed line; coal (black) and other continental strata to the right. (From H. R. Wanless, 18th International Geological Congress, 1950.)*

erally in the course of time, back and forth. The vertical and the horizontal variations in facies are commonly nearly identical.

Walther's law is one of the stratigrapher's most valuable tools. It helps him to decide what successive beds to put together in a formation—namely, those that are found as contemporaneous facies—and to predict what changes a stratum is likely to undergo downdip from an outcrop. Many such predictions have been verified by drilling.

The facies changes expressed in Walther's law are demonstrated especially well by the coal measures of central and eastern North America (Fig. 4-7). In Illinois the whole coal-measure succession is marked by complex alternations of marine and continental sediments, including continental sandstone, under-

clay (perhaps ancient swamp soil), coal, and fresh-water limestone, as well as marine shale, sandstone, and limestone. One striking facies is an intensely black fossiliferous marine shale, widespread and only a few inches or a few feet thick, which occurs time after time in the section. If one follows the coal measures eastward from Illinois, through Kentucky to West Virginia, the marine facies pinch out one by one, and the sequence becomes an almost unbroken series of continental sandstones, underclays, coals, limestones, etc. If one starts from the original point in Illinois and goes west and then southwest, through Iowa, Missouri, and Kansas to Oklahoma and northern Texas, the coal and other continental members gradually disappear, the sequence becoming wholly marine and largely limestone. From the Illinois section alone we might predict the gradual disappearance of the continental facies in one direction, of the marine facies in the other. Moreover, the facies observed in Illinois, succeeding one another in one section (Figs. 4-4 and 4-7), might be expected to occur also in one contemporaneous association, extending from Texas or Oklahoma or Kansas, in the marine west, to West Virginia or Pennsylvania, in the continental east. These are the relationships generalized in Walther's law.

4-6. *Eustatic and Local Changes of Sea Level*

The rise of sea level, relative to a point on land, may be either **eustatic,** due to a general rise of the ocean level, or **tectonic** and local, due to the subsidence of this particular part of the land, with respect to a stationary general sea level. Similarly, the emergence of the land may be due to a general eustatic fall of sea level or to actual local rise of the land. At any one place the distinction between eustatic and local change ordinarily cannot be made, though local tilting is proof that the change was not wholly eustatic. If it can be shown that the sea level has risen simultaneously all over the world, it is safe to conclude that the rise was really eustatic. Such a conclusion is an important one, for a eustatic rise (or fall) demands an explanation, and the explanation—as of the Pleistocene changes of sea level (§ 16-6.a)—may have notable implications.

Local changes of sea level may involve such large areas as all of Scandinavia or most of eastern Canada—or, with less certainty, most of central and southern Africa or almost all the shores of the Mediterranean; but deformation on such a scale is very difficult to distinguish from eustatic change.

4-7. *Onlap and Offlap*

As the result of eustatic or local changes of sea level, shore lines have moved back and forth many times, on all coasts. At one time or another in the earth's history, the sea has penetrated deep into every part of every continent except central and southern Africa (and perhaps Antarctica). In North America, during late Carboniferous time, when the coal measures were forming, a seaway covered the mid-continent from Texas northward. The eastern shore of this seaway moved repeatedly back and forth, west into Kansas when the continental sand plains and coal swamps were most extensive, east into Illinois and beyond during inter-coal marine expansions (Fig. 4-7). Each oscillation of the shore line, from Kansas to Illinois and back, may be divided into two parts: **marine onlap,** advance of the sea, and **marine offlap,** retreat of the sea. Each part of the oscillation leaves its characteristic record in the rocks (Fig. 4-8). Onlap followed by offlap may be caused by more than one sequence of events, and so a unique explanation requires unusually complete evidence from an exceptionally large area. One set of circumstances, which seems to fit the case of the American coal measures, would include continuous rise of sea level, producing a constant tendency toward eastward migration of the shore line. Sedimentation, whether marine or continental, perhaps provided an equally constant tendency to raise the depositional base and so to drive the shore line westward. During offlap, perhaps, the shore line was pushed westward by an exceptional bulk of clastic sediments, which was perhaps due to an exceptionally great rise of the land far away to the east. Readvance of the sea—onlap—would then immediately follow any slackening in the supply of clastic sediments, perhaps when the highland to the east had been worn down a bit and before its next upsurge. The slacken-

Fig. 4-8. *Onlap* (a) *and offlap* (b).

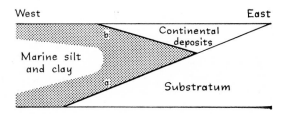

ing in the supply of clastic sediments would even lead to erosion in the lower courses of the streams, but probably not enough to explain the channels, 100 or more feet deep, that are now filled with the lower parts of some sandstone units.

The succession of onlap by offlap can be recognized in the coal measures from the evidence of the Illinois section alone. Looking at the outcrop shown in Figure 4-4 (or the diagram, Fig. 4-7), one realizes that the marine band above the coal represents onlap, a **transgression** of the sea, and that the return to continental deposition above the marine band represents offlap, a **regression** of the sea. The change from continental to overlying marine strata is a **transgressive sequence,** and the change from marine to overlying continental strata is a **regressive sequence.** "Transgression" and "regression" are common words in historical geology. The celebrated French geologist Emile Haug concluded long ago (1900) that every folding episode in a geosynclinal region produces a regression from that region and a transgression onto continental platforms. T. C. Chamberlin of the University of Chicago concluded independently (1909) that (1) ocean basins sink periodically and at the same times continents rise, (2) the resulting unconformities on the continents are universal, and (3) diastrophism "seems to be the ultimate basis of correlation." This generalization has been a bone of contention ever since. In later chapters we shall try to discover whether it can be proved or disproved.

If the higher beds of a stratigraphic succession cover broader areas than the lower ones, a condition especially common above an unconformity, the relation is called **overlap**

(Fig. 4-9). The beds of Formations B and C of the figure overlap successively onto Formation A. Overlap is a structural relation between rock bodies, but local time relations are also indicated. The sequence at *y*, by itself, shows only that the deformation was post-A and earlier than the deposition of part of C. The sequence at *x* shows that the deformation occurred before the deposition of the upper part of B. Figure 4-9 as a whole suggests, but does not prove, that the deformation occurred before the deposition of any beds of the horizontal BC sequence, even those out of sight to the left.

The existence of overlap, in a marine or other basin, may have more than one explanation. The overlap may be merely the result of basin filling, or it may have been induced by eustatic rise of sea level. In either case, there may have been no warping of the earth's crust in the region and there may not be the slightest unconformity between Formations B and C. On the other hand, the overlap may have accompanied the steady or spasmodic sinking of the whole basin of deposition. If the sinking was spasmodic, it may have occurred in two episodes, one before and one after the deposition of Formation B. The second episode may have involved the deformation of Formation B outside the area represented by the section. Study of the rocks and fossils of a region may show which of the several possible histories actually occurred.

All along the unconformity at the top of Formation A (Fig. 4-9) there is a gap in the record, a **lacuna,** or **hiatus,** and this lacuna becomes successively greater from *x* to *y*. If the strata were followed to the left, the angular unconformity might be found to decrease until the beds of all three formations became parallel (Fig. 3-12), and the lacuna might or might not disappear. In general, lacunas seem to be greatest around the margins of depositional basins; they usually decrease toward the centers of the basins and finally disappear. But some unconformities—the greatest ones—go right under whole depositional basins and make their floors.

Fig. 4-9. *Overlap above an unconformity.*

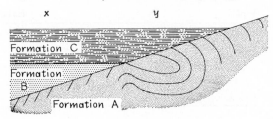

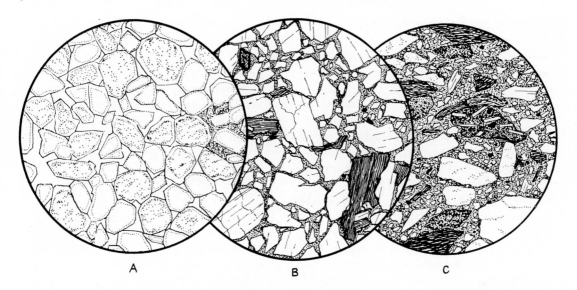

Fig. 4-10. *Microscopic features of sandstones. (From Williams, Turner, and Gilbert,* Petrography, *W. H. Freeman & Co., 1954.)*

A. Quartz sandstone, Cretaceous, Texas. Diameter 2 mm. Interstices filled by angular enlargements of the rounded clastic quartz grains.

B. Arkosic graywacke, Cenozoic, New Zealand. Diameter 2.5 mm. Angular grains of feldspar (with cleavage cracks) and quartz (clear), and flakes of biotite (dark-lined), in a matrix of silty clay.

C. Graywacke, Ordovician, Newfoundland. Diameter 1.5 mm. An unsorted aggregate of angular sand and silt grains in a clayey matrix. Larger grains are in part quartz and feldspar, in part volcanic and other rock fragments.

4-8. *Quartz-sandstone, Arkose, and Graywacke Suites*

The sandstone members of a sedimentary sequence are especially useful indicators of the geological conditions both in the areas of erosion and in those of deposition. If the sandstones are made up almost entirely of quartz grains, without fine matrix or cement (Fig. 4-10A) or with quartz or calcite cement, a long background of weathering and winnowing is indicated, with deposition under conditions that prevented contamination. The final stage may have been movement by currents along shore (typified among present-day sediments by the American East Coast sands, from the Carolinas southward to Florida) or by the wind (desert or coastal dunes). If the sandstones are arkoses (commonly more than 30 percent feldspar) or arkosic graywackes (with abundant fine-grained matrices, as in Fig. 4-10B), derivation from granitic or granodioritic source rocks, short transport, and quick burial are indicated. If the sand grains are mostly bits of volcanic rocks, as in clean volcanic sandstone or clayey volcanic graywacke, derivation from volcanic rocks is indicated. If the rock is the commonest kind of graywacke, with grains of varied texture and composition in a fine-grained matrix (Fig. 4-10C), derivation from varied sources and deposition without winnowing are indicated.

A sequence of shale, limestone, and quartz sandstone may be called a *quartz-sandstone suite;* one made up of arkose, conglomerate, and siltstone, commonly with little limestone, an *arkose suite;* and one made up of graywacke, siltstone, and shale, with or without limestone or conglomerate, a *graywacke suite*. At least two kinds of graywacke should be distinguished, volcanic and non-volcanic, with corresponding subdivision of the graywacke suite.

The arkose suite is rather rare. The somewhat similar *desert suite* is also somewhat rare. It is made up chiefly of wind-deposited, cross-bedded sandstone, poorly sorted pebbly stream-deposited red sandstone, red or purple or green clays and shales, and salts.

At least half of the well-described sandstones have between the sand grains the fine matrix that is characteristic of graywacke. In most graywackes the original clay matrix has been transformed, largely into a chloritic mineral. Some graywackes are composed wholly of quartz sand grains and the interstitial matrix, but more commonly the sand grains are of varied composition, some quartz, some feldspar, some bits of fine-grained volcanic or slaty rocks. The commonest graywacke association is marine, usually low in limestone and without abundant fossils, though some North American Paleozoic graywackes are interbedded with richly fossiliferous marine shales and even limestones. The classic graywacke suite in the lower Paleozoic of Wales was described in § 3-4.c.1. Examples in the western United States will be discussed in § 5-3.b.

4-9. *Sedimentary-tectonic Units*

a. Introduction

The principal structural units of each continent are one or more central platforms and one, two, or more marginal geosynclinal belts. The typical **platform** is made up chiefly of Precambrian rocks and has a flattish top with elevations ranging from a few hundred feet below sea level to several thousand feet higher. The major platform of a continent may be called a **plate** (Chap. 1, Ref. 1) or a **craton** (Chap. 6, Ref. 4). Each major continental platform contains several equidimensional, relatively shallow synclinal basins. **Geosynclines** are, or were, elongated mobile belts. They usually include masses of deformed sedi-

ments tens of thousands of feet thick and hundreds of miles long. Some geosynclines contain local basins separated by structural highs within the geosynclinal belt. The Caledonian folding in northwestern Europe at the end of Silurian time (§ 3-4.c.2) occurred in a geosynclinal belt that included Welsh and Irish-Scottish basins and extended from Wales and Ireland through Scotland to Scandinavia.

b. Platform and Geosynclines in North America

In North America a broad flat-topped platform of Precambrian rocks, mostly metamorphic and plutonic, has an exposed portion called the Canadian Shield (Fig. 4-11). South of the Great Lakes the Precambrian rocks are covered by thin flat sheets of Paleozoic and younger sedimentary rocks, largely of the quartz-sandstone suite. This central platform is slightly complicated by shallow structural basins, including the Illinois and Michigan basins, formed, in part, after the sedimentary cover was deposited. The upper, younger layers of that cover, which have been removed by erosion from up-arched parts of the platform, are preserved in the basins.

The North American central platform is bounded by complex marginal areas made up, in part, of local platforms and basins, but marked especially by geosynclines—great belts of downwarping, sedimentation, and subsequent close folding. The geosynclines at the eastern and western margins are the largest. The Appalachian geosyncline (Folded Appalachians, Blue Ridge and Piedmont, and New England Upland of Fig. 4-11) is close to the eastern margin of the continent, and the Cordilleran geosyncline covers a broad western marginal belt. The southern, deformed Ouachita Belt is mostly covered by the flat-lying Cretaceous and Tertiary strata of the Coastal Plain but emerges in southern Oklahoma and Arkansas. The northern (Arctic) marginal geosynclines are outside the limits of Figure 4-11. Note also, in that figure, the small Florida platform, southeast of the Appalachian geosyncline, and the small platform

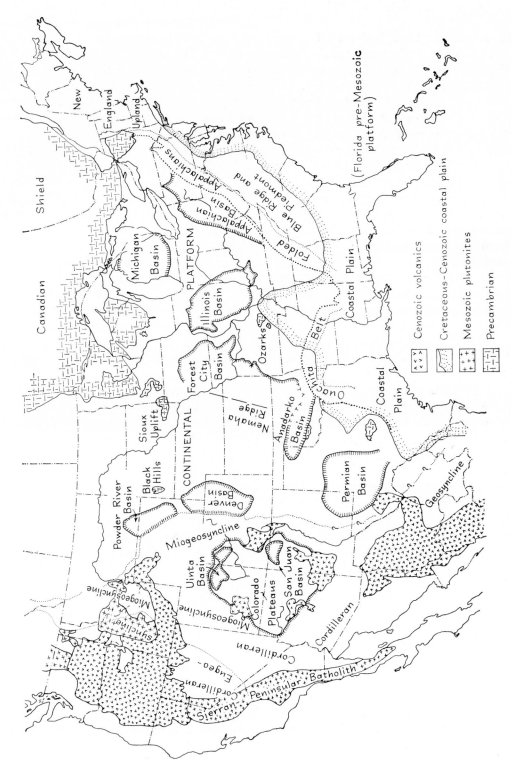

Fig. 4-11. *Tectonic units of central North America, from southern Canada to Cape San Lucas and the mouth of the Rio Grande.* (Adapted from Tectonic Map of the United States, 1961, and Carta Geológica de la República Mexicana, 1956.)

called the Colorado plateaus (to be described in Chap. 5), almost isolated in the Cordilleran geosynclinal belt.

The major structural features of North America go back to the beginning of the Paleozoic for their inception, and structure and sedimentation have developed together. The primary distinction is between two types of marine sedimentation: (1) that on the continental platform, with formations tens or hundreds of feet thick, aggregating only a few thousand feet altogether; (2) the narrower, thicker, marginal sedimentation of the geosynclines. In the geosynclinal belts two parts can be distinguished: adjacent to the platform, a **miogeosyncline** (Folded Appalachians), in which vulcanism was lacking; farther out, a **eugeosyncline** (including the Piedmont belt and the New England Upland), which experienced volcanic activity during sedimentation, as shown by lavas, tuffs, and volcanic graywackes. The proportion of volcanic material varies greatly from one portion of a eugeosynclinal belt to another—from nearly 100 percent in some places to practically none elsewhere. Individual formations in both kinds of geosynclines may be thousands of feet thick, and the aggregate thickness of the formations in the folded belts that have developed on the sites of geosynclines is usually 40,000 feet or more.

The miogeosynclinal and eugeosynclinal portions of the great folded belts are distinguishable in both North and South America, perhaps less so elsewhere. In both continents the eugeosynclinal zones were the first to undergo intense folding. These zones were also the principal sites of large plutonic batholiths, though granitic material also penetrated into miogeosynclinal rocks in some places. Finally, the American eugeosynclines exhibit vast expanses of graywackes, black shales, and chert, analogous to the much smaller graywacke and black shale facies of the Welsh lower Paleozoic (Fig. 3-13) and in contrast to the platform-like, commonly shelly facies of the miogeosynclines. The eugeosynclinal sediments are almost all silicoclastic; the miogeosynclinal

sediments are largely carbonates, with some shales and quartz sandstones.

The most varied and stratigraphically the most rewarding formations are those of the platforms. One illustration of this rule is furnished by the strata on the northwest European platform, where stratigraphy originated (compare Chap. 3). In the United States the outstanding illustration is found in the broad area that extends from western New York and Pennsylvania to Oklahoma and Texas. Here the epicontinental Paleozoic limestones and shales are crowded with brachiopods and other shallow-water marine invertebrates. The vertical changes in the fossil faunas are notable, often even between adjacent formations.

The sedimentary rocks of the miogeosyncline are similar to those on the platform. Some formations extend from platform to geosyncline; others can easily be correlated, especially because identical species of shallow-water marine fossils are commonly present in both regions. The fossils often indicate that both regions were covered by the same shallow seas. But the miogeosynclinal deposits are vastly thicker. The mass of miogeosynclinal sediments must therefore have sunk about as fast as the sediments accumulated, keeping the water shallow.

The subdivision of the eugeosynclinal graywackes, dark-colored siltstones and shales, and volcanic rocks into formations is difficult. The sedimentary units are discontinuous, and angular unconformities are common. Metamorphism by granodioritic or granitic batholiths has obscured the stratigraphy and destroyed a large part of the few fossils. Fortunately, some guide fossils of wide distribution are just common enough so that correlation problems are not insoluble. The best guides in the lower Paleozoic are graptolites, and the best in the upper Paleozoic and the Mesozoic are ammonoids. Rare nests of brachiopods and pelecypods have also proved useful.

Apparently the typical eugeosyncline, during its active depositional stages, had a geography similar to that of the East Indies today, with one or more belts of volcanic islands bounded by deep troughs. Perhaps the East Indies region will, in future ages, be transformed by close folding, metamorphism, batholithic invasion, uplift, and erosion into a mountain belt similar to the circum-Pacific ranges.

The process by which deep troughs, in a eugeosyncline or elsewhere, became filled with tens of thousands of feet of sediments is not completely understood. The currents that scour the shore zone lose their power in deep water. How, then, are graywackes and even pebbly or bouldery beds spread widely on the floor of a deep trough? The best suggestion is furnished by the turbid flows (products of turbidity currents) that form thin layers of clastic sediment as far from shore as the middle of the Mediterranean or even the center of the western North Atlantic basin. These modern deposits are muddy sand at the base, grading upward into mud. The sandy portions of such layers might become graywacke on consolidation. Graywackes predominate in the eugeosynclinal belts, but clean, sharply bounded sand and shale beds are found there too. Some of the metamorphosed sandstones are pure quartzites. The variation in the composition of eugeosynclinal sandstones may indicate large fluctuations in the depth of water or several sources of sediments. In any case, it is clear that the whole explanation of eugeosynclinal sedimentation has not yet been worked out.

The geosynclinal areas are so complex that even a general understanding of the North American examples must await further description in Chapters 5 and 6. In the meantime, the principal features may be outlined for easy reference:

I. Sedimentary column tens of thousands of feet thick.
II. Miogeosyncline at edge of platform; eugeosyncline farther out (especially well marked in North and South America).
   A. Miogeosyncline.
      1. Pre-orogenic sedimentation: shallow-water marine and continental; similar to that on platform; marine fossils abundant; almost no vulcanism.

      2. Orogeny: folding and thrust faulting with little or no metamorphism.
      3. Post-orogenic erosion, with minor deposition on depressed fault blocks.
   B. Eugeosyncline.
      1. Pre-orogenic sedimentation: volcanic sediments and lava flows locally dominant; much deep-water marine deposition; fossils rare.
      2. Orogeny, etc.: folding and thrust faulting earlier than in miogeosyncline; pronounced metamorphism; emplacement of granodioritic or granitic batholiths, some of which are many hundreds of miles long.
      3. Post-orogenic events complicated, involving vulcanism as well as deposition on coastal plains and depressed fault blocks in at least some parts of the belts.

c. Basins

The central platform and the geosynclines are the major structural elements of a continent. Basins are somewhat smaller features, but geologic interest has become centered on them, especially because they contain the world's principal accumulations of coal, oil, and other useful substances. Typical basins, such as the forty-two major non-Soviet oil-yielding basins studied by a group of oil geologists (Ref. 3), range in size from those only a few miles across to one giant, along the northeastern side of the Persian Gulf, that is 600 miles long and another, equally large, beneath the Texas-Louisiana portion of the American Gulf Coast. Most basins are approximately equidimensional, but some, including those of the Persian Gulf and the American Gulf Coast, are somewhat elongated.

A distinction must be made between sedimentary and structural basins. A sedimentary basin is one that has been more or less completely filled with sediments. A structural basin is one in which central subsidence has occurred after sedimentation was well advanced. Most large basins are both sedimentary and structural. Sedimentation and subsidence often proceeded together and were followed by marked deformation of the basin's margins. In general, the center of a basin tends to go down and its margins up. As a result, the present

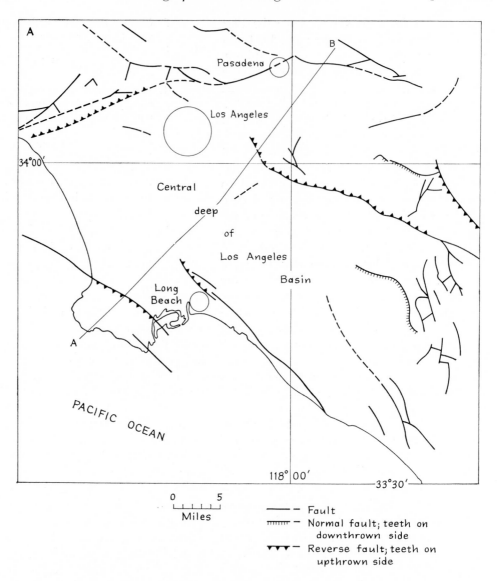

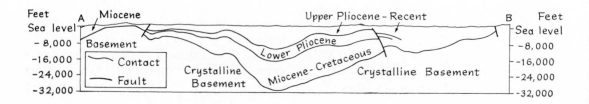

Fig. 4-12. *Map (A) and section (B) of the Los Angeles Basin, southern California, showing the central depressed area and the folded, faulted margins. (Redrawn from T. H. McCulloh, U.S. Geological Survey, 1960.)*

structural basin is usually somewhat smaller than the earlier basin of deposition (Fig. 4-12). The sediments in the central basin are the least disturbed and the most completely preserved. A sedimentary basin lying in a mobile belt may have its margins folded and faulted, as shown in Figure 4-12, whereas basins developed on the platform—for example, the Illinois Basin—may show only slight marginal deformation.

Neither a structural basin nor a filled sedimentary basin is necessarily low topographically. The Illinois and Michigan basins are neither much lower nor much higher than their surroundings, and the Appalachian Basin is the region of the Appalachian plateaus.

4-10. *Examples of Stratigraphic Assemblages*

Conditions of sedimentation are so complex and varied that the generalizations presented in this chapter can be made convincing and useful only by example. Two examples, one local and the other regional, are given here. Others are to be found elsewhere in this book, especially in Chapters 5 and 6.

a. Gressly's Facies

Local variations in the marine facies early became apparent to Swiss geologists. In 1838, Amanz Gressly described a notable example in the Upper Jurassic of the Jura Mountains and gave the word "facies" the special stratigraphic definition that geologists still use. A generalized section across Gressly's area (Fig. 4-13) shows the sequence of Upper Jurassic rocks. Units 2 and 3 clearly represent contemporaneous facies. Unit 2 is composed of many smaller interfingering rock units, in part coralline rock. The corals are largely concentrated in unbedded reef facies, shown in the center of the section. The remainder of unit 2, northwest of the reef facies, is mostly oolitic limestone, finer-grained limestone layers (consolidated limy muds of lagoonal type), and fossiliferous layers with corals and echinoids. As the reef facies is traced to the southeast, it

rises in the stratigraphic section, and at each level it is bounded on its southeast side by unit 3, an open-sea marl-limestone facies, locally containing fossil sponges and ammonites. One may imagine that the coral reefs marked lines of Jurassic breakers that separated shallow seas to the northwest, perhaps extending as far as Paris, from deeper and broader seas to the southeast, perhaps extending far beyond the present site of the Alps.

The lithologic facies and the faunal facies in units 2 and 3 are more different from each other than they are from rocks lower and higher in the section. How, then, can they be correlated with each other? The evidence for correlation is three-fold. First, units 2 and 3 are interbedded with each other, as shown diagrammatically by the jagged contact between them in the figure. Second, these units have the same stratigraphic position, between unit 1 and unit 4. Unit 1 and its fauna extend almost across the bottom of the section, right past the line of change from unit 2 to unit 3. In unit 4, a somewhat complex entity itself, at least one thin zone also extends across the whole unit. Third, the association of facies has a modern analogue. Unit 2 is similar to a modern reef and the lagoon (back-reef) facies it guards; unit 3 is like fore-reef and open-sea deposits. We use the present to interpret the past: the modern reefs and associated sedi-

Fig. 4-13. *Generalized northwest-southeast section through the Upper Jurassic facies distinguished by Amanz Gressly (1838): 1, Oxfordian; 2, Rauracian; 3, Argovian; 4, Sequanian. The Oxfordian is a widespread unit named from Oxford, England; the other units are local. (Adapted from Swiss Geological Commission, Sheet 3, 1936.)*

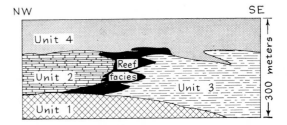

Fig. 4-14. *An aerial view southeast over the Jura Mountains near Moutier, northwest of Solothurn, Switzerland. (Photograph by Swissair.)*

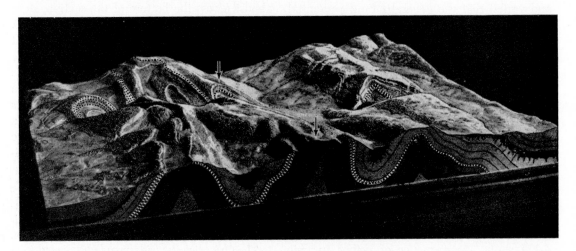

Fig. 4-15. *Block diagram of the Moutier area in the Jura Mountains, Switzerland, looking southeast at the strata pictured in Fig. 4-14 and shown schematically in Fig. 4-13. Units 2 and 3 of Fig. 4-13 stippled; 2 at left and 3 at right, with the transition in the anticline marked by vertical arrows (also visible in the upper left of Fig. 4-14). (Modified from Albert Heim,* Geologie der Schweiz, *1919.)*

Fig. 4-16. *The Permian Basin of western Texas and southeastern New Mexico. (Modified from Ref. 7.)*
    A. *Map of Permian Basin in Late Permian time. Arrows show the direction of movement of sediment.*
    B. *Diagrammatic west-east section across the Basin.*
    C. *Diagrammatic northwest-southeast section across the Basin.*

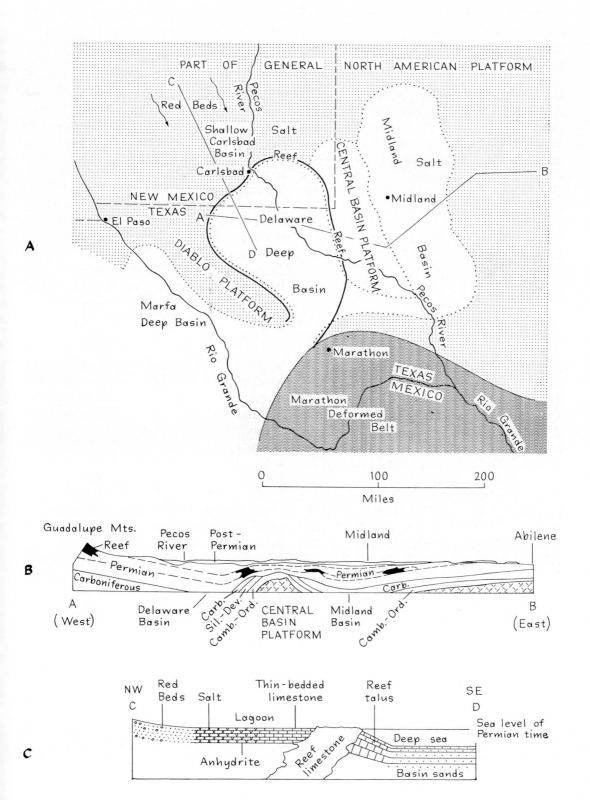

ments help us to understand the meaning of the facies in the rocks, and they also tend to confirm our conclusions as to the contemporaneity of those facies.

We must not leave this particular part of the Swiss Jura without making clear the stages of development of Gressly's idea, from the folded limestones one sees at first glance (Fig. 4-14) through a carefully prepared structure section and three-dimensional model (Fig. 4-15) to the diagrammatic *unfolding* achieved by Gressly and modified somewhat by his successors (Fig. 4-13). It is only after getting a concept of the rock mass as it was before folding that we can obtain an idea of the conditions of deposition.

b. Permian Basin Facies

An example on a much larger scale—a good example of **paleogeography,** or geography of an ancient epoch—is furnished by the evaporites and associated continental and marine sedimentary rocks of the Permian Basin in western Texas and southeastern New Mexico (Figs. 4-11 and 4-16A). The great Carlsbad Cavern of southeastern New Mexico is in Permian limestone, the Carlsbad potash salts are Permian evaporites, and the majority of the oil fields in the basin obtain their yields from Permian rocks.

Both the basin's structure and the Permian stratigraphy are complex. Structurally, the main basin has three parts, separated by two platforms (Fig. 4-16AB). The two principal sub-basins, the Delaware Basin and the Midland Basin, and the intervening Central Basin Platform with its Precambrian core, are shown as they are today in Figure 4-16B. The varied facies of a rather late part of Permian time are shown in Figure 4-16C. At this late time both the shallow Carlsbad Basin on the main platform and the originally deep Midland Basin were evaporating pans, where calcium sulphate, sodium chloride, and, near Carlsbad, even the very soluble potassium and magnesium salts were deposited from solution. Farther north, continental red beds were ac-

cumulating. The evaporating pans were separated from the sea by a reef surrounding the Delaware Basin (Fig. 4-16A). The great masses of salts can have come only from the evaporation of great quantities of sea water, perhaps provided by continuous or nearly continuous inflow through the bounding reefs.

The reefs sloped off steeply into the deep Delaware Basin (Fig. 4-16AC), with steep slopes of reef debris in roughly outlined beds now preserved as giant cross stratification in the limestones of El Capitan (Fig. 4-17) and other parts of the southern Guadalupe Mountains. Down in the Delaware Basin the calcareous reef debris graded laterally into silicoclastic sands and silts thousands of feet thick (Fig. 4-18). These clastic sediments may have been derived from the south, or they may have been sluiced through the Carlsbad Basin and narrow gaps in the surrounding reefs at times when at least some routes through the Carlsbad Basin were temporarily filled with largely clastic sediments. The clastic materials may have been distributed over the whole floor of the deep Delaware Basin by turbid flows like those of the present Atlantic or Mediterranean deep-sea floor.

The evidence on which the facies correlations were based is complex, and the relations became apparent only after long study by many geologists. The varied facies were correlated by field mapping of the rocks exposed at the surface, aided by stratigraphic paleontology, and by subsurface study of the large fraction of the rocks, including the valuable potash deposits, that can only be guessed at from surface exposures alone. The subsurface study was based mostly on findings in the thousands of wells drilled for oil.

The most critical points are the correlations between facies—from the red beds and salts to the back-reef marine strata, the reef limestones, and the deep-basin clastics. The distribution of these facies varied considerably in the course of Permian time. Note that the rather late Permian reef shown in Figure 4-16A blocked the entrance to the Midland Basin. At

Fig. 4-17. *Aerial view, from the west, of the Permian rocks of the Guadalupe Mountains, western Texas. (Photograph by J. S. Shelton.)*

a slightly earlier time the Midland Basin held deep water, was connected with the Delaware and Marfa Basins, and was surrounded by the earlier Permian reefs shown in section on the two sides of the Midland Basin in Figure 4-16B.

The final structural synthesis of the whole area demonstrated a series of changing paleo-geographies that had economic as well as scientific interest. The reef zones and their neighborhoods make up some of the richest sources of petroleum in the world; the area is known to oil men everywhere as the Permian Basin. Despite its somewhat complex structure, its fragmentation by faults (not shown in the figures), and the partial erosion of one fault block, producing the rather grand mountain front of Figure 4-17, that name is well

justified. The Permian Basin is a region where Permian sedimentary rocks are thick. Its floor is complex, with marginal minor basins and a central platform, but no part of the general structural depression has the shape or depth of a geosyncline, and the central platform is only a few scores of miles across. In the large view, the Permian Basin must be considered a marginal part of the main North American platform, with unusual facies and with a Permian history all its own.

4-11. *Use of Fossils in Local and Regional Correlations*

In this chapter we have relied on fossils as little as possible for correlations, but the fact is that guide fossils are used so regularly by

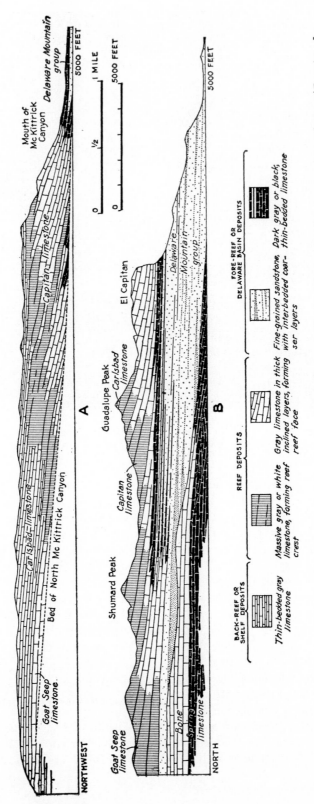

Fig. 4-18. *Two sections through the Permian reefs and related structures of the Guadalupe Mountains, western Texas. (Reprinted from The Evolution of North America by P. B. King, by permission of Princeton University Press. Copyright © 1959 by Princeton University Press.)*
A. *The upper part of the succession, exposed in a canyon wall.*
B. *The succession exposed in the escarpment at the west side of the mountains (pictured in Fig. 4-17).*

stratigraphers that occasional mention of correlation by fossils has been necessary—for example, in connection with the Permian Basin. As we have seen in Chapter 3, William Smith and his successors, having been convinced of the reliability of guide fossils while they were establishing the standard column in northwestern Europe, used them for some regional correlations in the same way they used rock units such as clay or siltstone. Before accepting the use of fossils in correlation as a fundamental method, however, we shall test the results of its use by means of the law of superposition (Steno's first law) in the fossiliferous stratigraphic sequences of other areas. We turn first, in Chapter 5, to the Grand Canyon of northern Arizona, a place where superposition seems perfectly clear.

4-12. Summary

The present assemblages of marine facies, such as those off the southeastern and southwestern United States and those in the East Indies, are obviously the products of particular geographies and climates. Coordinated assemblages have been worked out similarly for parts of many local geologic columns. A notable example is the Permian of western Texas and southeastern New Mexico, the sedimentary record of an arid land beside one or more shallow evaporating basins and at least one connected deep marine basin.

A stratigraphic synthesis, such as that of the Permian Basin, is a great accomplishment, commonly slowly achieved. The mapping of interfingering and therefore contemporaneous facies, as in the classic work of Gressly (Ref. 9), is the most important step. Even before detailed mapping, however, a clue to the probable contemporaneity of a set of facies is their interbedding in a single section, as, for example, in the interbedded continental and marine strata of the Illinois coal measures.

Where marine and continental strata are interbedded, onlap and offlap of the marine deposits have occurred. Under favorable circumstances the stages in the advance and retreat of the sea can be traced. Once again the Illinois coal measures furnish an example.

The probable changes of sea level demonstrated at any one spot, as at a place where continental deposits are covered by marine deposits, may have been either eustatic or tectonic. Proof of a eustatic change is always difficult, but on later pages we shall present the evidence that such changes have occurred during several widely separated geological periods.

Climate has been an important factor in the geologic past, sometimes with extremes of temperature and precipitation as great as those prevailing today or even greater. The climatic complications of the late Paleozoic and of the Pleistocene will be given special attention in later chapters. Here we may note that the reefs emphasized in the examples from Gressly and the Permian Basin may have been associated with tropical climates, as are the reefs of the present day.

The grandest conclusions concerning facies have structural (tectonic) implications. Thin and widespread limestones, quartz sandstones, and shales characterize the continental platforms. Thicker, but otherwise similar, sediments occur in the inner geosynclinal (miogeosynclinal) belts. Outer geosynclinal (eugeosynclinal) belts are commonly characterized by the abundance of tuffs and lavas, as well as by deep-seated granitic intrusives. Since the special features of the various tectonic elements of a continent are perhaps most clearly shown in North America, the details are left for description in special chapters (5 and 6) on parts of this continent.

REFERENCES

General

1. Maurice Gignoux: *Stratigraphic Geology* (Freeman, San Francisco, 1955)

2. C. O. Dunbar and John Rodgers: *Principles of Stratigraphy* (Wiley, New York, 1957)

3. G. M. Knebel and Guillermo Rodríguez-Eraso: "Habitat of Some Oil," BULLETIN, Amer. Assoc. Petrol. Geol., vol. 40, pp. 547–561 (1956)

4. G. A. Neeb: "The Composition and Distribution of the Samples," REPORTS, Snellius Expedition, vol. 5, Part 3, pp. 55–268 (Brill, Leiden, 1943)

North America

5. P. B. King: *The Tectonics of Middle North America: Middle North America East of the Cordilleran System* (Princeton University Press, 1951)

6. P. B. King: *Geology of the Southern Guadalupe Mountains, Texas,* Prof. Paper 215, U.S. Geol. Surv. (1948)

7. P. B. King: *The Evolution of North America* (Princeton University Press, 1959)

8. G. E. Murray: *Geology of the Atlantic and Gulf Coastal Province of North America* (Harper, New York, 1961)

Classics

9. Amanz Gressly: *Observations géologiques sur le Jura soleurois,* Nouveaux Mémoires de la Société Helvétique des Sciences Naturelles, vols. 2, 4, and 5 (Neuchâtel, 1838–1841)

10. Johannes Walther: *Einleitung in die Geologie als historische Wissenschaft,* 3 vols. (Fischer, Jena, 1893–1894), especially vol. 3, chap. 27

CHAPTER 5

The Grand Canyon Platform and the Cordilleran Geosyncline

THE BEST introduction to the geologic history of the Grand Canyon region would be a visit to the Grand Canyon itself, in northern Arizona. As a rather poor second-best, study the accompanying map (Fig. 5-1) and an aerial view in which the observer is looking northwest, down the river. Note, in the latter (Fig. 5-2), the narrow Granite Gorge, 1,000 feet deep, through which the river flows away out of sight and which is walled with Precambrian crystalline rocks, and the contrast of its massive ruggedness with the banded erosion forms carved out of two sets of overlying strata, the lower with inclined bedding, the upper horizontal. The lower set, at the right along the upstream part of the river's course, we shall call the wedge series because it makes a wedge between the crystalline rocks, on which it lies unconformably, and the horizontal higher strata. The horizontal beds, which extend for a thickness of 4,000 feet to the tops of the Canyon walls, lie unconformably across the eroded edges of both the crystalline rocks and

the wedge series. The local geologic column (Fig. 5-3) includes the Grand Canyon rocks and also higher strata that overlie the rocks of the Canyon rim farther north, especially in southern Utah.

Note, in Figure 5-3, the formation names of parts of the horizontal sequence. Study in museum or laboratory, if possible, specimens of Grand Canyon rocks, especially those from the more significant formations, including at least the Tapeats sandstone, the Bright Angel shale, the Muav limestone, the Supai formation (red beds), the Kaibab limestone, and the Shinarump conglomerate. (The Shinarump occurs at a level somewhat above the canyon-rim Kaibab limestone and crops out in the higher region to the north.) Study also tracks of land animals from the Supai and marine fossils from the Bright Angel shale and the Kaibab limestone. Clear ideas about the rock types and kinds of fossils in a few selected formations will be exceptionally useful in the reading of this chapter.

5-1. *Rocks of the Grand Canyon Region*

The Grand Canyon region is part of the geographic area called the Colorado plateaus (Figs. 5-1 and 5-15). Geologically it is an isolated part of the North American Precambrian platform covered by nearly horizontal Paleozoic and Mesozoic rocks, locally capped by Cenozoic rocks. The Colorado plateaus are bordered on the northwest by the Cordilleran geosyncline (Fig. 4-11), which has a thick sedimentary sequence and complicated structure.

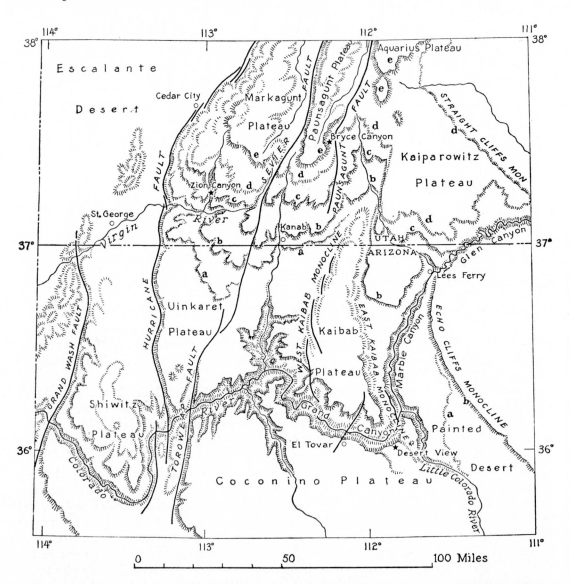

Fig. 5-1.   *Map of Colorado plateau region in Arizona and Utah, showing Grand Canyon, plateaus, escarpments, faults, and the monoclines that warp the strata up or down: a, Chocolate Cliffs (Shinarump conglomerate); b, Vermillion Cliffs (Jurassic); c, White Cliffs (Jurassic); d, Cretaceous; e, Tertiary. (Reprinted from* The Evolution of North America *by P. B. King, by permission of Princeton University Press. Copyright © 1959 by Princeton University Press.)*

The geography and geology of the plateau region became known fairly recently. It was in 1869 that Major John Wesley Powell, one-armed veteran of the Civil War and a pioneer geologist who later headed the U.S. Geological Survey, first explored the Colorado River canyons. He started from the newly built Union Pacific Railroad in southwestern Wyoming and led a little party down the Green and Colorado Rivers in rowboats, to explore the deep gorges and run the tumultuous rapids. The last and greatest of the Colorado's gorges that he explored was the Grand Canyon in northern Arizona. He finally emerged into open country in southern Nevada, where now the waters of Lake Mead are backed up behind Hoover Dam.

In this whole region Steno's first law may be applied easily and with considerable confidence. The lowest rocks are surely the oldest, for the possibility of overturning seems excluded by the obvious circumstances. All but the lowest strata are still horizontal, and we shall assume that the beds of the wedge series have been rotated only the amount required by their dip. For a description that will lead to a history of the events recorded here, in their chronological order, we begin at the bottom of the Canyon and work up.

a. Pre-Paleozoic Rocks

The rocks of the Granite Gorge are mostly schist and gneiss, cut by pegmatite dikes and masses of granite. The granite and pegmatite

Fig. 5-2. *Low oblique air view of the Grand Canyon, looking northwest and showing the wedge series between steeply banded gneiss and the horizontal Paleozoic. At the right the Tapeats sandstone, the lowest Paleozoic unit, abuts against a ridge of quartzite in the wedge series. (From J. S. Shelton, Geology Illustrated, W. H. Freeman & Co.)*

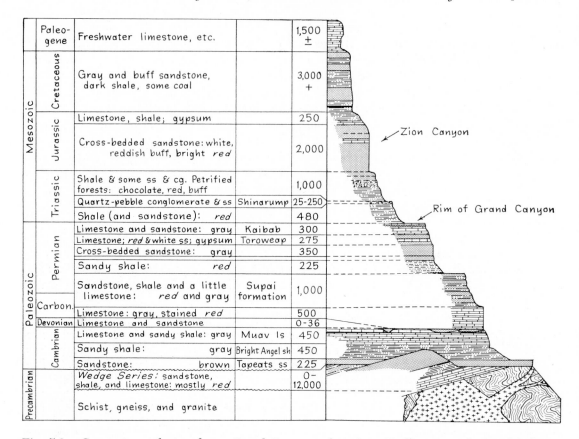

	Paleo-gene	Freshwater limestone, etc.		1,500 ±
Mesozoic	Cretaceous	Gray and buff sandstone, dark shale, some coal		3,000 +
Mesozoic	Jurassic	Limestone, shale; gypsum		250
Mesozoic	Jurassic	Cross-bedded sandstone: white, reddish buff, bright *red*		2,000
Mesozoic	Triassic	Shale & some ss & cg. Petrified forests: chocolate, red, buff		1,000
Mesozoic	Triassic	Quartz-pebble conglomerate & ss	Shinarump	25-250
Mesozoic	Triassic	Shale (and sandstone): *red*		480
Paleozoic	Permian	Limestone and sandstone: gray	Kaibab	300
Paleozoic	Permian	Limestone; *red* & white ss; gypsum	Toroweap	275
Paleozoic	Permian	Cross-bedded sandstone: gray		350
Paleozoic	Permian	Sandy shale: *red*		225
Paleozoic	Permian	Sandstone, shale and a little limestone: *red* and gray	Supai formation	1,000
Paleozoic	Carbon.	Limestone: gray, stained *red*		500
Paleozoic	Devonian	Limestone and sandstone		0-36
Paleozoic	Cambrian	Limestone and sandy shale: gray	Muav ls	450
Paleozoic	Cambrian	Sandy shale: gray	Bright Angel sh	450
Paleozoic	Cambrian	Sandstone: brown	Tapeats ss	225
Precambrian		*Wedge Series:* sandstone, shale, and limestone: mostly *red*		0-12,000
Precambrian		Schist, gneiss, and granite		

Fig. 5-3. *Composite geologic column, Grand Canyon and southern Utah; not to scale. (Modified from L. F. Noble and H. E. Gregory, U.S. Geological Survey.)*

occur in pink and gray masses that are separated by thicker vertical bands of schist and gneiss (Figs. 5-3 and 5-4). Parts of the schist are metamorphosed volcanic rocks; other parts are mica schists that were originally silty sandstones. Some of the gneiss is recrystallized feldspathic quartz sandstone. Even after the formation of folds, which now stand almost on end, and complete recrystallization during metamorphism, bedding planes have been well preserved (Fig. 5-5). Even the original thicknesses of the stratified series can be estimated; one well-exposed sequence appears to have been at least 25,000 feet thick. The granite sends intrusive tongues into the schist and gneiss, showing that it is younger.

Unconformably overlying the granite and gneiss, but also faulted against them, is the wedge series, 12,000 feet of unmetamorphosed sandstone, shale, limestone, and lava, dipping to the northeast (Fig. 5-2). This series is present in rather widely separated parts of the Grand Canyon. At each place it forms a great wedge, between the granite and gneiss of the Granite Gorge and the 4,000-foot sequence of horizontal strata composing the upper part of the Canyon walls.

b. Paleozoic Formations

The horizontal Paleozoic sedimentary rocks above the wedge series are shown in Figure 5-3. The lowest part of the Paleozoic sequence is Cambrian in age and lies across the eroded edges of the up-ended gneiss, with its intru-

Fig. 5-4. *Schist and gneiss of the Granite Gorge, cut by pegmatite dikes and overlain unconformably by the wedge series; at the very top, Tapeats sandstone. (From J. S. Shelton,* Geology Illustrated, *W. H. Freeman & Co.)*

Fig. 5-5. *Relic bedding in gneiss of the Granite Gorge. The scale is six inches long. (Photograph by J. H. Maxson.)*

sive granite, and also across the beveled edges of the formations that make up the tilted wedge series. The Cambrian is divided into three formations: at the base the coarse, pebbly Tapeats sandstone, 225 feet thick; then the Bright Angel shale, up to 650 feet thick; and at the top the Muav limestone, 125–150 feet thick at the east and becoming very much thicker to the west. The Tapeats sandstone is resistant to erosion and forms the rim at the top of the inner gorge (Granite Gorge). The weak Bright Angel shale has been easily eroded, leaving a broad bench (terrace) on each side of the river. The Muav limestone is exposed at the bases of the next higher cliffs.

The Tapeats sandstone and conglomerate, the Bright Angel shale, and the Muav limestone form a succession that seems to be characteristic of an encroaching sea. In this particular case, the succession represents a continuous series of events. The Precambrian surface was already a nearly flat surface formed by subaerial weathering and erosion, a peneplain, very smooth on the gneiss of the western Grand Canyon, marked by hogback ridges in the wedge series near Grand Canyon village (El Tovar in Fig. 5-1), and somewhat hilly farther east. It was strewn with partially weathered rock debris, much of which is still preserved. Waves beating on the Cambrian shore picked up and redistributed the loose, pebble-sized rock fragments, as well as sand and gravel lying on the pre-existing land surface, and spread this material about rather evenly, making the sandy gravel layer that is now the Tapeats basal conglomerate. The pebbles in the thin basal conglomerate are mostly small, rather angular masses of quartz. As the sea advanced farther onto the land, the area was covered successively by the sand and mud preserved as the Tapeats quartz sandstone and the Bright Angel shale. Finally,

when the sea had advanced still farther, and this area was more distant from the sources of sand and mud, the shells of organisms accumulated here, became mingled with mud, and produced in time the sandy-silty Muav limestone (Fig. 5-6).

Only a few remains of organisms are still preserved in the Bright Angel shale and Muav limestone. The most numerous are trilobites (Fig. 5-7; compare also § B-8), the primitive arthropods whose remains are common in the lowest fossiliferous rocks of many regions. The trilobites of Horizon A in Figure 5-6 are similar to those characteristic of the Lower Cambrian, and those of Horizon B are similar to those characteristic of the Middle Cambrian, in other parts of North America. If each of the fossil horizons is **isochronous**—formed at the same time throughout its extent—then the basal bed of the Tapeats sandstone was not deposited everywhere at one time; in the western part of the Canyon it is older than Horizon A but at the east contemporaneous with Horizon A or even younger. That is, the sea apparently advanced slowly from west to east, depositing sand near the shore, mud and limy beds farther out. If the guide fossils can be trusted, the base of the Tapeats is millions of years younger at the east end of the section than at the west end. Conversely, the eastern

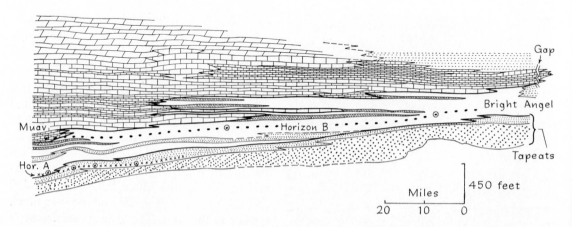

Fig. 5-6. *Diagrammatic section showing relations of Tapeats sandstone, Bright Angel shale, and Muav limestone. Two fossil horizons are marked. (Adapted by J. S. Shelton from E. D. McKee, 1945.)*

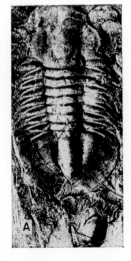
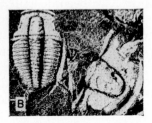

Fig. 5-7. *Cambrian trilobites from the Grand Canyon.* (From C. E. Resser, 1945.)
A. Glossopleura mckeei, *Bright Angel shale, Indian Gardens.*
B. Ehmaniella basilica, *Bright Angel tongue above Rampart Cave member of Muav limestone, Peach Springs Canyon.*

Tapeats was deposited at the same time as part of the Bright Angel shale farther west. This illustrates the important fact that a formation is a rock unit, but not necessarily a time unit.

The Cambrian section is overlain by thin, discontinuous remnants of sandy Devonian limestone containing poorly preserved marine invertebrates and bony plates that were parts of the external skeletons of primitive fishes. The remnant lenses lie between two unconformities; their maximum thickness is only 130 feet. The fish remains represent the most characteristic Devonian animals, the primitive vertebrates that we shall discuss in some detail in a later chapter.

Overlying the remnants of the Devonian or, more commonly, lying directly on the Cambrian rocks, is the prominent Redwall limestone, a 500-foot layer of gray limestone stained red on the cliff surface by a muddy pigment washed down from overlying red sediments. The limestone contains a few marine fossils that establish it as Early Car-

boniferous (Mississippian, in prevalent American usage) in age.

The Redwall limestone is overlain by the Supai (soo-pie) formation, a red-bed group that includes brownish or pinkish gray sandstone as well as dark red shale. This series of beds is easily eroded and so produces a stepped slope above the Redwall limestone. The Supai formation is mostly Permian, but the lowest member seems, from its plant fossils, to be Upper Carboniferous. Though this lowest member is of about the same age as the Coal Measures, it contains no coal. A dull, pinkish-gray sandstone that lies a little above the Supai is quarried for the flagstones that pave patios all over the Southwest. Here

Fig. 5-8. *At left, tracks of a reptile in Permian sandstone; at right, natural molds of the same tracks; from five miles north of Seligman, Arizona. The meter stick gives the scale.* (From Raymond Alf Museum, Webb School, Claremont, California.)

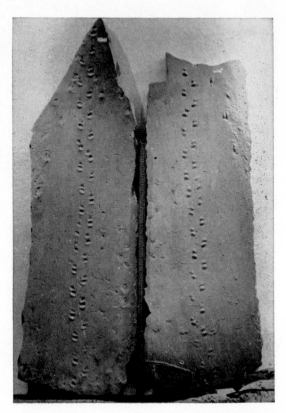

and there a flagstone slab is marked by a double row of footprints similar to those made by salamanders or some kinds of small reptiles. Thus we know that animals capable of walking on land must have lived during the Permian.

Above the Supai are 1,150 feet more of Permian formations (Fig. 5-3): first a red sandy shale, then steep cliffs of white sandstone, complexly cross-bedded, unfossiliferous except for tetrapod tracks (Fig. 5-8), then the gray fossiliferous marine limestone and barren red beds of the Toroweap formation, and finally, at the top of the Canyon cliffs, the Kaibab limestone (and sandstone), mostly gray and mostly marine. The Supai-Kaibab sequence shows that the conditions of deposition in this region must have changed repeatedly during Permian time. The Supai sandstones are, at least in part, continental and perhaps were deposited by wandering streams that moved about over flood plains or alluvial fans. The red mudstones of the lower Supai may have been deposited in temporary lakes. The curved, complex cross-stratification in the white sandstone is similar to that in modern sand dunes. The overlying, interbedded marine limestone and continental red beds of the Toroweap formation indicate alternation of land and sea—a movement of the shoreline

Fig. 5-9. *Three brachiopods from the Kaibab limestone of the Grand Canyon:* Derbya *at left,* Meekella *at center, and a productid at right. (Museum of Northern Arizona, Flagstaff; from J. S. Shelton,* Geology Illustrated, *W. H. Freeman & Co.)*

back and forth across this area. The cliff-top
Kaibab limestone with its marine shells (Fig.
5-9) is evidence of a final marine phase of the
Permian.

c. Mesozoic and Cenozoic
Formations

In high mesas from 50 to 100 miles north
of the Grand Canyon (and in the little Cedar
Mountain mesa and other isolated patches
southeast of the Canyon) the uppermost
Paleozoic strata are overlain by Mesozoic
rocks. As the regional dip is toward the north
(Fig. 5-10), Mesozoic strata appear northward
at lower and lower elevations until in southern
Utah they are at valley level.

Directly above the Kaibab of the Grand
Canyon are about 500 feet of weak Triassic
red shale and sandstone, overlain by the resistant cliff-forming Upper Triassic Shinarump
conglomerate and sandstone, commonly 50–
100 feet thick. Then come thousands of feet of
higher Triassic, Jurassic, Cretaceous, and
Paleogene sandstones and other sedimentary
rocks. The greater part of the Triassic and
Jurassic strata lack marine fossils and hence
are probably continental. Their brilliant colors,
commonly red, bright yellow, brown, or
creamy gray, indicate lack of the organic
matter that keeps most marine beds, especially
marine shales, a somber gray. Some beds contain occasional remains of land animals, such
as dinosaurs.

The Triassic formations at a few localities
contain numerous tree trunks, some three or
four feet thick. The most notable examples
are the petrified "forests" of northern Arizona,
made up of drifted logs that were left exposed
on the plateaus after the weak enclosing shale
was washed away. But below the log-bearing
stratum, in southwestern Utah just north of the
Grand Canyon area, two thin limestone units
contain characteristic Lower Triassic ammonites, indicating brief incursions of the sea.

The most striking Jurassic formation is the
thousand-foot non-marine white-to-brownish
Navajo sandstone that forms the White Cliffs
escarpment (Fig. 5-10), the walls of Lake

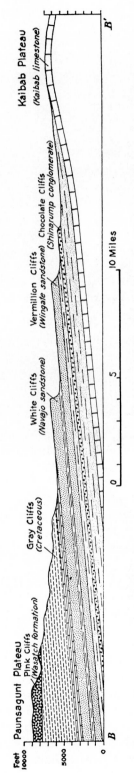

Fig. 5-10. *North-south structure section, from southern Utah to the Grand Canyon's northern rim. (Reprinted from The Evolution of North America by P. B. King, by permission of Princeton University Press. Copyright © 1959 by Princeton University Press.)*

Fig. 5-11. *Erosion landscape on the Navajo (Jurassic) sandstone. View southeast down Escalante River to Colorado River and Navajo Mountain, Utah. (Photograph by J. S. Shelton.)*

Powell above Glen Canyon dam on the Colorado River, the walls of Escalante Canyon (Fig. 5-11), and the dome of Navajo Mountain just south of the Colorado River in northern Arizona.

The Cretaceous of the Utah plateaus is mostly non-marine sandstone, siltstone, limestone, and conglomerate, thousands of feet thick and moderately deformed. Farther east, in the downwarped San Juan, Denver, and other basins of Colorado and New Mexico, the Cretaceous rocks are largely marine shale. The west-to-east succession—from coarse continental clastic sediments to fine-grained marine sediments—suggests a western source land for the sediments, perhaps in what is now Nevada and westernmost Utah.

At the top of the plateau sequence are found nearly horizontal Paleogene fresh-water limestone and shale, as well as land-laid yellow and white clastic rocks of the types seen in the middle distance of Figure 5-12, unconformable on tilted Cretaceous strata.

5-2. Unconformities in the Grand Canyon Section and Their Historical Significance

a. Positions of the Great Unconformities

In the Grand Canyon two obviously great unconformities can be seen from the edge of the plateau. The lower is the smooth surface between the granite-gneiss complex and the wedge series. The higher is between the ridged surface of the wedge series and the Cambrian sedimentary rocks. These two unconformities divide the Grand Canyon rocks into three groups: (1) the granite, gneiss, and schist of the Granite Gorge; (2) the wedge series; (3) all the overlying horizontal strata from the Cambrian through the Paleogene.

b. Comparison with the Present Erosion Surface

The magnitude and variety of the events represented by the two great unconformities are perhaps not immediately apparent. If we compare the two surfaces of unconformity with the present erosion surface, we shall get some idea of the probable succession of events and of the long period of time required to produce a flat erosion surface across rocks of varied age and structure. The present complex drainage system of the Colorado River and its tributaries can be explained only as the result of the long-continued operation of the erosive

and transporting forces that are still obviously at work in the region. The slowness of the processes of erosion is indicated by the long survival of cliff dwellings along tributaries of the Colorado. These habitations were constructed by Indians 700 or 800 years ago and then abandoned; they are still virtually intact even after being left untended for hundreds of years. These facts and all the other available evidence on the rate of erosion in the region, taken together, suggest somewhat vaguely that at least a million years (more probably several million years) were required for the cutting of the great canyon that we see today. Yet the removal of the whole mass of rocks above sea level has little more than begun. At the start of the present cycle of erosion Paleozoic strata extended in unbroken sheets across the present site of the Canyon and were overlain by Mesozoic and Paleogene strata. The volume of material already removed by erosion is indeed impressive, but the amount left is still more impressive. The surfaces of unconformity, on the other hand, are the

Fig. 5-12. *Wasatch formation (Paleogene), lying unconformably on Cretaceous strata, northeast of Bryce Canyon, southern Utah. View northeast toward the light-colored cliffs of a Wasatch mesa. (Photograph by J. S. Shelton.)*

finished products of erosion, perhaps just such erosion as we see in an early stage when we look at the Grand Canyon today.

c. Reconstruction of Past Stages

With the facts of recent canyon-cutting in mind, let us consider what must have happened in this region during its earlier geologic history. We shall work backward, step by step. We commence by restoring to the Canyon and plateau region all the sedimentary rocks that were there before the processes that have produced the present relief began their work (Fig. 5-13B). The top of this sedimentary pile, including the brown and white Jurassic sandstone (not shown in Fig. 5-13B), will then be 10,000 or more feet above the present sea level, with the uppermost marine formation (a Triassic bed) at about 7,000 feet elevation.

Now we make a clean sweep of all Cambrian and younger strata, so as to see the landscape as it was before Cambrian deposition began. The result is the exposure of a flat plain, with low ridges representing the outcrops of quartzite in the wedge series (Fig. 5-13C). The smoothness of the surface, indicated by the present canyon-wall exposures, was only in small part the result of marine erosion by the advancing Cambrian sea. To restore the landscape that existed just before the advance of that sea, we need roughen the surface very little.

To show the wedge series in its still earlier, uneroded state requires some imagination. The fragments of the wedge series in Figure 5-13C are terminated on the right by faults, and we may imagine that the central block was similarly terminated at the left (Fig. 5-13D). Having made this reconstruction, we can imagine continuation of the wedge series beyond the faults to the right and left. After restoring the expanded series to its original horizontal position (Fig. 5-13E), we remove it, exposing a flat plain eroded across the granite masses and the upturned edges of schist and gneiss (Fig. 5-13F). Next we must show the gneiss and

schist as they were just after the intrusion of the granite and pegmatites; this requires even more imagination than the restoration of the wedge series, for here we have even less evidence to go on. But Figure 5-13G shows what seems a reasonable guess: a set of sedimentary rocks compressed into closely spaced folds of steeply inclined strata and then metamorphosed and cut by intrusions of granite and pegmatite. Finally, we can remove the intrusive rocks and show the ancient sediments, the present-day schist and gneiss, in their original nearly horizontal positions (Fig. 5-13H). We have now carried the restoration as far back as the direct evidence will allow.

d. Geologic History Indicated by Grand Canyon Strata and Unconformities

Now that the oldest rocks of the region are lying flat before us, we can begin the story of the rocks in historical order. First were deposited the ancient sediments and volcanic materials that have since become schist and

Fig. 5-13. *Diagrammatic sections representing the history of the Grand Canyon region (adapted from block diagrams by J. S. Shelton): 1, Bass limestone of wedge series; 2, Hakatai shale of wedge series, with intrusive lava; 3, Shinumo quartzite of wedge series; 4, upper wedge series; 5, Tapeats sandstone; 6, Bright Angel shale; 7, Muav limestone; 11, Redwall (Mississippian) limestone; 12, Supai formation, etc.; 13, Kaibab (Permian) limestone, etc.; 14, pre-Shinarump Triassic; 15, Shinarump conglomerate.*

A. *Present state.*
B. *Paleozoic and Triassic rocks restored.*
C. *Rocks down to wedge series removed.*
D. *Fault blocks of wedge series restored.*
E. *Wedge series rotated to horizontal.*
F. *Wedge series removed.*
G. *Pre-wedge series structure restored by use of one possible extrapolation.*
H. *Schist and gneiss restored to state of horizontal sediments and volcanics.*

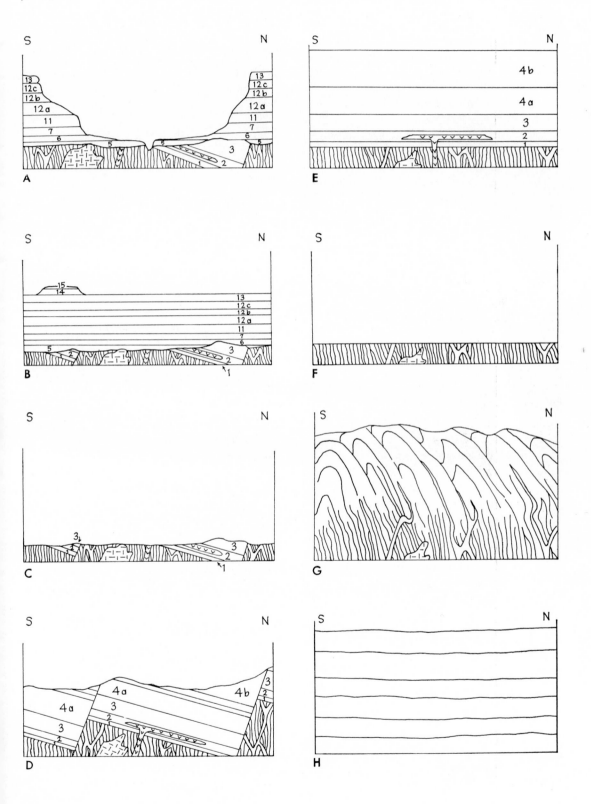

gneiss (Fig. 5-13H).* The sediments were made up of materials that came from other areas. Then occurred folding, granitic invasion, metamorphism of the sediments and volcanic rocks to schist and gneiss (Fig. 5-13G), and erosion to a nearly flat plain (Fig. 5-13F). Perhaps the plain was the final stage in the erosion of a block that had previously gone through plateau, canyon, and rugged mountain stages.

The enormous mass of schist, granite, and other rocks eroded from the Grand Canyon district before the time of the wedge series must have been deposited somewhere else. So we have evidence of another, second episode of erosion and deposition, this time erosion in the Grand Canyon region and deposition elsewhere. All this is indicated by the unconformable contact between the granite-gneiss complex and the next stratigraphic unit, the wedge series.

A third episode is demonstrated by the deposition of the wedge series from material that had been eroded elsewhere (Fig. 5-13E). The tilting (Fig. 5-13D) of the beds of the wedge series from their original horizontal position lifted parts of the schist, as well as parts of the wedge series, high above sea level (the base level for erosion). This was all that was needed to start a fourth episode, marked by erosion in this area (Fig. 5-13C) and deposition elsewhere. A fifth episode involved the deposition of the Paleozoic and later strata (Fig. 5-13B).

Finally, the region was uplifted and eroded in a sixth episode, in which the Mesozoic and Cenozoic strata were removed from the

EXPLANATION I

A. Deposition of Ordovician and Silurian strata

B. Partial erosion of Ordovician and Silurian, in latest Silurian time

C. In early Devonian time, complete removal of remaining Ordovician and Silurian

EXPLANATION II

A. In Ordovician and Silurian times, no deposition, very little erosion

B. In early Devonian time, perhaps a little erosion

Fig. 5-14. *Diagrams showing two possible histories leading to the Devonian-Cambrian unconformity in the Grand Canyon.*

plateaus and the Grand Canyon was cut deep into the older rocks (Fig. 5-13A). In this case we know well where the eroded material has gone. Much of it has been transported to the Gulf of California or the area at the head of the Gulf in southeastern California. This erosion cycle, as we have already seen, is only well started.

* A sedimentary episode of this sort was called a *cycle* by W. M. Davis of Harvard in his Grand Canyon lectures. Davis considered that such an episode implied the whole round of events from (incipient) uplift and (concomitant) erosion to a final stage of eroded flatness. With this assumption, attention moves back and forth between the Grand Canyon region and a vague somewhere else, to give six cycles of erosion and sedimentation, though only half of the evidence for each cycle is preserved in the Grand Canyon region.

Fig. 5-15. *Geologic map of Nevada and adjacent areas to the east and west, showing the Colorado plateaus and the distribution of the rocks of the Cordilleran geosyncline. (Adapted from* Tectonic Map of the United States, 1961, *with modifications from the geologic maps of Utah and California, from* Mineral and Water Resources of Nevada (*U.S. Senate Document 87, 1964), and from other sources.*

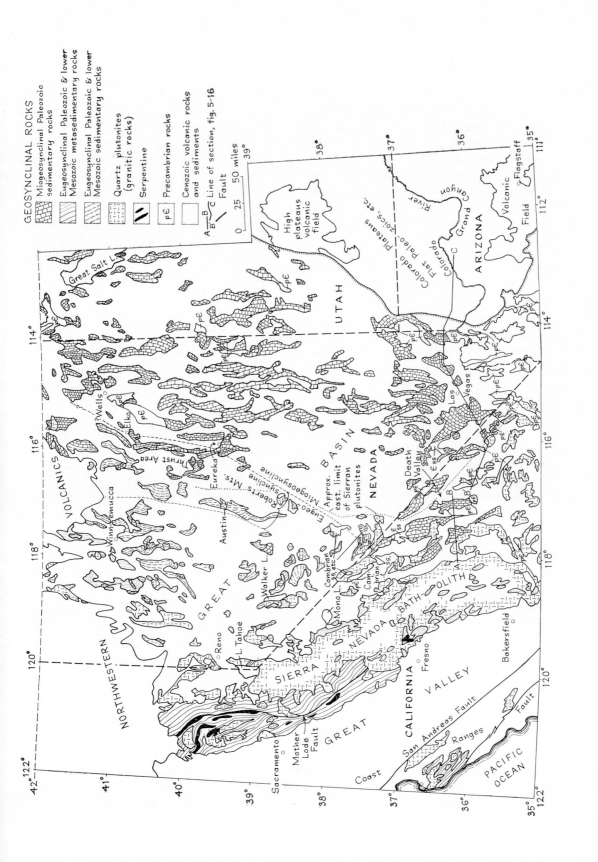

GEOSYCLINAL ROCKS

Miogeosynclinal Paleozoic sedimentary rocks

Eugeosynclinal Paleozoic & lower Mesozoic metasedimentary rocks

Eugeosynclinal Paleozoic & lower Mesozoic sedimentary rocks

Quartz plutonites (granitic rocks)

Serpentine

pЄ   Precambrian rocks

Cenozoic volcanic rocks and sediments

A——B Line of section, fig. 5-16
B'——C

Fault

0   25   50 miles

e. The Ordovician-Silurian Lacuna

In comparison with the standard European section, the Grand Canyon section has a gap where the Ordovician and Silurian systems should be. What happened in this region during those periods? There are two quite different possibilities. One (Fig. 5-14–I) is marine deposition here during Ordovician and Silurian time, followed by complete removal of the resulting sedimentary rocks by erosion at and just after the end of the Silurian, producing the unconformity beneath the Devonian lenses. This supposition is consistent with the very irregular erosional contact between Cambrian and Devonian, but it is made somewhat improbable by the lack of any remnant of the supposed Ordovician and Silurian sediments. The second possibility is non-deposition in this area during all of Ordovician and Silurian time (Fig. 5-14–II). This requires almost complete lack of erosion of the previously deposited Cambrian strata during a very long period of time; the region must have remained close to sea level for many millions of years, for any considerable rise would have invited erosion and any considerable depression would have invited Ordovician or Silurian sedimentation. Perhaps it is now impossible to discover whether the true history was that shown in Explanation I, in Explanation II, or in some intermediate sequence of events, such as Ordovician deposition and Silurian erosion. Evidence bearing on this problem will appear in the description of the Cordilleran geosyncline, in the following section.

5-3. The Cordilleran Geosyncline

a. Geography and Geology

Between the Grand Canyon and the Great Valley of central California the earth's outer layers are broken into blocks by faulting. The westernmost block is the broad and westward-tilted Sierra Nevada. Along the various possible lines of section between the great Sierra and the Colorado River plateaus there are from six to ten mountain ranges of widely varying sizes and heights, separated by intermontane basins. Geographically, this region is the Basin and Range province (or just the Great Basin). Geologically, it and the Sierra Nevada and perhaps much of the continental margin in California west of the Sierra have been parts of the Cordilleran geosyncline of Paleozoic and early Mesozoic time. This belt is now, even after compression by folding and thrust faulting, 300–400 miles wide (Figs. 5-15 and 5-16).

b. Miogeosyncline and Eugeosyncline

The Cordilleran geosyncline has two parts, an eastern, miogeosynclinal portion, developed typically in southern and east-central Nevada, where most formations are the same as those of the plateaus but thicker, and a western, eugeosynclinal portion, developed typically in the Sierra Nevada of California and west-central Nevada (Fig. 5-15), where the rocks are so different that the Paleozoic and early Mesozoic formations of the plateaus cannot be recognized. The Cordilleran geosyncline as a whole perhaps included, at one time or another, most of North America west of the Front Range in central Colorado, but in this discussion we shall consider chiefly the Utah-Nevada-California portion.

In the miogeosynclinal eastern Basin Ranges, close to the Colorado River plateaus, there is almost the same sequence of Paleozoic formations as in the Grand Canyon region, from Tapeats sandstone to Kaibab limestone, though almost every formation is much thicker and some are lithologically different enough to have been given different names. The whole Paleozoic section is 4,000 feet thick in the Grand Canyon; it becomes 40,000 feet thick in some parts of the southern Great Basin. The Cambrian strata, which are only about 1,000 feet thick in the Grand Canyon, increase to

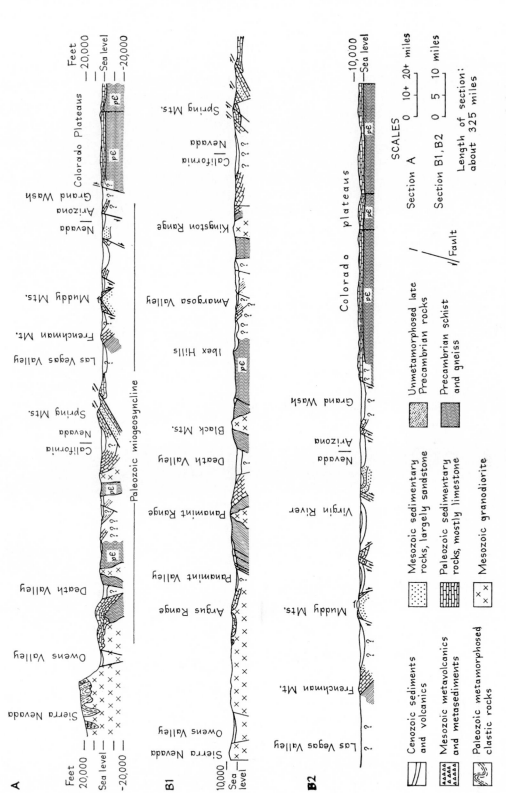

Fig. 5-16. *Structure section from the Sierra Nevada to the Colorado plateaus, along the line AC of Fig. 5-15. (Compiled from many sources.)*

A. *Generalized section, with eugeosynclinal rocks of the northern Sierra Nevada projected southward and upward into the plane of the section. (Along the line of section the Sierra Nevada is only 8,500 feet high.)*

B. *A more detailed section, at twice the horizontal scale of A and without vertical exaggeration.*

5,000 or 6,000 feet in southern Nevada (Fig. 5-17) and to 15,000 feet near the California-Nevada boundary. The Cambrian of the geosyncline is in part limestone, but also includes thick units of sandstone and other clastic rocks. The Cambrian sandstone unit corresponding to the Tapeats, several thousand feet thick in southern Nevada and eastern California, is conformably underlain by still earlier, non-fossiliferous sedimentary rocks. The middle Paleozoic (from Ordovician to Devonian) is better represented in the geosyncline than in the Grand Canyon region. Ordovician and Silurian (absent from the Grand Canyon) are represented here by marine limestones and clastic rocks, as is the Devonian, but each system is thin. The aggregate Ordovician-Silurian-Devonian section—limestone, quartzite, and shale—is in few places more than 2,000 feet thick. The upper Paleozoic increases in thickness from 2,000 feet of mostly Permian strata on the plateaus to 7,000 feet in the geosyncline. This part of the section becomes mostly marine limestone of Carboniferous (Mississippian and Pennsylvanian) and Permian ages.

The early Mesozoic (Triassic and Jurassic) rocks of the platform and the adjacent geosyncline show the same general similarities and differences as the Paleozoic. On the plateau platform the Triassic and Jurassic rocks are mostly continental deposits, with red and white sandstones the most striking (in Zion Canyon, southern Utah, for example). The same continental formations are present in the eastern Basin Ranges, but here they are considerably thicker. Farther west and northwest, in west-central Nevada, the red beds completely disappear, and the general aspect of the rocks becomes eugeosynclinal, dark-colored volcanic rocks, black shale, and black limestone being

Fig. 5-17. *Paleozoic and Mesozoic rocks of the miogeosyncline, tilted steeply down toward the east. Precambrian gneiss at the right, overlain successively by Tapeats and other plateau formations, with a limestone equivalent to the Redwall (arrow) at the summit of the mountain. Frenchman Mountain, southern Nevada. (From J. S. Shelton,* Geology Illustrated, *W. H. Freeman & Co.)*

perhaps the commonest rocks, and ammonites being abundant at several levels.

In order to gain an understanding of the eugeosynclinal facies of the whole section, Paleozoic and all, one must consider both west-central Nevada and the Sierra Nevada of California. Several late Paleozoic and early Mesozoic formations are made up wholly or in part of volcanic rocks. Limestones, though thick in some places, are geographically restricted. Most striking of all, the greater part of the sedimentary record has been swallowed up or rendered undecipherable by an enormous granodiorite batholith. This batholith intrudes into the marine Jurassic, the Triassic, and the pre-Triassic volcanic and sedimentary rocks. In the southern part of the Sierra Nevada (western end of Fig. 5-16B), almost all the geosynclinal rocks making up the roof of the batholith have been removed by erosion. Farther north much of the roof has been preserved, with abundant metamorphosed shale, chert, and volcanic rock—a typical eugeosynclinal assemblage.

In southeastern California and west-central Nevada, east of the Sierra Nevada, the lower and middle Paleozoic rocks are mostly miogeosynclinal limestones and quartzites. The uppermost Paleozoic and the Mesozoic rocks, however, also include graywackes and metavolcanics and are invaded by large bodies of granodiorite (Fig. 5-16B) that are no doubt in subsurface continuity with the Sierra Nevada granodiorite. This relation almost certainly prevails as far east as the Panamint Range just west of Death Valley, California, where the granodiorite also intrudes into thick, folded, Precambrian, metamorphosed sedimentary rocks (Fig. 5-16B). Apparently in southern California eugeosynclinal conditions spread eastward in the latest Paleozoic and in the Mesozoic.

In north-central Nevada, between Winnemucca and the Roberts Mountains thrust area (Fig. 5-15), Paleozoic eugeosynclinal sediments, mostly Cambrian and Ordovician, are interbedded with miogeosynclinal carbonates and quartzites. This area is therefore a part of the original transition belt between eugeosyncline and miogeosyncline, now considerably obscured by later thrust faulting.

c. Precambrian Strips in the Geosynclinal Belt

Strips of Precambrian rocks, mostly schists and gneisses but also including unmetamorphosed sedimentary rocks similar to the Grand Canyon wedge series, are present in the miogeosynclinal part of the Cordilleran belt. The most numerous Precambrian exposures are in the south, extending southeast from the ranges on the two sides of Death Valley. In this same region the Cambrian is some miles thick, and the Ordovician-Permian sequence has about the usual make-up and thickness. Probably the Paleozoic geosynclinal strata once covered the whole area. The Precambrian outcrops represent, not islands in the Paleozoic seas, but rather areas previously covered by Paleozoic strata, transformed into structural highs during post-depositional deformations, and finally eroded to the present state of Precambrian exposure.

Farther north, in northeastern Nevada and northwestern Utah, Precambrian strips appear again (Fig. 5-15); that is, the Precambrian floor of the Cordilleran geosyncline, which in the west is eaten away by plutonism and elsewhere is deeply buried, is here above sea level and preserved intact, though deformed. The Precambrian strips mark structural highs. But the overlying and surrounding Paleozoic limestones are typically thick and normally fossiliferous. Here also the exposure of the Precambrian rocks must be the result of post-Paleozoic deformation and erosion rather than a sign of persistent emergence during Paleozoic time.

d. Western Boundary of the Geosyncline

The Cordilleran eugeosyncline fades westward into uncertainty. It may always have been bounded by the deep Pacific, at times with chains of volcanic islands rising above the surface. Or there may have been high granite land in what is now the marginal belt of the ocean, especially during the Mesozoic (and Cenozoic). Jurassic and Cretaceous fossils have been found in clastic sequences tens of thousands of feet thick in the California Coast Ranges, west of the Great Valley. These strata are mostly fossil-poor eugeosynclinal sediments, but the volcanic element is minor. The clastic rocks were derived chiefly from granitic terrains that may have been west of the present coast line, though no evidence has yet proved that there actually were any pre-Cretaceous granitic rocks in or west of the California Coast Ranges. Farther southeast, in the San Gabriel Mountains near Los Angeles (100 miles southeast of Bakersfield; Fig. 5-15), a large mass of Precambrian plutonic rock and associated gneisses may be part of the floor of the Paleozoic miogeosyncline (compare Fig. 5-15). On the other hand, this mass may have been part of a southwestern source of the thick and extensive, quartz-rich, clastic sedimentary rocks of the Cambrian and Precambrian section southeast of the Sierra Nevada. These clastic rocks will be described and discussed in Chapter 10. For the present, we can only emphasize the fact, stimulating to the young investigator, that the nature of the western margin of North America in Paleozoic and Mesozoic times is not yet known.

e. Deformation and Plutonism in the Geosynclinal Belt

The Cordilleran geosynclinal belt, including the Front Range and other ranges in Colorado as well as the main part of the belt west of the Colorado plateaus, was greatly deformed in late Paleozoic and Mesozoic times. The most extreme deformation of all, affecting chiefly the Roberts Mountains thrust area in north-central Nevada and the eugeosyncline immediately to the west (Fig. 5-15), seems to have occurred between latest Devonian and early Pennsylvanian times. In the Roberts Mountains thrust area, at least sixty miles wide, eugeosynclinal sedimentary rocks, notably Ordovician chert and graptolitic shale, were thrust eastward as an upper plate covering Cambrian-Devonian (and Mississippian) miogeosynclinal limestone, dolomite, quartzite, and shale.

More widespread deformation occurred considerably later, in the Mesozoic and immediately thereafter. West-central Nevada underwent further thrust faulting in the Triassic, and then, between the end of the Jurassic and a time early in the Paleogene, the whole belt was deformed. One major episode occurred in the Sierra Nevada between the deposition of Upper Jurassic shale, now transformed into vertical slate, and that of Upper Cretaceous sandstone, still practically horizontal. Not only were the strata of the Sierra Nevada and the country just to the east profoundly deformed and moderately metamorphosed, but they were also invaded by the great granodiorite batholith (Figs. 5-15 and 5-16) and eroded to a nearly flat surface in which the granodiorite was broadly exposed before being partially covered by Upper Cretaceous sediments. The granodiorite must have crystallized beneath a considerable cover, and its exposure by erosion demonstrates that the deformation involved mountain-making and therefore was truly **orogenic** (*oros*, mountain + *genic*, making).

Finally, before or at or just after the end of the Cretaceous, the other parts of the great Cordilleran belt underwent extreme deformation, commonly involving not only close folding but also the eastward movement of thrust sheets (Fig. 5-16B).

The late Mesozoic (and Paleogene) deformations, accompanied as they were, in the west, by batholithic intrusions that extended all the way from Lower California to Alaska (compare Fig. 4-11) and were largest of all in British Columbia, marked the end of the depositional phase of the geosyncline as a whole. By late Cretaceous time most of the region, including practically all of Nevada, was being eroded. Marine deposition still went on at the Pacific margin, from Lower California to British Columbia, including, in California, both the Coast Ranges and the Great Valley. At the other edge of the Cordillera there was an end of the great epicontinental seaway that had extended from Texas to the Arctic during the Cretaceous, at times including very large portions of Montana, Wyoming, Colorado, and New Mexico. Now, with the beginning of the Tertiary, appeared the Rocky Mountains of the eastern Cordillera, which thereafter were chiefly the site of uplift and erosion, though in the Paleogene large intramontane lake basins were filled with finely banded, fine-grained sediments. To the east, the Great Plains were places of almost continuous continental deposition during the Cenozoic.

Looking back over the history of the part of the Cordilleran geosyncline between the Colorado plateaus and the Pacific, we see a difference between the Paleozoic pattern of deposition and deformation, determined by northeast trending belts parallel to the northwest edge of the plateau region, and the pattern of late Mesozoic and Cenozoic deformation, which has produced north-south structures in the Great Basin and northwest trending structures in California. In the Coast Ranges the latter are only slightly truncated by the north-northwest trend of the Pacific shore (Fig. 5-15). Some of the rocks still preserve records of much of their complex history. The Ordovician strata near Convict Lake in the Sierra Nevada (Fig. 5-18), for example, were in existence during both the Mississippian and the Mesozoic orogenies. They survived with graptolites intact. This part of the Sierra, which has a superb summer climate, is now a magnet for geologists interested in what happens to strata that apparently have been through two wringers.

The late-Mesozoic Sierran-Peninsular batholith (Fig. 4-11) probably continues below the surface far to the east, both in California and

Fig. 5-18. *Aerial view of Ordovician roof pendant (banded rock), enveloped by apparently structureless granodiorite. Near Ordovician graptolite locality at Convict Lake, Sierra Nevada. (From J. S. Shelton, Geology Illustrated, W. H. Freeman & Co.)*

in Nevada. Granitic bosses are numerous as far as the sinuous dotted line of Figure 5-15, from a point in southern California southeast of Death Valley north to the vicinity of Winnemucca, Nevada. Paleozoic and Mesozoic eugeosynclinal metamorphic rocks, represented by the pattern of solid parallel lines in the figure, extend almost as far east as the dotted line in some places, especially in the north. Structural trends in the metamorphics, indicated by the pattern, are, in part, parallel to plutonic contacts. Perhaps this concordance is due to a relation between the development of the metamorphic structures and the emplacement of the batholith.

The faults that separate the thick geosynclinal sediments of the Basin and Range province from the thin sediments of the present Colorado plateaus (Fig. 5-16B) break apart formations that were once continuous, with rise on the plateau side. The faults must have developed after the deposition of the Mesozoic sedimentary rocks that they cut and displace. The plateaus may owe their elevation primarily to thousands of feet of vertical movement on these faults in late Cenozoic time.

5-4. Paleogeographies in the Grand Canyon Region

a. General

The thin Paleozoic and early Mesozoic rocks of the Grand Canyon platform and the thick contemporaneous rocks of the geosyncline make a typical stratigraphic and structural assemblage. In translating the evidence furnished by these rocks into geologic history, geologists must work step by step, first studying the formations individually, then putting contemporaneous formations together, and finally deriving the general conclusions of geologic history. For each formation or set of contemporaneous formations, a prime objective is the location of the approximate position of the shore line, which will indicate the distribution of land and sea during the time represented by the rocks under consideration. The shore line is the most important element

in geography or in paleogeography. In the succeeding pages the Paleozoic and early Mesozoic paleogeographies of the western United States will be considered, with special attention to the Grand Canyon region.

b. Onlap and Offlap in the Grand Canyon Paleozoic

Two of the commonest kinds of evidence for the position of an ancient shore line are illustrated by the Paleozoic rocks of the Grand Canyon region.

The Permian Toroweap formation has preserved a record of onlap and offlap (Fig. 5-19). Members A and C, wholly continental and fresh-water, are composed mostly of red beds at the west, of cross-bedded white sandstone (eolian?) at the east. Even the limestone high in Member C at its western edge is a fresh-water deposit. Member B is a wedge of marine limestone, pinching out eastward between Members A and C. The shore line—the boundary between marine and continental deposition—moved gradually eastward during A-B time and then moved sharply westward at the beginning of the time represented by Member C.

The previous paragraph is an interpretation of Figure 5-19, which is a small-scale interpretation of the field evidence. This interpretation may not be the only one possible. In particular, the apparently very rapid western offlap indicated by the figure is so different from the symmetry of Figure 4-8 that it invites confirmation or disproof by further study in the field.

A combination of onlap and offlap is not required to prove a shore line. Equally good evidence is furnished by simple overlap. An example is the overlap of the Tapeats sandstone across the various Precambrian rocks of the Grand Canyon. As we have seen, the relation between the Tapeats and the other Cambrian formations suggests that the Cambrian sea advanced slowly east or southeast, incorporating fragments of the underlying rocks into a basal conglomerate. The Tapeats sandstone certainly extends southeast about as far

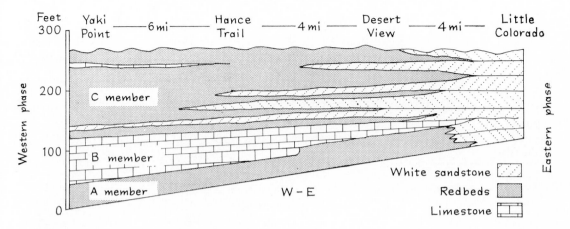

Fig. 5-19.   *Onlap and offlap recorded in the facies of the Toroweap formation, Permian of northern Arizona. (After E. D. McKee, Memoir 39, Geol. Soc. Am., 1949.)*

as Flagstaff, Arizona, about 60 or 70 miles southeast of the Grand Canyon, and may be continued another 75 miles south, to the vicinity of Jerome, Arizona, where a doubtful equivalent is overlain conformably by Devonian limestone. Farther east, Devonian rocks lie unconformably on the Precambrian.

c. Paleozoic Shore Lines in the Cordilleran Region as a Whole

Study of the Paleozoic rocks in western North America shows that formations representing every system are distributed widely throughout the miogeosynclinal belt. A succession of vast shallow seas covered most, but not all, of Nevada and spread northward as far as British Columbia. During considerable parts of this time, perhaps one-third of all Paleozoic time, the seas also extended onto the adjacent platform—for example, into the Colorado plateau region. The rocks and fossils of the Grand Canyon region, in particular, show that in Cambrian, mid-Devonian, early Carboniferous (Mississippian), and middle Permian times seas covered that region (compare Figs. 5-3 and 5-20).

The lands at the eastern and southeastern edges of the Paleozoic seas must have been very low, as the shore line moved back and forth several times, apparently without encountering serious obstacles. At each advance

of the sea a wedge of marine sediments was deposited in a belt several hundred miles wide.

The Ordovician and Silurian shore lines have special interest because rocks representing these systems are absent from the Colorado River plateaus. Ordovician and Silurian shore lines must have been east and southeast of the fossil-coral localities shown in Figure 5-21, but we do not know how far east and southeast. Indeed, Ordovician or Silurian seas may possibly have covered the whole region of the Colorado River plateaus, uniting the known seas of southern New Mexico with those of Nevada. But the thinness of the Ordovician and Silurian limestones near the southeastern edge of the geosyncline makes one wonder if they did not pinch out quickly to an original margin—a shore line—near the boundary between Cordilleran geosyncline and plateau platform.

The withdrawals of the Paleozoic shore line toward the west may have been greater than shown in Figure 5-20. We know, at least, that the sea retreated from the whole of the plateau region four times during the Paleozoic: (1) during or after the Ordovician and Silurian, as shown by the Cambrian-Devonian unconformity; (2) during late Devonian time, as shown by the Devonian-Carboniferous unconformity; (3) during the late Carboniferous

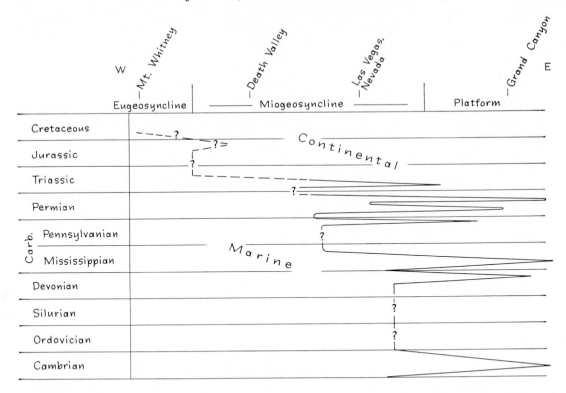

Fig. 5-20.   *Shore-line diagram for the Paleozoic and Mesozoic, from the Sierra Nevada to the Grand Canyon.*

Fig. 5-21.   *Ordovician and Silurian coral localities in the western United States. (After Helen Duncan, U.S. Geological Survey, 1956.)*

and the pre-Toroweap part of the Permian, as shown by a probable unconformity and widespread continental formations; (4) between the times represented by the Toroweap and Kaibab marine tongues. Continental deposits are present in both the upper part of the Toroweap and the lower part of the Kaibab. In fact, the Kaibab equivalent is wholly continental in easternmost Arizona and western New Mexico. Still farther east is the marine Permian Basin described at the end of Chapter 4.

d. Early Mesozoic Shore Lines in the Southern Cordilleran Region

The shore lines of the early Mesozoic—Triassic and Jurassic—changed position less. Almost uninterrupted continental deposits on the Colorado plateaus show that this more or less isolated part of the western North American platform was a lowland region of nonmarine deposition. In the eastern part of the

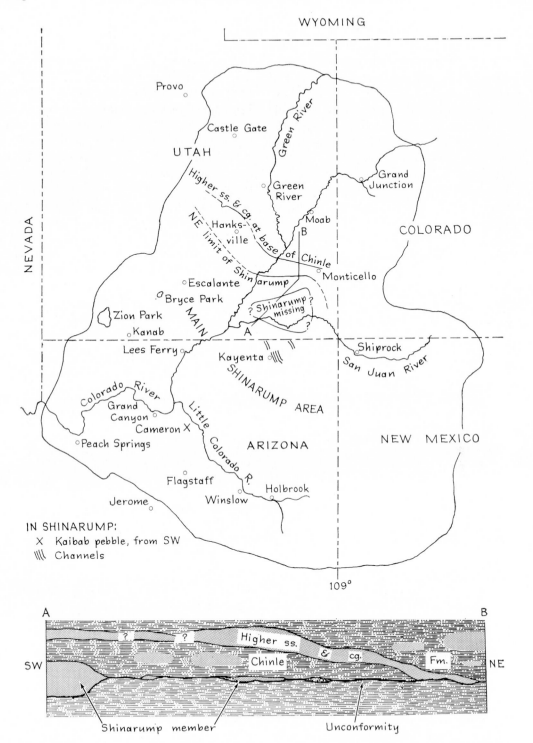

Fig. 5-22. *Map and section showing the distribution of Shinarump and higher (Chinle) conglomerate-sandstone units on the Colorado plateaus. (After J. H. Stewart, Am. Ass. Petrol. Geol., 1957; I. J. Witkind, U.S. Geological Survey, 1956; E. D. McKee and others, Atomic Energy Commission, 1953; E. D. McKee, Am. Jour. Sci., 1936.)*

geosyncline, in eastern Nevada, western Utah, and western Wyoming, early Mesozoic strata are alternately marine and continental. Farther west and northwest, in California and west-central Nevada, marine Triassic and Jurassic limestones, shales, sandstones, and tuffs prevail. By the beginning of the Mesozoic, the increased abundance of volcanic products in this western part of the geosyncline demonstrated its eugeosynclinal character, soon to be emphasized by plutonism. The eastern edges of Triassic and Jurassic seas connected with the Pacific Ocean may have been mostly in the eastern geosynclinal belt, 100–200 miles west of the typical Paleozoic shore and just where the Paleozoic marine sediments had been exceptionally thick and nearly continuous. The oceanic connections of the marine bands in the eastern Great Basin and in the Colorado plateaus, however, may have been northeastward to the Arctic, by way of Wyoming.

e. Paleogeography of a Plateau Unit

If we go into more detail concerning the distribution of land and sea, we find that conditions varied so much from system to system, even from formation to formation, that we cannot go into all the complications. So we shall select one unit, the Shinarump sandstone and conglomerate, a member of the Upper Triassic Chinle (chin-lee) formation, for more detailed treatment. A few general facts about this unit tell much about the conditions of its deposition, the climate, and the relief of the land.

The Shinarump has a nearly unvarying thickness, mostly between 50 and 100 feet, throughout its whole extent, an area of tens of thousands of square miles in the southern plateau region, in northern Arizona and southern Utah (Fig. 5-22). A similar conglomerate is also present in the Chinle formation in the miogeosyncline of southern Nevada, but it may not be at the Shinarump horizon. Everywhere the Shinarump is composed chiefly of quartz sand grains and quartzite and chert

pebbles (Fig. 5-23), though locally, especially in and above channels cutting the underlying Lower Triassic strata, a few mudstone layers and clay balls are largely composed of clay minerals derived from the underlying beds. Logs and smaller fragments of petrified or carbonized wood and very rare impressions of other parts of land plants, together with the absence of marine fossils, are evidence that this formation was a continental deposit. The fragmentary nature of the plant remains makes one think that they were washed into the area of deposition. The pebbles, apart from the wood, decrease in size from a maximum of six inches in diameter in the southern part of the plateau region, sixty miles south of the Grand Canyon, to one inch or less in northeastern Arizona, near the Utah line. Limestone pebbles, though rare, are of prime importance because one specimen contains Kaibab fossils of types known only in the southwestern part of the plateau, southwest of a line through Grand Canyon and Flagstaff (Fig. 5-22). It is also worth noting that the Shinarump and other Triassic formations are missing from central Arizona.

Here we have three important types of evidence: (1) horizontal variation in the sizes of the clastic grains from larger at the south to smaller at the north; (2) fragments of an older formation known in a nearby area; (3) a nearby gap in the record, rocks of Shinarump age being among those missing. These three lines of evidence, taken together, point to the conclusion that in Shinarump time central Arizona was a region of erosion from which some of the Shinarump sediments were derived. This region was a nearly flat lowland, whose northern part has been preserved in the belt of flat-lying Kaibab at the southern edge of the northern Arizona plateau. It was the former southern continuation of this belt of Kaibab that contributed pebbles to the Shinarump.

Since quartz grains and quartzite or chert pebbles predominate so strongly in the composition of the Shinarump, the granite, schist, and most other rocks of this late Triassic erosion

Fig. 5-23. *Hand specimens, × 0.7.*
A. *Shinarump conglomerate, northwest of Colorado River bridge, east of Kanab, Utah.*
B, C. *A correlative(?) conglomerate, Bar-Nothing Ranch, west of Las Vegas, Nevada.*

area must have been thoroughly weathered. At the time central Arizona must have had moderately heavy rainfall.

The bottom of the Shinarump is marked by stream channels that cut into the underlying Lower Triassic and Permian formations (Fig. 5-24). Some channels contain important uranium deposits, which were among those that made this region a new Eldorado in the years 1945–1955. The channels in the Monument Valley of northeastern Arizona and southeastern Utah show a tendency toward a southeast-northwest trend. In 53 out of 103 cases the trend is in the range of 50° between N10°W and N60°W. The channel trends are moderately strong evidence for the conclusion that

the Shinarump sediments in this central area were moving toward the nearest part of the Cordilleran geosyncline, in what is now central and southern Nevada.

The main mass of the Shinarump deposits forms a continuous sheet above the separate channel fillings. In this sheet the directions of cross-bedding, minor filled troughs, and other structures are highly variable, no doubt because of frequent changes in the courses of streams moving about over nearly flat plains. Yet these structures, too, conform to a general pattern of movement toward the northwest. The cross-bedding, for example, tends to dip either northwest or toward the center of a local channel. The sands are fairly clean—an

Fig. 5-24. *A view southeast toward Shinarump conglomerate* (Trs) *filling a channel in Moenkopi* (Trm, *Lower Triassic*) *sediments and Permian* (P) *sandstone, Monument Valley, northern Arizona. (Modified slightly from I. J. Witkind, U.S. Geological Survey, 1956.)*

indication that most of the fine sediment was carried farther, perhaps to the sea in which were deposited the contemporaneous marine rocks of the eugeosyncline far to the northwest (Fig. 5-15). The Upper Triassic marine sediments in the Sonoma Range of central Nevada contain logs of the species of tree that is common in the Shinarump. The logs in central Nevada may have come from trees that grew on a nearby land area in the geosynclinal belt, but some of the Triassic silt in central Nevada may have come from the Grand Canyon region. Anyway, the silt and clay carried by Shinarump streams were washed beyond the area of Shinarump deposition. Sand and silt could be transported for hundreds of miles only by streams supplied with an abundance of water. The lack of coarse boulder beds in any part of the Shinarump shows the absence of nearby highlands, torrents from which would have washed large blocks into the accumulating sediments.

The Chinle formation contains, at higher levels, similar but finer-grained sandstone and pebbly sandstone units, notably one that is limited mostly to a northwest-southeast belt 150 miles long and 50 miles wide, in east-central Utah just northeast of the Shinarump area. This unit, overlapping the Shinarump and the intervening claystone member toward the northeast, becomes the basal unit of the Chinle formation northeast of a line shown in Figure 5-22, extending northwest from the Utah-Colorado line. The relations are shown in the section at the bottom of the figure; the vertical scale is greatly exaggerated, the sandstone units actually being only 15–175 feet thick.

The pinch-out of the Shinarump at the northeast is consistent with the previous evidence for its southern, southwestern, and southeastern sources. The sources of the higher, finer-grained sandy unit shown in Figure 5-22 are not definitely known, but the dips of cross-strata, measured in the channels of the unit in ten widely distributed areas, indicate movement from southeast to northwest.

The plateau region in Shinarump and later Chinle time must have been an area of low relief and widespread continental deposition, where shifting streams flowed in a general northwest direction and discharged into the sea that occupied the central part of the Cordilleran geosyncline, off to the northwest in what is now west-central Nevada. Apparently the major belt of northwest-flowing streams moved northeast as time went on, overlapping onto the northeastern part of the plateau, which had earlier been a region of very mild erosion. The later Chinle gravels may have been derived from central and southern Colorado uplands (compare Fig. 5-22). Note that, northeast of the Shinarump pinch-out, Shinarump time is represented by the stratigraphic lacuna involved in the unconformity at the base of the Chinle.

5-5. *Historical Summary*

The rocks and structures of representative portions of the southwestern United States, described in this chapter, furnish the evidence for the geologic history of the region. The succession of the strata in the Grand Canyon is so obvious that its section has been called "geologic history at a glance." There is no reasonable question about the relative ages of most units, especially the larger ones. For example, the Mesozoic rocks that contain dinosaurs are obviously much later than the Cambrian beds and their included trilobites. In most other regions one must work to discover the order of the strata hidden beneath green hills. In the Grand Canyon the succession of the strata is so clear that it can be read like a book.

In glancing at the Grand Canyon we should not miss the significance of the folding, metamorphism, and unconformities of the Precambrian record. The complications of the Precambrian cycles make it easy for us to believe that Precambrian time was longer than all subsequent time.

The Paleozoic history of the Grand Canyon platform and the adjacent Cordilleran geosyn-cline was mostly one of varied sedimentation, with marine deposition predominating over continental and lacustrine deposition. In the western part of the geosyncline vulcanism became increasingly important toward the end of the era. In the early Mesozoic, sedimentation was marine in the western part of the geosyncline and accompanied by vulcanism, but predominantly continental in the eastern part of the geosyncline and almost exclusively continental on the platform. Then there was a transformation, which terminated the long history of orderly geosynclinal sedimentation. The last of a long series of notable episodes of folding and thrusting occurred. The western part of the geosyncline, invaded from below by plutonic rocks, was transformed by the plutonism and accompanying metamorphism into a mostly crystalline, relatively rigid mass. Then both this mass and the somewhat less rigid miogeosynclinal belt to the east were broken into elongated north-south blocks, some of which were elevated into mountain ranges, which in late Mesozoic and Cenozoic times became the sources of new accumulations of sediments, in part deposited in the intermediate depressed areas but mostly carried east or west beyond the limits of the region here considered.

The later Mesozoic and Cenozoic history of the region must be passed over lightly, at least for the present. We must emphasize, however, the independence of the Paleozoic and early Mesozoic geography from that of today. The streams that deposited the Shinarump conglomerate and sandstone, for example, flowed northwest, at right angles to the present course of the Colorado River. Since the early Mesozoic the plateau region has been mightily uplifted, and a wholly new drainage system, that of the Colorado, has been developed there.

PROBLEMS

1. W. M. Davis (footnote, p. 108) considered that the Cambrian–Paleogene sequence in the Grand Canyon region represented a single cycle of erosion elsewhere and sedimentation in the Canyon region. Should this concept be modified in any way because of (a) unconformities in the Cambrian–Paleogene sequence of the Grand Canyon platform, (b) the presence of sediments conformably below the Cambrian in the Cordilleran geosyncline, (c) late Paleozoic orogeny in the geosyncline, or (d) late Mesozoic or early Cenozoic orogeny in the geosyncline? If so, how?

2. W. M. Davis assumed that Cambrian and later deposition in the Grand Canyon region was accompanied by erosion to peneplanation elsewhere. Can the sedimentary record be used to test this assumption? How? Work from sediments to paleogeography. Use the Shinarump as one example.

3. Was the wedge series of the Grand Canyon region a platform or a geosynclinal deposit? Give reasons for your answer.

4. Were the oldest sediments in the Precambrian of the Grand Canyon region geosynclinal or platform deposits? Give reasons for your answer.

5. Expand the Grand Canyon geologic history of pages 106–108 into a summary statement of the geologic history of west-central North America, using cycles of erosion and deposition as well as platform-geosyncline theory.

REFERENCES

Reading

1. John H. Maxson: *Geologic History of the Bright Angel Quadrangle* (Grand Canyon Nat. Hist. Ass., 1961)

2. Herbert E. Gregory: *Colorado Plateau Region,* Guidebook 18, 16th Int. Geol. Cong., 38 pages (Washington, 1933)

3. Chester R. Longwell: "Tectonic Theory Viewed from the Basin Ranges," BULLETIN, Geol. Soc. Am., vol. 61, pp. 413–434 (1950)

Background

CAMBRIAN

4. Edwin D. McKee and Charles E. Resser: *Cambrian History of the Grand Canyon Region,* Pub. 563, 232 pages, Carnegie Institution of Washington (1945)

PERMIAN

5. Edwin D. McKee: *The Environment and History of the Toroweap and Kaibab Formations of Northern Arizona and Southern Utah,* Pub. 492, 268 pages, Carnegie Institution of Washington (1938)

SHINARUMP

6. John H. Stewart: "Proposed Nomenclature of Part of Upper Triassic Strata in Southeastern Utah," BULLETIN, Am. Ass. Petrol. Geol., vol. 41, pp. 441–465 (1957)

7. I. J. Witkind: "Uranium Deposits at Base of the Shinarump Conglomerate, Monument Valley, Arizona," Bulletin 1030-C, U.S. Geol. Sur., pp. 99–130 (1956)

8. E. D. McKee, C. G. Evensen, and W. D. Grundy: *Studies in Sedimentology of the Shinarump Conglomerate of Northeastern Arizona,* RME-3089, U.S. Atomic Energy Commission, 48 pages (1953)

GENERAL

9. C. R. Longwell (editor): *Sedimentary Facies in Geologic History,* Memoir 39, Geol. Soc. Am. (1949), papers by McKee, Spieker, and Muller

10. R. J. Roberts, P. E. Hotz, James Gilluly, and H. G. Ferguson: "Paleozoic Rocks of North-central Nevada," BULLETIN, Am. Ass. Petrol. Geol., vol. 42, pp. 2813–2857 (1958)

11. R. P. Sharp: "Ep-Archean and ep-Algonkian Erosion Surfaces, Grand Canyon, Arizona," BULLETIN, Geol. Soc. Am., vol. 51, pp. 1235–1270 (1940)

CHAPTER 6

Platform and Geosyncline in East-central North America

BETWEEN the Mississippi River and the Atlantic Ocean the stream patterns and the shapes of the hills change in ways that reflect changes in the geologic structure. In the broad platform area, which extends as far east as western Pennsylvania (see Fig. 6-5), the stream pattern is a complex, irregular network, and the low interstream hills have irregular shapes. All this changes at the Allegheny Front (Fig. 6-1), beyond which lies the miogeosynclinal belt of southwest-northeast trending folds, in which the principal rivers, such as the Potomac, Susquehanna, and Delaware, break across structure to the sea but are nourished by large tributaries that follow zones of weak rock in valleys separated by ridges of resistant sandstone (Fig. 6-2). East of the miogeosyncline are successive belts of varied composition and structure, including the Triassic lowland and the New England upland (Fig. 6-3).

6-1. *Land Forms and Structure in East-central North America*

A structural and geomorphic diagram of a northwest-southeast strip across the central Appalachian region (Fig. 6-4) shows most of the structural features, the origin of which will be a major theme of this chapter. Five geomorphic provinces are represented, as follows:

(1) The Coastal Plain, from New Jersey south, is underlain by weak, easily eroded Cretaceous and Cenozoic sediments.

(2) The Piedmont belt and the Blue Ridge, which to the north become the New England upland, are underlain by hard crystalline plutonic and metamorphic rocks of Precambrian and early Paleozoic age, invaded by later Paleozoic plutons.

(3) The Triassic Lowland extends, with some interruption, from northern New Jersey to North Carolina. A second sizable belt lies

[125]

Fig. 6-1. *The Allegheny Front, separating the Appalachian Plateau (left) from the folded Appalachians (center and right); looking northeast near Lockhaven, Pennsylvania. (From J. S. Shelton, Geology Illustrated, W. H. Freeman & Co.)*

Fig. 6-2. *Folded miogeosynclinal Paleozoic rocks near Harrisburg, Pennsylvania. (From J. S. Shelton, Geology Illustrated, W. H. Freeman & Co.)*

Fig. 6-3. *The Triassic lowland along the Connecticut River, around Northampton, Massachusetts, with the New England Upland, surmounted by Mt. Monadnock, in the distance.* (*Photograph by J. S. Shelton.*)

along the Connecticut River in Massachusetts and Connecticut (Fig. 6-3).

(4) The folded Appalachians (western miogeosyncline of Fig. 6-5) extend west from the vicinity of Harrisburg to the Allegheny Front. This province is bordered on the southeast by a narrower lowland belt, the Great Valley, developed on a succession of Ordovician and other early Paleozoic limestones that in most places lack interbedded ridge-making sandstones. The Great Valley is rich farming country. In Pennsylvania it contains the cities of York and Lancaster, southeast of Harrisburg. Farther south, in Virginia, it is followed

by the north-flowing Shenandoah River, a tributary of the Potomac.

(5) West of the Allegheny Front, the Appalachian Plateaus, mostly from 1,200 to 3,500 feet above sea level, lie at the eastern edge of the continental platform, in western Pennsylvania, West Virginia, eastern Ohio, and eastern Kentucky. Rather surprisingly, these plateaus are approximately the area labeled Appalachian Basin in Figure 6-5. The presence of moderately high plateaus in the center of a structural basin is explained by the outcrop here of the youngest rocks of a thickened stratigraphic section. The strata are either flat-

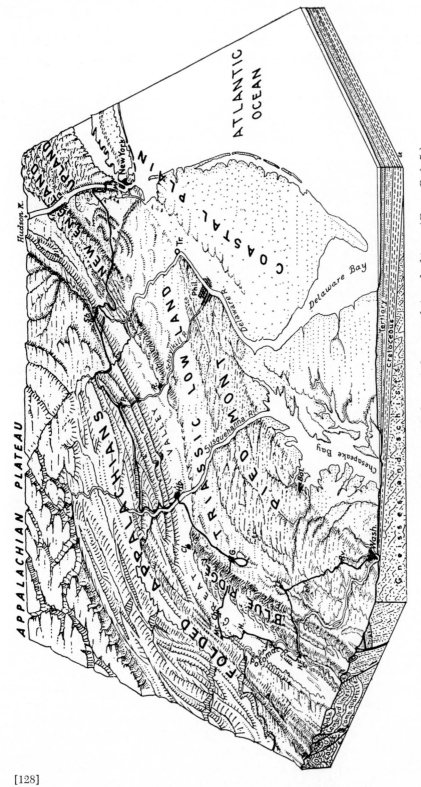

Fig. 6-4. *A block diagram showing the structure and geomorphology of the central Appalachians. (From Ref. 5.)*

Fig. 6-5. *Tectonic map of east-central North America. (After Tectonic Map of the United States, 1961).*

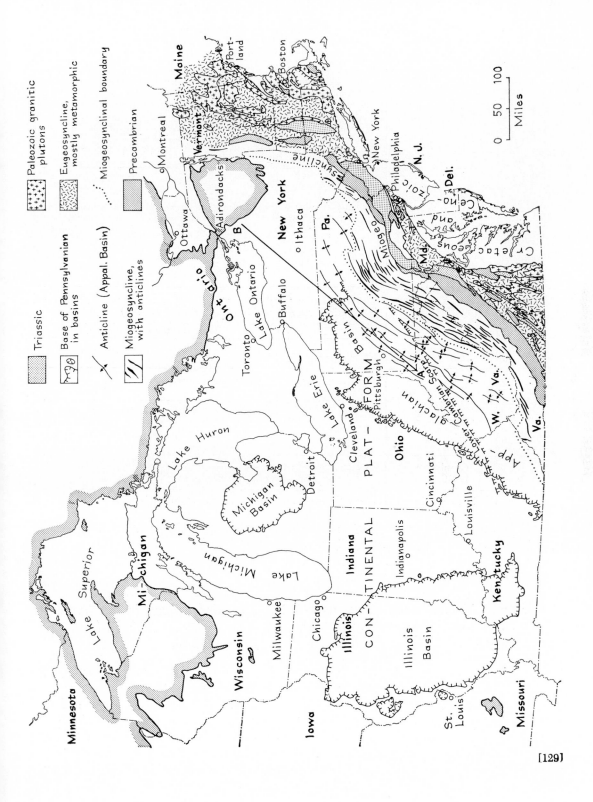

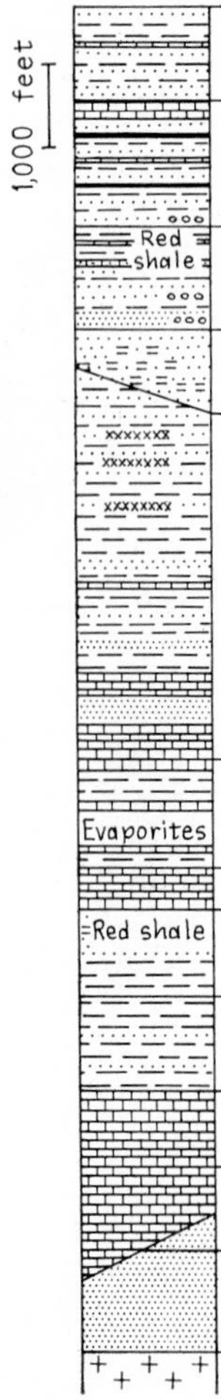

	Permian 1,100 feet	Gray shale and sandstone; thin limestone and coal beds; non-marine plant remains.
	Pennsylvanian 1,500 feet	Gray sandstone and shale; fresh-water limestone; coal beds; basal sandstone and conglomerate; non-marine plant remains; four thin marine bands.
	Mississippian 1,200 feet	Gray sandstone topped by red shale; mostly non-marine; thin marine limestone in southwestern Pennsylvania.
	Devonian (continental) 500-1,000 feet	Red and green shale; brown and green sandstone (Catskill facies).
	Devonian (marine) 4,100-4,600 feet	Mostly sandstone and shale with brachiopods and other marine fossils; marine limestone near base. xxxxxxx *Tropidoleptus* zone
	Silurian 2,800 feet	Upper Silurian: salt and other evaporites; red and green shales; sparse marine (and fresh-water?) faunas.
		Middle Silurian: marine shale, limestone, dolomite.
		Lower Silurian: sandstone and shale, mostly marine.
	Ordovician 3,000 feet	Upper Ordovician: shale and sandstone; marine.
		Middle Ordovician: limestone (Trenton, etc.); marine.
		Middle and Lower Ordovician: limestone (and sandstone); marine; north of Adirondacks.
	Cambrian 1,200 feet	Upper Cambrian: sandstone (and limestone); marine; north and west of Adirondacks.
	Precambrian	Plutonic and metamorphic rocks of Adirondacks.

Fig. 6-6. *Columnar section of the platform rocks of central New York and western Pennsylvania, approximately as found along line AB of Fig. 6-5.*

lying or gently folded along southwest-northeast axes. (The Appalachian Plateaus merge westward into the Central Interior lowlands, which lie beyond the western margin of Fig. 6-4 and even extend beyond the western limit of Fig. 6-5. Another name for this region is the Upper Mississippi Valley. It is all part of the continental platform, with Paleozoic rocks exposed at the surface and underlain at depths of a few thousand feet by crystalline Precambrian rocks.)

6-2. Standard Paleozoic Section in Western New York and Pennsylvania

The standard Paleozoic succession, with which other North American sequences are compared, is the New York Section, derived mostly from the series of nearly flat, gently south- or southwest-dipping strata that crop out on the easternmost part of the continental platform between the Black River Valley of north-central New York and the plateaus of western Pennsylvania. Middle Ordovician strata are exposed along the Black River and are overlain to the southwest, in successive belts, by a nearly complete Silurian and Devonian marine sequence, topped in Pennsylvania by non-marine Carboniferous and Permian. The part of this section found in New York State was described in some detail between 1837 and 1843 by James Hall the paleontologist (not Sir James Hall the structural geologist and friend of Hutton) and his associates on the New York Geological Survey. At the bottom of the principal continuous section, in central New York, Middle Ordovician limestones lie unconformably on the plutonic Precambrian rocks of the Adirondack massif (Fig. 6-5), but on the north and southeast edges of this massif older Ordovician strata and Upper Cambrian sandstone are also present. The New York–Pennsylvania section represents

moderately well the body of Paleozoic rocks that extends as far west as Colorado, beyond the western margin of Figure 6-5. This complex sheet of rocks is the most informative mass of Paleozoic strata in the world. Its type section was very nearly the first to be described in adequate detail. The type lower Paleozoic of Wales was briefly outlined by Sedgwick and Murchison in 1835, Murchison's great Silurian System appeared in 1839, and the Devonian was named in 1839. The description of the British column had barely been completed when the New York section was made known.

The New York–western Pennsylvania section is shown in columnar form in Figure 6-6. The base of the main part of the section is near Lowville, New York, at the northeast end of the line *AB* in Figure 6-5, the top in the southwest corner of Pennsylvania.

Upper Cambrian sandstones, 800–1,800 feet

Fig. 6-7. *Upper Ordovician limestone, composed largely of brachiopods and bryozoans; Cincinnati, Ohio. (Photograph by Robert C. Frampton.)*

thick, crop out north of the Adirondacks and extend west along the Great Lakes to Minnesota. These sandstones are widespread on the platform, even in the subsurface of western New York. In the Adirondack region, the upper members grade north and northwest into limestone.

The Ordovician rocks are mostly limestones, but black and gray shales are also common. Thicknesses are variable, with 3,000 feet an approximate total for the composite section derived from the northern and southwestern margins of the Adirondacks. The Lower Ordovician, both north and south of the Adirondacks, is mostly dolomite. Middle Ordovician limestones, mostly southwest of the Adirondacks, include the thin-bedded, very fossiliferous Trenton limestone (named from Trenton Falls southeast of Lowville), which is several hundred feet thick. Limestones called Trenton have been found over most of the North American platform, from Trenton Falls west, though forty miles east-southeast of the type locality

the place of the Trenton in the section is taken by black shale with graptolites, which allow probable correlation with strata in England somewhat above the middle of the type Ordovician. The Upper Ordovician in central New York is made up of shales and sandstones, which in southern Ohio become thin-bedded limestones and shales, with abundant fossils at all levels. A Cincinnati fossiliferous limestone is shown in Figure 6-7.

Above the Ordovician are Silurian sandstones, shales, limestones, dolomite, iron ore, and rock salt—a most varied system. The middle of the system is marked by a prominent dolomite, which makes the lip of Niagara Falls (Fig. 6-8). The underlying shale is being eroded at the base of the falls. The Niagara dolomite extends for long distances east and west, making a prominent escarpment along the south shore of Lake Ontario. This rock was originally a normal marine fossiliferous limestone, which probably changed to dolomite soon after its deposition. The Silurian strata

Fig. 6-8. *Aerial view southward toward the Niagara escarpment—Silurian carbonate rock on shale, dipping gently south—and the Niagara Falls and Gorge; Lewiston, N.Y., in the foreground. (Photograph by J. S. Shelton.)*

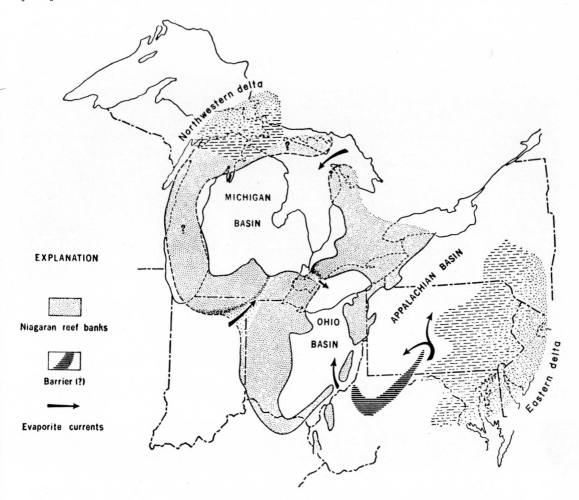

Fig. 6-9. *Salt basins and carbonate reefs in the Silurian of east-central North America. (Modified slightly from Ref. 7.)*

are up to 3,000 feet thick, though at the Falls they are much thinner.

An unusual rock in the Silurian of central New York is red hematite (iron oxide), which occurs in beds from one to five feet thick slightly below the stratigraphic level of the scarp-forming dolomite. The ore is in part oolitic, in part the replacement of calcium carbonate fossils. It was once mined extensively in New York and is still important at Birmingham, Alabama, far to the southwest.

A second unusual set of rocks, the salt formation of the Upper Silurian, is missing at the surface because the salt dissolves in the surface waters. Downdip from the outcrop the salt is 400 feet thick in western New York and increases to more than 2,000 feet farther west, in the center of the Michigan Basin. It was formed when an inland sea, previously connected with the ocean through gaps in the surrounding coral reefs (Fig. 6-9) and containing an abundant shallow-water fauna, contracted into land-locked basins under conditions of such extreme aridity that the water evaporated almost completely, precipitating first calcium sulphate (anhydrite) and then sodium chloride (rock salt), the latter to the amazing thickness of 1,230 feet in the uppermost of four beds.

Fig. 6-10. *The Helderberg escarpment of Devonian strata, south of Utica, N.Y., from the northwest. (Photograph by E. J. Stein, New York State Museum, courtesy of L. V. Rickard.)*

The reefs were somewhat similar to those of the West Texas Permian Basin (Chap. 4), but the sea outside the reefs was shallow instead of deep. The Silurian salt, an important industrial raw material, is now produced chiefly from brine wells. Some geological implications of its presence will be developed later in this chapter.

In New York State, the Devonian section, overlying the Silurian, starts at the base with fossiliferous marine limestones and sandstones, which are overlain by the marine limestone that makes the Helderberg escarpment near Albany (Fig. 6-10). This limestone, in the Catskill Mountains of east-central New York, is in turn overlain by thick and varied strata, largely non-fossiliferous conglomerates, red sandstones, and varicolored shales, which change to finer-grained, fossiliferous marine sediments in west-central and western New York (Fig. 6-11). Between the line *AB* of Figure 6-5 and Ithaca (New York), just short of the point where the last of the eastern red beds has changed to the western marine facies, the Devonian has a thickness of 4,000–5,000 feet, increasing to the east and south, decreasing to the west. Even here, two upper

Devonian fossil facies have been distinguished in the marine section, each with its characteristic brachiopods. The *Tropidoleptus* fauna is repeated several times as one goes up the section (Fig. 6-6), probably indicating shifts back and forth, between east and west, of the conditions that favored this fauna. The simplest explanation of the shifting facies is change in the depth of the sea. The *Tropidoleptus* fauna is probably a shallow eastern near-shore biofacies, which is replaced, still farther east, by the unfossiliferous and apparently non-marine red-bed (Catskill) lithofacies of the Upper Devonian.

In southwestern New York and northwestern Pennsylvania, Upper Devonian and other sandstones are reservoirs of oil. The world's first commercial well drilled for oil, 69 feet deep, was completed near Titusville, in northern Pennsylvania, in 1859. Now, more than a hundred years later, oil is still being produced in this region, largely from the Upper Devonian but also from other levels, including the Ordovician.

In the plateaus of western Pennsylvania, the Devonian rocks are overlain by gray sandstone and red shale, commonly called Missis-

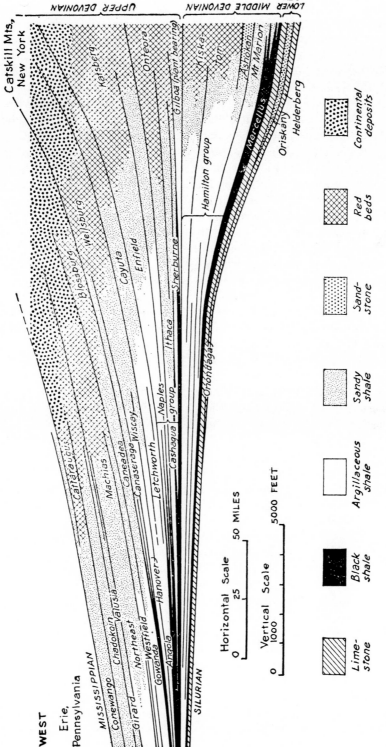

Fig. 6.11. *Devonian lithofacies in New York.* (Reprinted from *The Evolution of North America* by P. B. King, by permission of Princeton University Press. Copyright © 1959 by Princeton University Press.)

sippian (Lower Carboniferous), usually with land plants as the only fossils. At the southwest, south of Pittsburgh, the apparent equivalent of this unit contains thin bands of marine limestone containing characteristic Mississippian fossils. Farther west, in the northern Mississippi Valley, the type Mississippian is wholly marine limestone and shale, with abundant fossils. Around the margins of the Illinois Basin, just outside the Pennsylvanian boundary shown in Figure 6-5, a broad belt of Mississippian limestones crops out. In these limestones large caves are common, including the one near Hannibal, Missouri, just west of the Mississippi River, which Tom Sawyer made dramatic and famous.

In western Pennsylvania, the predominantly continental strata called Mississippian are overlain by the Pennsylvanian (Upper Carboniferous) coal measures: sandstone, underclay, coal, etc. In most of the region these are the highest strata preserved. The coal measures are about 1,500 feet thick and extend from western Pennsylvania into West Virginia, Ohio, and Kentucky. East of Pittsburgh they are folded into flat anticlines and synclines, which trend southwest-northeast. In these folds the dips are mostly less than ten degrees.

The lowest Pennsylvanian strata, the Pottsville sandstone, grit, and conglomerate, are very much like the Millstone Grit* of England and probably of about the same age. The Pottsville is overlain successively by Lower Productive Coal Measures, Barren Measures containing four marine bands, each about ten feet thick, and Upper Productive Coal Measures. About half a dozen coal beds are thick and pure. The richest bed, the Pittsburgh seam at the base of the Upper Productive Measures, has an average thickness of seven feet in an area of 12,000–15,000 square miles and is, perhaps, the most valuable bonanza of any sort in the whole world, probably surpassing the largest Mesozoic oil fields of the Persian Gulf and the Cenozoic borax of California.

---

* The Millstone Grit is largely made up of very coarse sandstone (grit), but it also includes conglomerate, medium-grained sandstone, and shale.

In the southwest corner of Pennsylvania and adjacent parts of Ohio and West Virginia, the Pennsylvanian is overlain in a rather small area by capping Permian strata: continental plant-bearing shales containing thin layers of sandstone and limestone and a few poor seams of coal. In West Virginia these beds contain bones of typical Permian land reptiles. The Permian makes up the highest part of the stratigraphic section.

The whole Paleozoic section represented in Figure 6-6 is approximately 16,000 feet thick. This figure is the sum of many approximate values, for all the units vary in thickness from place to place. Perhaps at no single place is the whole section quite so thick. The greatest thickness at one place may be near the southern boundary of Pennsylvania and may be 12,000 or 13,000 feet. Thicknesses increase in the adjoining miogeosyncline of central Pennsylvania and West Virginia, probably to 25,000 or even 30,000 feet. Thicknesses on the platform decrease westward.

6-3. Structural Units of East-central North America

a. Basins and Inter-basin Areas of the Central Platform

Although the Paleozoic strata are almost horizontal on the central North American platform, notable structural features appear when the platform is viewed in the large, as in Figure 6-5. The principal such features within the area of that figure are three structural depressions, the Illinois, Michigan, and Appalachian Basins. Between the basins are two very flat structural highs, the Findlay Arch in northern Ohio, between the Michigan and Appalachian Basins, and the Cincinnati-Indiana Arch extending from central Kentucky northwest across Indiana along the east and northeast sides of the Illinois Basin. At the southwest corner of the map, south of St. Louis, a more pronounced high, with Precambrian exposures, is part of the Ozark Dome of Missouri and Arkansas.

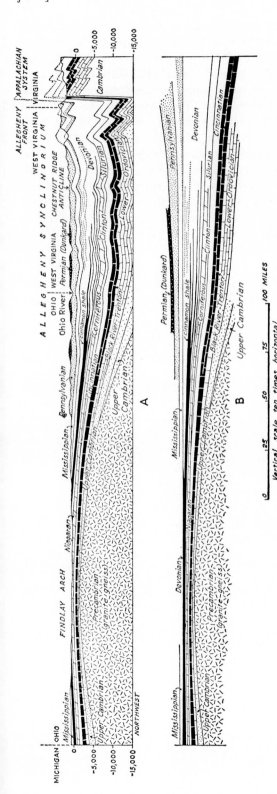

1. APPALACHIAN BASIN. The Appalachian Basin is centered near the southwest corner of Pennsylvania. Its general basin structure (Fig. 6-12) can be read from the distribution of the Pennsylvanian (and Permian) strata. The Basin region includes the low plateaus on both sides of the Ohio River. Several of these plateaus are capped by Permian strata, but in most places the river has cut through the Permian to the underlying Pennsylvanian. Pennsylvanian outcrops also completely surround the Permian area. On the west flank of the Basin, Ordovician rocks crop out at Cincinnati and are succeeded to the east by all the younger Paleozoic systems.

Structurally, the Appalachian Basin is little more than a half-basin, cut off sharply on the southeast by the folded Appalachians of the Valley and Ridge province. The strata pass into those of the folded Appalachians without any break, showing that the depositional basin of Paleozoic times included both the present Appalachian half-basin, at the eastern edge of the continental platform, and the originally rather broad area of deposition of the rocks in the folded Appalachians.

The structure in the older Basin rocks is more complicated than the outcrops indicate. In the center of the Basin the Carboniferous and Permian rocks are almost horizontal. The slight surface folds become somewhat accentuated in the older rocks. Below the Middle Ordovician (Trenton), two unconformities appear, as suggested in Figure 6-12B and shown with great vertical exaggeration in Figure

Fig. 6-12. *Strata of the Appalachian Basin in Ohio and West Virginia. (Reprinted from* The Evolution of North America *by P. B. King, by permission of Princeton University Press. Copyright © 1959 by Princeton University Press.)*
A. *Structure section from northern Ohio to western Virginia.*
B. *Stratigraphic diagram along the line of the section, showing the absence of any stratigraphic change at the Allegheny Front; the apparent thinning in A, east of the Front, is an effect of vertical exaggeration.*

6-13. There is also a pronounced scarp (shown too in Fig. 6-5), bounding the Lower Cambrian wedge of the southeastern part of the Basin on the northwest, but crossed without any break by late Middle Cambrian strata. The Lower Cambrian wedge is up to 4,500 feet thick (Fig. 6-14). Clearly, the Appalachian Basin had a long history of complicated deformation, with the appearance of a scarp (fault scarp?) right across the Basin in early Cambrian time, with two slight deformations in early Ordovician time, and with marked folding and the development of 10° dips in post-Pennsylvanian (probably post-Permian) time.

Notable features of the Precambrian surface northwest of the scarp (the steep platform margin of Fig. 6-14) are the abundant "Granite Wash" found in most Ohio wells and the seemingly fresh granite of the Precambrian surface close to Lake Erie. Apparently the Late Cambrian sea, which was probably the first to encroach upon the continental platform, advanced over a nearly flat plain of subaerial erosion and weathering, a peneplain, in Ohio, without wholly destroying the weathered zone until the vicinity of the present Lake Erie was reached. As we found a similar condition on the Grand Canyon platform (Chap. 5), we

Fig. 6-13. *Section of the lower Paleozoic strata, Ohio–West Virginia, showing a Lower Cambrian scarp and Lower Ordovician unconformities. (After Ref. 8.)*

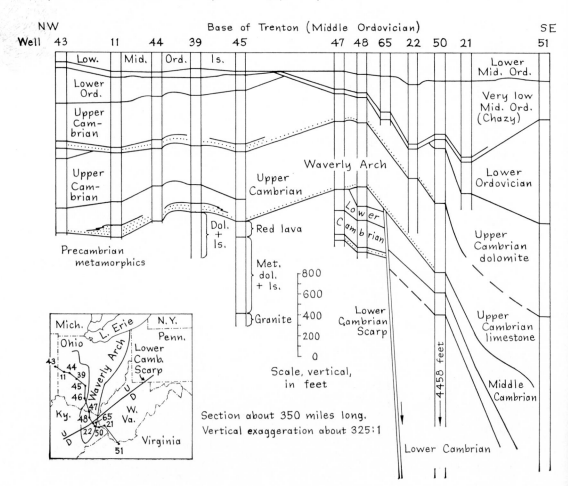

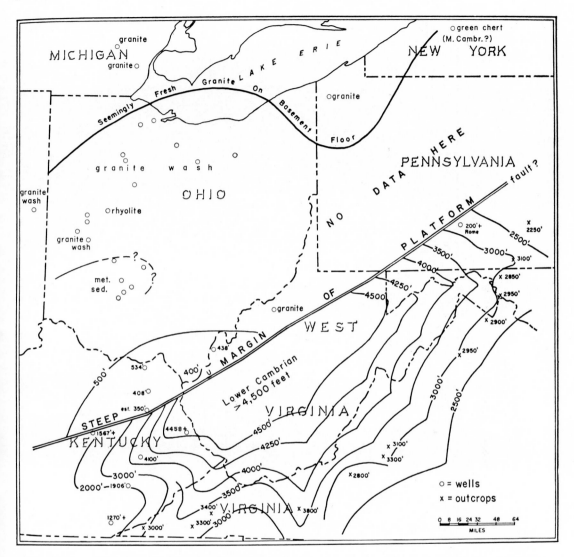

Fig. 6-14. *Contours of sediment thickness (in feet) in the Lower Cambrian along the southeastern margin of the Appalachian Basin, and, on the platform, the spot lithology at points in the Precambrian floor. (Modified from Ref. 8.)*

conclude that peneplains covered most of the North American platform in Cambrian time— the results of many millions of years of erosion during late Precambrian and early Cambrian times. In early Cambrian time the sea level must have been stable for millions of years, to permit the final production of broad, smooth erosion surfaces. Cambrian conditions were therefore unlike the present unstable condi-

tions, under which no continent has a peneplain at sea level.

2. MICHIGAN BASIN. The Michigan Basin (Fig. 6-15) is a nearly circular structural depression centered in east-central Michigan, its flanks marked by Lake Michigan and Lake Huron. The lake surfaces are about 600 feet above sea level, and most of the land between

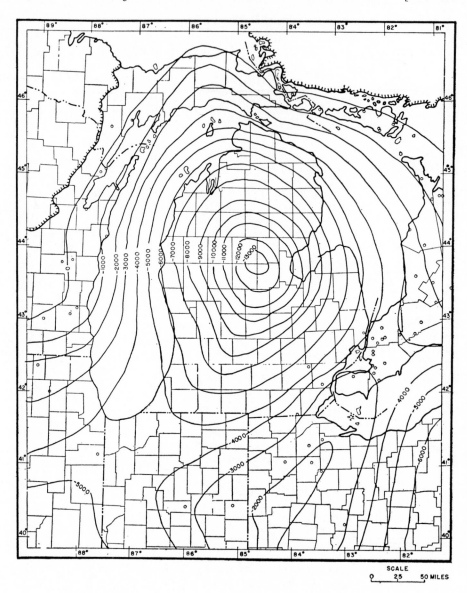

Fig. 6-15. *Contour map of the Precambrian floor of the Michigan Basin. (From G. V. Cohee,* BULLETIN, *Am. Ass. Petrol. Geol., 1948.)*

and around the lakes is not much higher. The rocks of the Basin are Paleozoic—Cambrian–Pennsylvanian—and crop out in concentric belts round a thin and rather small central tablet of lower and middle Pennsylvanian (Fig. 6-5) that lacks workable coal beds.

The Precambrian floor of the Michigan Basin is 13,000 feet below sea level at its lowest

point in east-central Michigan. The Precambrian rim of the Basin rises above sea level in Wisconsin and north of the Great Lakes; it is lower beneath northern Indiana and Ohio but nowhere as much as 5,000 feet below sea level. Thus the closed part of the basin is more than 8,000 feet deep.

The Michigan Basin is not wholly post-

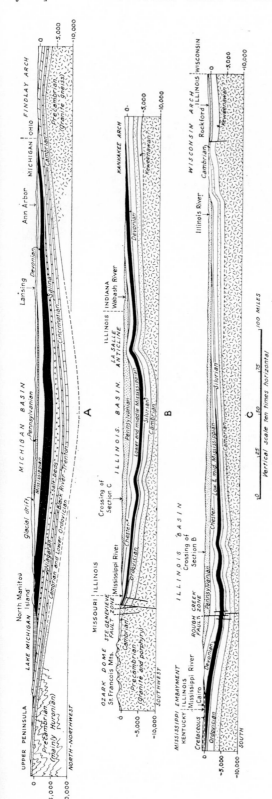

Pennsylvanian; in fact, though post-Pennsylvanian warping occurred round the margin of the basin, as will be shown below, the basin itself began to subside earlier, as shown especially well by Upper Silurian shallow-water marine sediments and evaporites, which were formed approximately at sea level but whose base is as much as 9,000 feet below the base of the Pennsylvanian—a sedimentary sequence that also formed within a few hundred feet of sea level and is still about at the elevation of formation. Between late Silurian and Pennsylvanian times, the floor of the Michigan Basin must have sagged 9,000 feet, filling with sediments as it sank.

3. ILLINOIS BASIN. The Illinois Basin (Fig. 6-16BC) lies southwest of the Michigan Basin, beyond the flat and narrow Indiana (or Kankakee) Arch. Its form is shown by the elongated area of Carboniferous outcrops, mostly in Illinois but also extending into southwestern Indiana and western Kentucky. The Pennsylvanian coal measures crop out in the parts of the area not covered by a thin layer of Pleistocene glacial and fluvio-glacial deposits. The coal measures dip a few feet per mile toward a central low in east-central Illinois. They overlie Mississippian marine limestones, sandstones, and shales unconformably and overlap northward onto Devonian, Silurian, and Ordovician strata. The unconformity at the base of the Pennsylvanian is also shown by the truncation of pre-Pennsylvanian folds.

The thickest pre-Pennsylvanian Paleozoic is in southern Illinois, where the Precambrian

Fig. 6-16. *Structure sections across the Michigan and Illinois Basins. (Reprinted from* The Tectonics of Middle North America *by P. B. King, by permission of Princeton University Press. Copyright, 1951, by Princeton University Press.)*

A. *Michigan Basin, from north-northwest to south-southeast.*
B. *Illinois Basin, southwest-northeast.*
C. *Illinois Basin, south-north.*

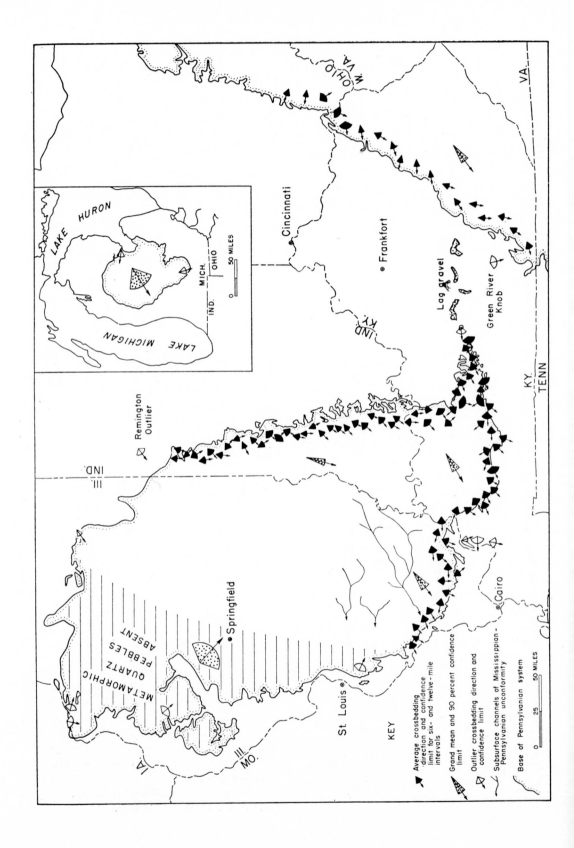

KEY

Average crossbedding direction and confidence limit for six- and twelve-mile intervals

Grand mean and 90 percent confidence limit

Outlier crossbedding direction and confidence limit

Subsurface channels of Mississippian-Pennsylvanian unconformity

Base of Pennsylvanian system

METAMORPHIC QUARTZ PEBBLES ABSENT

Lag gravel

Remington Outlier

Green River Knob

Springfield

St. Louis

Cairo

Frankfort

Cincinnati

ILL.
IND.

MO.
ILL.

KY.
IND.

KY.
TENN.

OHIO
W. VA.

VA.

LAKE HURON

LAKE MICHIGAN

IND. MICH.
OHIO

50 MILES

0   25   50 MILES

floor of the Basin probably sinks to 10,000 feet below sea level. The numerous wells drilled for oil show that many formations, especially of the Pennsylvanian, Mississippian, and Ordovician systems, thicken in the center of the Basin; the deepest wells commonly reach the Middle Ordovician at depths about 7,000 feet below sea level. The additional depth to the Basin's Precambrian floor is estimated from the probable thicknesses of Lower Ordovician and Cambrian strata and from the travel times of seismic waves produced by artificial earthquakes and bounced off the floor. The occurrence of shallow-water sediments at many levels shows that the Illinois Basin, too, was subsiding throughout the Paleozoic.

All the basins of the platform were areas of sinking and deposition. But it does not follow that the arches and domes between the basins were regions of uplift and erosion. The sedimentary rocks representing the Cambrian and at least part of the Ordovician are similar throughout the platform region and are preserved on the arches as well as in the basins. For the distribution of later Paleozoic rocks on the platform, before the erosion that produced the present conditions, the study of the Pennsylvanian formations has given useful suggestions.

4. DEPOSITION OF PENNSYLVANIAN STRATA ON THE PLATFORM. Were the coal measures deposited only in the basins where they are now found? Or did they originally form sheets that covered practically the whole platform area represented in Figure 6-5? There is compelling evidence for the second alternative.

The most varied evidence is found in Kentucky (Fig. 6-17). The basal Pennsylvanian—Pottsville sandstone and gravel—is represented on ridges all the way across the flat Cincinnati Arch by masses of residual pebbles called lag

Fig. 6-17. *Basal Pennsylvanian cross-bedding, channels, and lag gravels in the Illinois Basin and elsewhere.* (*Adapted from Ref. 6 by permission of the University of Chicago Press. Copyright 1956 by the University of Chicago.*)

gravels, which are up to 50 feet thick. There are even some blocks of cemented sandstone. Clearly, the lowest Pennsylvanian strata once extended across the Arch and have not been completely removed by erosion. The lag gravels lie mostly on Mississippian rocks, but the northernmost gravel area provides evidence that here, near the crest of the Arch, the basal Pennsylvanian sandy conglomerate lay unconformably on Devonian and even Ordovician rocks. In this part of Kentucky the solid basal Pennsylvanian outcrops show that a channel in the pre-Pennsylvanian rocks is filled by the basal Pennsylvanian (Pottsville) sandstone and conglomerate; the channel is west-southwest of the "Lag gravel" of Figure 6-17.

That figure also shows, over the whole region, including even the Michigan Basin (inset), the directions of cross-bedding in the basal Pennsylvanian sandstones. Except in the northwest part of the Illinois Basin, the mean direction of cross-bedding is everywhere southwest. Cross-bedding (compare § 1-6.a) indicates the directions of currents. The evidence of Figure 6-17 points overwhelmingly to currents moving southwest over almost the whole region. Exceptionally, in the western Illinois marginal area, they moved southeast. Flow was not, in general, into the Illinois, Appalachian, and Michigan Basins, but was rather a general southwestern movement of widely spread sand and gravel, complicated slightly by inflow into the Illinois Basin from a local northwestern source. In general, the sand and gravel must have come from the Canadian Shield and the northern Appalachians and been spread over the whole region of deposition, including the arches between the present basins.

Information about the higher Pennsylvanian strata is less abundant, but all that is known is consistent with our interpretation of the basal beds. In particular, the drainage systems shown for the basal channels in southern Illinois (Fig. 6-17) are roughly paralleled by very well-known and thoroughly surveyed channels at higher levels in the Pennsylvanian. Winding channels a half mile wide cut **down**

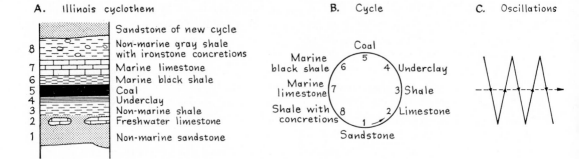

A. Illinois cyclothem

8	Sandstone of new cycle
	Non-marine gray shale with ironstone concretions
7	Marine limestone
6	Marine black shale
5	Coal
4	Underclay
3	Non-marine shale
2	Freshwater limestone
1	Non-marine sandstone

B. Cycle

Coal
5
Marine black shale 6 — 4 Underclay
Marine limestone 7 — 3 Shale
Shale with concretions 8 — 2 Limestone
1
Sandstone

C. Oscillations

Fig. 6-18. *Illinois cyclothem as a cycle rather than an oscillation.*
    A. *Generalized cyclic succession in the Pennsylvanian of Illinois.*
    B. *Cyclic lithologic diagram.*
    C. *Oscillation diagram.*

50 or 100 feet into earlier Pennsylvanian beds, completely eliminating some coal seams from the channel area and replacing all the eroded materials with channel sands. The channel sands grade upward into sheets that covered broad areas. Records showing these relations in detail have been published by the Illinois Geological Survey.

In Illinois the Pennsylvanian is 500–1,800 feet thick, the smaller figure representing western sections that are incomplete because of fairly recent erosion. The basal, sandy, Pottsville-like portion of the system is overlain by Productive Coal Measures that are not divided by a middle zone of Barren Measures similar to those in Pennsylvania. Some thirty or forty beds of coal or coaly shale are more or less extensive, and six or seven of these are economically important. As in Pennsylvania, each coal bed is associated more or less uniformly with a particular set of other strata, notably sandstone and underclay below the coal and marine shale and limestone above it (Fig. 6-18). Note that the sequence (A) is a one-way cycle (B) rather than a symmetrical oscillation (C). The underclay, for example, occurs only once in the cycle, not twice as it might in an oscillation through a middle condition (as in C). Marine bands are commoner than in Pennsylvania; in western Illinois twelve of the nineteen principal coals or coaly beds are overlain by marine black shale or limestone

or by both. The coal-measure cycles commonly range from two to forty feet in thickness, but they are usually thicker where basal sandstones fill channels. Five of the eight principal members of one Illinois cycle were shown in Figure 4-4: underclay overlain successively by coal, fossiliferous black platy marine shale, soft black shale, and gray fossiliferous marine limestone. The term **cyclothem** is often used for the set of sediments formed during a Pennsylvanian cycle of sedimentation. A cyclothem containing all the units represented in Figure 6-18A is somewhat unusual. As we saw in Chapter 4, the continental units tend to pinch out west of Illinois, so that in Kansas the Pennsylvanian section is mostly marine. The great Pennsylvanian seaway of North America was in Texas, Oklahoma, and Kansas.

Possibly the one-way cycle was the result of a slow rise of the sea level, each cycle being ended by a sudden event—perhaps by a deformation involving rise to the east and a new flood of clastics in Illinois.

5. POST-PENNSYLVANIAN WARPING AND EROSION. If the Upper Carboniferous (Pennsylvanian) complex just described was originally spread over the whole platform south of the Great Lakes, as seems definitely demonstrated, it has since been removed, by erosion, from the structural arches of the platform. The

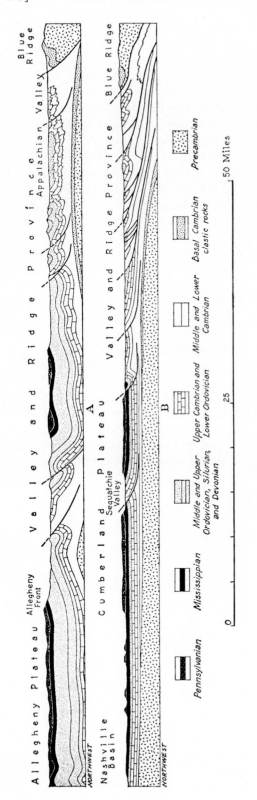

Fig. 6-19. *Structure sections across the Appalachian miogeosyncline.* (*Reprinted from* The Evolution of North America *by P. B. King, by permission of Princeton University Press. Copyright © 1959 by Princeton University Press.*) A. *In southern Pennsylvania; folding dominant.* B. *In southern Tennessee; faulting dominant.*

original sheet must have been deformed by upwarping of the arches and then the upwarped Pennsylvanian strata, with some of the underlying rocks, removed by erosion. That erosion has not gone far below the base of the Pennsylvanian is suggested by the lag gravels represented in Figure 6-17. The present wide exposure of Ordovician rocks on the arches may be due as much to pre-Pennsylvanian as to post-Pennsylvanian erosion.

The date of the post-Pennsylvanian warping is uncertain, for the uncomformably overlying strata are mostly Pleistocene. The Permian beds in and near southwestern Pennsylvania are so like the Pennsylvanian strata that the two systems probably are conformable and belong together structurally. The warping may have occurred at the end of the Paleozoic, but this supposition is, after all, only a reasonable guess.

b. Appalachian Geosyncline

The Appalachian geosyncline is the belt of deformed, thick, Paleozoic sedimentary rocks along the eastern edge of the great central platform of the North American continent. The geosyncline extends southwest from Newfoundland and the Maritime Provinces of Canada through New England, southeastern New York, and eastern Pennsylvania to northern Alabama. The close folding in part of it—in West Virginia and Pennsylvania—is expressed in Figure 6-5 by the crowding of anticlinal axes.

The geosyncline is rather cleanly divided into two parts. A western miogeosyncline is made up of shales, sandstones, limestones, coals, and other rocks very similar to platform strata of the same ages but much thicker (Figs. 6-12 and 6-19). In Pennsylvania the total thick-

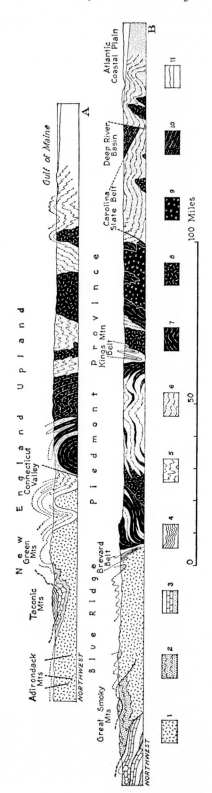

ness of the Paleozoic in this western belt is 25,000 feet; farther south the total may reach 40,000 feet. Marine fossils are present at many levels. An eastern eugeosyncline is so different from the western belt that its recognition as a correlative part of the great geosyncline has been a slow process and is only now approaching a satisfactory conclusion. The eastern belt is intensely deformed, highly metamorphosed, marked by thick layers of volcanic rocks interbedded with the sedimentary, and invaded by plutonic batholithic rocks such as granite. Fossils are rare; discoveries of fossils here and there in the sedimentary rocks have been triumphs that have made correlations with the western facies possible.

New England is typical of the eastern belt. A section across New England (Fig. 6-20A) shows a great overthrust of eastern (eugeosynclinal) rocks over western rocks along Lake Champlain, numerous folds, steep-angle thrusts, and late Paleozoic batholithic intrusions. The Ordovician, Silurian, and Lower Devonian stratified eugeosynclinal rocks, including some volcanics, are 30,000–40,000 feet thick. Addition of the locally developed Cambrian and Upper Carboniferous sedimentary rocks makes a total Paleozoic thickness of at

Fig. 6-20. *Sections across the Appalachian eugeosyncline: 1, basement rocks, mainly granite and gneiss; 2, late Precambrian clastic sedimentary rocks; 3, Paleozoic limestone, quartzite, and shale of miogeosynclinal origin; 4, Paleozoic slate, schist, quartzite, and marble, in Taconic, Brevard, and Kings Mt. belts; 5, schist and gneiss, mostly Paleozoic; 6, Paleozoic metaclastic and metavolcanic rocks of the Carolina slate belt; 7, foliated Paleozoic quartz plutonites; 8, massive Paleozoic quartz plutonites; 9, Paleozoic quartz-free plutonic rocks; 10, Triassic strata; 11, Cretaceous and Tertiary strata. (Reprinted from* The Evolution of North America *by P. B. King, by permission of Princeton University Press. Copyright © 1959 by Princeton University Press.)*
   A. *From Adirondack Mountains to Gulf of Maine.*
   B. *In Tennessee and North Carolina.*

Fig. 6-21. *Structural evolution of the eugeo-syncline in New England, illustrated in New Hampshire. (From M. P. Billings,* Geology of New Hampshire, *Concord, 1956.)*

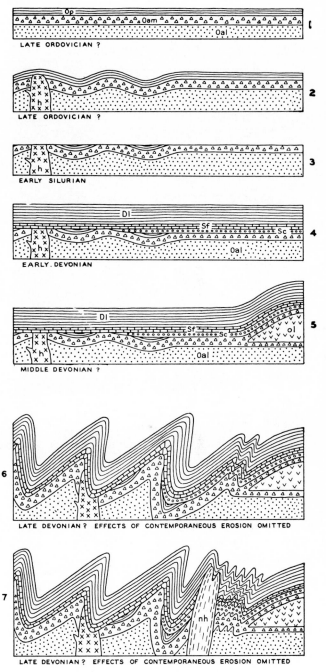

least 50,000 feet. A section across the southern Appalachians (Fig. 6-20B) is similar.

The most notable unconformities in the eugeosynclinal belt are probably (1) in western New England, between Cambrian and Ordovician; (2) in eastern New England, between the principal mass of Paleozoic rocks, topped by the Lower Devonian, and Pennsylvanian conglomerate, shale, coal, etc. The Pennsylvanian rocks occur in eastern Massachusetts and Rhode Island and again in the Maritime Provinces of Canada. The best data on the relative ages of deformation and plutonism seem to come from the Maritime Provinces. Apparently both close folding and plutonic intrusion occurred in mid-Devonian time. The principal metamorphism and the most widespread plutonism may have been somewhat later, but they were clearly pre-Pennsylvanian. The Pennsylvanian rocks are only moderately deformed and mildly metamorphosed, though an especially susceptible rock, coal, has been changed to anthracite in Rhode Island. The alteration to anthracite is not limited to New England; it occurred on a much larger scale in eastern Pennsylvania, in the eastern part of the miogeosyncline or in an area transitional from miogeosyncline to eugeosyncline. The geologic history of New England during the Paleozoic is summarized diagrammatically in the sections of Figure 6-21.

6-4. *Horizontal Variations in Sedimentary Facies*

The horizontal changes in contemporaneous Paleozoic surface rocks are extreme in east-central North America. Volcanic rocks were piling up in eastern New England at the same time as continental clastics in eastern New York and marine shale and limestone on the

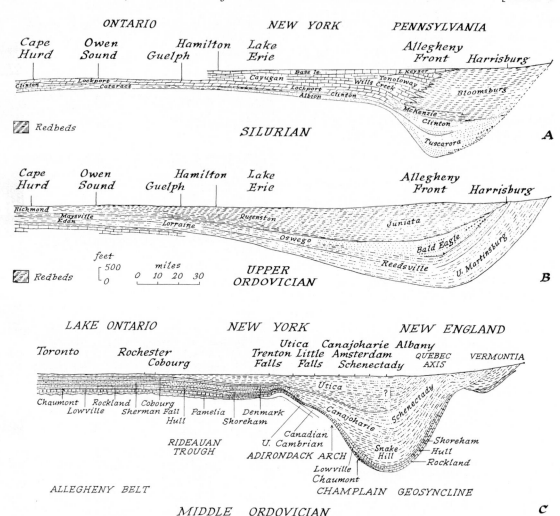

Fig. 6-22. *Ordovician and Silurian geosynclinal and platform facies. (Adapted from Marshall Kay, BULLETIN, Geol. Soc. Am., 1942.)*

platform. The miogeosynclinal and platform portions of facies sets of three ages are shown in Figure 6-22: A, Silurian; B, Upper Ordovician; C, Middle Ordovician, including the change from graptolitic shale to Trenton limestone mentioned at the beginning of this chapter. Figure 6-23 is a Cambrian–Middle Ordovician composite that includes the eugeosyncline. The northwestern ends of the sections are well out on the platform, at Cape Hurd on the east side of Lake Huron and at Toronto north of Lake Ontario. Note the general thin-

ning from east to west, or from southeast to northwest, not only from eugeosyncline through miogeosyncline to platform, but also, in Fig. 6-22AB, on the platform itself, marking the change from the Appalachian Basin to the central structural high. Note also two modes of facies change, a sharp change to limestone on the platform in A and C and a gradual change in clastic facies in B. Farther west, and south of the Ohio River, the Upper Ordovician becomes platform limestone and dolomite.

6-5. Post-Paleozoic History of East-central North America

The principal events in the geologic history of this region were surely Paleozoic. We can briefly summarize the subsequent events by interpreting the evidence indicated in Figures 6-4 and 6-5.

At the end of the Paleozoic the region ceased to be the site of extensive epicontinental deposition, especially of marine deposition. Appalachian folding occurred, perhaps in a series of episodes beginning in the Devonian, but ultimately involving Pennsylvanian and possibly Permian strata. The Appalachian folds, at least from Newfoundland to Alabama, trend southwest-northeast.

In late Triassic time the Appalachian belt was subjected to block faulting, and red sandstone was deposited in the fault troughs, notably along what is now the Connecticut River Valley (in Massachusetts and Connecticut) and in a strip extending from Newark (New Jersey), opposite New York City, southwest past Philadelphia to western Virginia and North Carolina. Extensive vulcanism must then have occurred, as shown by lava flows and by great sheets and dikes of shallow igneous intrusives, including the one that makes the Hudson Palisades opposite New York City. The age of the sandstone is attested by the abundant footprints and rare bones of Triassic dinosaurs (compare Chap. 14).

The Jurassic, which was important in western Europe, left no record in this part of America.

In Cretaceous and Cenozoic times, sedimentary deposits accumulated along the eastern edge of the continent. In New Jersey and farther south the Lower Cretaceous sediments are clays and sands containing the remains of land plants. These sediments are overlain by Upper Cretaceous and Cenozoic marine deposits, still flat-lying, which are thin where exposed on land by slight erosion but thicken to many thousand feet beneath the continental shelf.

In the Pleistocene, continental ice sheets extended as far south as New York City, producing the terminal moraines and outwash sand plains that make up much of Long Island. Glacial deposits now more or less obscure the bedrock geology in western New York and in the Middle West north of the Ohio River— that is, in the greater part of the area shown in Figure 6-5. Minor topographic features in the northern part of the glaciated area were mostly determined by a very late glaciation at the end of the Pleistocene. Undrained lakes and bogs are common; stream valleys are not fully developed into complex, regular, and all-pervasive systems.

6-6. Why Geosynclinal Deformation, Plutonism, and Metamorphism?

The Appalachian geosyncline was the site of folding, thrust faulting, and, in the eugeosyncline, metamorphism and plutonism. As the New England part of the eugeosyncline was deformed, especially in Devonian time, a great prism of sediments, in part continental, in part marine, accumulated to the west, in the miogeosyncline and beyond. Devonian mountains must have existed in New England; in other words, a Devonian orogeny occurred in New England. A later orogeny, near the end of the Paleozoic, affected the whole miogeosynclinal belt.

The depositional and orogenic events of the Appalachians were paralleled—in a general way, but with differences—in the Cordilleran region. In both regions, folding occurred first in the eugeosyncline, then in the miogeosyncline; thrusting was widespread in both types of geosyncline and was accompanied almost everywhere by overthrusting toward the central continental platform; the eugeosynclinal rocks, in the largest thrusts, formed plates overlying miogeosynclinal rocks; and, at and immediately after times of extreme deformation, batholiths formed, made up of light-colored quartz-bearing granodiorites and granites. Some of the similarities are represented on the structure sections reproduced as Fig-

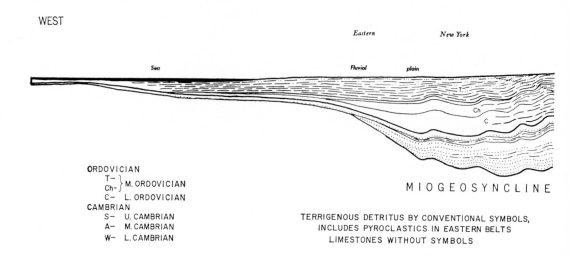

Fig. 6-23. *Appalachian geosynclinal facies, in diagrammatic section, from Cambrian through Middle Ordovician, between New York and Maine. (Adapted from Ref. 4.)*

ures 5-16, 6-20, and 6-23. Others can be imagined with the aid of generalized geologic maps, such as Figures 5-15 and 6-5.

Among the differences, some may be merely apparent. For example, the change from eugeosyncline to miogeosyncline in central Nevada is spread over a belt 100 miles wide, where an upper plate of western volcanics, chert, graptolitic shale, etc. overlies miogeosynclinal limestones of about the same ages as the western siliceous rocks. The corresponding Appalachian thrust sheet, east of Lake Champlain, crops out only in a narrow belt, but the upper, eastern plate may have been removed from the Adirondacks by erosion. Similarly, the differences in the positions of the strips of Precambrian rocks may be more indicative of the degree of general uplift and erosion than of the relative heights of the structures. In the Cordilleran region, the general level reached by erosion exposes lower and lower rocks toward the south until, in southeastern California and westernmost Arizona, most of the mountain masses are made up of Precambrian rocks. In contrast, long strips of Precambrian are exposed throughout the length of the Appalachian geosyncline. A third difference is expressed on the maps (Figs. 5-15 and 6-5)

by the sizes and shapes of the Paleozoic and Mesozoic intrusive bodies (plutons)—long narrow strips in the Appalachians, larger and less obviously linear bodies in the Cordilleran region. The different sizes of the exposed plutons are probably due, in part, to different degrees of removal of the roofs by erosion. A single western plutonic body, in the Sierra Nevada, is broadly exposed in the south but hidden by roof rocks in the northwest. Even if some Appalachian granitic strips unite at depth, however, it is very improbable that they become a pluton as large as that of the Sierra.

The major difference between the Cordilleran and Appalachian geosynclines is in the time of culminating orogeny. In New England the eugeosynclinal orogeny must have culminated in the Middle Devonian or somewhat later, for the metamorphosed stratified rocks are Cambrian–Lower Devonian, and an erosion surface across Lower Devonian rocks and intrusive plutonics is overlain by Carboniferous rocks. Farther south the culmination of eugeosynclinal deformation may have been as early as Ordovician. In the miogeosyncline of eastern Pennsylvania the Upper Carboniferous (Pennsylvanian) coal measures are involved

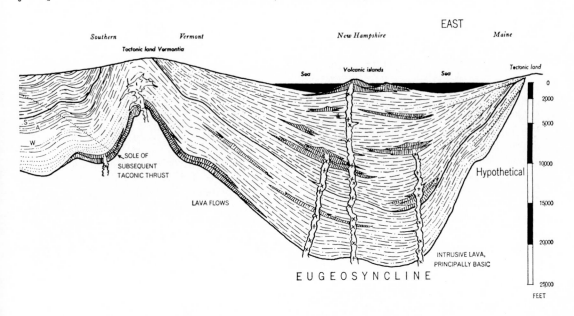

in the principal folding, with the shales changed to slates and the coal to anthracite (pure carbon). In the Cordilleran region, mountain-making folding occurred in the late Paleozoic, but the latest considerable orogeny and the time of metamorphism and vast plutonic intrusion were Cretaceous. The Appalachian region was block-faulted in the Triassic but was then eroded to low mountains and has been fairly quiet ever since as part of the main mass of the continent, periodically and marginally slightly submerged. The Cordilleran region has been repeatedly block-faulted in the Cenozoic, and the marginal Coast Ranges were closely folded just yesterday. The region is still an active orogenic belt.

With the histories of the Cordilleran and Appalachian geosynclines in mind, we may begin to think about the processes of orogeny. In each region mountains were made primarily by close folding, beginning near the oceans, and by major thrust faulting toward the main mass of the continent. The associated metamorphism was much more intense near the oceans, and the plutonism was nearly limited to the eugeosynclines, which had earlier been the sites of intense vulcanism. We may imagine that the earliest sagging of the geosynclinal floor was greater close to the ocean, that magma rose through the sinking sediments to the surface, producing submarine and finally subaerial eruptions, that plutonic invasion followed, that the weakened floor of the geosyncline partially collapsed, apparently first in an outer and then in an inner belt, and that the overlying sediments were then more easily compressed into folds. We still have no explanation of the compressive folding or even of the compound geosynclinal belts—each belt having an outer part marked by plutonism, vulcanism, and early folding and an inner belt lacking these features. We shall get more evidence bearing on these questions when we consider Precambrian times and Gondwanaland, but even then the problems of geosynclinal orogeny will remain, at most, only partially solved. We can arrange the facts in order, but we cannot fully explain them.

PROBLEMS

1. Why has the sequence of strata in northern Pennsylvania, between the coal measures and the marine Devonian, been considered Mississippian? Why not include this sequence in the Catskill facies of the Devonian? Why not give both sets of rocks, in New York and in Pennsylvania, the name Old Red Sandstone? (Tentative answers, based on the summary statements in Chaps. 3 and 6, may need revision after Chaps. 11 and 12 have been read.)

2. Discuss the origin of the Michigan Basin. Can the depression or excavation of the Precambrian bedrock have occurred before Cambrian time, perhaps as a result of meteoritic impact? Was a pre-existing basin filled with Paleozoic sediments? If this was not the sequence of events, what was the history of the Basin, and what is the evidence?

REFERENCES

1. P. B. King: *The Evolution of North America,* 190 pages (Princeton University Press, 1959)

2. P. B. King: *The Tectonics of Middle North America,* 203 pages (Princeton University Press, 1951)

3. Pittsburgh Geological Society: *Field Guidebook of Appalachian Geology, Pittsburgh to New York,* 110 pages (Am. Ass. Petrol. Geol., New York, 1955)

4. Marshall Kay: *North American Geosynclines,* Memoir 48, Geol. Soc. Am., 143 pages (1951)

5. Douglas Johnson: *Geomorphology of the Central Appalachians,* Guidebook 7, 16th Int. Geol. Cong., 50 pages (Washington, 1932)

6. P. E. Potter and Raymond Siever: "Sources of Basal Pennsylvanian Sediments in the Eastern Interior Basin," Journal of Geology, vol. 64, pp. 225–244, 317–335 (1956)

7. H. L. Alling and L. I. Briggs: "Stratigraphy of Upper Silurian Cayugan Evaporites," Bulletin, Am. Ass. Petrol. Geol., vol. 45, pp. 515–547 (1961)

8. H. P. Woodward: "Preliminary Subsurface Study of Southeastern Appalachian Interior Plateau," Bulletin, Am. Ass. Petrol. Geol., vol. 45, pp. 1634–1655 (1961)

CHAPTER 7

Correlation by Fossils

CORRELATION—the relating to each other of two or more rock masses that are thought to have about the same age—may be achieved locally in more than one way, as we found in Chapter 4. But for long-distance correlations, and hence for coordinated geologic history of the whole earth, the kind of correlation that makes use of fossils is by far the commonest and the most significant. In Chapters 5 and 6 we assumed without discussion a whole series of correlations by fossils between North American sections and the European type section described in Chapter 3. Only by making these assumptions could we use the terms Cambrian and Permian and Triassic for American rocks.

Locally, especially in the Grand Canyon region, it seemed that, after Steno's first law—superposition—had given the age succession in a single section, the obvious continuity of the rock layers for tens or hundreds of miles would justify time correlations in which fossils were not involved. But we soon found that, even in the Grand Canyon, the time significance of correlations from place to place, in what appears to be the same rock layer, may be questioned. In the Cambrian System the fossil zones cut obliquely across the Bright Angel shale at a slight angle to the base of the formation (Fig. 5-6). The fossil species were used as guides to time correlations, and then interfingering beds

of limestone and shale that corroborated the fossil evidence were found.

Now we must examine the assumption that fairly precise long-distance time correlation through the use of fossil taxa is possible and also estimate the degree of refinement that can be achieved. We are interested in the correlation not only of systems—the placing of the American Permian on the same stratigraphic level as the Russian Permian, for example—but also of smaller units. Did the supposed Middle Cambrian trilobites, on which we relied for correlations between rock facies in the Grand Canyon, appear, here and elsewhere, only after the extinction of the trilobites that are considered guides to the Lower Cambrian? Just how minutely can the strata be divided into fossil-controlled units? Are these units time-stratigraphic?

7-1. Guide Fossils

Correlation by fossils involves two steps: the first is to discover changes in the successive fossil faunas (or floras) at one locality; the second is to learn how to use those changes in correlating one local column with another. Even though most fossil faunas are probably only minor relics of the original populations, the changes in them at successively higher levels are presumed to represent fairly the evolutionary or other changes in those populations. As we study the faunas, we ask ourselves two kinds of questions: Paleontologically, what can we learn about the faunas? (For one thing, we may get hints concerning the way evolution occurred.) Stratigraphically, to what extent can the local geologic columns be subdivided, and what does the subdivision mean?

Subdivision of the column depends primarily on how fossiliferous the rocks are and how clearly the succession is exposed. If the faunas are composed of many species, each represented by many individuals, we must choose between two possible methods of work: (1) statistical study of a large sample of each fauna (or a large sample of the ammonites or brachiopods or other selected group), a procedure that has been excessively slow; (2) use of selected guide species (or genera), the usual procedure. Computers now being available for making the calculations, statistical studies have become practical, but they are not yet numerous enough to be used as bases for general statements. We must stick chiefly to selected guide species or genera.

When similar successions of faunas or guide taxa are found, especially if they are in widely separated areas, such as Europe and North America, the similarity may be called **homotaxis,** a term based on Greek roots and meaning "the same arrangement." If a pair of closely similar faunas can then be proved to have lived during the same time interval, they are said to be **synchronous,** a term derived from Greek roots and meaning "formed at the same time." The enclosing strata are then linked in **time correlation.*** The correlated

strata are said to occur at the same **stratigraphic horizon.** (Alternatively, since the strata in question have real and variable thicknesses, the term "horizon" may be used for the bases or the tops of the correlated strata.) If we find the same fossil fauna or the same guide species in northwestern Europe and northeastern North America, we may, after weighing other possibilities, decide that the enclosing strata represent the same horizon and should be time-correlated.

Having decided to use guide fossils rather than whole faunas, we must pick the kind or kinds of fossils to use. The ideal group of guides would be one that had evolved rapidly, occurred abundantly in all kinds of stratified rocks, and was worldwide in distribution. The fossils that approach this ideal most closely are the Ordovician-Silurian graptolites, the upper Paleozoic fusuline foraminifers, the upper Paleozoic goniatitic ammonoids, and the ammonites of the three Mesozoic systems. The ammonites seem to be the best of the lot. Among the Mesozoic systems, the Jurassic seems to be the most fossiliferous, with the best preservation and the most favorable set of well-studied exposures, that of northwestern Europe. Almost every aspect of stratigraphic subdivision by the use of guide fossils can be illustrated from the Jurassic System.

7-2. *Stratigraphic Zones*

The Jurassic has been divided and subdivided, into stages and substages, zones and subzones. We shall take as our starting point the stratigraphic zone. It is true that zones were not the first divisions of the Jurassic to be invented: several of William Smith's formations were put together to form the Jurassic System (compare Chap. 3). Then, between 1842 and 1849, Alcide d'Orbigny, using ammonites primarily, reversed the process and divided most of the Jurassic into ten paleontologically defined stages. Finally, the stages were divided into about sixty zones by d'Orbigny and others, notably (1856–1858) by

---

* The term "homotaxis" was invented and the distinction between it and "synchronism" was emphasized in 1862 by Thomas Henry Huxley, the man who popularized Darwinism. Huxley asserted that "a Devonian fauna and flora in the British Islands may have been contemporaneous with Silurian life in North America, and with a Carboniferous fauna and flora in Africa." Among the principal objectives of this chapter are demonstrations of the value of Huxley's distinction and the incorrectness of his assertion.

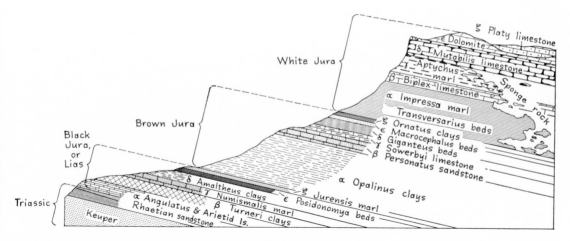

Fig. 7-1. *Generalized Jurassic section for the Swabian Alb and other parts of southwestern Germany, showing facies variations in the Upper Jurassic. (After Edgar Dacqué, 1915.)*

Albert Oppel of Germany. Oppel had a single nearly complete section to use as a standard (Fig. 7-1).

a. The Zonal Concept

A **zone** is made up of a succession of strata characterized by a particular assemblage of fossils. This definition is vague and avoids the vital question of time, but it has proved easy to use. We shall come back to the possible time significance of a zone.

The implications of the zonal concept are grasped most easily in connection with an idealized example. First, we study in detail a sequence of beds at one locality, *A*. We study and identify the fossils, bed by bed, emphasizing, in the Jurassic, the ammonites. Almost always the ammonite succession is discontinuous; the section yields several distinct, successive faunas. We choose one member of each fauna as a special index species and use its name to label the fauna. The ranges of the faunas do not usually coincide with rock boundaries: frequently a fauna is restricted to a small part of a thick clay or shale; less commonly the range of one fauna involves several beds, such as a shale, a sandstone (perhaps non-fossiliferous), and part of another shale. We call the set of beds with a single fauna a **zone**.

We repeat the process at a second exposure, *B*. The rock succession is different, but the faunal succession has elements in common with that at *A*. In particular, some of the faunal zones established at *A* can be recognized at *B*, even though others cannot and vice versa. We go on thus, comparing faunal successions in ever widening geographical extent. We find that some of our faunas at *A* can be identified over distances of hundreds of miles but that others are very local. By synthesis of successive faunas of suitably wide extent we can construct a table of standard zones for a particular area, such as northwestern Europe, just as we constructed the standard geologic column in Chapter 3. The names of the standard zones are derived from those of faunal index species. One particular zone, named after the ammonite shown in Fig. 7-2AB, is called the Zone of *Parkinsonia parkinsoni* or merely the Parkinsoni Zone (No. 30 in Table C-1—that is, the first table of Appendix C). The Parkinsoni Zone is a set of strata, not a collection of fossils.

Now, returning to our starting point, *A*, we see that some of our original local zones at that place, including the Parkinsoni Zone, have become standard zones. Others, which proved to be less widespread, are attached, as subzones, to one or another of the standard zones. We

TABLE 7-1

Distribution of Ammonite Specimens in Bethel Brick Quarry at Bielefeld, Northwestern Germany*

Zone	Bed	Parkinsonia acris, raricostata	G. (Subgarantiana) depressa	G. (Subgarantiana) tetragona	G. (Subgarantiana) suevica	G. (Subgarantiana) alticosta	G. (Subgarantiana) subgaranti	G. (Subgarantiana) wetzeli	G. (Subgarantiana) trauthi	G. (Subgarantiana) pompeckji	G. (Subgarantiana) coronata	G. (Subgarantiana) cyclogaster	G. (Subgarantiana) subangulata	G. (Garantiana) garantiana	G. (Garantiana) dubia	G. (Garantiana) baculata	G. (Garantiana) althoffi	G. (Garantiana) filicosta	G. (Pseudogarantiana) minima	G. (Pseudogarantiana) dichotoma	Perisphinctids	Bigotites (species undetermined)	G. (Orthogarantiana) inflata	G. (Orthogarantiana) schroederi	G. (Orthogarantiana) densicostata	Strenoceras subfurcatum	Strenoceras bajocensis	Strenoceras latidorsatum	Strenoceras robustum	Strenoceras rotundum
Garantiana–Parkinsoni Transition	1																				1									
Upper Garantiana: 13 m, calcareous shale	3–4	6																			1									
	7		1^a	4	1																									
	8		1	3																										
	15		1	6		1																								
	16–17																				1									
	19																				1	2								
	21													1							1									
Lower Garantiana: 12 m, micaceous clay	22		1		2^a	1								1	1				1	1										
	23				1		1							1	1					2										
	24																													
	25							1^a																						
	26						1								4					8										
	27				4		2	1						1	1															
	A^b				2		3	2																						
	28						1	1	1^a																					
	29–32					6		4																						
	34									1	1			1	1															
	35											1		1	1															
	36												1						1		1									
	41																													
	42		1										1												2					
Subfurcatum: 4 m thick	Upper															2	3	4					2$^?$			5	15	2	11	
	Lower																1	4					2	1	4					4

^{a} Close to the species listed.

^{b} Here are listed specimens from nodules at about this horizon.

* Modified from Bentz (Ref. 6). Bentz did not use the term Garantiana Zone. W. J. Arkell (Ref. 11) assigned Beds 2–21 to the Garantiana Zone but considered Beds 22–42 passage beds between the Subfurcatum and Garantiana Zones.

may find, moreover, that not all the standard zones are represented at A. That is, the section at A may not be paleontologically complete; it may contain paleontological lacunas. Of the non-fossiliferous beds between zones (not those contained within zones) we can say nothing.

Note (1) that we need, for the recognition of a zone, both rocks and fossils; (2) that a zone is characterized by an *assemblage* of species (especially that of the type locality), and that the index species may be rare or missing at a particular locality; (3) that the decision to call some units zones and other units subzones is a matter of convenience, based usually on geographical extent; (4) that the existence of a standard-zone table implies widespread homotaxis; (5) that such homotaxis, if it is explainable only in terms of synchronism (time correlation), makes the standard-zone table a table of time correlation also, each zone being made up of the rocks deposited during the time when the group of zonal guide fossils was living, a time different from that of any other zone in the table.

Zones are always paleontologically bounded. At a particular place, the kind of rock may change at a zone boundary, but the change can be used only as a local guide in mapping the boundary. If one wishes to show individual faunal zones on a map, the making of the map is likely to involve an enormous amount of paleontological study. Ordinarily a geological map shows the boundaries between rock units, such as shales and limestones; zones are then represented only on local sections or in diagrammatic charts compiled from the sections.

b. Recognition of Zones

The first table of standard Jurassic zones was set up for northwestern Europe by Oppel in 1856 (Ref. 3). Now forty-one Northwest European Lower and Middle Jurassic zones are commonly recognized (Table C-1), each with its ammonite guide species and each named for one of these species.

The recognition of zones at a particular place can be illustrated by a specific example.

The place is a brick quarry in clay and shale near Bielefeld in northwestern Germany (Table 7-1). One standard zone lies at the base of the section, and a second apparently includes almost all the overlying beds exposed in the quarry. Standard Zone 28 (Table C-1), at the base of the exposed section, is characterized by eleven specimens of the index species *Strenoceras subfurcatum* (Fig. 7-2E), found throughout the four meters of the zone that could be seen here. This zone is here divided paleontologically into two parts (possible subzones), the lower characterized by the presence of several species of *Strenoceras*, the upper by the presence of the *Garantiana* subgenus *Orthogarantiana*. The next twenty-five meters are assigned more or less certainly to Standard Zone 29, though only four specimens of the index species, *Garantiana garantiana* (Fig. 7-2CD), were found. The contrast between the ammonite species of the two zones is a striking one. *Strenoceras* is here limited to the lower zone and most species of *Garantiana* to the upper one. The Garantiana Zone itself can be divided into two parts, for perisphinctids (similar to Fig. 7-2FG) are limited to an upper unit (Beds 2–21, a possible subzone) and the subgenus *Pseudogarantiana* to a lower unit (Beds 22–42, a second possible subzone). In Bed 1, at the top of the quarry section, two species of *Parkinsonia* are associated with two species of *Garantiana* and a single perisphinctid, making up a fauna that appears to be transitional from the Garantiana to the Parkinsoni Zone.

At Bielefeld the Garantiana Zone is vaguely bounded. At the top there is a mixed fauna; and Bed 42, at the base of the zone, might as well be placed in the Subfurcatum Zone, for its single ammonite species is common to the two zones.

c. Ammonite Evolution, Lacunas, and Short-distance Correlation

Thus far the ammonite species and genera have been assumed to be clean-cut units, easily distinguished from all others. For some guide species (and genera) in the Northwest Euro-

Fig. 7-2.   *Selected Jurassic guide ammonites; for list of zones, see Appendix C. (A–D, from Photographic Unit, University College, London; C and D, from Alfred Bentz, 1928; E, H, and I, from J. H. Callomon, London; F and G, from W. J. Arkell, 1956, via J. M. Edmonds, Oxford.)*

A,B. Parkinsonia parkinsoni, *Zone 30, Dorset, England; 125 mm across.*

C,D. Garantiana garantiana, *Zone 29, Calvados, France; 82 mm across.*

E. Strenoceras subfurcatum, *Zone 28, Auerbach, Bavaria, Germany; 30 mm across.*

F,G. Perisphinctes plicatilis, *Upper Jurassic (Oxfordian), Berkshire, England; 100 mm across.*

H,I. Oppelia aspidoides, *Zone 26, Württemberg, Germany; 100 mm across.*

pean Jurassic section this is quite true. Some of the commonest ammonites, however, exhibit continuous or nearly continuous evolutionary changes from one species to another, and some of these vaguely bounded species are used as guide fossils. Such forms are important for our understanding of the zones.

An ammonite succession near the city of Peterborough, England, involving 3,035 specimens assigned to the genus *Kosmoceras*, was studied statistically by Roland Brinkmann of Germany in the late nineteen-twenties (Ref. 7). Specimens of *Kosmoceras* are the commonest fossils here, but other ammonites are also present, as well as members of other animal groups, including numerous pelecypods. Brinkmann collected from about forty-two feet of the formation called the Oxford Clay (Smith's Clunch Clay in our Chap. 3), in a group of brick pits, and recorded the height of each occurrence above the base of the succession. The four *Kosmoceras* sequences are summarized as a pictorial diagram in Figure 7-3. Fourteen *Kosmoceras* species were distinguished in the material collected from the walls of the pits. The successive forms in each

sequence—each evolutionary lineage—are very similar, as shown in Figure 7-4, representing the *aculeatum* branch of the last lineage of Figure 7-3. Gradation is so prevalent in each lineage that the number of species might conceivably have been reduced to four, one for each lineage, or even to two if the curious prongs called lappets are sexual features. In these sequences the number of species is somewhat arbitrary. Yet the species names used in Figure 7-3 are worth keeping. Most of them have been recognized for a century or more,

Fig. 7-3. *Evolutionary sequences in* Kosmoceras *from Oxford Clay at Peterborough, England.* (*Adapted from Ref. 7.*)

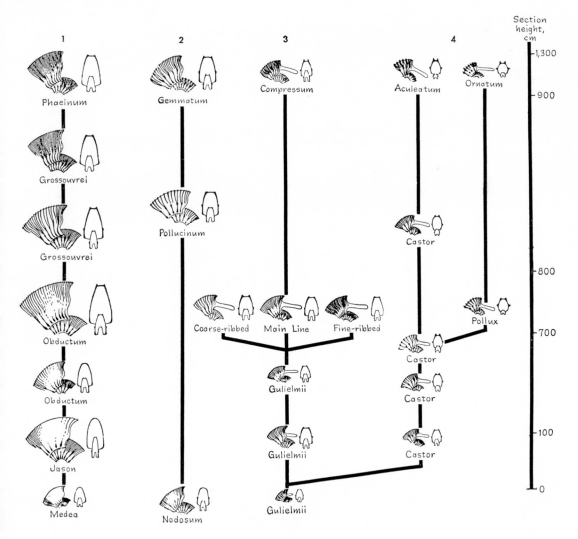

A   B   C   D

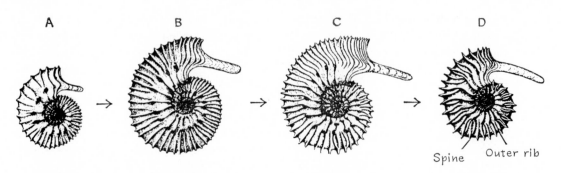

Spine   Outer rib

Fig. 7-4. *Evolution of one of the lappeted lineages of* Kosmoceras *at Peterborough. (Modified slightly from Ref. 7.)*
    A. *312 cm above the reference level.*   C. *988 cm above the reference level.*
    B. *670 cm above the reference level.*   D. *1,277 cm above the reference level.*

and, despite the gradations, they are useful in distinguishing four zones, 37–40 inclusive, in Table C-1.

A notable feature of Brinkmann's study was the discovery, from statistics, of lacunas in the sedimentary record. The lacunas are indicated by breaks in the statistical means (averages) of the measured features of the shells. An especially sharp break was found at 1,093.5 cm (centimeters) above the base of the succession, at the top of Zone 39 (Table C-1), at a thin white coquina composed of ammonite fragments. A break at this level was shown by several measurements, involving at least three of the four lineages of Figure 7-3. An example is furnished by the ratio of the number of outer ribs to the number of peripheral spines. In Figure 7-4 one sees that a change occurred between the approximately 1/1 ratio at *C* (a shell from the 988-cm level) and the approximately 2/1 ratio at *D* (a shell from the 1,277-cm level). The detailed statistics, represented graphically by Figure 7-5A, in which the rib-spine ratio is plotted against height above the base of the stratigraphic succession, show that a large part of the change occurred at 1,093.5 cm. In Figure 7-5B the break is eliminated and the graph is transformed into a somewhat hypothetical plot of rib-spine ratio against time, with the aid of two assumptions: (1) that the clay at Peterborough was deposited at a uniform rate; (2)

that the ammonite coquina represents a long period during which clay was not deposited at all. There is, then, so far as the clay is concerned, a depositional lacuna at 1,093.5 cm. The figure suggests that this lacuna stands for a time as long as that required for the deposition of 80 cm (2.5 feet) of clay at the normal rate.

Another investigator (J. H. Callomon, Ref. 10) has found that part of the Peterborough *Kosmoceras* succession is paralleled in the Oxford Clay near Oxford, seventy miles southwest of Peterborough. Callomon used only about 200 complete specimens of *Kosmoceras* in his statistical work, instead of Brinkmann's 3,035, but they were in a single succession and adequate for the use to which they were put. The changes in shell size and sculpture show that 500 cm (16+ feet) of lower Oxford Clay near Oxford are equivalent to 135 cm (4+ feet) at the bottom of the Peterborough section. The number of shell coquinas is not the same in the two sections, but at least one coquina, and the corresponding lacuna, are present at corresponding positions in the two sections, despite the seventy miles of separation and the changes in thickness of the strata involved. The similarities show that the Peterborough section is not merely local, but the dissimilarities show that the Peterborough lacunas do not all extend throughout central England.

d. The Northwest European Province

The zones found at Bielefeld and in central England have also been recognized elsewhere in northwestern Europe, notably in other parts of Germany and England, in eastern France, and in the Jura Mountains of Switzerland (Table C-2, columns 1–5). The geographic ranges of the different zones are so similar that we may profitably recognize a Northwest European Province for Lower and Middle Jurassic ammonite faunas (Fig. 7-6).

The Lower and Middle Jurassic zones of the Northwest European Province form a succession of flat-lying sheets on the European platform and extend also into adjacent deformed areas. On the platform, they crop out in one belt that crosses England from southwest to northeast, including Oxford; in a second belt that almost surrounds the Paris Basin; and in plateaus on both sides of the Rhine, in south-

Fig. 7-5. *Ratios between numbers of outer ribs and peripheral spines for part of the* Kosmoceras *sequence illustrated in Fig. 7-4: (a) plotted stratigraphically; (b) expanded to show the relative length of time represented by the lacuna at 1,093.5 cm. (After Ref. 7.)*

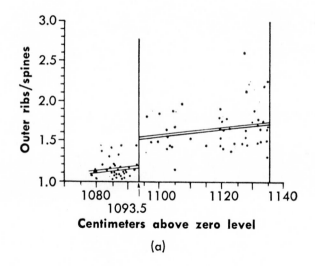

(a)

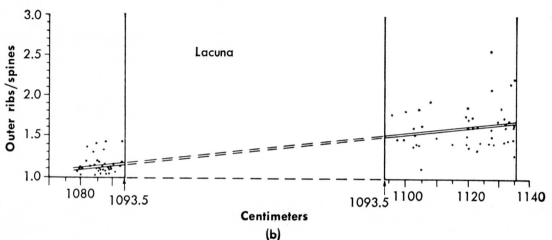

(b)

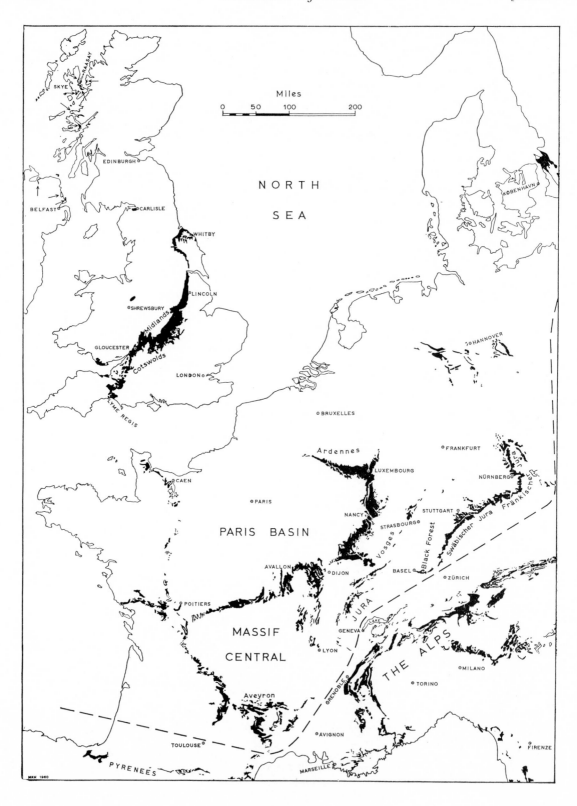

Fig. 7-6. *Map showing Lower Jurassic (Lias) outcrops in northwestern Europe. Hannover is in northwestern Germany, the Swäbischer Jura in southwestern Germany; dashed line is limit of Northwest European Province. [From Ref. 15, reproduced by courtesy of the Trustees of the British Museum (Natural History).]*

eastern France and southwestern Germany. The slightly-to-moderately folded and faulted portions of the province are at the edges of the northwest German basin (the Bielefeld area) and in the Jura Mountains on the French-Swiss border. Altogether, the Northwest European Province is 700–1,000 miles in diameter, about as large as the part of the United States that lies east of the Mississippi River between the latitude of Chicago and New York, on the north, and that of Vicksburg and Charleston, on the south.

Provincial, rather than worldwide, faunas (and floras) have prevailed since the begin-

ning of Cambrian time, though the degree of provincialism has varied greatly. Early and Middle Jurassic times were less provincial than most others.

7-3. Distinction Between Time-stratigraphic and Biofacial Zones

a. Time-stratigraphic and Biofacial-stratigraphic Units

We must now establish criteria by which we can determine the significance of the Northwest European Lower and Middle Jurassic zones. Is each zone a time-stratigraphic unit, formed during a distinct part of geologic time, later than that represented by any part of any zone lower in the zone table (Table C-1) and earlier than any part of any zone higher in the table? Or may some pairs of zones be local or biofacial equivalents, with faunas that are different because of isolation by physical barriers or of differences in depth of water, tempera-

Fig. 7-7. *Time-stratigraphic and biofacial-stratigraphic units.*

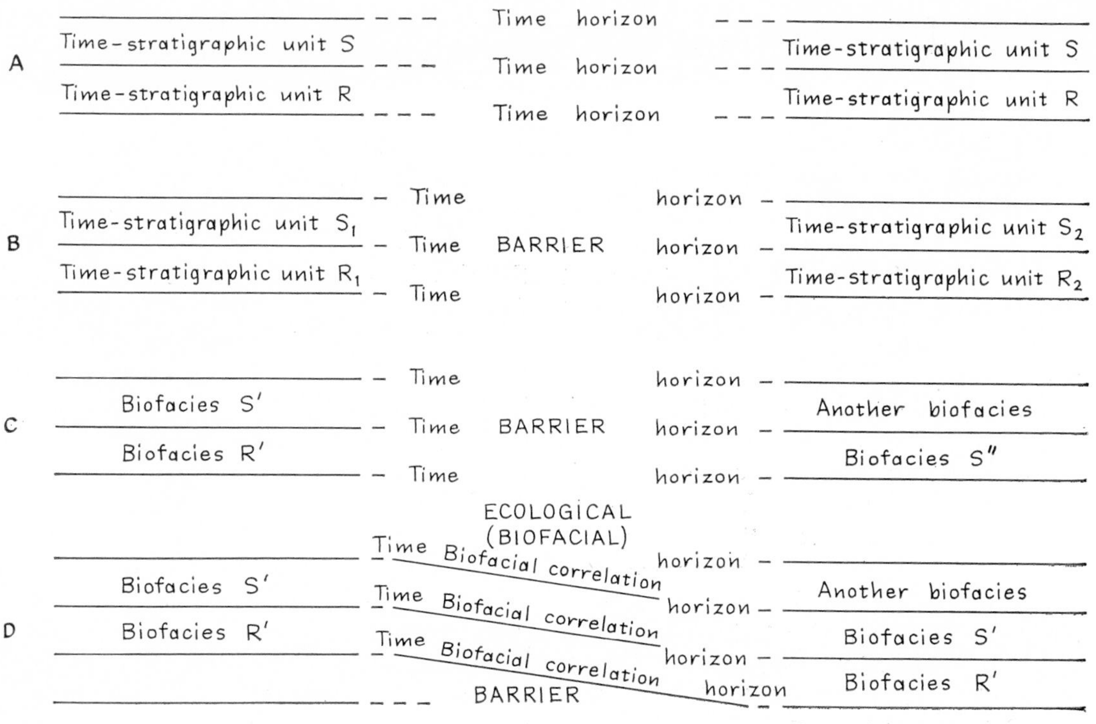

ture, or bottom conditions at the times of their formation? If the zones are time-stratigraphic, is their usefulness limited to northwestern Europe, or is it worldwide, or is it intermediate between these extremes?

Some of the possible relations between local columns are represented diagrammatically in Figure 7-7, which was devised for marine faunas (like the Jurassic ones in question). If the boundaries of a zone can be shown to be time horizons, the zone is a time-stratigraphic unit. If there are no known geographic limits to its extent, it may be represented schematically by the two correlated columns of Figure 7-7A. If the zone has only provincial extent and seems to be bounded by deep ocean, land, or other barriers, it may be represented by such a unit as S_1 in Figure 7-7B and may have a dissimilar but recognizably contemporaneous analogue, S_2, beyond the barrier. Biofacies co-existing on opposite sides of a barrier, with the two most similar facies, S' and S'', non-contemporaneous, are represented in Figure 7-7C. Finally, the way a variable environmental condition, such as depth of water, may lead to the misleading correlation of non-contemporaneous strata is shown in Figure 7-7D. We shall give more details about biofacial zones, especially depth zones, in the next section.

A doubt about time correlation through the use of fossils that has occurred to many persons is not represented in the foregoing discussion. This doubt is based on the obvious slowness with which many marine animals get about. Would not evolutionary changes that occurred in England appear later in France and Germany, to say nothing of eastern Asia and North America, because of the slow migration of any new form? The rate of migration of extinct mollusks, such as ammonites, is obviously hard to determine, but we can make some rough comparative estimates. The migration of marine invertebrates between two localities in the same shallow-water belt is represented schematically in Figure 2-15, in which four units of time are required for migration from L1 to L2. If the distance is a thousand miles, data on the present migration

of marine clams and snails (Chap. 2) show that the time unit is likely to be 1,000 years or less, certainly not hundreds of thousands or millions of years. In Chapter 8 we shall show that the time for the deposition of the whole Jurassic System was probably about 50,000,000 years. If we divide the Jurassic into about sixty zones (41 for the Lower and Middle Jurassic, 20+ for the Upper), the average zone, which, so far as we yet know, may be only a stratigraphic measure of *local* time, probably required between 800,000 and 900,000 years for its deposition. That is, if the ammonites got around as quickly as the clams and snails (and they probably did), the establishment of a new zonal fauna throughout northwestern Europe was, in terms of geologic time measured by zones, practically instantaneous. One may conclude that the broad distribution of an ammonite or other marine guide species can be prevented only by a barrier of some sort. That is, dissimilar faunas are either biofacial or time-stratigraphic.

b. Biofacial Zones

If zonal faunas recur in a single rock succession, as Upper Devonian faunas do in central New York (Fig. 6-6), the zones must be biofacial rather than time-stratigraphic units. Biofacial zones recognized in this or other ways occur at several levels in the geologic column. They are easiest to deal with in the youngest rocks, where many forms are indistinguishable from species living today and therefore have known ecological relationships (§ 2-12).

Biofacial change in a single area of deposition can be caused by climatic change affecting that area. A probable example is furnished by successive shallow-marine Pleistocene beds containing alternately warm and cold molluscan faunas at many places along the east and west coasts of North America and also in other parts of the world. No doubt these faunas, in the northern hemisphere, moved south during glacial epochs and north during interglacial periods. Almost all the species are living somewhere along the same coasts today, the cold-water species in the north and the

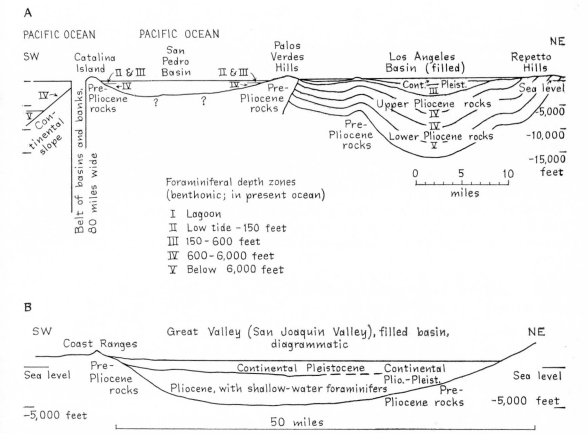

A

PACIFIC OCEAN　　　PACIFIC OCEAN

Foraminiferal depth zones
(benthonic; in present ocean)

  I　Lagoon
 II　Low tide – 150 feet
III　150 – 600 feet
IV　600 – 6,000 feet
 V　Below 6,000 feet

B

Fig. 7-8.　*Foraminiferal facies in the Pliocene and Pleistocene of California.*
    A. *Diagrammatic section across the Los Angeles Basin, southern California, and the sea floor offshore, with foraminiferal zones of the rocks and the living benthos.*
    B. *Diagrammatic section across the Pliocene-Pleistocene strata of the San Joaquin Valley, California (shallow-marine and continental).*

warm-water species in the south. But, as we shall learn in Chapter 16, all the species are likely to occur in deeper and cooler offshore water somewhat south of their inshore, shallow-water range; that is, temperature seems to control their occurrence. There can be no doubt that these molluscan species, which are still living, are facies fossils in their Pleistocene occurrences rather than guides to some particular parts of Pleistocene time, but there may be some uncertainty whether, at any particular place, the facies succession is due to climatic change or to change in the depth of the water in which the Pleistocene animals lived. In either case, the Pleistocene facies

successions at different localities are homotaxial rather than synchronous.

In other biofacial successions, depth may be treated as the variable factor, though temperature differences are involved. Examples are to be found in the Los Angeles and Ventura Basins of southern California. Each of these basins is some 25 by 50 miles in horizontal dimensions, and in each the sediments and faunas have been studied thoroughly in connection with oil-field exploitation (Ref. 13). The Pliocene and Pleistocene strata, made up of alternating beds of sandstone, shale, and minor marginal conglomerate (Fig. 7-8A), are from 10,000 to 20,000 feet thick. The Foraminifera characteristic of the Pliocene and Pleistocene zones are shown in Figure 7-9. In both basins these species are locally satisfactory guide fossils. The zones occur in the same order in the two basins and are of comparable thickness. They conform to the structure shown in Figure 7-8A, just as do the sandstone layers that are the reservoir rocks of the numerous oil fields. But the foraminiferal assemblages found as fossils in the basins are also found living offshore at different depths (left side of Fig. 7-8A). In a way, the order offshore is the same as in the rocks. The shallowest foraminiferal fauna of the oil-well sequence is found on the sea floor in shallow water, and the oil-field zones follow in order down the slope of the sea floor, with some members of the deepest oil-well foraminiferal assemblage living in the deeper offshore basins and on the

continental slope at depths greater than 3,500 or 4,000 feet. The very few extinct species in the basin strata, perhaps eleven species out of 150, are almost all in the two lowest fossil zones. Apparently all the zones in the rocks, including the lowest, are primarily *depth zones*, each distinguished by the faunal facies of a particular depth—namely, the depth of water at the time of deposition of the strata involved. Apparently the lowest strata, those containing several extinct foraminiferal species, were deposited in water more than 3,500 feet deep, and all the higher strata were deposited in shallower and shallower water as the basins filled. Some uncertainty exists, it is true, about the exact correspondence between the living facies and the fossil faunas, partly because of mixing by turbid flows, both in the strata and on the present sea floor. Despite the complica-

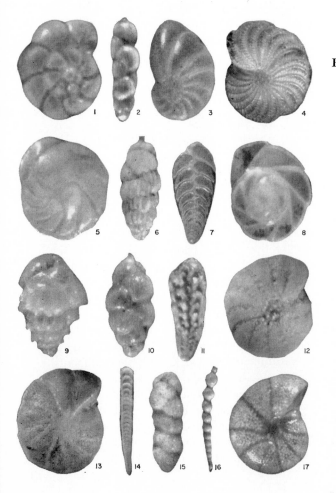

Fig. 7-9. *Foraminifers from the Pleistocene and Pliocene strata of the Los Angeles and Ventura Basins, southern California, selected, identified, and photographed by M. L. Natland. Specimens mostly between 1/2 and 1 mm in length or diameter.* **Upper Pleistocene** *of local usage, also living (in lagoons)*: 1, Ammonia beccarii. **Lower Pleistocene** *of local usage, also living (sublittoral, from low tide to 900-foot depth)*: 2, Uvigerina juncea; 3, Nonion grateloupi; 4, Elphidium crispum; 5, Cassidulina limbata. **Upper Pliocene** *of local usage, also living (upper bathyal zone, 900–2,000 feet)*: 6, Uvigerina peregrina; 7, Bolivina argentea; 8, Epistomella pacifica. **Middle Pliocene** *of local usage:* 9, Bulimina subacuminata, *also living (middle bathyal, 2,000–4,000 feet)*; 10, Uvigerina *species near* U. canariensis *of the living fauna;* 11, Bolivina sinuata, *extinct;* 12, Elphidium *new species, extinct.* **Lower Pliocene** *of local usage:* 13, Cibicides mckannai, *also living (low middle bathyal, 4,000–6,000 feet)*; 14, Plectofrondicularia californica, *extinct;* 15, Karreriella milleri, *extinct;* 16, Siphonodosaria insecta, *extinct;* 17, Nonion pompilioides, *also living (lower bathyal, perhaps 5,000–12,000 feet)*.

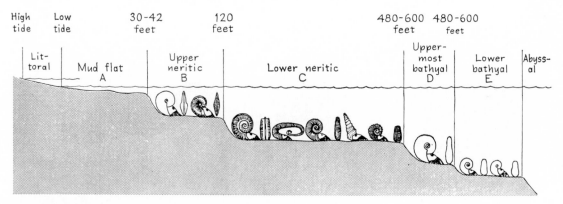

High tide	Low tide	30–42 feet	120 feet		480–600 feet	480–600 feet	
Lit-toral	Mud flat A	Upper neritic B	Lower neritic C		Upper-most bathyal D	Lower bathyal E	Abyss-al

Fig. 7-10. *Hypothetical depth zones for ammonites.* (*Redrawn from Gayle Scott,* JOURNAL OF PALE-ONTOLOGY, *1940.*)

tions, the foraminiferal zones in the rocks correspond approximately to depth facies in the present ocean.

Now, if we turn to a comparison between the two filled basins of southern California, the Los Angeles Basin of Figure 7-8A and the Ventura Basin a few tens of miles to the northwest, we have an example of homotaxis of foraminiferal zones that does not necessarily involve synchronism. We do not know whether any particular facies zone was deposited at the same time in both basins, though the identical extinct species in the lowest zones of the Pliocene rocks may justify time correlation for these zones.

Even if the depth-zone foraminifers are good local guides to relative age in both southern California basins, they are worthless for time correlation with other regions. This has been demonstrated by comparisons with the faunas found in the Neogene strata of the Great Valley of California, 200–300 miles to the north (Fig. 7-8B). All the Pliocene beds in the Great Valley contain assemblages of shallow-water foraminifers, assignable to living species. It is impossible, with Foraminifera alone, to develop even a homotaxial parallelism between subdivisions of the Pliocene strata of the Great Valley and the zones set up for the southern California basins.

Facies fossils are harder to recognize in the older rocks. The stratigrapher feels his way, working back from the present. He can usually

avoid facies that merely indicate depth differences by looking for organisms whose structures (or relationships to living forms of known behavior) suggest the swimming or floating mode of life. The very fact of wide geographic distribution, essential for a guide species, suggests a mobility that is unlikely in organisms narrowly restricted in facies. If, in addition, the occurrences are in varied lithofacies, the organisms were surely not narrowly biofacial.

Among living shellfish, some genera or subgenera are associated with one lithofacies or one depth range, and rather closely related forms are associated with other depths of water or other bottom conditions. In an extinct group, such as the ammonites, the interpretation—even the recognition—of biofacies is more difficult. The ammonite facies that have been suggested are not accepted by all ammonite specialists.

The Jurassic ammonites of northwestern Europe, discussed earlier in this chapter, are found in most marine lithofacies and biofacies, though they did not penetrate behind coral reefs (compare Gressly's facies, Fig. 4-13) and are unknown in deltaic or estuarine deposits. Within the ammonite-bearing facies of the Northwest European and Western Tethyan provinces, the smooth globose genera *Lytoceras* and *Phylloceras* [depth(?) zone *E* of Fig. 7-10] are abundant in Tethyan (deep?) geosynclinal deposits of Jurassic and Creta-

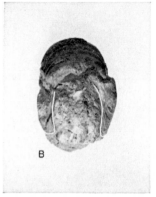
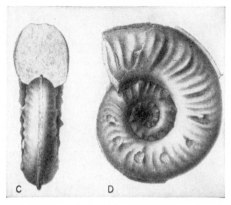

Fig. 7-11.   *Biofacial Middle Jurassic (Bajocian) ammonites; somewhat reduced.*
AB. *A representative of the stephanoid facies,* Otoites contractus, *Sherborne, Dorset, England: side and aperture views, with lappets and aperture outlined in white. (Courtesy of Dr. Raymond Casey, Geol. Survey, Great Britain.)*
CD. *A representative of the sonniniid facies,* Sonninia biplicata, *Somerset, England: edge and side views. (From J. H. Callomon, University College, London.)*

ceous ages but are almost unknown on the northwest European platform. A Texan named Gayle Scott, in 1940, attempted to show that in his home state other smooth forms [Fig. 7-10, depth(?) zone *D*], which were characteristic of certain Cretaceous marls and marly limestones, lived in moderately deep water, between depths of 480 and 600 feet, but that highly sculptured quadrate forms [Fig. 7-10, depth(?) zone *C*], found in marls, clays, chalk, and dense limestone, lived at the mostly shallower depths of 120–600 feet and that sharp-keeled ammonites [Fig. 7-10, depth(?) zone *B*], found in sandy limestones and sandy shales, lived at the still shallower depths of 30–120 feet. Scott's evidence was little more than suggestive, and since his time ammonites of his zone *D* have been found in a Fort Worth quarry associated with sea weeds and with genera of Foraminifera that today live attached to plants in shallow water.[*]

Gerd Westermann (Ref. 9) recognized two alternating ammonite facies in the calcareous-sandy clays of Middle Jurassic zones No. 26

and No. 27 (Table C-1), 200 feet thick, at Alfeld, east of Bielefeld, northwestern Germany. In one biofacies, stephanoid ammonites such as that shown in Figure 7-11AB are abundant; in the other biofacies, keeled sonniniid ammonites such as that shown in Figure 7-11CD. The stephanoid facies occurs thrice, the sonniniid twice, but the whole sequence can be divided satisfactorily between the two zones, partly because the guide species for both zones are stephanoids. Gayle Scott might have considered the sonniniid facies the shallower one, because its ammonites are rather sharply keeled, but the issue is still uncertain, to say the least.

The evidence concerning ammonite facies may be summarized in few words. The only ammonite biofacies that have been demonstrated by repetitions in a single section are the German ones just described, which are subzonal in magnitude. The major facies, such as the Tethyan one with *Lytoceras* and *Phylloceras,* are provincial in scope and may be the products of persistent regional conditions. The *Lytoceras-Phylloceras* fauna is geosynclinal and perhaps deep; the Northwest European Jurassic and Cretaceous faunas developed on

[*] Information furnished by Professor Claude Albritton of Southern Methodist University.

the continental platform and may have lived in shallower water.

For one specific case, the Oxford Clay between Peterborough and Oxford, we may attempt a more definite description of the environment, in a speculative way. The *Kosmoceras* living chamber is only about half a whorl, and therefore *Kosmoceras* was probably a swimmer, like *Nautilus* (compare § 2-13.d). We may imagine that *Kosmoceras* preyed on fish or other mobile animals near the surface of a sea a few hundred feet deep. When the individuals died, their shells sank slowly to the bottom, to accumulate along with the shells of bottom dwellers such as pelecypods and brachiopods. The ammonite shells were usually incorporated in the muddy bottom sediments, but during long periods of clear water, when mud was not deposited, the fragile shells accumulated in layers, which, crushed during subsequent compaction, made the thin shell-fragment coquinas.

7-4. Lower and Middle Jurassic Zones of Northwest Europe

a. Evaluation of the Zones

Most of the Northwest European Lower and Middle Jurassic zones are present throughout the area. They are everywhere in the same stratigraphic order. Despite some mild structural complexities here and there, all the successions are trustworthy; they correspond to the order of deposition. The crudest calculation of probabilities, after the fashion of § 1-2, would show that the uniform sequence in all the columns, without a single transposition, is extremely improbable as the result of chance. What, then, is the explanation of the uniform succession? Can the zones represent a series of depth facies, as in the southern California Upper Neogene?

The European Jurassic ammonite zones differ from the facies zones of the California Upper Neogene in several ways. The guide fossils, instead of being sedentary bottom forms with living relatives confined to depth zones, were probably active swimming ani-

mals of the *Nautilus-Kosmoceras* type. Moreover, ammonite shells may occasionally have been spread rather widely after the deaths of the animals, just as the shells of *Nautilus* are now carried as far as Japan, many hundreds of miles northeast of the animal's habitat. Finally, the unfailing ammonite homotaxis in the large European area contrasts with the failure of Upper Neogene foraminiferal homotaxis between the southern California basins and the Great Valley of California.

There seem to have been no barriers within the Northwest European Province during the Lower and Middle Jurassic (Ref. 11). There is little or no evidence that slowness of migration caused any local lag in faunal change. The nearly complete homotaxis throughout the faunal province, zone by zone, indicates easy intermigration between all parts of the northwest European area. The local evolution of successive faunas (Fig. 7-3) is especially important. If we take this indigenous evolution into account, it seems necessary to conclude that *Kosmoceras jason*, for example, spread over the whole area occupied by its zone (No. 38) before the fauna of the next higher zone came into existence. Perhaps the whole succession of changes in the Lower and Middle Jurassic ammonites occurred in similar consecutive fashion, though the evidence is not equally conclusive for all the zones.

The barriers at the margins of the Northwest European Province seem to have varied in effectiveness. Partial barriers (compare Fig. 2-15) seem to have existed, either intermittently or continuously, between the Lower and Middle Jurassic faunas of the northwestern European platform and the faunas of adjacent regions, such as the eastern European (Russian) platform and the Tethyan geosyncline of the Mediterranean region. The species of *Kosmoceras* characteristic of Zones 38 and 39 occur eastward into central Russia, where these zones also contain other species of the same genus, species that are not present in northwestern Europe. These geographic ranges are consistent with the existence of a directional filter so delicate that it was capable

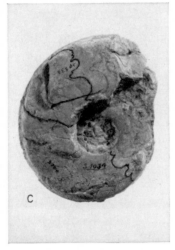

Fig. 7-12.   *Provincial guide fossils of the Lower Toarcian (Lower Jurassic).*
AB. Dactylioceras tenuicostatum, *Whitby, England; index species for Zone 15 (Table C-1). × 2/3. (British Museum photographs, courtesy Dr. M. K. Howarth.)*
CD. Bouleiceras nitescens, *Jebel Tuwaiq, Arabia; guide to the Lower Toarcian of the Ethiopian Province; note the simple suture. × 1/2. (Photographs of plaster cast of a W. J. Arkell specimen, figured 1952, by Photographic Unit of University College, London.)*

Fig. 7-13.   *Correlative Lower Jurassic (Sinemurian) ammonites of Europe and Mexico. (AB, British Museum photographs, courtesy of Dr. M. K. Howarth; C and F, H. K. Erben, 1956, photographs courtesy of Dr. Héctor Ochoterena F.; DE, Alpheus Hyatt, 1889.)*
AB. Echioceras raricostatum, *Radstock, Somerset, England. Diameter 69 mm. Index species for Zone 9 (Tables 7-2 and C-1).*
C. Echioceras densicosta, *Huayacocotla district, Veracruz, Mexico. Diameter 33 mm.*
DE. Coroniceras lyra, *Gmünd, Switzerland. Diameter 85 mm. Guide for Zone 4 (compare Table 7-2).*
F. Coroniceras pseudolyra, *Huayacocotla district, Veracruz, Mexico. Diameter 29 mm.*

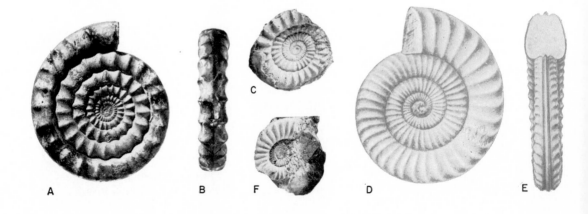

of letting some animals through while it barred the way to closely related animals. The directional aspect of the filtration may mean that currents flowed mostly toward the Russian part of the platform (compare Fig. 2-15C). Whatever the explanation, one might be somewhat less certain of the precise time correlation of Zones 38 and 39 between Russia and England than between two localities with more species in common, within northwestern Europe.

The Lower and Middle Jurassic faunas of northwestern Europe contain many guide fossils that appear suddenly in this region but are similar to persistent forms in the geosynclinal sediments of Tethys. An example is the flat "horn of Ammon" of Figure 7-12A. Apparently ammonite migration between Tethys and the platform was hampered by a partial (directional?) barrier of some sort, perhaps depth of water, perhaps temperature. One of the most interesting aspects of this relationship

is the removal of some of the mystery about the origin of the guide fossils that are strange invaders of the northwest European section. The guides that are closely related to persistent Tethys types probably came from Tethys.

b. Recognition of the Zones Elsewhere

Most of the European Lower and Middle Jurassic ammonite zones have been recognized, more or less certainly, at one or more places outside Europe, through the presence of their guide ammonites or closely related species. Take, for example, the Lower Jurassic correlations between Europe and east-central Mexico (Table 7-2). Note that Zones 4, 5, 9, and 10 are confidently correlated even though no index (zone-name) species is common to the two regions. Some Mexican species are similar to guides for the European zones; two examples are shown in Figure 7-13. There are difficulties with Zones 6, 7, and 8. Ammonites

TABLE 7-2

Lower Jurassic Correlations Between Northwestern Europe and Eastern Mexico[*]

STAGES	EUROPEAN AMMONITE ZONES	AMMONITE "FAUNIZONES" OF EAST-CENTRAL MEXICO
Pliensbachian	10. *Uptonia jamesoni*	*Uptonia* sp.
Sinemurian	9. *Echioceras raricostatum*	*Microderoceras bispinatum altespinatum* / *Echioceras burckhardti*
	?	*Pleurechioceras? james-danae* / *Pleurechioceras subdeciduum*
	8. *Oxynoticeras oxynotum*	?
	7. *Asteroceras obtusum*	[a] *Vermiceras bavaricum mexicanum*
	?	[b] *Oxynoticeras* sp.
	6. *Caenisites turneri*	?
	5. *Arnioceras semicostatum*	*Euagassiceras subsauzeanum* / *Arnioceras geometricoides*
	4. *Arietites bucklandi* (*Coroniceras* subzones)	*Coroniceras pseudolyra*

[a] Poor correlation.
[b] Perhaps equal to European Zone 8.

[*] The European column is based on Arkell (Ref. 11; cf. Table C-1), the Mexican column on Erben (Ref. 12).

similar to those of Zone 6 have not been recognized in Mexico. The author of Table 7-2 (H. K. Erben, Ref. 12) seriously considered correlating the *Oxynoticeras* sp. zone of Mexico with the Oxynotum Zone (Zone 8) of the European standard sequence, but finally chose the Zone 7 correlation shown—*Asteroceras-Vermiceras*. This drops *Oxynoticeras* two notches. The correlation presented in this table—or any other possible set of matches—leaves two zones in each region unmatched in the other.

The incomplete and contradictory character of the Liassic zonal homotaxis between east-central Mexico and western Europe is a representative (but unusually clear-cut) example of the difficulties encountered by those who attempt Mesozoic zonal correlations over long distances. It is apparent that larger and more generalized units are needed for worldwide correlation. These units will be described on later pages.

c. Conclusions

The conclusions about the Lower and Middle Jurassic zones of northwestern Europe that one can reach by generalizing from the data compiled by European stratigraphers may now be listed. These generalizations have been illustrated rather than proved in the preceding pages.

Conclusion 7-1: The Lower and Middle Jurassic zones of northwestern Europe are 41 sets of strata, characterized by 41 faunal assemblages, that occur in an orderly succession, Zone 1 at the bottom and Zone 41 at the top.

Conclusion 7-2: The 41 zones, which differ from one another in thickness and lithology and also vary in these respects from place to place, have differing horizontal dimensions. *Each, however, is represented over a large part of the whole area.* Most of the zones are found in at least a part of every major subdivision of the Northwest European Province (England, eastern France, etc., as shown in Table C-2).

Conclusion 7-3: Each zone is characterized by its assemblage of ammonite species and is independent of lithologic boundaries. Even specialists find lists of zone species hard to agree upon, but the Bielefeld faunas (Table 7-1) give some idea of the make-up of two assemblages. At least part of the zonal assemblage is present wherever the zone is recognized. Where no ammonites are present, commonly no zonal boundaries can be drawn. Exceptionally, as with Gressly's coral facies (§ 4-10.a), a non-ammonitic biofacies may be brought into at least approximate alignment with the ammonite zones.

Conclusion 7-4: The northwestern European Lower and Middle Jurassic zones, established on data from local sections, *are almost perfectly homotaxial throughout the region.* Correlations in the Oxford Clay between Peterborough and the vicinity of Oxford have been given as an example.

Conclusion 7-5: The northwestern European Lower and Middle Jurassic zones can be time-correlated throughout the region. That is, each zone was deposited during approximately the same portion of geologic time throughout its extent. This conclusion follows upon the elimination of other possibilities, especially that of biofacial zones. The evolutionary zonal succession at Peterborough is an important detail in the argument.

Conclusion 7-6: The individual northwestern European Lower and Middle Jurassic zones can be extended varying distances beyond the boundaries of the region, with varying degrees of confidence in the correlations. The European-Mexican comparison (Table 7-2) shows that the northwestern European column is not a complete standard for the world; it may contain large paleontological lacunas that represent measurable portions of geologic time. Outside Europe, species similar to, but not exactly the same as, the standard guide species frequently occur in the standard homotaxial order, and these differences are illustrated in the European-Mexican comparison. Such extra-European sequences are commonly considered satisfactory for time correlations with Europe. As a matter of fact, differences in contemporaneous faunas are to be expected, by analogy with the geographical faunal differences that exist today.

7-5. Mesozoic Stages

a. Lower and Middle Jurassic Stages

1. ZONES AND STAGES. The zones of Table C-1 are grouped into stages. Though stages were established before zones, a **stage** is most easily defined in terms of the zones that make it up. The Callovian Stage is made up of Zones 36–41, the Bathonian of Zones 31–35, etc. The Lower and Middle Jurassic stages used today (Table 7-3) are about the same as those established by d'Orbigny. The Middle Jurassic stages were based fairly closely on William Smith's formations. The Callovian Stage was named after Smith's Kelloways Stone, the name Callovian being a Latinization of Kelloways. The Bathonian Stage includes Smith's "Great Oolyte, or Bath Freestone," named from Bath, England, and also the "Forest Marble and Clay." The Bajocian is Smith's "Under Oolyte," but the type locality is across the Channel at Bayeux, Normandy. The four Lower Jurassic stages were all carved out of Smith's Lias clay, shale, and limestone, but the type localities for these four stages are in France and Germany. The stages have remained practically unchanged since 1864.

Since the stages are based on zones, they too are defined on a paleontological basis. Stages have boundaries that may cross formation boundaries obliquely, even in the type areas; stages may be represented by different lithologic facies in different areas; stages can be identified in isolated distant places—all because stages are based on guide fossils. These characteristics were clearly stated by d'Orbigny in 1850. A little later fossil zones were given their current definition by Oppel. In 1956, just before his death, the British stratigrapher W. J. Arkell said of the Jurassic stages: "As units of the single world scale of classification stages must be based on zones. . . . They are essentially groupings of zones, but they transcend zones both vertically and horizontally" (Ref. 11). Vertically, several zones make one stage. Horizontally, the characteristic zone assemblages of fossils may disappear, but the stage, or a substage such as the Upper Bajocian, may still be recognizable, as will be shown in subsequent paragraphs.

2. WORLDWIDE HOMOTAXIS. Sample Lower and Middle Jurassic columns in Asia and America are shown in Table 7-4. The Callovian is the only stage represented in all eight columns. The three lowest stages are absent

TABLE 7-3

Lower and Middle Jurassic Stages

STAGE	TYPE SEQUENCE
Middle Jurassic	
Callovian Stage[a]	Kelloways Stone and Oxford Clay, central England
Bathonian Stage	Oolitic limestone of Bath, England
Bajocian Stage	Oolitic and other limestones of Bayeux, northwestern side of Paris Basin, France
Lower Jurassic	
Toarcian Stage	Marls and shales of Thouars, southwestern side of Paris Basin, France
Pliensbachian Stage	Shale and marl, Pliensbach, southwestern Germany
Sinemurian Stage	Black limestone of Semur, southeastern side of Paris Basin, France
Hettangian Stage	Limestone of Hettange, near Metz on eastern side of Paris Basin, France

[a] Considered the lowest Upper Jurassic stage by many French, North American, and other stratigraphers.

TABLE 7-4

Eight Selected Non-European Lower and Middle Jurassic Columns (Marine Units Only)*

STAGE		1 CAUCASUS	2 ARABIA	3 KUTCH, INDIA	4 EAST GREENLAND	5 WESTERN CANADA	6 WYOMING	7 EASTERN MEXICO	8 CENTRAL AND SOUTHERN ANDES
MIDDLE JURASSIC									
Callovian	U	ss		ss			ss	ss	
	M	ss	ss	ss		ss		x	S
	L	ss		ss	ss	ss	ss		
Bathonian	U		ss?	ss?		ss?			
	M	S	ss	ss	S			S?	
	L		ss?					ss	
Bajocian	U	ss	ss						
	M	ss	ss		S	ss	ss	S	ss
	L	ss				ss			ss
LOWER JURASSIC (LIAS)									
Toarcian	U	S			ss	ss			ss
	L		ss		ss	ss			ss
Pliensbachian	U	S				S			
	L				ss			ss	ss
Sinemurian	U					ss?		ss	ss?
	L					ss		ss	ss
Hettangian						S			S

* U = Upper, M = Middle, L = Lower; S = stage present but substages more or less uncertain, ss = substage; x = fauna with both Middle and Lower Callovian elements.

from many areas but are quite fully represented in such widely separated regions as Europe (Table 7-3), western Canada, and the central and southern Andes. No extra-European column is complete, but each of three, in the Caucasus, western Canada, and the Andes, contains more than half of the worldwide (stage and substage) units. The unique completeness of the Northwest European column is in part, but only in rather small part, the result of Northwest Europe's position as the standard of comparison.

Substages became the units of worldwide correlation as a result of confusion caused by attempts at correlation by zones. In eastern Mexico, for example, some Sinemurian zones cannot be placed in the European sequence (Table 7-2), but Lower and Upper Sinemurian substages can be distinguished, with the two lowest Mexican zones in the Lower, the remainder in the Upper division. Even in the Caucasus and the Andes, where many Northwest European zones have been recognized, substages are the most rewarding units for general, systematic correlation. It is nevertheless noteworthy that nine European zones have been reported in the central and southern Andes, two-thirds of the way to the opposite side of the globe.

The Callovian Stage, here considered the uppermost stage of the Middle Jurassic, is especially interesting as a worldwide unit. Some standard Callovian zones are recognizable outside western Europe—for example, in the Caucasus. In most places, however, only substages or special superzones can be correlated with Europe. The most complex extra-European Callovian is in Kutch, India, at the northeastern edge of the Arabian Sea (Fig. 7-14), where the Upper Callovian is represented and the Middle and Lower Callovian have been divided into twelve local, paleontologically determined subdivisions. These twelve subdivisions can be grouped into three zones with some similarities to particular European zones; but *Kosmoceras* is absent, and many species are wholly Oriental in their relations.

In the southern hemisphere some of the most characteristic European Callovian genera do not exist, but the Callovian Stage can be recognized "by the general grade of evolution of the ammonite fauna as a whole and by a chain of overlapping correlations carried link by link round the world" (Arkell, Ref. 11, p. 12).

3. TIME CORRELATION FROM STAGE AND SUBSTAGE HOMOTAXIS. Arkell, in the statement just quoted, assumed (1) that the presence of the same guide ammonites at two localities provides sufficient evidence of synchronism and (2) that local "overlaps" of provincial ammonite guides are almost equally good evidence of synchronism. We must now consider whether the assumptions are justified.

With respect to the ammonite guides of the Lower and Middle Jurassic stages and sub-stages, we shall assume that facies variations within provinces have been taken care of at the zone level (compare earlier pages of this chapter). There seem to be two possible sources of significant error at the substage level: (1) different time ranges of the substage guides in two or more districts or provinces, as by survival in a distant province after extinction in the homeland, or vice versa; (2) misinterpretation of differences in the faunas of two provinces separated by a barrier.

We take the Toarcian Stage of the Lower Jurassic as an example. Typical Toarcian faunas can be followed round the world in the northern hemisphere (Fig. 7-14), from western Europe to the Donets Basin of southern Russia, the Caucasus, Iran, Baluchistan, Indonesia, Indo-China, Korea, Japan, Alaska, a Canadian Arctic island, eastern Greenland, and back to northwestern Europe. Everywhere European guide genera are found and in many places European guide species. *Grammoceras thouarsense* is a guide fossil for a zone in the midst of the stage at Thouars, France, the place that was the source of the name Toarcian. The same species is found, apparently at the same stratigraphic level, in the Toarcian of the Caucasus. Other west European guides also occur in the Caucasus, in about the standard order (the thick section has structural complexities, however, and definitive studies have not yet been made). In Japan the Toarcian zones are almost the same as in western Europe, with typical European genera but peculiar Japanese species. In eastern Greenland the Upper Toarcian substage and one Lower Toarcian zone can be distinguished, in part with European guide *species*. The Toarcian localities range in latitude from the equator (Indonesia) nearly to the North Pole (the Arctic island). The facies range from thin platform-type sheets of shale and limestone to thick geosynclinal strata with interbedded volcanics (Caucasus). In the Caucasus the shales and sandstones of this single Liassic stage, mostly but not entirely marine, have a total thickness of 15,000 or 20,000 feet.

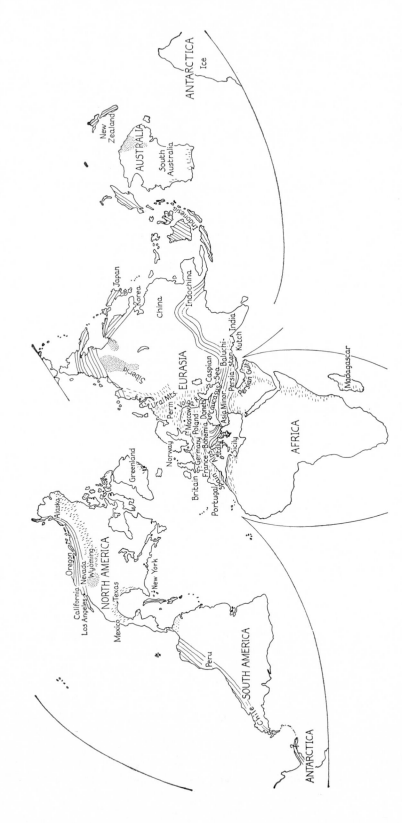

Fig. 7-14. *Map of the world on Bartholomew's modified regional projection, showing Jurassic geosynclines (continuous lines), epicontinental seas (dashes), and continental sediments (stippled). (Data from Roland Brinkmann, 1954, and Bernhard Kummel, 1961.)*

Two successive Toarcian faunas, characterizing Lower and Upper Toarcian substages, can be generally recognized. Let us imagine that each originated in northwestern Europe and migrated eastward round the world, evolving slowly as it migrated. By the time the migrants reached Japan, all might have become new species. Thus far the hypothesis seems to fit the facts. But evidence of the supposed eastward migration ends with Japan: the Japanese species did not get to Alaska or Greenland. The somewhat scanty facts suggest a different hypothesis: migration both east and west from an evolutionary center that may have included both Tethys and the European platform, with development of local species in distant, more or less isolated areas, such as Japan, but with communication sufficiently good and rapid to permit the earlier Toarcian fauna to be everywhere overwhelmed by the second soon after the second had become well characterized anywhere. This hypothesis explains the similar succession of Toarcian genera all round the world, in Japan as well as in Europe; that is, the evidence favors interpretation of the Toarcian homotaxis in Europe, Japan, etc. as evidence of the time correlation of the highly varied enclosing strata, substage by substage or even, in some places, zone by zone.

The Toarcian is a specially instructive stage, for one must work round the world with some care in order to find at all localities the same assemblage of typical European Lower Toarcian genera. A more southern course from Europe to the Indian Ocean yields a somewhat different set of results for the Lower Toarcian. This route goes from the Northwest European platform to Portugal and then jumps to Arabia, East Africa, and Madagascar, where, on the south side of Tethys, a peculiar fauna, containing *Bouleiceras* (Fig. 7-12CD) and other ammonites unlike anything in northwestern Europe, characterizes a province called Ethiopian by Arkell (Ref. 11). *Bouleiceras* is found with European guides in Portugal, and the Ethiopian Lower Toarcian fauna has Oriental affinities that perhaps make possible correlation with Baluchistan and eastern Asia, but these correlations are not as well established as those on the northern route. One cannot assert positively that the faunas called Lower Toarcian in the Ethiopian and Northwest European provinces were synchronous, but one can say that this time correlation is more probable than any other.

b. Middle and Upper Jurassic Provincialism

Ammonite provincialism considerably more marked than that of the Toarcian or any other Lower Jurassic stage begins in the Middle Jurassic and increases upward. The Oriental and other provincial peculiarities in the Callovian have already been mentioned. In the upper part of the Upper Jurassic three European provinces have become well defined: Northwest European, Tethyan, and Russian-Arctic or Boreal. Their zones and stages are given in Table C-3. The uppermost Jurassic faunas most satisfactory for worldwide homotaxis and time correlation are the Tethyan, with type localities in or near the Alps. For these uppermost Jurassic levels northwestern Europe cannot furnish a standard for the world. From the uppermost Bajocian on, in fact, there is less uniformity than in the lower part of the Jurassic. The fine exposures of Jurassic rocks in East Greenland, east of the great ice cap, illustrate the point. Above the continental plant-bearing lowermost Jurassic, three Pliensbachian and Toarcian zones and the Upper Toarcian substage contain the Northwest European guide fossils. Then come seven local ammonite zones, probably all Middle Jurassic, that have partial analogues on the Arctic islands but cannot be correlated with Europe or any other temperate region. These zones are overlain by the two lowermost Callovian zones, with European guide ammonites. Then there is a large lacuna, above which many Upper Jurassic zones have been recognized, with guide ammonites of the Northwest European or the Russian province.

The Russian-Arctic faunas may reflect a cold-water facies, though some of the genera

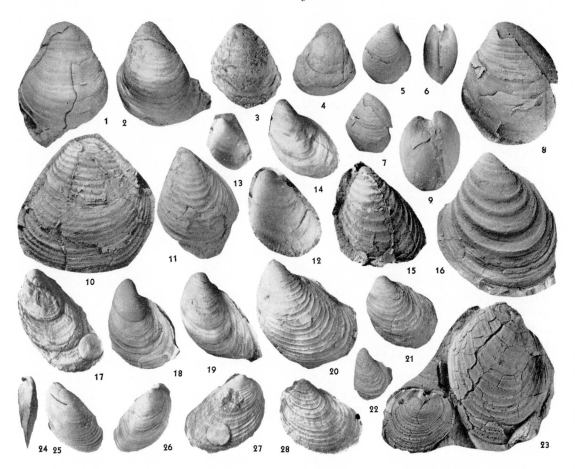

Fig. 7-15. Buchia (*and the related genus* Aucellina) *from the Upper Jurassic and Lower Cretaceous of western North America (mostly Alaska), somewhat reduced* (1–16, *Lower Cretaceous;* 17–28, *Upper Jurassic*): 1–9, Buchia crassicollis; 10–11, B. subokensis; 12–14, Aucellina; 15–16, Buchia okensis; 17, B. spitiensis; 18–19, B. mosquensis; 20–23, B. rugosa; 24–28, B. concentrica. (*Courtesy of R. W. Imlay, U.S. Geological Survey.*)

are known from widely separated parts of the great Pacific region, including California, Mexico, and New Zealand—particularly the very abundant oyster-like pelecypods assigned to the genus *Buchia* (Fig. 7-15; also called *Aucella*) and related genera. The Northwest European sequence (first column of Table C-3) may represent the alternation of cold-water and warm-water conditions, since northern ammonite genera appear in the Mediterranean at the base of the Oxfordian (lowest Upper Jurassic stage). Nonetheless, Upper Oxfordian coral reefs are present as far north as central England.

c. Precision in Determining the Base of the Jurassic

Recent improvements in the radiometric dating of rock masses (Chap. 8) make possible the estimation in years of the precision of horizons established through correlation by fossils. For a test of the precision of a world-wide horizon based on ammonite correlation, we take the base of the Jurassic.

Most worldwide Jurassic horizons are substages. The lowest stage, the Hettangian, however, is not formally divided into substages. The guide ammonites of the three Hettangian zones and six subzones are present in all parts of the Northwest European Province, but Hettangian ammonites are scarce almost everywhere else. No marine Hettangian is known in Australia, Africa, southwestern Asia, Russia, or Siberia. A few Hettangian ammonites have been found in Tibet, Japan, New Caledonia, and Alaska. *Psiloceras*, the guide genus for Zone 1 of Table C-1, has been found in loose blocks in the island of Babar, Indonesia, and in bedrock on the South Island of New Zealand and in Peru. *Psiloceras* (lower Hettangian) and *Schlotheimia* (upper Hettangian) are known from a limestone mass near Palermo, Sicily, and from an area 110 miles north of Vancouver, British Columbia. Near Luning, Nevada, a *Psiloceras* fauna (with *Schlotheimia* also present) occurs in a conformable shale-limestone sequence, thirty feet above Upper Triassic guides and seventy-five feet below Sinemurian guides (Ref. 8).

If the Jurassic System accumulated in 50,-000,000 years, as suggested earlier in this chapter, the sixteen worldwide stratigraphic units of the Middle and Lower Jurassic—mostly substages but including the Hettangian Stage as a single unit—had average lengths of approximately 2,000,000 years. The probable maximum difference between the ages of two Hettangian faunas is therefore about 2,000,000 years. Such an uncertainty would apply especially to the correlation of a *Psiloceras* fauna in one area with a *Schlotheimia* fauna in another. The age of the *Psiloceras* fauna near Luning, Nevada, might be considered somewhat closer to the age of the base of the system in Northwest Europe, possibly within 1,000,000 years, but such an estimate would not be safe, for clean-cut Hettangian substages have not been demonstrated.

An uncertainty of 2,000,000 years seems large in itself, but it should be thought of in connection with the probable age in years of the base of the Jurassic, which will be shown in Chapter 8, from radiometric data, to be approximately 180,000,000 years, perhaps ±15,-000,000 years. The probable variation of ages within the Hettangian Stage is therefore only about 1–1.2 percent of the age of the stage as a whole.

d. Jurassic Geographies

In a world view (Fig. 7-14), the most striking fact about Jurassic geographies is the emergent state of all the continents. Second is the strong development of two great geosynclinal belts: the Tethyan belt, extending from Portugal to the East Indies and perhaps to New Zealand, and the West American (Cordilleran) belt, extending from Alaska to southern Chile and perhaps to Antarctica (compare the columns of Table 7-4; columns 5 and 8 are largely geosynclinal). The geosynclinal belts are mostly marine, but the distribution of ammonite occurrences is spotty. The only broad and persistent Jurassic epicontinental sea was on the Northwest European platform, with an extension into Russia that was especially well developed in the Late Jurassic.

In Late Triassic time the continents were even more emergent than at any time during the Jurassic. Seaways were present only in a few geosynclinal areas, notably in the eastern Alps and in Nevada. At the end of the Triassic, the flooding of the Northwest European platform was completed rapidly, so that the marine-lagoonal Rhaetic beds (uppermost Triassic) were immediately and generally succeeded by the ammonite-bearing Hettangian and overlying Jurassic zones. Outside Europe, the Lias is a record of gradual marine expansion, with some oscillations, as suggested in the lower part of Table 7-4. With the Pliensbachian, the Caucasus geosyncline and the East Greenland troughs were flooded. The maximum spread of Jurassic seas was probably in the Callovian, with marine deposits on the Northwest European–Russian platform, in many parts of the Tethyan and Cordilleran geosynclines, and also in Arabia, East Africa, Madagascar, Japan, Spitsbergen, and East

Greenland, and on the Montana-Wyoming-Dakota platform.

e. Triassic and Cretaceous Homotaxis and Correlations

The Triassic and Cretaceous systems have been zoned, and the zones have been grouped into stages, in about the same way as the Jurassic. Ammonites are the principal marine guide fossils. Homotaxis for large parts of each system is worldwide. The marine Cretaceous is considerably more extensive than the Jurassic, the marine Triassic considerably less extensive. The type sections for the six Triassic stages (§ D-2) are in the eastern Alps. The type sections for the twelve Cretaceous stages are mostly in France, and some are just outside that country (§ D-1). The uppermost Cretaceous, in many regions, contains few ammonites; echinoids, foraminifers, and members of other groups frequently take the ammonites' place as guide species, especially for local correlations. Study of the ammonite (and planktonic foraminiferal) faunas indicates that correlations to the substage level are generally justified, as in the Jurassic.

f. Conclusions Concerning Mesozoic Stages

Now, at the end of our consideration of Mesozoic stages and their ammonite faunas, several conclusions may be drawn and added to those concerning zones.

Conclusion 7-7 (definition): Mesozoic stages are groupings of the rock sheets called zones, based on ammonite assemblages.

Conclusion 7-8: Though zones are more or less local, Mesozoic stages and even substages are mostly worldwide, made so by step-by-step correlations of geographically changing ammonite assemblages.

Conclusion 7-9: Mesozoic stages and substages are time-stratigraphic units. Each stage or substage is composed of strata that accumulated at about the same time in all the places where the stage or substage has been properly identified.

Conclusion 7-9 is vitally important. It contains two weasel phrases, "about the same time" and "properly identified"; these must be interpreted. The second is easier to handle. A proper identification should involve the presence and skilled use of ammonites or acceptable substitute guides, whose stratigraphic range should be connected with the ranges of the guide ammonites in the pertinent European stages by methods indicated on previous pages and summarized in Conclusion 7-8. "About the same time" expresses confidence that the stages and substages do not overlap more than a little. Almost all of the marine Hettangian (Zones 1–3), for example, was probably deposited before the accumulation, in any region, of any ammonite-bearing strata that have been assigned to the Sinemurian. That is, all or almost all of the Mexican Sinemurian (Table 7-2) was probably deposited after the end of any deposition called Hettangian on the basis of good ammonite evidence. This conclusion is based primarily on unvarying stage and substage homotaxis in all parts of the world.

Conclusion 7-9 would stand unchanged even if some Northwest European zones should prove to be biofacial. One slightly suspect group of zones and subzones is that of the Hettangian. The ammonites of the six Hettangian subzones (two in each zone) may represent six biofacies of a transgressing sea. These subzones follow in sequence above the non-marine Upper Triassic and the thin uppermost Triassic marine-lagoonal Rhaetic, with its bone-bed and pelecypods. The Northwest European Province was in process of submergence at the end of the Triassic, and the cover of water may have continued to deepen. It is perhaps significant that Hettangian zones and subzones have not been found outside Northwest Europe. Even the two hypothetical Hettangian substages of § 7-5.c have been found in few if any clearly homotaxial extra-European successions. On the other hand, the Hettangian ammonites are closely related, and the European subzonal assemblages may reasonably be considered an evolutionary se-

Fig. 7-16. *Paleozoic marine invertebrate guide taxa.* (A, B, E, F, G, *and* H *from the* Treatise on Invertebrate Paleontology, *courtesy Geological Society of America and University of Kansas Press;* C *from R. H. Flower,* JOURNAL OF PALEONTOLOGY, *1955 and 1958;* D *and* I *from Bernhard Kummel,* History of the Earth, *1961.)*

   A. *The trilobite* Olenellus, *Lower Cambrian, 120 mm long.*
   B. *The trilobite* Elrathia, *Middle Cambrian, Utah, 63 mm long.*
   C. *Straight nautiloids of the Ordovician:* C1, Dideroceras magnum, *Montreal, 70 mm long;* C2, *section through* Stereospyroceras champlainense, *Vermont, 125 mm long.*
   D. Strophomena, *a brachiopod limited to the Middle and Upper Ordovician.*
   E. *The Lower Ordovician graptolite* Didymograptus, *60 mm long.*
   F. *Graptolite of the Silurian genus* Monograptus, *25–30 mm long.*
   G. Halysites, *the chain coral, Silurian, about 30 mm long.*
   H. Hallia, *a Devonian rugose coral, 55 mm long:* C, *cardinal septum.*
   I. Atrypa, *a Silurian–Mississippian brachiopod, especially common in the Devonian.*

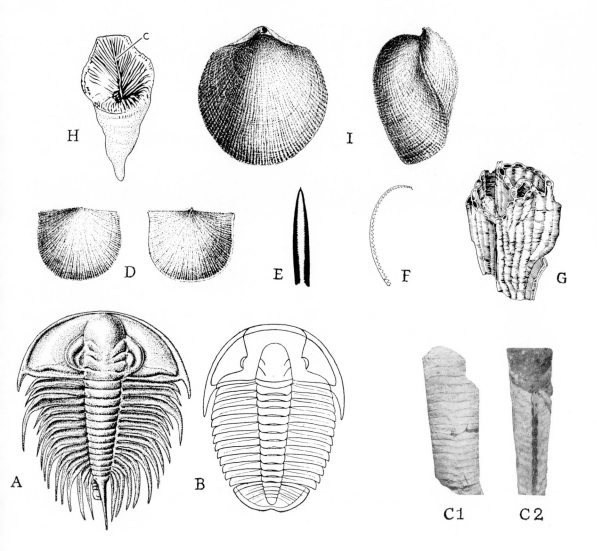

Fig. 7-17. *Upper Paleozoic marine invertebrates.* (A, C, E, *and* F, *from the* Treatise on Invertebrate Paleontology, *courtesy Geological Society of America and University of Kansas Press;* B *and* G, *from T. Davidson, 1858–1863, via Bernhard Kummel, op. cit.;* D, *from J. J. Galloway and H. V. Kaska, Memoir 69, Geol. Soc. Am., 1957;* H, *from Mark Rich,* JOURNAL OF PALEONTOLOGY, *1961.*)

A. *The primitive ammonoid* Manticoceras, *Devonian.*

B. *A spiriferoid brachiopod, with a long hinge line, Devonian.*

C. Phacops schlotheimi, *a coiling trilobite with big eyes, Middle Devonian, Germany, 18 mm across.*

D. Pentremites, *Mississippian: 1, side view of specimen 34 mm long; 2, top view; 3, side view of P. conoideus, from Kentucky, with the rarely preserved stem, the whole specimen 60 mm long.*

E. Imitoceras rotatorium, *a typical goniatitic ammonoid, Mississippian, Indiana;* × 2/3.

F. Gonioloboceras goniolobum, *a goniatitic ammonoid, Pennsylvanian, Kansas,* × 3/4.

G. *A productid brachiopod, Permian.*

H. *A fusuline foraminifer,* Schwagerina, *Permian, Nevada; longitudinal section, enlarged.*

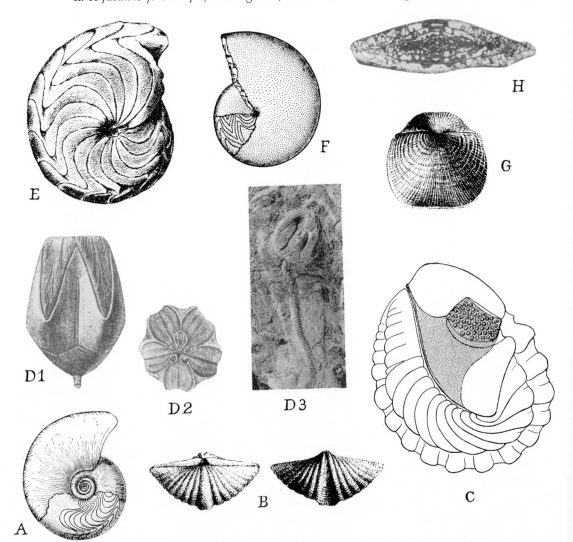

quence. However this European problem may be settled, the Hettangian zones are only provincial units. The time-stratigraphic nature of the worldwide Mesozoic stages and substages, including the undivided Hettangian, seems so probable that a discussion of their precision, as in § 7.5.c, seems justified.

7-6. Paleozoic Guide Fossils and Correlations

a. Paleozoic Guide Fossils

No single group of animals has provided an adequate set of guide fossils for the Paleozoic. Goniatitic ammonoids are useful in the upper Paleozoic, but they are less numerous and less widely distributed than their Mesozoic relatives. Goniatite zones probably represent about the same lengths of time as Mesozoic stages. Zones of almost equal value may be based on other organisms. Trilobites are outstanding in the Cambrian, graptolites in the geosynclinal facies of the Ordovician and Silurian, and fusuline foraminifers in the Pennsylvanian (Upper Carboniferous) and Permian. In the highly fossiliferous and widespread limestones and shales of the broad continental platforms the most useful guide fossils, especially for short-distance correlations, are the brachiopods. Almost all these groups of animals, and others too, are represented in the panels of typical Paleozoic guide fossils (Figs. 7-16, 7-17, and 7-18.

b. Paleozoic Stages

Many Paleozoic stages have been set up in Europe, on the basis of fusulines or ammonoids or other guide fossils, but these stages—except perhaps the marine Devonian stages set up in Belgium—do not have worldwide authority. Another set of nearly parallel stages is, in fact, growing in North America, with American names based on American type sections and American fossil species.

In general, a three-fold subdivision of each Paleozoic system is about as far as one can go in discussing worldwide correlations. Lower Cambrian, Middle Cambrian, Upper Cambrian, Lower Ordovician, etc. are useful as worldwide time-stratigraphic subdivisions of the systems, but further subdivision into worldwide stages is not ordinarily fruitful.

c. Lower Paleozoic Correlations

For the Cambrian, Ordovician, and Silurian, trilobites or graptolites provide guide fossils that make intercontinental correlations fairly easy for the geosynclinal facies. Trilobites are equally useful on the platforms, but graptolites have rarely been found there, perhaps because they have not been sought for with sufficient perseverance.

Olenellus (Fig. 7-16A) or closely related, shaggy-looking trilobites mark the Lower Cambrian on the border between England and Wales, in northwestern Scotland, in Norway, in Poland, in Vermont, in eastern California, in Siberia, and elsewhere. Other sets of trilobite genera are characteristic of Middle Cambrian (Fig. 7-16B) and Upper Cambrian respectively. Most species, however, have regional rather than worldwide distribution. For the Cambrian, most of North America makes up one faunal province.

Now we can answer the question with which this chapter began, concerning the Lower and Middle Cambrian faunas of the Grand Canyon: they are moderately cosmopolitan. They are everywhere homotaxial—arranged in the same order—not only with respect to one another but also with respect to whole series of overlying units based on other fossils. Some of the overlying units are also impressively subdivisible and the subdivisions homotaxial. All these homotaxial divisions and subdivisions are probably time-stratigraphic units that have earned at least tentative precedence over lithologic units in the determination of relative age, in the Grand Canyon or elsewhere. Faunal and lithologic evidence must finally be combined to give a single consistent historical interpretation. For the Grand Canyon Cambrian this has been done successfully.

The eugeosynclinal Ordovician and Silurian are easily and generally divided into Lower, Middle, and Upper portions by the use of graptolites, which are especially abundant in Britain and which there and elsewhere also

A

Fig. 7-18. *Fusuline foraminifers of the Upper Paleozoic.*
    A. Triticites, *Pennsylvanian, eastern Kansas;* × *4.*
    B. *A model of Triticites (Pennsylvanian-Permian), showing external ribbing, coiling about the long axis, and internal structure; greatly enlarged. (From H. K. Brooks.)*
    C. Parafusulina(?), *Permian, southeastern California;* × *2.*

B   C

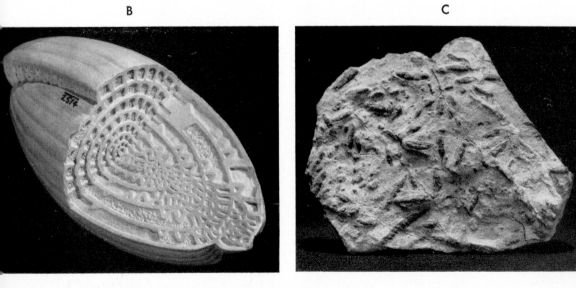

make finer subdivision possible. But even the graptolites are provincial. For the Lower Ordovician, three regions—American, European, and Australian—have recently been distinguished (W. B. N. Berry, 1960). The Silurian graptolites (species of *Monograptus*, Fig. 7-16F) were more cosmopolitan.

Graptolites are widely distributed in the North American geosynclinal belts, from Newfoundland and Quebec to Alabama, in the Ouachitas of southern Oklahoma, and in the Cordillera from Nevada and California north. But in many geosynclinal areas the graptolitic and shelly facies are so sharply separated, commonly by faults, that correlation from one to the other is difficult. Away from the folded geosynclinal belts, in the enormous expanses of the continental platforms, graptolite finds are somewhat rare but locally spectacular, as in the Upper Ordovician at Cincinnati. Within the shelly facies, almost all Ordovician and Silurian correlations have been made by other means. The more or less local guides are furnished mostly by genera and species of brachiopods, some of which are similar or identical on the two sides of the North Atlantic.

d. Upper Paleozoic Correlations

In the Devonian, Carboniferous, and Permian the goniatitic ammonoids (Fig. 7-17 AEF), found at some places in almost all regions, are perhaps the best group of guides for intercontinental correlations. For the latest Paleozoic (Pennsylvanian and Permian), fusuline foraminifers (Fig. 7-18) are, at least locally, more useful because they are more abundant, especially in certain broad platform areas, as in Kansas, western Texas, and the eastern part of European Russia, where they characterize what appears to be a moderately deep-water facies. Fusulines are also present in geosynclinal belts, as in Nevada and the Urals. Certain fusuline genera, since they seem to be present in the same order in all these places, have become useful in intercontinental Carboniferous and Permian correlations, for example, between eastern Russia and the western United States. Upper De-

vonian zones based on microscopic conodonts (§ B-11) may also become useful, as some such zones have been found both in Europe and in western America.

e. European–North American Correlations

The correlations between the type sections in Europe and sections in eastern and western North America are important to us because of the use of these sections in Chapters 3, 5, and 6.

Correlations between the lower Paleozoic portions of the British and the two American sections are shown in Figure 7-19. Trilobites make the Cambrian correlations possible, either directly or through the more fossiliferous European sections in Scandinavia. The trilobite correlations are reinforced, in some minor ways, by evidence furnished by some brachiopods (§ B-6). The Ordovician and Silurian correlations between Britain and west-central New York shown in Figure 7-19 were made only in small part by the use of graptolites, for graptolites are found not at all in central New York and only in parts of the Ordovician sequence in eastern New York. Most of the Ordovician and Silurian correlations are based primarily on the similarities between the brachiopod faunas at several levels.

From the Devonian to the Permian the correlations between Britain and New York–Pennsylvania, or between western Europe and eastern North America generally, are easy because even the facies are nearly identical. In each region marine and red-bed continental Devonian facies are succeeded by Lower Carboniferous, which in turn is overlain by Upper Carboniferous coal measures. The two Permian sections are alike in lacking typical marine facies, but the scanty eastern American continental sandstones and shales make only a partial analogue to the western European Permian, which also includes marine dolomite and thick salt deposits.

The Grand Canyon Paleozoic section, taken as a whole, has European correlatives at every

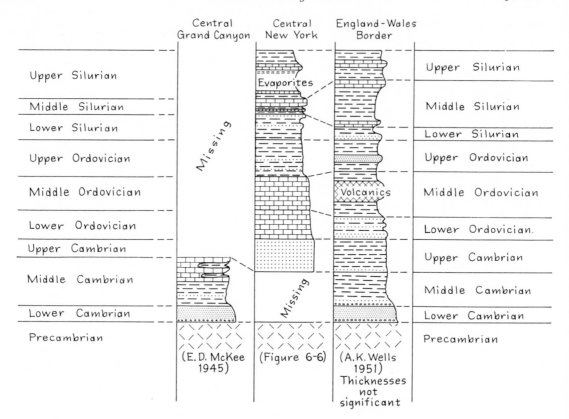

Fig. 7-19. *Diagrammatic correlation chart of lower Paleozoic systems: Welsh Border—central New York—central Grand Canyon. Relative thicknesses not precise.*

level, though these correlatives cannot all be found in Britain or any other one part of Europe. That is to say, the Grand Canyon, which is far from Europe, exhibits a succession of facies and lacunas not matched by any one European section. Table 7-5 shows the best correlations.

Most striking are the lacunas in the Grand Canyon record, especially when this is compared with that of Britain or eastern North America (or even of the Cordilleran geosyncline). But the relatively few fossil faunas and floras found in the Grand Canyon section are closely similar to faunas and floras known in Europe, eastern North America, and elsewhere. There are, in particular, no reversals in order: the Cambrian is at the bottom of the Grand Canyon pile, the Permian is at the top, and all the intermediate units are in the same

order as in Europe. The system names used for the rock units in the Grand Canyon seem justified, and the lacunas in the Grand Canyon section seem to be real.

7-7. Cenozoic Guide Fossils and Correlations

With the beginning of the Cenozoic, gastropods, pelecypods, echinoids, and foraminifers replace the ammonites as marine guide fossils. The ammonites get scarcer as the top of the Cretaceous is approached from below. One stage, the Danian, with type locality in Denmark, was formerly considered Cretaceous in spite of the absence of ammonites in its type area and in units elsewhere that are convincingly correlated with the type Danian. Since 1955, most American stratigraphers and many Europeans have put the Danian in the Cenozoic, largely because its most widespread guides, the planktonic Foraminifera, are like those of the Paleogene and unlike those of the Upper Cretaceous. In 1960 the International Geological Congress at Copenhagen debated the Danian question. The Russian A. L. Yanshin advocated the retention of the Danian in the Cretaceous because of such things as a dinosaur genus in a Crimean formation called Danian and a fine ammonite specimen recently found in the supposed Danian of southwestern France. The whole discussion has emphasized the uncertainties in some stage correlations. If the Danian is finally discarded, some strata previously called Danian will be put in the Paleogene and others in the Maestrichtian, which is now commonly considered the uppermost stage of the Cretaceous (§ D-1).

The Cenozoic Era is well named, for it is indeed the era of modern types of life. Most of the earliest marine Paleogene pelecypods, gastropods, echinoids, and foraminifers had hard parts rather similar to those of animals living today. On land, the Cenozoic is the age of mammals. The last dinosaur probably died before the Cretaceous ended. Small mammals became fairly abundant in the latest Cretaceous, and in the earliest Paleogene the mammals became the dominant land animals.

Within a single marine faunal province, such as the Gulf or Pacific coastal regions of North America, small foraminifers are the most useful guides for Cenozoic correlations, especially below the surface from oil well to oil well. Worldwide correlations of marine Cenozoic strata are almost as far behind those of the Paleozoic as Paleozoic correlations are behind those of the Mesozoic. The difficulties are especially great in the Neogene, probably because of the gradual intensification of the differences between temperature zones that culminated in the cold-zone glaciations of the Pleistocene.

In the Paleogene, the larger Foraminifera (nummulites and similar forms; compare § B-2.b) are good and fairly widespread guides for the distinction of the three or four main subdivisions of the system, especially in tropical and subtropical regions. Some pelecypod and gastropod genera are equally useful, though most members of these groups show regional differences that reduce their value for worldwide correlations. The best Paleogene guides may turn out to be small pelagic foraminifers and microscopic discoasters (§ B-1.b).

The Neogene marine strata can be distinguished from the Paleogene by the disappearance of nummulites and some other large foraminifers, by the first appearance of the small spherical *Orbulina*, a planktonic foraminifer, and by marked changes in the pelecypods, gastropods, and echinoids. Many

TABLE 7-5

Grand Canyon–European Correlations

GRAND CANYON	EUROPE
Marine Permian	Marine Permian: Perm district of Russia
Continental Permian	Continental Permian: eastern Russia
Continental Upper Carboniferous (no coal)	Continental Carboniferous: Germany (poor correlation)
Marine Lower Carboniferous limestone	Marine Lower Carboniferous limestone of Britain
Marine Devonian with rare fish	Marine Devonian of Belgium & Britain in which fish form a minor element in a varied fauna
Middle Cambrian	Marine Cambrian: Scandinavia (good Lower Cambrian correlation); Britain (poor correlations)

pelecypod, gastropod, and echinoid genera disappear at about the top of the Paleogene and are replaced by related new genera. But species and even subgenera are likely to be different in the Neogene of different parts of the world; distant correlations, as from California or Oregon to France or Italy, are therefore extremely difficult and commonly vague at best. There is also a dispute about the exact position of the Paleogene-Neogene boundary in Europe.

Few if any worldwide marine Cenozoic stages are yet valid. Progress in this direction is still being made, especially by the use of planktonic Foraminifera.

Many Cenozoic continental formations, in all the continents except Australia (and Antarctica), contain bones representing large mammalian faunas. These faunas have been used to define a dozen or more stages that seem to be fairly generally valid and to be represented in formations widely distributed in North America, Europe, and some parts of Asia. In a few places, such as France and California, continental and marine Cenozoic strata interfinger. As a result, some marine strata in California may be defined in terms of continental stages, though thus far such correlations have been only moderately helpful in the making of geologic history more precise.

The Lower, Middle, and Upper Pliocene of the Los Angeles Basin (Fig. 7-8A) are divisions in local use that have not been justified by precise correlations with the type sequence in the Po Valley of northern Italy, useful guide fossils common to the two areas not having been found. One important horizon, the Pliocene-Pleistocene boundary in the type sequence, was defined by the International Geological Congress of 1948. The mammalian fauna just above this horizon, unfortunately, has not been found in the Los Angeles Basin. Similar correlation problems, important for discussions of glaciation and human prehistory, will be considered in Chapter 16; partial solutions are already possible.

7-8. *Conclusions Concerning Paleozoic and Cenozoic Time-stratigraphic Units*

We can now add to the generalizations about Mesozoic zones and stages some conclusions that apply to Paleozoic and Cenozoic time-stratigraphic units.

Conclusion 7-10: Paleozoic and Cenozoic systems, such as the Devonian and the Paleogene, and subsystems, such as the Lower Devonian and the Oligocene, are fairly well-established worldwide time-stratigraphic units.

Conclusion 7-11: Most Paleozoic and Cenozoic stages and zones are regional or continental in extent, rather than worldwide. This conclusion is a cautious one and does not do justice to some Paleozoic stages (or divisions called zones that actually have about the same significance as Mesozoic stages).

7-9. *Divisions of Geologic Time*

Systems and stages are divisions of the rocks. Now, if we agree that the procedures by which sedimentary rocks all over the world are assigned to particular systems and subsystems, or even to stages and substages, are correlations of contemporaneous strata, we can pass easily from the stratigraphic division of the rocks to the division of geologic time. In the remainder of this book this transition is assumed to be justified. The discussion will be limited almost entirely to the larger divisions of geologic time—the **periods,** or times of deposition of the sedimentary systems (see Table 2-1, p. 21)—and to the primary subdivisions of the periods: Early Cambrian time, the time of deposition of the Lower Cambrian rocks; Middle Cambrian time, the time of deposition of the Middle Cambrian rocks; Late Cambrian time, the time of deposition of the Upper Cambrian rocks; etc.

A question at once arises: Do the times of

deposition of the fossiliferous sedimentary rocks of all the subsystems, from the Lower Cambrian up, cover all time since the beginning of Early Cambrian time? In particular, how about the lacunas emphasized in Chapter 4? This question has disturbed geologists for almost a century. Now it seems that a definite answer is possible. Numerous detailed studies of sedimentary basins, supplemented by the most precise worldwide correlations that are possible, make it appear that no lacuna of measurable size is worldwide. Most lacunas are like the one diagrammed in Figure 3-12: they disappear when traced into the larger sedimentary basins of the conti-nental platforms. A few, which extend into the basins of a platform, or into a miogeosyn-cline, are not recognizable in a eugeosyncline and surely are not present on the floors of the great oceans. Somewhere, on some continent or island, or beneath some small or moderate-sized sea, there are, almost certainly, sedi-mentary rocks that formed during the time represented by every unconformity in the type section in Europe. And all these sedimentary rocks, even though they do not occur in the European type sections, are assimilated into the standard rock systems. In a later chapter we shall give the evidence on the well-marked and extensive sub-Cambrian unconformity.

CHRONOLOGICAL SUMMARY

1815–1819	William Smith of England: some fossil species limited to particular groups of strata.
1838–1841	Amanz Gressly of Switzerland: rock facies and fossil facies.
1850–	Alcide d'Orbigny of France: Jurassic and Cretaceous stages.
1858	Albert Oppel of Germany: Jurassic zones of England, France, and Germany.
1862 & 1870	T. H. Huxley of England: homotaxis.
1929	Roland Brinkmann of Germany: Jurassic ammonite evolution.
1956	W. J. Arkell of England: Jurassic geology of the world.

REFERENCES

1. Alcide d'Orbigny: *Paléontologie française: terrains jurassiques, céphalopodes,* 642 pages (Paris, 1842–1851)

2. Alcide d'Orbigny: *Cours élémentaire de paléontologie et de géologie stratigraphique* (Paris, 1849–1852)

3. Albert Oppel: *Die Juraformation Englands, Frankreichs, und des südwestlichen Deutschlands,* 857 pages (Stuttgart, 1856–1858)

4. T. H. Huxley: Anniversary Addresses, QUARTERLY JOURNAL, Geol. Soc. London, vols. 18 and 26 (1862 and 1870)

5. Emile Haug: *Traité de géologie:* II, *Les périodes géologiques,* 2 vols. (Paris, 1911), pp. 539–1922; the work on stratigraphy that never loses its value.

6. Alfred Bentz: "Über Strenoceraten und Garantianen insbesondere aus dem Mittleren Dogger von Bielefeld," Jahrb. Preuss. Geol. Landesanstalt, vol. 49, pp. 138–206 (1928)

7. Roland Brinkmann: *Statistisch-biostratigraphische Untersuchungen an mitteljurassischen Ammoniten über Artbegriff und Stammesentwicklung,* 249 pages, Abhandlungen Gesell. Wiss. Göttingen, N.F., vol. 13, No. 3 (1929)

8. S. W. Muller and H. G. Ferguson: "Mesozoic Stratigraphy of the Hawthorne and Tonopah Quadrangles, Nevada," BULLETIN, Geol. Soc. Am., vol. 50, pp. 1573–1624 (1939)

9. Gerd Westermann: *Monographie der Otoitidae* (*Ammonoidea*), Heft 15, Beihefte z. geol. Jahrb. (Hannover, West Germany), 364 pages (1954)

10. J. H. Callomon: "The Ammonite Succession in the Lower Oxford Clay," etc., PHILOS. TRANS., Roy. Soc. London, vol. B239, pp. 215–264 (1955)

11. W. J. Arkell: *Jurassic Geology of the World,* 806 pages (Oliver and Boyd, Edinburgh and London, 1956)

12. H. K. Erben: *El Jurásico inferior de México y sus amonitas,* 393 pages (20th Int. Geol. Cong., 1956)

13. M. L. Natland: *Paleoecology of West Coast Tertiary Sediments,* Memoir 67, Geol. Soc. Am. (1957), vol. 2, pp. 543–572

14. A. L. Yanshin: "Stratigraphic Position of the Danian Stage and the Problem of the Cretaceous-Paleogene Boundary," Part V, 21st Int. Geol. Cong., pp. 210–215 (1960)

15. W. T. Dean, D. T. Donovan, and M. K. Howarth: "The Liassic Ammonite Zones and Subzones of the North-West European Province," BULLETIN, British Museum (Nat. Hist., Geology), vol. 4, pp. 437–505 (1961)

CHAPTER 8

Radiometric Ages

In previous chapters we have found (1) how William Smith established a local column in Britain, based mainly on the section from Wales to London, (2) how nineteenth-century stratigraphers completed this section and developed from it a standard column and time scale, and (3) how, by the use of fossil assemblages, correlations with the standard column have been made in all parts of the world. Relative age can be expressed in terms of the standard column and time scale.

In this chapter we shall consider age-determination and correlation without the use of fossils. Procedures developed in the twentieth century, following the discovery of radioactivity, make it possible to determine age in years (absolute ages). It is now possible, for example, to say that some Cretaceous strata are about 100,000,000 years old. What is more, we can say that a granite determined to be 100,000,000 years old (by methods to be described in this chapter) is probably Cretaceous. The year used here is an astronomic unit, the length of time during which the earth makes one revolution round the sun. A second and independent astronomic unit is the day, during which the earth makes one rotation. Other, ultra-short scientific time units are based on intramolecular and intra-atomic vibrations of extreme rapidity that can be precisely, though indirectly, measured. No variation in the length of the year, in terms of

non-astronomic time units, has yet been demonstrated.*

This chapter will close with the discussion of two other, related topics: the ages in years of the solid earth and the ocean.

8-1. Elements and Isotopes

Determination of the absolute ages of rocks is based on the steady, spontaneous decomposition of atoms, the chemical building blocks once considered indestructible. Before discussing this kind of decomposition we must review briefly some aspects of the structure of matter. Atoms are small units; a hundred million of them, side by side, would make a row about an inch long. Each atom consists of a **nucleus** and one or more **electrons.** The nucleus is very small indeed, with a diameter about 1/10,000 that of the atom itself. The mass (or

---

* The day, however, is slowly getting longer. Professor J. W. Wells of Cornell University has shown [*Nature,* vol. 197, p. 948 (1963)] that certain Middle Devonian corals had growth cycles that were probably annual, each marked by about 400 growth lines that were probably daily. If the interpretations of the coral structures are correct, there are about thirty-five fewer days in the year now than there were in the Middle Devonian. The estimated braking effect of the tides, for the length of time since the Middle Devonian (according to estimates of Devonian ages in years that will be set forth later in this chapter), is about enough to produce this much retardation in the rate of the earth's rotation.

[191]

weight) of the tiny nucleus is small, but that of the electron is very much smaller, 1/1,836 that of the lightest nucleus. The electron or electrons of an atom seem to move about rapidly, for they effectively fill the space that is called the volume of the atom, preventing other atoms from intruding. The smallest and lightest nucleus is a single **proton** (for which we shall attempt no further definition). It carries one unit of positive charge; with an electron, which carries one unit of negative charge, it forms a neutral atom of the chemical element called hydrogen. **Elements** are the substances that cannot be decomposed by ordinary chemical reactions.

Most hydrogen atoms are made up of one proton and one electron, but in elemental hydrogen or in compounds such as water about one part in 5,000 is made up of hydrogen atoms that are approximately twice as heavy. Each heavy hydrogen atom has a nucleus composed of two parts, a positively charged proton and a neutral **neutron.** A neutron has about the same mass as a proton. The two kinds of hydrogen atoms are called **isotopes.** (In addi-

tion to these two, found in nature, hydrogen has a third isotope, artificially produced.) Most of the hundred or so chemical elements are composed of two or more isotopes. The isotopes of an element are atoms whose nuclei contain the same number of protons but different numbers of neutrons. The **atomic number** of an element is the number of protons in the nucleus of an atom of the element. The **mass number** of an isotope is the number of protons plus the number of neutrons in its nucleus. The hypothetical structures of some atomic nuclei are shown in Figure 8-1. Ordinary hydrogen, made up of atoms containing one proton and one electron, is called hydrogen 1, and heavy hydrogen, made up of atoms containing one proton, one neutron, and one electron, is called hydrogen 2 (heavy hydrogen, deuterium). The element with two protons, and hence with atomic number 2, is helium. The heaviest element known in nature is uranium, with atomic number 92. Uranium 235 (the uranium isotope with mass number 235) has a nucleus containing 92 protons and 143 neutrons; it also contains 92 electrons.

Some atoms of an element are short one or more electrons or carry one or more extra electrons that are easily detached. If an atom is short one electron, it has a positive electrical charge of 1; if it has an extra electron, it has a negative charge of 1. An atom with a charge is called an **ion.**

Each element has a symbol, H for hydrogen, O for oxygen, C for carbon, Ca for calcium, U for uranium, Pb for lead, etc. These symbols are used in the chemical formulas of compounds. Water's formula, H_2O, shows that water is made up of two hydrogen atoms to each oxygen atom. Note that the subscript follows the H, to which it refers. A subscript position having been used up in this way, a superscript position is commonly used for the mass number of an isotope, such as H^1 or H^2 (Fig. 8-1). In this book, however, isotope mass numbers are used so often that they are written, for convenience, as full-size numerals in normal alignment: H1 for hydrogen 1, H2 for hydrogen 2, C12 for carbon 12, U238 for

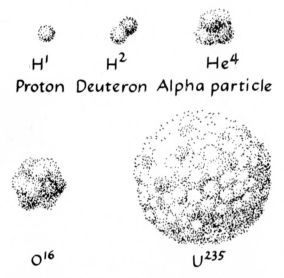

Fig. 8-1. *Range of complexity in atomic nuclei: proton and deuteron of hydrogen; alpha particle (helium nucleus); nuclei of oxygen and uranium. (From Linus Pauling,* General Chemistry, *W. H. Freeman & Co., 1953.)*

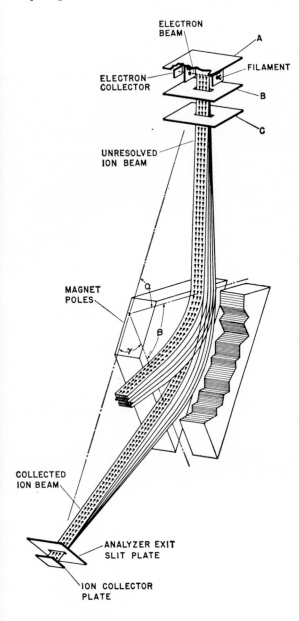

Fig. 8-2. *Nier's 60° mass spectrometer. (Courtesy of A. O. C. Nier.)*

uranium 238, etc. The names, atomic numbers, and symbols, and selected isotope mass numbers, of the elements considered in this chapter are given in Table 8-1.

The larger the mass number of an isotope, the heavier are its atoms and ions. As a result, the isotopic composition of a sample of gaseous ions of an element can be determined in a low-pressure chamber called a mass spectrometer (Fig. 8-2), where the attraction of a powerful electromagnet deflects moving ions in inverse proportion to their masses.

8-2. *Spontaneous Transmutation of Elements*

Spontaneous change, called **decay,** of one element into others was demonstrated by Pierre and Marie Curie in the eighteen-nineties. They and those who followed showed

TABLE 8-1

Some Chemical Elements and Isotopes

ELEMENT	SYMBOL	ATOMIC NUMBER	MASS (WEIGHT) NUMBERS OF SOME ISOTOPES				STATE AT USUAL TEMPERATURE AND PRESSURE
Argon	Ar	18		36	38	40	Gas
Calcium	Ca	20			40		Solid
Carbon	C	6			12	14	Solid
Helium	He	2			4		Gas
Hydrogen	H	1			1		Gas[a]
Lead	Pb	82	204	206	207	208	Solid
Nitrogen	N	7			14		Gas[a]
Oxygen	O	8			16		Gas[a]
Potassium	K	19		39	40	41	Solid
Radium	Ra	88	223	224	226	228	Solid
Rubidium	Rb	37			85	87	Solid
Strontium	Sr	38		86	87	88	Solid
Thorium	Th	90			230	232	Solid
Uranium	U	92			235	238	Solid
Zirconium	Zr	40	90	91	92	94	Solid

[a] Occurs commonly in compounds that are liquid or solid.

that uranium changes into a series of other substances, including radium (which the Curies discovered). All the newly formed substances are called **radiogenic.** One of the radiogenic substances, early called the *alpha particle,* is now known to be a helium nucleus, an ion with two positive charges from its two protons (Fig. 8-1). An atom of uranium 238 loses eight successive alpha particles, finally reaching a stable state as lead 206 (Fig. 8-3). After a few hundred thousand years the transmutations are in a steady state, with an almost unchanging amount of each intermediate substance, all these amounts being small compared with that of uranium. The amount of the parent isotope, uranium 238, decreases continually, and the amount of the stable daughter isotope, lead 206, increases continually, both at approximately the same low rate. Laboratory studies of the uranium–lead and other radioactive series have shown that changes of temperature, pressure, and chemical environment have practically no effect on the **decay rate,** or rate of transmutation. A logical extrapolation, basic for our purposes, is the con-

clusion that the radioactive transmutations must have gone on at the present rates under all the conditions that have existed on earth in the geologic past.

The decay of uranium 238 to lead 206 would produce, after 4.5 billion years, new lead atoms equal in number to the uranium atoms re-

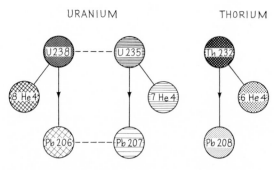

Fig. 8-3. *Decay of uranium and thorium.*
ABOVE. *Simplified diagram.*
RIGHT. *Diagram showing series through intermediate to final products. (Adapted from J. N. Rosholt, U.S. Geological Survey, 1959.)*

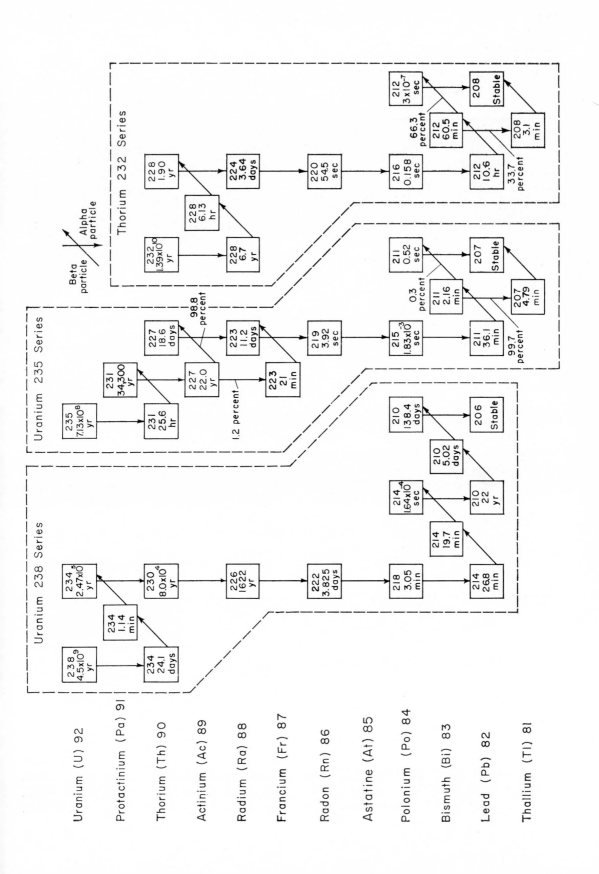

TABLE 8-2

Transmutations of Chemical Elements Useful in Determinations of Age

FROM	TO	DECAY CONSTANT (PER YEAR)	PARENT'S HALF-LIFE	METHOD FIRST USED
Carbon 14	Nitrogen 14		5,730 years	1947
Potassium 40	Argon 40 and calcium 40	To Ar40, 5.85×10^{-11}; to Ca40, 4.72×10^{-10}		1948
Rubidium 87	Strontium 87	1.39×10^{-11}, geologically determined, used here; 1.47×10^{-11}, experimentally determined	47,000 m.y.	1946
Thorium 232	6 α-particles + lead 208	4.99×10^{-11}	13,900 m.y.	1938
Uranium 235	7 α-particles + lead 207	9.72×10^{-10}	713 m.y.	1938
Uranium 238	8 α-particles + lead 206	1.54×10^{-10}	4,510 m.y.	1938
Uranium	Lead (ordinary weighing on chemical balance)			1907

Note: m.y. = million years.

maining (Table 8-2); that period is therefore said to be the **half-life** of uranium 238. The other decay rates that we shall consider in this chapter are similarly low. One geologically important transmutation, the change of carbon 14 into nitrogen 14, is much more rapid. Carbon 14 is half gone after about 5,700 years. Its decay will be useful in Chapter 16, on the Pleistocene, where we shall be interested in ages of the same order of magnitude as carbon 14's half-life.

8-3. Age from Radioactivity

If the exact quantities of parent and daughter isotopes in a mineral are known, the ratio of these quantities—for example, Pb206/U238 —can be used in an appropriate formula to give the **radiometric age** of the mineral—the number of years since it crystallized.

a. Some Transmutations Useful in Dating Rocks

Existing uranium is 99.3 percent U238. The remaining 0.7 percent is practically all U235, which, decaying somewhat faster than U238,

yields seven alpha particles and a final stable lead 207 (Fig. 8-3 and Table 8-2). Thorium 232, associated with uranium in some minerals, yields six alpha particles and a final stable lead 208. The age of a uranium-thorium mineral may be calculated from any one of the three ratios: Pb206/U238, Pb207/U235, and Pb208/Th232. Each of these ratios involves an original parent isotope and a final daughter isotope; each such pair may be called a **decay pair.**

The ages of the potassium-bearing micas— muscovite, biotite, and lepidolite—and of some other potassium minerals, such as potassium feldspars, can be calculated from transmutations less disruptive than those involving the discharge of alpha particles. Potassium 40 changes to argon 40 (and calcium 40), and rubidium 87 changes to strontium 87, as results of minor internal rearrangements. Potassium 40 is a subordinate but ever-present potassium isotope that changes to argon 40 if an electron is captured by the nucleus. Rubidium is a nearly constant minor associate of potassium. Rubidium 87 is usually somewhat less rare in a potassium mineral than potassium 40, though both are usually measured in parts per million.

Rubidium 87 changes to strontium 87 by emission of a beta particle (an electron).

Before we use a decay pair in dating rocks, we need to know the assumptions involved, so that we can make the necessary qualifications. The present-day procedures and computations are moderately complicated. We shall consider first the simpler calculations made a half century ago, when the relative quantities of the elements lead and uranium, rather than those of specific isotopes, were used, and the formula was crude.

b. A Simple Treatment

The first radiometric ages were calculated by Professor B. B. Boltwood of Yale University. In 1905 he reached the conclusion that the lead in uranium minerals must be the end product of uranium decay, and in 1907 he used the simple lead/uranium ratios to obtain the approximate ages of ten mineral occurrences. Estimating that one ten-billionth of the uranium changes to lead each year, he multiplied each lead/uranium ratio by 10 billion to get the age of the mineral in years. Boltwood's youngest specimen was a uraninite (uranium oxide) from Glastonbury, Connecticut, with a Pb/U ratio of 0.041 (average of five analyses) and hence an estimated age of 410

million years. This age is surprisingly close to the latest estimates, 250–275 million years, and would have been much closer had the uranium–lead decay rates been accurately known. The material Boltwood thought oldest was a thorianite (thorium and uranium oxide) from Ceylon with a lead/uranium ratio of 0.22 and a supposed age of 2,200 million years. This age was far too high because Boltwood considered thorium a stable element that did not yield radiogenic lead.

c. Proper Calculations

Boltwood did not use properly the rate of uranium decay. He treated the change from uranium to lead as though the material were sand passing through an hourglass (Fig. 8-4A). In his hourglass the parent material would lose one ten-billionth of its original amount every year. In 10 billion years it would all be gone (straight-line relation, Fig. 8-4B). Actually, an unchanging fraction of the *remaining* uranium is lost each year (Fig. 8-4C). Let us consider an individual isotope, even though here a distinction between isotopes is not necessarily involved. The decay constant for uranium 238 is 1.54 ten-billionths per year (Table 8-2); that is, this fraction of the remaining uranium, if at least a few trillion

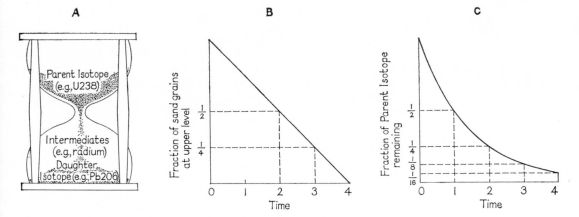

Fig. 8-4. *Hourglass diagram and decay curves for radioactivity.*
   A. *Section through hourglass.*
   B. *Hypothetical graph of the hourglass type of decay.*
   C. *Graph of actual radioactive decay.*

atoms are involved, will decay each year. The loss the second year would not be appreciably different from that for the first year, and even after a billion years the amount lost per year would be five-sixths of the first year's loss. But after 4.5 billion years the U238 would be half gone, and the quantity decaying each year would be only half of what decayed each year at the beginning. As worked out mathematically by H. Bateman of England in 1910, the decay curve is logarithmic (Fig. 8-4C); the original uranium would never be completely exhausted, though after 50 or 100 billion years the amount remaining might not be detectable. The time of decay of a particular atom is not predictable; Bateman's equations apply only to large numbers of atoms.

d. General Assumptions and Qualifications

Even though the hourglass analogy is not applicable to decay rates, it is useful in other ways. The material in the upper part of the glass (Fig. 8-4A) is the parent isotope, that at the bottom is the daughter isotope, and the band of dots between represents intermediate substances such as radium. In determining age, we assume not only that the decay rate is logarithmic and constant but also that all the parent isotope entered the hourglass (the mineral grain or grains) at the time it started operating (the time of mineral crystallization) and that at this time none of the daughter isotope was present. If these assumptions are not correct, we must find means of measuring departures from them. We also either assume that the enclosing rock has provided impermeable walls for the hourglass, so that no measurable amount of either isotope can be added or removed, or attempt to compensate for any such changes. Any compensation must be rigorously justified.

e. Ages from Ratios Involving Lead

1. INTRODUCTION. In calculations of isotopic ages from lead/uranium and lead/thorium ratios, some of the assumptions mentioned

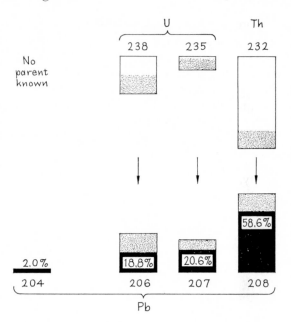

Fig. 8-5. *Relations between uranium, thorium, and lead isotopes. Black: primeval lead (proportion in Canyon Diablo meteorite); gray: uranium and thorium decayed to radiogenic lead during 4.55 billion years of earth history; white: remaining uranium and thorium. (Redrawn from R. S. Cannon Jr. and others,* Economic Geology, *1961.)*

above can be checked. In particular, non-radiogenic lead can be recognized and allowed for, because, fortunately, one isotope, lead 204, has no known radioactive source (Fig. 8-5). The non-radiogenic lead indicated by the presence of Pb204, including appropriate amounts of Pb206 and Pb207, is therefore subtracted. The proportions of the lead isotopes in non-radiogenic lead vary somewhat from place to place, but are always of the order shown in Figure 8-5.

The minerals whose ages have been determined by Pb/U and Pb/Th ratios fall into two groups, one made up of a few minerals with high percentages of uranium or thorium, the other made up of zirconium and rare-earth minerals that are hospitable to the substitution of uranium or thorium in a particular structural position. In the second group, of which the most important minerals are monazite (a rare-earth phosphate) and zircon (zirconium silicate, Fig. 8-6), the radioactive elements have partially replaced elements of similar atomic volume and similar chemical bonding characteristics. Only a few of the zirconium (or rare-earth element) positions in the crystal structure, perhaps one in ten thousand, are occupied by uranium atoms; in monazite, however, thorium is much more abundant.

Minerals of high uranium content commonly weather rather easily. Zircon, however, is extremely resistant to weathering and monazite moderately so. The few uranium atoms in zircon and monazite appear to be well protected, for they persist through many environmental changes, including those involved in weathering, transportation, and deposition in a sedimentary bed. The products of radioactivity are somewhat more likely to get away; the lead atom, for example, is too large for the zirconium position, and its chemical bonding is inadequate.

Two products of uranium and thorium decay are gases under ordinary conditions. One, helium, has been shown to leak slowly away. As the leakage cannot be estimated satisfactorily, ages involving helium are not now being used. A second gas, radon, isotopes of which are produced in both the U238–Pb208

Fig. 8-6. *The structure of zircon. (From W. L. Bragg*, Atomic Structure of Minerals, *with the permission of G. Bell & Sons, Ltd.)*

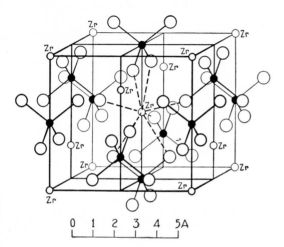

0 1 2 3 4 5A

and the U235–Pb207 series, is short-lived, the Rn222 of the U238 series having a half-life of 3.83 days, the Rn219 of the U235 series one of 3.92 seconds. The isotopes of radon probably do not, therefore, under natural conditions, escape from a crystal of zircon or other slightly radioactive mineral in significant amounts. If any radon does escape, it is probably in the U238 rather than in the U235 series. Therefore, if the Pb207/U235 age is the greater, loss of radon may be suspected; if the Pb207/U235 and Pb206/U238 ages are about the same, loss of radon has probably been unimportant. Even in minerals rich in uranium, loss of radon may be less serious than loss of radium if we may judge from analyses of Colorado Plateau uranium ores.

2. THE RATIO Pb207/Pb206. Since the half-life of U235 is much shorter than that of U238 (Table 8-2), the amount of Pb207 produced in a mineral per year drops off much more rapidly than the amount of Pb206 produced per year. As a result, the ratio Pb207/Pb206 is itself a radioactivity clock, one that becomes easier to read with increasing age, especially above 500 million years. This clock is independent of recent partial loss of lead, as the two leads behave similarly in all chemical reactions. It is also practically independent of recent loss of uranium and does not require the determination of the amount of uranium in the mineral. The ratio Pb207/Pb206 is one of the most important measures of age.

3. URANIUM-LEAD CONCORDIA AND LOSS LINE. The Pb207/U235 and Pb206/U238 ratios of a mineral, taken together, provide exceptionally important evidence of age. If the ages derived from the two ratios are about the same, they are called **concordant.** Few pairs of ages are exactly concordant, but many pairs—perhaps one-third of all that have been determined—are within about 10 percent of each other. Such approximately concordant ages corroborate one another. If the age discrepancy is greater than 10 percent of the larger, the ages are called **discordant.**

Even discordant pairs, under some circumstances, give useful indications of the age of a rock and also of its post-consolidation thermal history.

The Pb207/U235 and Pb206/U238 ratios and ages obtained in a region may be plotted against each other in a regional diagram. Figure 8-7 is such a diagram, representing analyses of three Rhodesian monazites. The Pb207/U235 ratios and the corresponding ages are scaled along the y-axis, the Pb206/U238 ratios and the corresponding ages along the x-axis. In the rare case where a pair of ages are exactly concordant, the point representing the pair is plotted on the curve labeled Con-

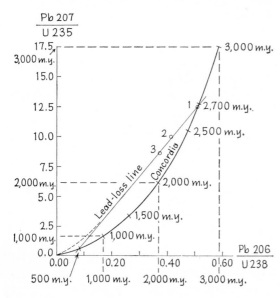

Fig. 8-7. *Concordia curve for Pb206/U238 and Pb207/U235 ratios, with loss line fitted to discordant ages at three African localities.*

cordia. If the Pb206/U238 ages are the smaller, as they are for all three analyses plotted, the pairs, which here vary from slightly to greatly discordant, plot to the left of the Concordia curve, on its concave side.

The ages calculated for the three Rhodesian monazites (perhaps all from pegmatites) are given in the table at the foot of Figure 8-7, The Bikita ages are almost concordant. The other two localities give discordant ages. The plots (1, 2, and 3 in the diagram) determine a straight line that, if extended, cuts Concordia at about 2,700 and 500 m.y. When one notes also that the Jack Claim and Irumi Hills Pb207/Pb206 ages are within 2.3 percent of Bikita's 2,680 m.y., one is tempted to consider the low Pb206/U238 and Pb207/U235 ages the effects of leakage of lead at the two northern localities (compare Fig. 8-8 for geographic positions), the two leads being equally affected, just as chemical considerations would lead one to expect. The oblique straight line in Figure 8-7 can then be considered a **loss line**. Its slope is determined by the Pb207/Pb206 ratios, for the ratio between U238 and U235 is everywhere the same at any one time, including the present, and therefore does not affect the slope. All the data may be explained as the result of two events: (1) the crystallization of the monazites, no doubt from a quartz-plutonite magma, 2,700 m.y. ago; (2) the partial recrystallization or other alteration of two monazites 500 m.y. ago. Since the

	Ages in Millions of Years					
	Pb206/U238	Pb207/U235	Pb207/Pb206	Pb208/Th232	Ar40/K40	Sr87/Rb87
1. Monazite, Bikita, Southern Rhodesia	2,675	2,680	2,680	2,645		
1A. Mica, same locality					2,310	2,500 (2,400–2,600)
2. Monazite, Jack Claim, near Salisbury, Southern Rhodesia	2,260	2,470	2,650			
3. Monazite, Irumi Hills, Northern Rhodesia (Zambia)	2,040	2,330	2,620			

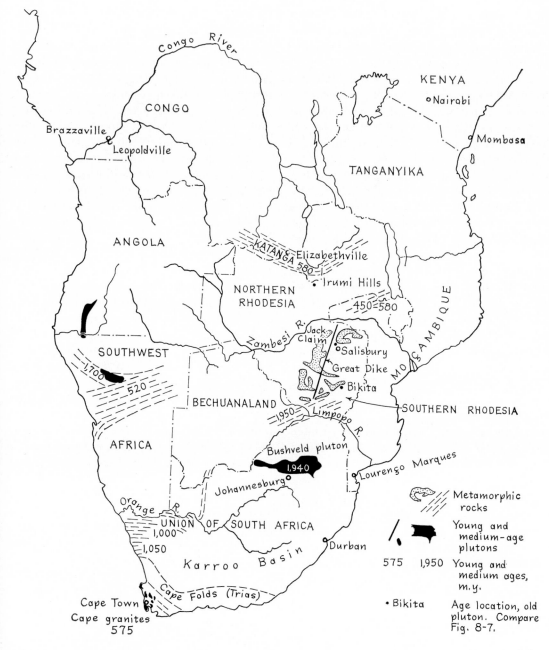

Fig. 8-8. *Map showing structures and some ages in central and southern Africa. (Structural lines adapted from L. O. Nicolaysen, Buddington Volume, Geol. Soc. Am., 1962.)*

second event was relatively recent, the lead dissolved at that time had attained a Pb207/Pb206 ratio that has not changed much since. The loss line gives nearly as good evidence for a single definite age of original crystallization

(here 2,700 m.y.) as concordant Pb206/U238 and Pb207/U235 ages would.

The field geological evidence is consistent with these conclusions. All three Rhodesian monazites might be expected to have about the same age, for all probably came from the same sea of quartz-plutonite rocks, in which roughly parallel belts of metasediments and metavolcanic rocks lie (Fig. 8-8). (There is some uncertainty about the Irumi Hills material, which was collected, not from bedrock, but from a natural alluvial concentrate.) In northeastern and northwestern Rhodesia, and in an adjacent part of Katanga Province of the Congo, pegmatites and veins yield minerals with ages of 485–640 m.y. (marked on Fig. 8-8). All the geological and geochemical evidence is consistent with the previously stated idea that the old intrusions of 2,700 m.y. ago were followed 600–500 m.y. ago by new localized northern intrusions. The latter may have reheated the whole northern part of the ancient mass of Rhodesian crystalline rocks. (One wonders a little why the belt of metamorphism southwest of Bikita, which is 1,950 m.y. old, did not affect that locality.) Finally, erosion of the Irumi Hills made possible the formation of heavy-mineral alluvial concentrates that seem to have lost lead and other substances, during weathering, without changing the Pb207/Pb206 ratio.

A short extension of the loss line to an intersection with Concordia is more reliable than a long extrapolation. In Figure 8-7 the age of

Fig. 8-9. *Diagram showing distribution of 226 Ar/K ages, northwestern Russia, by 100 m.y. intervals. (Ages recalculated with the American decay constants of Table 8-2 from data of E. K. Gerling and A. A. Polkanov, 1958.)*

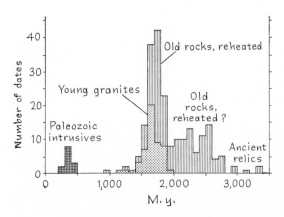

the original crystallization of the monazites, obtained by a short extension of the loss line, is therefore much better established than the supposed age of reheating and leakage, obtained by a long extrapolation. The latter would not be taken seriously were it not for the independent evidence of central African plutonism about 500 m.y. ago. Even so, another possible interpretation of the data, as the result of continuous solid diffusion, gives a curve that coincides for most of its length with the straight loss line previously discussed but curves away finally to the origin as shown by the dashed line of Figure 8-7.

4. LEAD/THORIUM AGES. The Pb208/Th232 age of a mineral or rock is often different from and usually less than the Pb206/U238 and Pb207/U235 ages, even if the latter are concordant. Under such circumstances the lead/thorium age is commonly ignored. Some Russian workers, however, consider a low lead/thorium age a warning (Vinogradoff and others, 1960). Stating that "experiments have shown that uranium is more easily leached out of different radioactive minerals than thorium," they interpret concordant lead/uranium ages greater than lead/thorium ages as the result of the leaching of both lead and uranium. The best ages are those for which the lead/uranium and the lead/thorium ages are all concordant, but most workers are willing to accept concordant lead/uranium, argon/potassium, and strontium/rubidium ages even if the lead/thorium age is much lower.

f. Ages from Argon/Potassium Ratios

Potassium 40 decays to argon 40 and calcium 40. Calcium 40 is not very useful for age determinations, for radiogenic Ca40 cannot be distinguished from Ca40 of other origin and is only a small part of the total Ca40 in most rocks. The argon 40 found in the analysis of a potassium mineral or rock is also only partly radiogenic; the remainder comes from the atmosphere. A correction, however, can be made for atmospheric argon 40 after the amount of

Fig. 8-10. *Geological sketch map of Finland and northwestern Russia, showing structural trend lines.* (*Generalized from official sources.*)

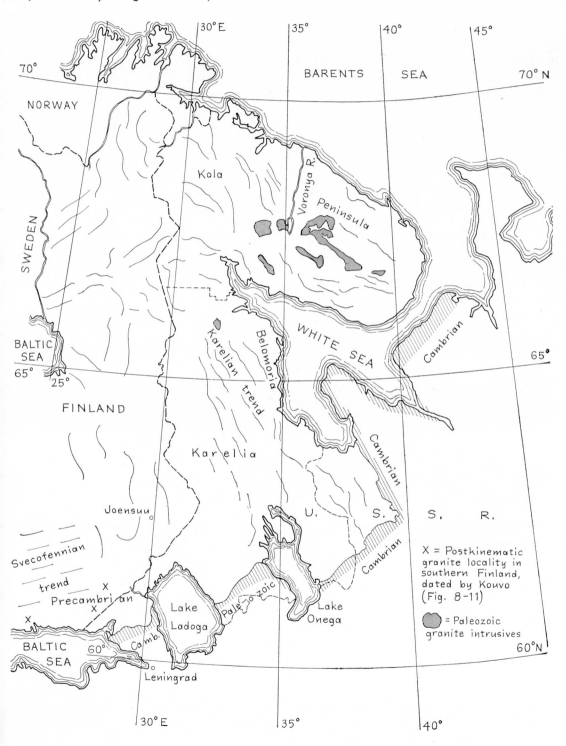

a non-radiogenic argon isotope has been determined. This correction is similar to that made for common lead. Argon, which is a gas under ordinary conditions, is quickly expelled from minerals at high temperatures. Nevertheless, the minute quantities of argon evolved from potassium seem to be retained for at least 100 million years in feldspar and for much longer periods in micas if the rocks containing these minerals have been neither reheated nor intensely deformed.

The behavior of argon in some rocks that were reheated during metamorphism, in large part near younger granite masses, is revealed by a set of argon/potassium ages for micas in the Russian part of the Baltic Shield. These ages are plotted in Figure 8-9, and a sketch geologic map of the region is given as Figure 8-10. The 226 ages, fortunately, have fairly wide geographical distribution and represent several parts of the Baltic geologic column. In Figure 8-9 the ages are shown in 100 m.y. groups. The ages between 200 and 500 m.y. are for the granites shown by shading on the map, mostly in the Kola Peninsula (Fig. 8-10), and these granites are known from independent evidence to be Paleozoic. The largest group of ages is made up of the eighty between 1,600 and 1,800 m.y.; it includes twenty-nine ages for two sets of relatively young ("postkinematic") Precambrian granites (one set in the Kola Peninsula, the other north of Karelia and west of the White Sea), which no doubt crystallized 1,800–1,600 m.y. ago. The remaining fifty-one ages in this group, however, are for older rocks, invaded and reheated by the granites. The long sequence of greater ages, extending to 3,400 m.y., with minor maxima at 2,200–2,300 and 2,500–2,600 m.y., may be interpreted as representing relics of ancient rocks that kept some early radiogenic argon through all vicissitudes.

Three lead/uranium loss lines (Fig. 8-11), for three sets of granite rocks in the Baltic Shield area of Finland and northwestern Russia, give ages consistent with those of Figure 8-9. They indicate that two groups of young Precambrian granites originated 1,650

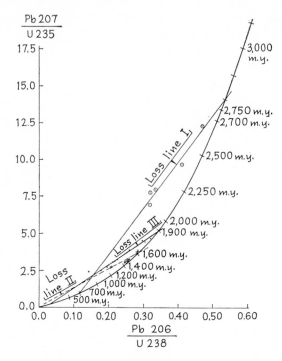

Fig. 8-11. *Concordia curve with loss lines for Baltic Shield granites. Loss line I and circles: southeastern Finland, after G. L. Davis and others (Ref. 5); loss line II and crosses: southern Finland, after O. Kouvo (1958); loss line III and small dots: Karelia, Russia, after E. K. Gerling (1958) and G. L. Davis and others (Ref. 5).*

and 1,900 m.y. ago and a group of older granitic gneisses 2,775 m.y. ago. One of the groups of young granites is in Belomoria (Fig. 8-10), west of the White Sea, and the other is in southern Finland (the crosses of Fig. 8-10); the granitic gneisses are also in southern Finland, near Joensuu. In view of the evidence of four areas of young Precambrian granites, distributed from the Kola Peninsula to southern Finland, it is no wonder that most of the older metasediments and recrystallized plutonic rocks of the region have lost part or all of the radiogenic argon accumulated before the intrusion of the young granites.

The argon/potassium ages for old rocks are probably minima. The very greatest ages of Figure 8-9, 3,300–3,400 m.y., for mixed sedimentary-plutonic rocks on the Voronya River on the north slope of the Kola Peninsula, probably show, therefore, that the formation of these particular plutonic rocks and the metamorphism of the associated sediments were at least that early.

One must not oversimplify the pre-1,900 m.y. record of the Baltic Shield. The 2,200–2,300 and 2,500–2,600 m.y. peaks of Figure 8-9 may represent events occurring at those times or earlier events whose apparent ages have been reduced by loss of argon during reheating. These peaks are less certain indicators of age than the loss lines are of events at 2,700, 1,900, and 1,650 m.y.

g. Ages from Strontium/Rubidium Ratios

Rubidium 87 is more abundant than potassium 40, but it decays to strontium 87 rather slowly (Table 8-2), and the mass spectrometer used for its determination is less sensitive than that used for argon. On balance, one might expect the Ar40/K40 and Sr87/Rb87 methods

Fig. 8-12. *Concordance of Ar/K and Sr/Rb ages, shown by data for Minnesota Precambrian rocks. (After S. S. Goldich and others, Bull. 41, Minn Geol. Survey, 1961.)*

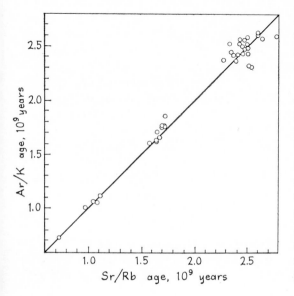

to be about equally effective, and they do commonly lead to similar ages (see Fig. 8-12).

The Sr87/Rb87 method has one advantage. The radiogenic Sr87 appears to stay in or near the source mineral even after mild metamorphism, as shown by a comparison of the analysis of a rock with analyses of its rubidium-bearing constituents mica, hornblende, and feldspar. Such analyses permit checks on strontium/rubidium ages similar to the loss-line checks on lead/uranium ages.

8-4. Precision and Accuracy of Determinations of Geologic Age

Statisticians make a distinction between precision and accuracy. The term **precision** refers to the scatter, or lack of it, among repeated determinations of what is thought to be a single value, such as the age of the biotite in a granite, determined by the argon/potassium method. The **accuracy** of the determinations, however, is a measure of their deviation from the true age, if that can be discovered.

Before comparing precision and accuracy we must have clearly in mind the kinds and causes of variation or error in the numbers that represent the age of a mineral occurrence. **Analytical errors** are those made during chemical treatment and analysis. **Sampling errors** are variations from the average composition that result from the selection of the mineral sample, which may, for example, be made up of hundreds of little crystals of zircon or flakes of mica. The two groups of errors are statistically similar, for both are discovered through repeated determinations on substances as they now exist. The probable analytical error can be calculated if 5 or 25 or 100 determinations are available. If the frequencies are plotted after the fashion of Figure 2-8, a bell-shaped curve is commonly obtained. For example, 40 out of 100 determinations might be exactly 100 m.y., 80 within the range 98–102 m.y., and all 100 between 95 and 105 m.y., with a mean of 100 m.y. The bell-shaped curve would then be very high and narrow, with a standard deviations smaller than ±2 m.y. One feels intuitively that the mean, 100 m.y., is probably within 2 m.y. of the true value for the sample —that is, that analytical precision equals analytical accuracy. But was the analyzed sample a fair sample? In order to answer this question, one collects multiple samples and prepares them for analysis, commonly with great labor. Then one treats the analyses of the different samples statistically to obtain a new mean and a standard deviation that applies to both analytical and sampling errors.

Even numerous samples of a radioactive mineral, however, are not likely to give the true age by simple analysis for parent and daughter isotopes. Allowances for **contamination** and **leakage** should be made. It is standard procedure, in analyses for radiogenic lead or argon, to make allowances for the amounts of non-radiogenic Pb206, Pb207, Pb208, and Ar40 indicated by the presence of other, wholly non-radiogenic lead or argon isotopes. Leakage from the radioactive hourglass is allowed for if the uranium–lead loss line is used, and error that is the result of recent leakage is by-passed in the Pb207/Pb206 method. In one way or another, more or less satisfactory estimates of the first four types of error are frequently available.

Systematic errors are those that have similar effects on whole arrays of determinations. One kind of systematic errors is not included in any of the previous groups: those in the decay constants. The constants have been revised several times; those now in use are not all identical in Russia and the United States. A hundred determinations with a mean of 900 m.y. and a standard deviation of ±18 m.y. might be changed to a hundred determinations with a mean of 950 m.y. and a standard deviation of ±19 m.y. as a result of a change in a decay constant. All other ages based on the same decay pair would be affected in exactly similar fashion.

In order to have geological application, a mineral age must be shown to have some specified relation to the age of a rock. The mineral may be older than the rock, contemporaneous with it, or younger. Some of the thousands of little zircons in a granite may, after being detrital in a sedimentary rock, have been incorporated into the granite without melting and without restarting the radioactive clock. A large zircon in a pegmatite may have formed in a crack or solution cavity produced at a late date, during a revival of pegmatitic activity. Even if the zircon crystals in a particular pegmatite were formed at the same time as all the other minerals in that rock, some other pegmatites in the district may have been formed at a very different time. These possibilities are examples of those that must be considered by persons who wish to date rocks by the ages of radioactive minerals. Every occurrence must be considered a special problem, to be solved individually.

The analytical variations for some samples have been studied rather thoroughly. One study involved lepidolite samples from five rocks, each analyzed in more than one laboratory, the number varying from two to four. The mean determined ages ranged from 100 to 2,760 m.y.; the standard deviations at any one laboratory were mostly below 4 percent, and the differences between the means obtained at different laboratories were also mostly less than 4 percent. Many lead and Ar40/K40 ages probably have equally good laboratory reproducibilities; some are somewhat better. Variability between samples (sampling error) is not so well known; here contamination and leakage may be involved. The Sr87/Rb87 ages of different samples of lepidolite from a pegmatite at Pala, California, determined in a single laboratory, varied, for unknown reasons, from 107 to 116 m.y.

The distinction between precision and accuracy can best be made in connection with a specific example. The Pacoima pegmatites, twenty miles north of Los Angeles, are a swarm of dikes striking northwest-southeast in coarse-grained crystalline country rock. One thick dike contains large crystals of zircon, some of which are two inches or more long. Analyses of the zircon by L. T. Silver and associates at the California Institute of Technology showed 41.6 ± 0.2 ppm (parts per million) of radiogenic lead (average of four analyses), 208.2 ± 1 ppm of uranium (average of 12 analyses), and 63.0 ± 1 ppm of thorium. The radiogenic lead was found to be made up as follows, in atom percentages: Pb206, 85.1 ± 0.2 percent; Pb207, 6.72 ± 0.02 percent; Pb208, 8.20 ± 0.03 percent. These data correspond to the following ages: Pb206/U238, $1,175 \pm 15$ m.y.; Pb207/U235, $1,185 \pm 15$ m.y.; Pb207/Pb206, $1,195 \pm 10$ m.y.; Pb208/Th232, $1,185 \pm 25$ m.y. A second set of analyses gave these ages: Pb206/U238, $1,160 \pm 20$ m.y.; Pb207/U235, $1,175 \pm 20$ m.y.; Pb207/Pb206, $1,200 \pm 15$ m.y. The average age from six other Pb207/Pb206 analyses was $1,195 \pm 10$ m.y. Thus all the zircon data, used in formulas with constants and corrections now thought most reliable, lead to ages of 1,160–1,200 m.y., with standard deviations of ± 25 m.y. or less.

Other workers collected, from another dike of the same swarm, two crystals of biotite mica, each an inch or two across, that yielded three different and much lower ages. One crystal gave an Ar40/K40 age of 379 m.y. and a Sr87/Rb87 age of 380 m.y., the other an Ar40/K40 age of 123 m.y. and a Sr87/Rb87 age of 183 m.y. The precision of each of the four mica analyses is probably good, perhaps almost as good as those of the zircon analyses, but the precision of a mean mica age for the pegmatite cannot be stated in any meaningful way, for the scatter in the mica ages is wholly unlike the symmetrical variation about a mean (compare Fig. 2-8A) that is the mathematical basis for the calculation of standard deviation.

If one tries to go beyond the analytical data and get some idea of the true ages of the pegmatites, leakage and contamination must be considered. A general leakage of argon and strontium from the whole rock is not enough to explain the complexly different ages of the two mica crystals. A difference between the true ages of the zircon-bearing and mica-yielding pegmatites cannot be the whole explanation, for the problem of the difference between the two mica crystals would still be left untouched. More promising is the hy-pothesis that a recent local reheating of the mica-yielding pegmatite developed in it a thermal gradient that caused a graded series of leaks of the daughter isotopes. This hypothesis gets a measure of support from the presence in the mica pegmatite of a thin, cross-cutting, fine-grained dike that may be much younger than the pegmatites (see Fig. 8-16 for the regional age range). If this explanation is accepted and the zircon age is considered accurate for the pegmatite swarm, the mica ages are inaccurate by 800 m.y. or more.

The accuracy of the zircon age must still be considered critically. This age was determined on large crystals that were intergrown with the other large crystals of the pegmatite. Because of this textural relation, the zircon must have about the same age as the other pegmatite minerals and therefore about the same age as the dike as a whole (though not necessarily, perhaps, the age of the dike as originally formed). In particular, it is not possible that the zircons were detrital grains incorporated in the rock at the time of its formation. Moreover, the zircon age was probably not affected by lead, uranium, or thorium leakage or contamination; for, if it was, three different decay pairs, Pb206/U238, Pb207/U235, and Pb208/Th232, with three experimentally determined and very different decay constants, and affected in complexly different ways, would have given nearly identical inaccurate ages. No matter how it is tested, the zircon age appears almost impregnably accurate. We should, however, preserve at least a tiny doubt, if only in remembrance of the seventeenth-century bishop who asserted that the earth was created at "the entrance of the night preceding the twenty third day of October" in 4004 B.C. (Julian calendar) and of the twentieth-century radio comedian who regularly asked his marvel-mongering stooge, "Was you there, Charley?" We may still say that the evidence seems to be consistent with the hypothesis of a true age of approximately 1,200 m.y. for one Pacoima pegmatite and, by successive extensions, more or less the same age for the rest of the swarm and for the larger plutonic mass from which the pegmatite dikes seem to come.

In general, a survey of radioactive age data for individual plutonic rock bodies leads to the conclusion that concordant lead/uranium and lead/thorium ages may be quite accurate. Moreover, the time of crystallization of a widespread plutonic or metamorphic formation or set of formations, as in Rhodesia or the Baltic region, may be determined with similar probable accuracy if the same concordant lead age is found at several localities or even if, as shown in Figures 8-7 and 8-11, discordant lead/uranium ratios yield loss lines based on several localities that point to a definite age on the Concordia curve.

In favorable cases the accuracy may be given a rough numerical estimate. One locality —the Bikita district in Southern Rhodesia— stands out for the concordance of its age data. The lead ages for its monazite are concordant, and two sets of strontium/rubidium ages for lepidolite are almost the same as the monazite age. The strontium/rubidium ages from one or two other laboratories are somewhat lower, and the argon/potassium ages are definitely lower, but the latter are no doubt affected by a loss of argon that occurred 500 or 600 m.y. ago. When the existing data are supplemented by a zircon age, a fairly satisfactory estimate of the approach toward accuracy may be possible. The best present value may be the 2,680 m.y. age for monazite. The monazite analysis was made in Professor A. O. C. Nier's laboratory at the University of Minnesota, which since 1938 has led in mass spectrometry. The analytical precisions of the Pb207/Pb206 and Pb207/U235 ages were given as ±30 m.y. and ±15 m.y., respectively. Obviously, the accuracy can be no closer. Should it be estimated, for the chosen value of 2,680 m.y., at ±25 m.y., ±100 m.y., or ±1,000 m.y.? The consistency of the great majority of the ages from decay pairs determined since 1938 stands against the choice of so large an uncertainty as ±1,000 m.y. At the other extreme, the known imprecisions of sampling, vague though they are, make it foolhardy to use ±25 m.y.

Therefore, ±100 m.y. may be the right order of magnitude for Bikita accuracy.

8-5. *Modes of Origin of Radioactive Minerals*

Potassium and rubidium occur together, notably in micas and feldspars, which are widespread and abundant minerals that crystallize during the formation of igneous and metamorphic rocks. A few potassium-rubidium minerals crystallize or recrystallize at the time of formation of sedimentary rocks; one that is moderately common is the green, platy glauconite. Most uranium and thorium minerals, in contrast, are rare. One, zircon, is almost as widespread as feldspar or mica but occurs in such small amounts that many pounds of granite or other rock must be crushed to yield the half thimbleful of zircon crystals needed for an age-determination. The other uranium and thorium minerals (Table 8-3) are most likely to be found in the ore veins or pegmatite dikes associated with some granitic rocks.

The rocks that have been dated by decay pairs can be divided conveniently into two groups, one made up of plutonic and metamorphic rocks and represented by many age-determinations, the other made up of sedimentary and volcanic rocks and represented by a smaller number of age-determinations.

8-6. *Temporal Distribution of Age-determinations of Plutonic and Metamorphic Minerals*

Plutonic and metamorphic ages are important for historical geology, for some of them apply to notable events that affected rock belts hundreds of miles wide and thousands of miles long. The radiometric ages of some plutonic rocks, such as granites and pegmatites, and completely metamorphosed rocks, such as micaceous gneisses, are represented in Figure 8-13. The ages are plotted vertically and the number of examples for age intervals of 10 m.y. horizontally. The solid black parts of the horizontal bands represent concordant lead/

TABLE 8-3

Principal Radioactive Minerals That Have Yielded Absolute Ages*

MINERAL	CRYSTAL STRUCTURE	COMPOSITION	MINOR RADIOACTIVE CONSTITUENTS	DECAY PAIRS (OF ISOTOPES)
Uraninite	Cubic	UO_2		U238–Pb206; U235–Pb207
Thorianite	Cubic	$(ThU)O_2$		Th232–Pb208; U238–Pb206; U235–Pb207
Sylvite	Cubic	KCl (K chloride)		K40–Ar40; K40–Ca40
Zircon	Prismatic (tetragonal)	$ZrSiO_4$	U, Th	U238–Pb206; U235–Pb207; Th232–Pb208
Monazite	Complex (monoclinic)	Rare-earth thorium phosphate	U	U238–Pb206; U235–Pb207; Th232–Pb208
K feldspar	Complex (monoclinic)	KAl silicate	Rb	K40–Ar40 (and Ca40); Rb87–Sr87
Muscovite mica	Platy	KAl silicate	Rb	K40–Ar40 (and Ca40); Rb87–Sr87
Biotite mica	Platy	KAlFe (etc.) silicate	Rb	K40–Ar40 (and Ca40); Rb87–Sr87
Lepidolite mica	Platy	KAlLi silicate	Rb	K40–Ar40 (and Ca40); Rb87–Sr87
Glauconite	Platy	KFe silicate	Rb	K40–Ar40 (and Ca40); Rb87–Sr87

* Lead ages have also been obtained from the rather common minerals allanite, galena, and sphene (silicate, sulphide, and silicate, respectively); from the rare oxide minerals betafite, brannerite, "davidite," euxenite, fergusonite, "hjelmite," microlite, "nohlite," samarskite, and yttrotantalite; from the rare silicates "cyrtolite" and thorite; and from the rare phosphate xenotime. Argon/potassium ages have been obtained from phlogopite mica and from clay minerals.

uranium ages and loss-line ages, most of them supported also by argon/potassium or strontium/rubidium ages. Groups of other, perhaps less trustworthy ages from single localities or small areas are shown by hollow rectangles. Single age-determinations or choices among discordant determinations are shown by crosses.

In the first column of the figure, representing North America, the 175 ages almost all fall into seven groups. Three groups are at or near 100 m.y., 300–400 m.y., and 500–550 m.y.; the two groups at 900–1,200 and 1,300–1,400 m.y. are so close to each other that they may not be separable; finally, there are groups at 1,600–1,850 and 2,500–2,700 m.y. Almost every group probably represents at least one real and widespread event, and some groups may represent several. We shall find later that the three youngest groups (to 550 m.y.) are probably all Cambrian or later and that the other groups

are all surely Precambrian. The Precambrian history of North America was therefore much longer than all subsequent time.

The second column shows 111 European ages, mostly for rocks in the Baltic Shield or Russian platform. The ages range from 150 to 2,700 m.y. but are concentrated strongly near 1,800 m.y., with a peak almost identical to that of Figure 8-9, even though none of the 226 argon/potassium ages of that figure are included. The other features of this column are also reminiscent of Figure 8-9, at least partly because the hollow rectangles and crosses of the column are so largely based on argon/potassium data.

The third column represents 76 African mineral occurrences. Nearly two-thirds of the dates are based wholly or in part on lead/uranium isotope ratios. Four rather well-marked groups of ages occur at 440–660 m.y., 900–1,040 m.y., 2,050–2,200 m.y., and 2,500–

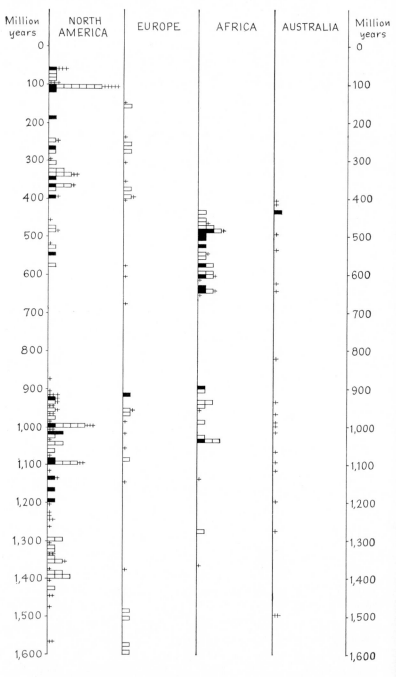

Fig. 8-13. *Regional distribution of age-determinations for deep-seated rocks: North America, Europe, Africa, and Australia. (Data from Ref. 6; A. F. Wilson and others,* Journal, *Geol. Soc. Australia, 1960; and others. Ages of Figs. 8-9 and 9-11 not included.)*

+ Single determination
□ Group of determinations: mean or selected value
■ Concordant Pb/U or loss-line value

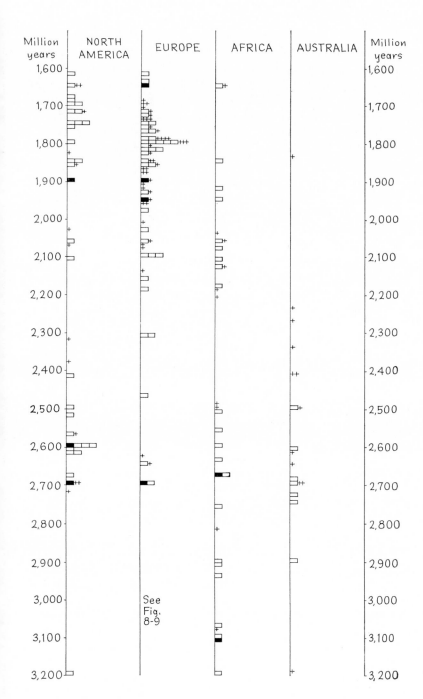

+   Single determination
□   Group of determinations: mean or selected value
■   Concordant Pb/U or loss-line value

3,200 m.y. The big North American concentrations at 100 m.y. and 300–400 m.y., and the European concentration at about 1,800 m.y., are not duplicated in Africa. Three of the African concentrations are matched more or less clearly in North America, but the modest one at 2,050–2,200 m.y. is almost unrepresented in the North American data included here.

The fourth column shows the distribution of 39 Australian ages ranging from 400 to 3,200 m.y. The only concentration is near 2,700 m.y.; notable also is the absence in this second southern continent of any concentration near 1,800 m.y.

From Figures 8-7, 8-9, and 8-13 one might conclude, after some hesitation based on doubts about the accuracy and adequacy of the data, that North America, Baltic Europe, Africa, and Australia all experienced notable plutonic and metamorphic events at about the same early dates, ranging about 2,700 m.y. ago, but that thereafter each area, or at least each of the first three, has had a history somewhat different from those of the others.

8-7. *Ages of Minerals in Stratified Rocks*

The ages of most stratified rocks cannot be determined directly from radiometric ratios. Such a ratio yields the time elapsed since the crystallization of a mineral containing uranium, thorium, or potassium (accompanied by rubidium). In sedimentary rocks, unfortunately, most minerals containing these elements occur as clastic grains in which the radiometric clocks were started long before sedimentation (compare Table 8-3). One or two sedimentary potassium minerals deserve consideration, but most sedimentary sequences must be dated radiometrically from the ages of interbedded tuffs or other volcanic rocks or, less satisfactorily, from the ages of intrusive plutonic rocks. Useful volcanic and plutonic rocks are rather rare. Whole systems, including the Silurian and practically all of the Carboniferous, lack, at this writing (1964), usable dates. The few available radiometric ages of

Cambrian and later fossiliferous rocks are, obviously, of minor value to the stratigrapher. Nevertheless, these dates make a consistent pattern that is useful in the solution of such problems as a local rate of sedimentation or a general rate of evolution per million years. After more and better-distributed dates have accumulated, it may become possible to estimate in years the lengths of most or all geologic periods, from the Cambrian up.

Two sedimentary rocks, three sedimentary minerals, four volcanic minerals, and one type of volcanic rock have yielded radiometric ages of greater or lesser value.

a. *Sedimentary Substances Used for Dating*

The two sedimentary rocks that have been used for dating are uranium-bearing black shale and a dark, fine-grained, uranium-bearing Scandinavian rock locally called kolm. The many $Pb206/U238$ ages for kolm are different from the $Pb207/U235$ ages for the same samples, and the pairs of values do not plot on a loss line. A Tennessee black shale looks more promising, but not conclusively so. Neither of these materials will be considered further here.

The three sedimentary minerals that have been used for radiometric ages, sylvite (potassium chloride), glauconite (iron-potassium silicate), and a potassium-bearing clay mineral, have commonly been dated from the argon/potassium and strontium/rubidium ratios, but at least two occurrences have been dated from the $Ca40/K40$ ratio. Most age-determinations for sedimentary rocks are based on $Ar40/K40$ ratios for glauconites. All three minerals have given some amazingly reasonable determinations of age, but each has an inherent defect that makes it an unsatisfactory guide to true age, at least in the present state of knowledge concerning it.

Sylvite, which has been dated by the argon/potassium and calcium/potassium methods, is soluble in water. Its recrystallization is therefore very easy and commonly also hard to recognize. Each recrystallization gives the radiometric clock a new start. Both concordant and discordant sylvite ages have been reported in the U.S.S.R. A Ca40/K40 age of 228 ± 7 m.y. was found for an apparently unrecrystallized Lower Permian sample and an age of 620 ± 20 m.y. for a Lower Cambrian sample. The Ar40/K40 age was slightly lower for the Permian material and very much lower for the Cambrian material. The Ca40/K40 Russian ages are consistent with those of volcanic and plutonic rocks, to be discussed later, and should be kept in mind, but the calcium/potassium method has been used too little to be relied on.

Glauconite, the principal radioactive sedimentary mineral used for dating, seems to have crystallized on the sea floor as sand-sized pellets (greensand) that got their chemical constituents largely from adjacent clay particles and even incorporated the remains of such particles. The clastic source material (clay) may have contained, at the time of deposition, radiogenic argon 40 and strontium 87, and these isotopes may not have escaped completely during the formation of glauconite; as a result, the determined glauconite ages may be high. On the other hand, since lower Paleozoic glauconites usually contain more potassium than later glauconites, this mineral can, perhaps, gain potassium long after its first crystallization. The result might be low argon/potassium ages, especially for the more ancient glauconites.

The third radioactive sedimentary mineral, a potassium-bearing clay, has the defects of glauconite in exaggerated degree. It will not be considered further here.

b. Volcanic Substances Used for Dating

The four volcanic minerals that have been used for dating stratified rocks are biotite, potassium feldspar, zircon, and monazite, all of which occur as crystals in tuffs. Monazite has been used only in an Ordovician sample that also contained zircon.

The most widespread tuffs, and hence those that are stratigraphically the most useful, are the high-silicon rhyolitic ashes, products of the explosive outbursts of viscous magmas. These tuffs commonly contain a few shiny black biotite crystals, uncommonly a few zircons. If the biotite crystals are still fresh, they give a usable argon/potassium age. If enough zircons can be concentrated from a tuff, they may give usable lead/uranium ages. Whole-rock samples of a few potassium-rich non-fragmental lavas, analyzed for potassium and radiogenic (or total?) argon, have provided data for age calculations.

c. Sample Dates for the Cretaceous System

The amount of scatter and some other facts about sedimentary radiometric ages become apparent from a sample graph. The example, Figure 8-14, is a rough graph of the apparent radiometric ages of rocks assigned to the upper and middle stages of the Cretaceous System. Argon/potassium ages only are listed, partly because they are much the most numerous and partly to eliminate variations due to the method used. The Cretaceous stages are listed in order at the left, with the highest stage at the top. The stratigraphic positions of the analyzed samples are given as closely as possible; if only the stage is known, the age is plotted in the middle of the space. The uncertainties as to radiometric age or stage assignment that were indicated by some analysts are not shown in the graph. Circles mark mean ages for stages.

A general trend is clear, especially for the stage means, from smaller numbers at the top to larger ones near the bottom. The scatter, however, is very large. Cenomanian dates range from 70 to 128 m.y., Middle Albian from 94 to 142. The scatter is too great for us to have much confidence in the individual ages. A single apparent radiometric age, chosen at random, would make an inadequate age datum and, from the stratigraphic point of view, would be greatly inferior to a guide fossil. The scatter can be reduced by elimination of some kinds of data. Glauconite dates show the widest scatter, from 70 to 128 m.y. in the

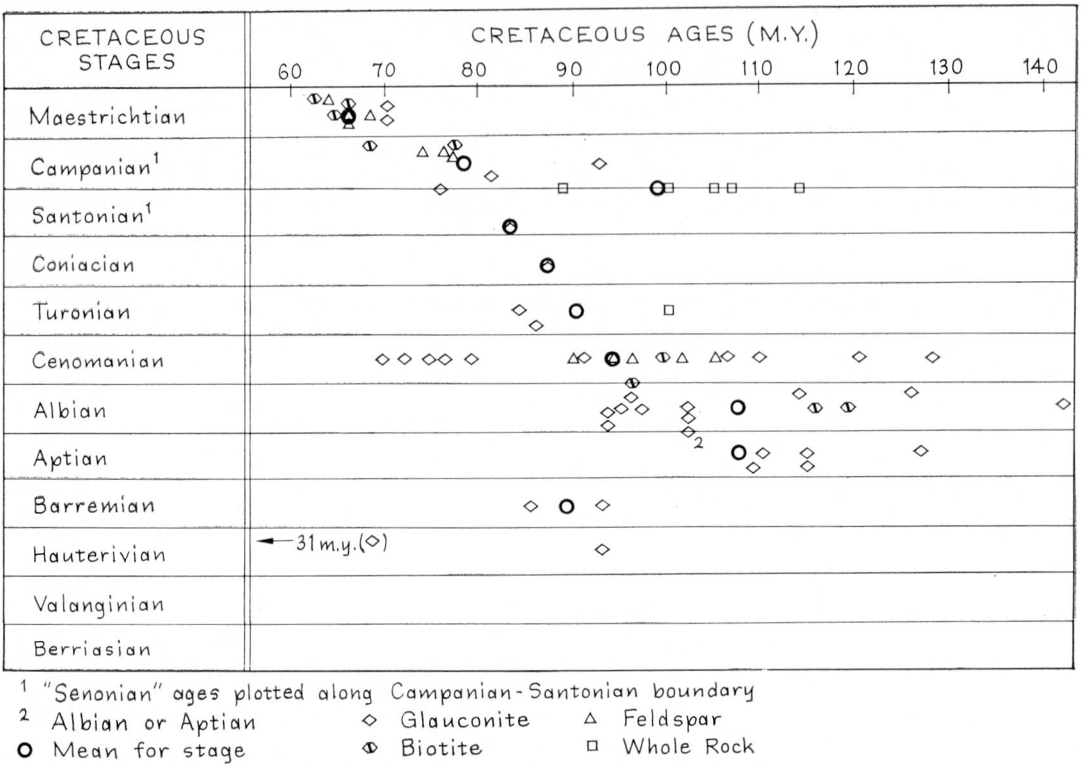

CRETACEOUS STAGES	CRETACEOUS AGES (M.Y.)							
	60	70	80	90	100	110	120	130	140
Maestrichtian								
Campanian[1]								
Santonian[1]								
Coniacian								
Turonian								
Cenomanian								
Albian								
Aptian								
Barremian								
Hauterivian								
Valanginian								
Berriasian								

[1] "Senonian" ages plotted along Campanian-Santonian boundary
[2] Albian or Aptian   ◇ Glauconite   △ Feldspar
O Mean for stage   ⬥ Biotite   □ Whole Rock

Fig. 8-14. *Cretaceous Ar/K ages. (Data mostly from C. F. Davidson, Liverpool and Manchester* Geol. Jour., *1960; J. F. Evernden and others,* Geoch. Cosmoch. Acta, *1961; G. A. Kazakov and N. I. Polevaya,* Geochemistry, *1958; and R. E. Folinsbee and others, 1961.)*

Cenomanian and from 94 to 142 m.y. in the Middle Albian. We might eliminate the glauconite dates, even though we should, at the same time, lose all the dates derived directly from sedimentary rocks. As the whole-rock volcanic ages also show considerable scatter, from 89 to 114 m.y. for the "Senonian," we might set them aside too. We should have left only a few ages for samples of biotite and potassium feldspar from volcanic rocks. These remaining ages make a regular progression, consistent with stratigraphic position, from 63–67 m.y. for the Maestrichtian through 75–76 m.y. for the Campanian and 93–96 m.y. for the Cenomanian to 115–119 m.y. for the Albian.

Lower Paleozoic glauconite ages are markedly lower than those for volcanic rocks. Because of this divergence and the glauconite scatter at most horizons, we should probably ignore glauconite ages (and the few other ages for sedimentary rocks) in constructing a radiometric age scale for the fossiliferous rock systems.

d. Age Scale for Stratified Rocks

The use of radiometric volcanic ages, supplemented by plutonic ones, makes possible a rather clean-cut, though tentative, age scale for Cambrian and younger rocks. Such a scale is shown in Figure 8-15. In this figure, stratigraphic position in the standard geologic column is plotted vertically. Ages in years are plotted horizontally, from zero at the left to 600 m.y. at the right. For each of the forty-nine ages, a cross shows stratigraphic position plotted against age in years. Cenozoic volcanic ages are so numerous that the crosses interfere with one another, at the upper left, and some crosses stand for two or more rock ages. The pre-Cretaceous ages are both sparser and less precise; for most of them the analytical and stratigraphic uncertainties are large enough to show on the graph. The analytical uncertainty (commonly the standard deviation; compare

Fig. 8-15. *Biotite, feldspar, zircon, and mona-zite ages of fossil-controlled volcanic and plu-tonic rocks, with ordinates determined qualita-tively by stratigraphic position but with period lengths, uncertain below the Cretaceous, ad-justed to bring crosses close to the diagonal straight line. Most ages in the Kulp list (Ref. 2), including Kulp Nos. 2, 5–9, 11, 13, 14, 17–19, 24, 30, 32, 33, 35, 42, 43, 45, 50, 52, 53, 55, 59, 63, 65, 68, 73, 75–77, 81, 80, 85, 84. Cross: single or mean age; elongated ver-tical bar: stratigraphic uncertainty; elongated horizontal bar: analytical uncertainty.*

Unlettered	*Biotite from tuff, Ar/K age.*
f	*Feldspar from tuff, Ar/K age.*
z	*Zircon from tuff, Pb/U age.*
b,di	*Biotite from diabase, Ar/K age.*
b,gr	*Plutonic biotite, Ar/K age.*
m,gr	*Plutonic monazite, Pb/U age.*
z,gr	*Plutonic zircon, Pb/U age.*
u	*Ore uraninite, Pb/U age.*
z,b,gr	*Nearly identical plutonic zircon and biotite ages.*

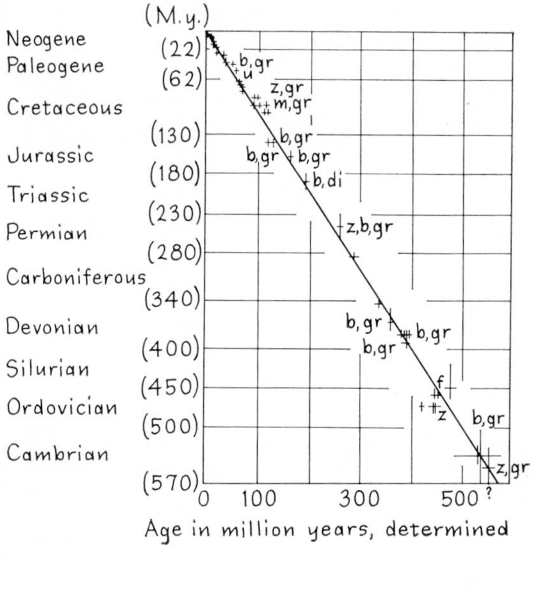

Fig. 2-8) is indicated by the length of the horizontal bar of the cross. The stratigraphic uncertainty is shown by the length of the vertical bar.

The tentative age scale in Figure 8-15 is the oblique straight line; it was fitted by alternate inspections and adjustments. The geological periods, which were largely established on changes in the fossil marine faunas (compare Chap. 7), were first plotted with equal lengths of 50 m.y. Several departures from this rule became necessary if the crosses were to be close to the oblique straight line. The base of the Neogene is now scaled at 22 m.y., the base of the Paleogene at 62 m.y., and the base of the Cretaceous at 130 m.y. (see the calibrations in Fig. 8-15). Finally, the vertical spaces for the Carboniferous and Devonian were in-creased to the equivalent of 60 m.y. and the Cambrian to 70 m.y.

The greatest stratigraphic uncertainties in Figure 8-15 are for the rather numerous ex-amples of intrusive rocks. Fourteen intrusive rocks are involved: twelve quartz plutonites, one diabase, and one ore-vein. In the pre-Cretaceous part of the array the intrusives provide about half of the ages (10 out of 21). The stratigraphic uncertainties of these in-trusives vary considerably. Among the least uncertain are the "z,gr" and "m,gr" mid-Cre-taceous dates, for granitic rocks in southern California and Lower California, respectively. The southern California occurrence, at River-side, is shown on the map of Figure 8-16, and its stratigraphic relations are represented in the accompanying structure section *CD*. The Riverside granite mass, 103 m.y. old by con-cordant $Pb206/U238$ and $Pb207/U235$ ratios based on zircon analyses, is stratigraphically one of the youngest units in the plutonic com-plex called the Southern California Batholith, which extends south from Riverside well into Lower California. The batholith as a whole (section *CD*) invaded Callovian (high Middle Jurassic) sedimentary rocks and Lower Cre-taceous(?) volcanic rocks, but was exposed by erosion before a thick sequence of Turonian and younger Upper Cretaceous sediments **was**

Fig. 8-16. *Geological sketch map and structure sections of an area in southern California, showing distribution of radiometric ages.*

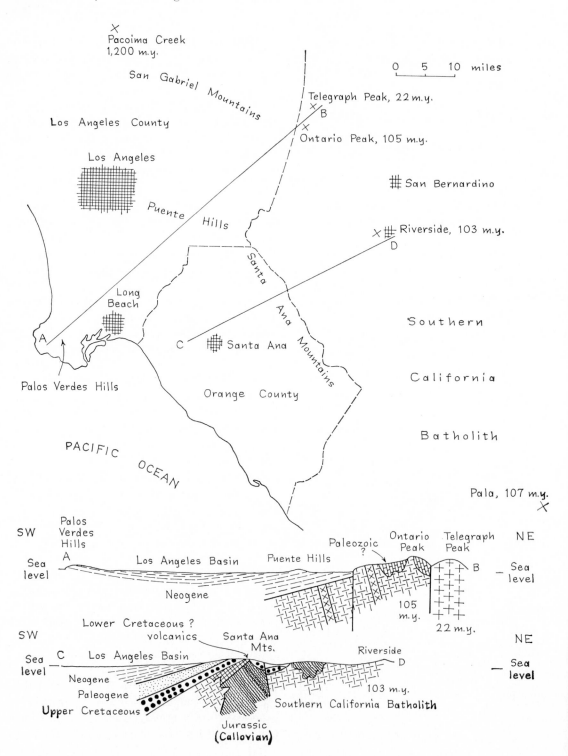

deposited. The volcanic rocks extend south discontinuously into Lower California. There the tuffs contain Middle Albian (high Lower Cretaceous) guide fossils and are invaded by the "m,gr" quartz plutonite of Figure 8-15, 116 m.y. old from concordant lead/uranium and lead/thorium ages of the mineral monazite. In the San Gabriel Mountains a few miles northwest of Riverside (Fig. 8-16, section *AB*), a possible extension of the Southern California Batholith has yielded, at Ontario Peak, a biotite age of 105 ± 10 m.y. by the Sr87/Rb87 method. A lower Ar40/K40 age of 83 ± 3 m.y. for the Ontario Peak rock is probably due to a loss of argon during reheating by the nearby Telegraph Peak Cenozoic intrusive (approximately 22 m.y. old by the Sr87/Rb87 and Ar40/K40 methods). The 103, 105, 107 (Pala, Fig. 8-16), and 116 m.y. ages may represent an actual duration of 10 or 15 m.y. for the solidification of the succession of intrusions, but a shorter time is perhaps almost equally likely. In either case the coarse-grained plutonic rocks of the Southern California Batholith are probably all mid-Cretaceous (post-Albian and pre-Turonian) in their stratigraphic relations.

The small Telegraph Peak pluton, 22 m.y. old, has fine-grained margins that indicate chilling by cool wall rocks. It is probably connected with fine-grained dikes of similar composition that cut through nearby pre-Neogene rocks (section *AB* of Fig. 8-16). The fine-grained dike cutting the Pacoima pegmatite, which may have caused the leakage of radiogenic argon and strontium discussed on a previous page, may, so far as now known, be either Cretaceous or Cenozoic. The southern California and Lower California coarse-grained and fine-grained intrusives invite further research and are now being studied by many geologists and geochemists. They may prove to have greater and more complex significance for age and structure than has been indicated here.

Below the Cretaceous the available volcanic and plutonic ages are sparse. They fit the oblique straight line of Figure 8-15 rather well because the diagram is the result of the

adjustment of period lengths to a stratigraphically consistent set of radiometric ages. In the future, new radiometric dates will no doubt make futher adjustments of period lengths necessary. Changes, large or small, should be welcomed as improvements on the present-day reasonable guesses.

An important horizon that does not yet have a well-established radiometric age is the base of the Cambrian. Most of the data are consistent with the age of 570 m.y. shown in Figure 8-15. Somewhat doubtful evidence against such great age comes, however, from central Siberia, where strata that are probably Lower Cambrian unconformably overlie metamorphic rocks cut by a vein containing mica 462 m.y. old by argon/potassium, zircon 450 m.y. old by Pb207/Pb206, and monazite 500 m.y. old by Pb208/Th232. The only safe conclusion at the moment is that any general age for the base of the Cambrian is uncertain.

8-8. *Relative Precision of Radioactive Ages and Fossil Correlations*

If, by radiometric dating, the range of Neogene ages is from 1 (or 3) to 22 m.y., if that of Paleogene ages is 22–62 m.y., and if that of Cretaceous ages is 62–130 m.y., should these numbers be used as new bases for the definition of the Neogene, Paleogene, and Cretaceous Periods? Or should stratigraphers stick exclusively to the definition of a period as the time of deposition of the rocks of the sedimentary system? This is a real problem in connection with plutonic rocks. Only a few batholiths are closely dated stratigraphically. Before making a decision, one should compare the uncertainties of radiometric ages and fossil correlations. For a radiometric age-determination, the indicated uncertainty, such as the ±7 m.y. in 228 ± 7 m.y., is usually the standard deviation for the mass-spectrometer readings, without any provision for the non-analytical errors discussed on previous pages. These other errors are likely to be at least as great as the uncertainty of the mass-spectrometer readings, making, for the example given, a total uncertainty of at least ±14 m.y., or 6 percent. For an estimate of the uncertainty in fossil correlations we can go back to the uncertainty in the age of the base of the Jurassic System. In Chapter 7 that uncertainty was estimated to be of the order of 1 or 2 m.y., a figure that is about 1 percent of a typical Jurassic age. On the other hand, as recently as the decade 1950–1960, competent stratigraphic paleontologists, when dealing with poor fossil specimens from mildly metamorphosed terrains, have made errors of approximately one geologic period in the ages of rocks in the western United States. Such errors can be compared with the apparent argon/potassium error of about one billion years for a pegmatite at Pacoima, California. We can only decide to use all the information available in making any specific age-determination. At present, fossil correlations seem to be safer guides in most cases. Possible Pleistocene exceptions will be discussed in Chapter 16.

8-9. *The Age of Our World*

The universe as a whole could conceivably have an infinite age but is thought by astronomers to have a finite age considerably greater than that of the earth. Estimates, based on considerations that sometimes include the assumption of an expanding universe, range from 8 to 25 billion years.

a. The Age of the Solid Earth

The earth became a solid, largely crystalline mass of about its present size before the oldest rocks whose ages have been determined invaded pre-existent rocks of the crust. The earth is therefore more than three billion years old. A further hint as to the earth's age is obtained from the radiometric age of meteorites, which may be debris from an exploded planet. The meteorite age that seems most reliable, determined from lead/uranium isotope ratios, is about 4.5 billion years. Estimates of the earth's age have also been based on the isotopic composition of terrestrial ore lead. A. Masuda of Japan (1958), summarizing the earlier work of

many men on different lead ores, listed eight ages for the earth ranging from four to five billion years.

b. The Age of the Ocean

Attempts have been made to estimate the age of the ocean from its salt content. For the sake of simplicity it is commonly assumed that the initial ocean was nearly pure water and had its present volume, since other, more probable assumptions would not make serious differences in the results. The sodium chloride that the ocean now contains—3.5 percent—is assumed to have been added gradually through the ages, mostly along with the water discharged into the sea by rivers. For a first estimate, the present annual rate of addition from rivers is used. The amount of salt in the ocean, when divided by the annual intake, should give, as a quotient, the ocean's age in years. Some corrections, however, should be made. For one thing, much salt has been precipitated out of the ocean in the course of geologic time and has been preserved as salt beds in the rocks.

Among the assumptions are not only constant volume for the ocean but also constant rainfall and constant runoff from the land. Such assumptions seem reasonable, especially for average conditions. Many of the Precambrian rock series, with their great volumes of quartzite, shale, dolomite, and the like, are evidence of conditions fairly close to those that prevail today. The climates must have been about the same, with similar regions of erosion and deposition, similar weathering, and similar runoff. The sea level may have varied somewhat. The ocean basins may have been deeper or less deep, the plateaus and mountains of the land higher or less high, the proportion of land to sea greater or less. But Precambrian oceans and continents much like those of today must have existed. In southern Africa, where the Precambrian section is the most nearly complete in the world and one of the best-dated (compare Chap. 9), the whole series of Precambrian sea levels was probably within a few thousand feet of the present sea level. It is still more probable that Cambrian and later seas had similarly close levels. It is somewhat less certain that the volumes of the successive oceans have been within somewhat such limits as 50 and 150 percent of the present volume.

After all the corrections have been made and the uncertainties estimated, it is still hard to calculate, from the salt content, an age of more than 200 million years for the ocean. The discrepancy between this age and the general tenor of the radiometric ages for the rocks has not yet been explained. Possibly the explanation is very simple. The present additions of salt to the ocean may come from areas of emergent land yielding ten or twenty times the geologic average of salt-forming elements, and therefore this rate may be ten or twenty times the average for all geologic time. The hypothesis of abnormally voluminous present continental bulges leads to corollaries that involve geophysical and geochemical problems that are wholly beyond the scope of this book.

8-10. *Summary and Conclusions*

Geologically useful mineral ages expressed in years are the products of careful collection of radioactive minerals at geologically significant spots, skillful isotopic analysis, and critical evaluation. Tests of reliability have been moderately well developed, with emphasis on concordant $Pb206/U238$ and $Pb207/U235$ ages and well-marked lead-loss lines. The numerous reliable Precambrian ages are especially valuable and in several continents go back about three billion years. There are also about fifty significant dates for the Cambrian–Pleistocene stratigraphic succession, with 100 m.y. dates for Cretaceous rocks, 350 m.y. dates for Devonian rocks, probable 450 m.y. dates for Ordovician rocks, and somewhat questionable 550 m.y. dates for Cambrian rocks. Long poorly dated intervals remain in the stratigraphic succession, however, and only Cretaceous and later radiometric ages are now useful supplements to biologic correlations of fossiliferous rocks.

The most important result of the systematic development of radiometric ages has been the cumulative effect of the now numerous determinations. Although the consistency of the sets of ages based on five independent decay constants—two for uranium, one each for thorium, potassium, and rubidium—and the interlocking of all these ages with the stratigraphic systems based on changes in fossil faunas and floras may not establish accurate individual ages in years, they do establish beyond doubt an enormous length for geologic time. No worker in this field is concerned any longer with the demonstration of this great central conclusion. The problems have become more specific: whether radiometric ages are the best guides for Pleistocene horizons; whether the Silurian is a short period and the Cambrian a long one; whether the base of the Cambrian is at 500 or 570 or 600 m.y.; and whether the probable accuracy of the estimated 2,680 m.y. age for an African pegmatite is ±50 or ±150 or ±250 m.y. However these details may be settled, an earth history extending back over billions of years has been established as one of the conditions with which thinking men must deal. Comparable concepts in other sciences are almost infinitely large astronomical space and almost infinitely small units of matter.

REFERENCES

General and Introductory

1. Adolph Knopf: "Measuring Geologic Time," SCIENTIFIC MONTHLY, vol. 85, pp. 225–236 (1957)

2. J. Laurence Kulp: "Geologic Time Scale," SCIENCE, vol. 133, pp. 1105–1114 (1961)

3. Arthur Holmes: "A Revised Geological Timescale," TRANSACTIONS, Edinburgh Geological Society, vol. 17, pp. 183–216 (1960)

Detailed or Technical

4. L. H. Ahrens: "The Convergent Lead Ages of the Oldest Monazites and Uraninites (Rhodesia, Manitoba, Madagascar, and Transvaal)," GEOCHIMICA ET COSMOCHIMICA ACTA, vol. 7, pp. 294–300 (1955)

5. G. L. Davis and others: "The Ages of Rocks and Minerals," Year Book 59, Carnegie Institution of Washington, pp. 147–158 (1960)

6. Gordon Gastil: "The Distribution of Mineral Dates in Time and Space," AMERICAN JOURNAL OF SCIENCE, vol. 258, pp. 1–35 (1960)

7. J. Laurence Kulp and others: "Geochronology of Rock Systems," ANNALS, New York Academy of Sciences, vol. 91, pp. 159–594 (1961)

8. L. R. Stieff and T. W. Stern: "Graphic and Algebraic Solutions of the Discordant Lead-uranium Age Problem," GEOCHIMICA ET COSMOCHIMICA ACTA, vol. 22, pp. 176–199 (1961)

9. G. W. Wetherill: "Discordant Uranium-lead Ages, I," TRANSACTIONS, American Geophysical Union, vol. 37, pp. 320–326 (1956)

10. J. A. Lowdon and others: "Age Determinations by the Geological Survey of Canada," Paper 62-17, Geol. Sur. Canada, pp. 1–122 (1963)

11. L. T. Silver, C. R. McKinney, Sarah Deutsch, and J. Bolinger: "Precambrian Age Determinations in the Western San Gabriel Mountains, California," JOURNAL OF GEOLOGY, vol. 71, pp. 196–214 (1963)

12. K. J. Hsu, George Edwards, and W. A. McLaughlin: "Age of the Intrusive Rocks of the Southeastern San Gabriel Mountains, California," BULLETIN, Geol. Soc. Am., vol. 74, pp. 507–512 (1963)

CHAPTER 9

Precambrian Times

PRECAMBRIAN times are known through the study of rocks that have been proved to be pre-Cambrian. The best proof is demonstration of stratigraphic position beneath beds containing the lowest Cambrian fauna. In some areas, as we shall find in Chapter 10, either the lowest fossils are not Lower Cambrian or Lower Cambrian fossils become rarer and rarer downsection, merely fading out below. Under such circumstances some rocks are questionably Precambrian. We shall, however, find ways of reducing the doubtful occurrences to small proportions.

In Precambrian as in other stratigraphy there are two primary procedures. First, one local column, made up of mappable formations, is selected as a standard; second, correlations are made from other local columns to the standard column. The primary sequence of formations in a Precambrian column, as in any other, is composed of sedimentary and volcanic surface rocks. Because of the almost complete absence of guide fossils, lithologic similarities have been used for local Precambrian correlations, with special reliance on successions containing unusual rocks, notably the widespread silica-iron complex called iron formation. Long-distance correlations of the surface formations, however, must be made indirectly, through the radiometric ages of minerals in intrusive rocks that are mostly quartz plutonites. These plutonites are the most abundant Precambrian rocks; the sedimentary and volcanic series form more or less isolated elongate bodies of stratified rocks, somewhat like archipelagoes in plutonic seas. If a sequence of one or more stratified series lies unconformably on one dated plutonic rock and is invaded by another, the sequence is bracketed in time between the two dates.

9-1. The Precambrian Record

a. Distribution of the Rocks

The continental platforms are made up mostly of Precambrian rocks (Fig. 9-1). In North America, as we found in Chapter 6, these rocks are exposed over most of the vast extent of the Canadian Shield* as well as at the centers of such local domes as the Black Hills of South Dakota and the eastern Ozarks, in Missouri. In the east-central part of the continent, between the domes, the top of the Precambrian, in most places, is only a few thousand feet beneath the surface and is easily reached by drilling.

In South America, the great eastern bulge of the continent in Brazil, the Guianas, and Venezuela, on both sides of the Amazon Basin, is mostly an exposed Precambrian platform (shield area). In Eurasia, large areas of Precambrian rocks crop out in the Baltic Shield and (in central Asia) around Lake Baikal. A Precambrian basement platform, partially cov-

---

* The Canadian Precambrian area was called a shield because its shape was thought to be similar to that of a Greco-Roman shield.

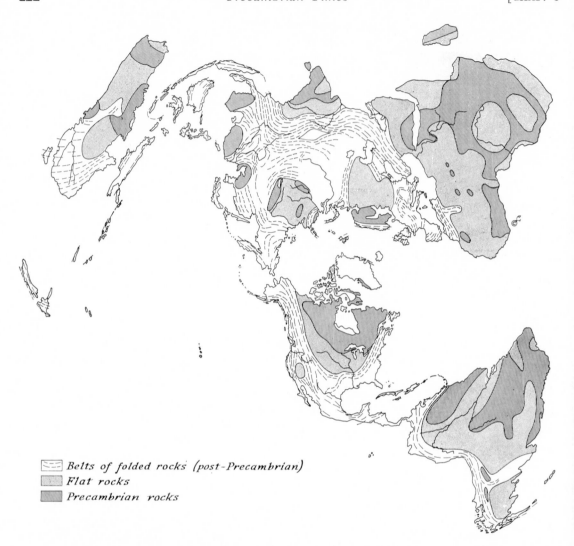

Belts of folded rocks (post-Precambrian)
Flat rocks
Precambrian rocks

Fig. 9-1. *Structural map of Precambrian and younger rocks of the world. (Adapted from J. H. F. Umbgrove by Bernhard Kummel,* History of the Earth, W. H. Freeman & Co., 1961.)

ered by later sediments, is also present in other parts of Eurasia, notably in European Russia, in the Arabian and Indian peninsulas, in northern China, southern China, and Vietnam, and in many small massifs of western and central Europe. In Africa, the largest and most varied high-standing mass of Precambrian rocks in the world crops out widely in the central and southern parts of the continent. Finally, somewhat more than the western half of Australia and most of Antarctica are Precambrian. Though the Precambrian rocks

of every continent have interesting features, we shall confine our attention chiefly to North America and southern Africa.

b. Subdivision and Correlation

The Precambrian of the Grand Canyon is very clearly divisible into two parts: (1) the schist, gneiss, and granite of the Granite Gorge; (2) the unconformably overlying sedimentary rocks of the wedge series. Similar though less obvious distinctions were found long ago in the Precambrian rocks north of

Lake Superior, in the northern Rocky Mountains of the United States and Canada, in northwestern Scotland, in Finland, and elsewhere. In some of these regions fossils have been found in the unmetamorphosed or slightly metamorphosed sedimentary rocks above the grand unconformity. The fossils are mostly algae, but they are unmistakably organic, and so these rocks have been called Proterozoic (belonging to the time of earlier life). The underlying crystalline rocks have been called Archean (very antique) or Archeozoic (belonging to the time of very ancient life). The Archean rocks were thought to be extremely old, the sedimentary rocks of wedge-series type much younger, perhaps little older than the lowest Paleozoic strata. The two-fold subdivision, however, has encountered difficulties. In central Arizona, not far south of the Grand Canyon, three Precambrian units occur, the upper two much like the two in the Grand Canyon, the lowest, beneath an unconformity, an older granodiorite. In South Africa, seven Precambrian groups (commonly called systems) have been distinguished. These developments have made a general two-fold subdivision of the Precambrian very difficult—in fact, hardly possible. The terms Proterozoic, Archean, and Archeozoic have therefore become useless.

New distinctions, based primarily on the radiometric ages of one chosen section and extended to other sections by the use of radiometric dating, have recently become possible. A revised classification of this sort will be suggested after a discussion of lacunas and metamorphism and descriptions of the South African and Lake Superior sections.

c. Lacunas and Metamorphism

Unconformities, and the lacunas of which they are evidence, are especially common in the Precambrian record. The types of evidence associated with an unconformity have been illustrated in Figure 8-16, representing Mesozoic terrains in southern California. It will be remembered that the development of the great unconformity there, as well as the intrusion of the Cretaceous granitic body, required only a small part of Cretaceous time, probably not more than 10 or 15 m.y. One may, with this example in mind, minimize the temporal importance of even so profound an unconformity as that between the gneiss and the wedge series in the Grand Canyon. Such an unconformity is useful for local correlation as far as it can be followed, either continuously or with minor interruptions, as from one part of the Grand Canyon to another; but one must be alert to possible changes in structure and in metamorphism. The size of the lacuna may change, either through simple overlap (§ 4-7 and § 5-1.b), through overlap complicated by deformation, or through the passage from platform to geosynclinal conditions. In the last case, the investigator must be on the lookout for the varied metamorphosing effects of a granite that is widespread in the geosyncline but sends only a few minor dikes into the rigid mass of the platform. It is here that the dating and correlation of a granite through its radioactive minerals become especially important.

A pair of examples from the Canadian Shield shows the difficulties in correlation by unconformities or intensity of metamorphism and demonstrates the value of radiometric ages. The Grenville series of limestones, quartzites, and metavolcanic rocks crops out in eastern Ontario and western Quebec, on both sides of the Ottawa River, extending from the Georgian Bay of Lake Huron, at the west, to a point northeast of Ottawa, at the east, with outliers almost as far east as Quebec city and south into the Adirondack region of New York. This series is invaded by granite and other plutonic rocks and has been transformed into coarsely crystalline metamorphic rocks that contain many high-temperature, high-pressure minerals, such as hornblende and garnet. The old volcanics, for example, are now coarse-grained plagioclase-hornblende rocks. The present upper surface of the Grenville series is an erosion surface, perhaps a peneplain, which cuts indiscriminately across all the rocks and their structures; the overlying, nearly horizontal Cambrian and Ordovician strata are strikingly unconformable on the Grenville. The Grenville rocks appear to be miogeosynclinal and eugeosynclinal strata that have reached a stage of deformation and metamorphism equal to that of the oldest rocks in the region. But the age of crystallization of the granitic rocks that invade the Grenville, determined at many localities and including some of the most concordant of all Pb/U ages, is only about one billion years. Fifteen hundred miles northwest, near the western edge of the Shield, the Athabasca series of northern Saskatchewan is made up largely of flat-lying clastic sandstones, unconformable on a complex of gneiss and granite (Fig. 9-16). Lithologic similarity might tempt one to correlate the gneiss with the Grenville series. But the Athabasca series is cut by uraninite-bearing veins at least 1,400 m.y. old. It must be older than the Grenville plutonism and metamorphism, rather than younger, as was long thought.

9-2. *Deformation of a Precambrian Platform*

We found, in Chapters 5 and 6, evidence of the development in late Precambrian and Early Cambrian times of two broad flat erosion surfaces in North America—one, rather small, in the Grand Canyon region and the other, much larger, in the eastern part of the continent. In both regions some of the products of weathering still lie on the erosion surface or have been moved but short distances ("granite wash"). The eastern surface, in part exposed as the Canadian Shield, in part hidden by younger rocks, is the top of a Precambrian platform that makes up most of the bulk of the northeastern half of the continent.

The eastern North American platform has been mildly deformed since Cambrian times, and the character of the deformation is probably significant, though its interpretation is not yet clear. The deformation structures are broad, flat-topped, low upwarps and perhaps

slightly smaller, mostly rather deep downwarps.

a. Upwarps

The upwarps are typified by the flat Cincinnati-Indiana Arch (§ 6-3.a). A second structural high is particularly important to us now, for in it we shall find our Precambrian type area. This area is, in the main, the Lake Superior region, but it also extends northward between Lakes Winnipeg and Athabasca, on the west, and Hudson Bay, on the northeast.

The geology of the Superior-Athabasca-Hudson area is shown in Figure 9-2. Lake Athabasca (not marked in Fig. 9-2; see Fig. 9-16) is at the western edge of the Shield, west of the widest part of Hudson Bay. The Athabasca series is mostly a nearly horizontal rock sheet (part of the undifferentiated Precambrian shown by a pattern of crosses in Fig. 9-2; marked VI in Fig. 9-16), whose eastern edge lies within the Province of Saskatchewan, 300 miles west of Hudson Bay. In part this edge is a steep front retreating slowly westward by erosion. One might imagine that the nearly flat surface of the Shield farther east, between this front and the Hudson Bay Paleozoic, is merely or mostly an exhumed portion of the sub-Athabasca erosion surface. But this is not exactly or wholly true.

The younger rocks adjacent to the Precambrian of this part of the Shield, with the exception of a thin and discontinuous cover of Pleistocene deposits, are represented in Figure 9-2. Beneath the Pleistocene, the rocks range in age from Cretaceous (stippled) to Cambrian. Ordovician, Silurian, and Devonian limestones are especially widespread. The pattern of the Paleozoic outcrops and the prevalence of limestones of platform type indicate strongly that after Cambrian time the whole area was covered by successive sheets of Paleozoic (and later) sediments, which were removed, in part, by erosion from two belts of uplift, whose axes (lines of greatest uplift) are shown in Figure 9-2 almost at right angles to each other. The first deformation occurred in the late Paleozoic, before the deposition of the Pennsylvanian coal measures. A broad, low, northwest-southeast anticline was formed, which at the south, in Wisconsin, is marked by central exposure of the Cambrian, with marginal belts of Ordovician and Silurian. This axis extends far northwest into Canada, as shown by central Precambrian exposures and marginal belts of Ordovician,

Silurian, and Devonian strata. Later, in post-Pennsylvanian time, but before the deposition of the Cretaceous, a southwest-northeast upfold formed, from which the coal measures and all the underlying Paleozoic were stripped, in southwestern Minnesota, southeastern South Dakota, and northern Nebraska, and which were then covered by Cretaceous strata

Fig. 9-2. *Intersection of pre-Pennsylvanian and pre-Cretaceous arches near Lake Superior: C, Cretaceous; C, Cambrian; D, Devonian; JT, Jurassic-Triassic; M, Mississippian; O, Ordovician; P, Pennsylvanian; PAL, Paleozoic; PC, Precambrian; PP, Pennsylvanian-Permian; S, Silurian. (Adapted from A. I. Levorsen,* Paleogeologic Maps, *W. H. Freeman & Co., 1960.)*

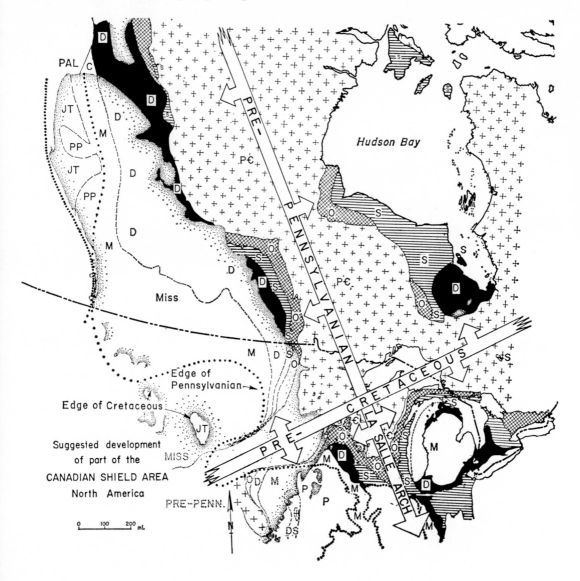

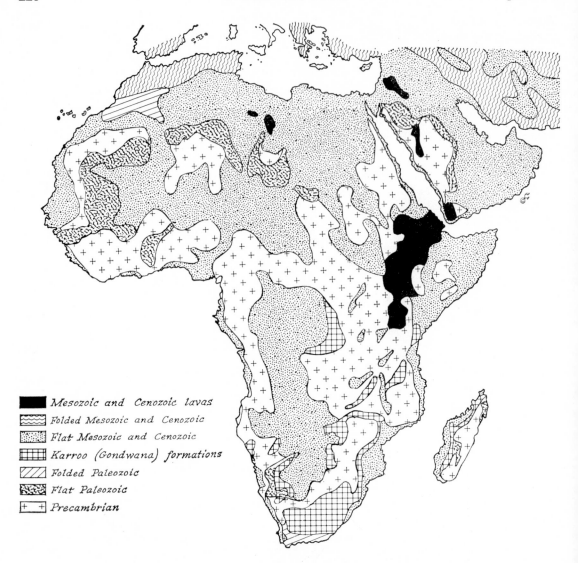

Legend:
- ■ *Mesozoic and Cenozoic lavas*
- ∿ *Folded Mesozoic and Cenozoic*
- ⋰ *Flat Mesozoic and Cenozoic*
- ⊞ *Karroo (Gondwana) formations*
- ⧄ *Folded Paleozoic*
- ▨ *Flat Paleozoic*
- ⊹ *Precambrian*

Fig. 9-3. *Geologic map of Africa. (Adapted from Ernest Neaverson by Bernhard Kummel, op. cit.)*

that extended far to the east, as shown by small remnants south of Hudson Bay. Later much of the Cretaceous was stripped away, and the valleys now occupied by the Great Lakes were hollowed out. In the Shield area the present surface of the Precambrian rocks is a complex product of several periods of erosion, separated by times of deposition and slight deformation. The deformations were not only the two represented by the axes of Figure 9-2 but also the earlier pre-Athabasca event and, after a great Ordovician overlap onto the Precambrian, later minor deformations following the deposition of the sediments of each Paleozoic system represented in the area. Nevertheless, the present exposed surface of Precambrian rocks at the southern edge of the Shield, in Michigan and northern Wisconsin, was formed in Cambrian or earlier time and has recently been exhumed; it is, in fact, covered by widely scattered remnants of the lower Paleozoic cover. The surface of the Shield farther north may have been developed partly in pre-Athabasca time, partly in post-Cambrian time, but the degree of post-Cambrian incision into the Precambrian rocks must have been slight. The anticlines shown in Figure 9-2 are very low upwarps, perhaps with crests no higher than the present base of the superjacent Upper Cambrian (about 1,000 feet above sea level) or the higher hills of exposed Precambrian rocks along the anticlinal axes (up to about 2,500 feet above sea level).

b. Downwarps

The principal downwarps in the main platform area are the shallow Hudson Bay Paleozoic basin in the center of the Shield and the deeper Illinois, Michigan, and Appalachian basins in the United States (Chap. 6). The Michigan Basin, filled with Paleozoic rocks, is only about 300 miles across, and its center is more than 13,000 feet below sea level (Fig. 6-15).

Even after we have taken all the post-Cambrian deformation into consideration, we find that the Precambrian platform of northeastern North America has been an exceptionally stable area since the beginning of the Paleozoic. So have other shield areas. Their Precambrian histories, however, were very different.

9-3. Precambrian Rock Systems

In most parts of the Precambrian shields the rocks are predominantly granitic. In a few areas sedimentary-volcanic sequences as thick as those of younger systems are also found. The areas of abundant Precambrian surface rocks and of varied relations between the granites and the surface rocks are the ones that yield the most interesting and most useful local Precambrian columns.

Exceptionally informative successions of Precambrian sedimentary and volcanic forma-

tions occur in two areas—one in South Africa, the other in the Lake Superior region of North America. We take the South African area first because of its clear succession and many clean-cut stratigraphic units.

a. South Africa

The dominance of the Precambrian in central and southern Africa is apparent in a geologic map of the continent (Fig. 9-3). Several complex Precambrian successions are known, including the Rhodesian one mentioned in § 8-3.e.3. Farther south, around Johannesburg in Transvaal, Union of South Africa, the exploitation of great gold mines has led to an especially sound knowledge of the succession. As the younger rocks of South Africa are interestingly unusual, and as we shall come back to them in Chapter 13, most of the South African geologic column will be outlined here. The only Paleozoic marine fauna that amounts to anything at all is Devonian, and even that European system name is not applicable to a natural unit of South African rocks. We have nine new names to consider, as shown in Table 9-1.

In most parts of southern Africa one must use radiometric dating even to ascertain which rocks are Precambrian. The bodies of Cape granite near Cape Town (Fig. 9-4), with probable ages of about 575 m.y., may be close to the Cambrian-Precambrian boundary (compare § 8-7.d). Cape granites invade the moderately metamorphosed shales and sandstones of the geosynclinal Malmesbury "System" (Table 9-1), which is therefore probably Precambrian even if it is only slightly older than the granite. Another folded and metamorphosed sedimentary sequence of geosynclinal aspect, in Southwest Africa, a thousand miles north of Cape Town, underwent its last metamorphism some 520 m.y. ago and may be an equivalent of the Malmesbury rocks. A third, similar sequence, south of the mouth of the Orange River (Fig. 9-4), has yielded ages of about 1,000 m.y.

The Waterberg "System" of Transvaal (northeastern South Africa, Figs. 9-4 and 9-5) is a platform deposit that has been moderately deformed. It is not in contact with the young Precambrian rocks previously mentioned, but it is probably somewhat older (Table 9-1). The Loskop "System" underlies the Waterberg and is probably only a little older.

The Transvaal "System" is a thick platform-and-basin sequence that is widespread in northeastern South Africa. It includes, at the base, conglomerate and quartzite, which are overlain successively by dolomite, shale, and quartzite, with some volcanic sheets high in the series. The deposition of the Transvaal "System" was probably followed immediately,

TABLE 9-1

South African Stratigraphy

(Top)	
Karroo "System" [a]	By much the most widespread unit. Continental; from Upper Carboniferous(?) to Upper Triassic.
Cape "System"	Lies conformably beneath the Karroo and includes the marine Devonian strata; mostly continental. Lowest unit the Table Mountain Sandstone that towers over Cape Town.
Nama "System"	Platform sheet of quartzites and carbonates in Southwest Africa. One Lower Cambrian guide fossil.
Malmesbury "System"	Deformed, moderately metamorphosed shales and sandstones in belts northeast of Cape Town; possibly 20,000 feet thick; invaded by Cape granites, 550–600 m.y. old; perhaps, in part, geosynclinal equivalent of Nama "System."
Waterberg "System"	Platform sheet of quartzites, shales, conglomerates, and volcanic rocks in northeastern South Africa. Probably older than dikes aged $1,290 \pm 180$ m.y. No fossils.
Loskop "System"	Platform sheet of quartzites, shales, and conglomerates. No fossils. Beneath Waterberg in northeastern South Africa.
	Unconformity
Bushveld Plutonic Complex	Shallow intrusive mass in Transvaal (northeastern South Africa), hundreds of miles across. Red granite, gabbroic rocks, etc. Age, $1,940 \pm 150$ m.y. (6 localities; Sr/Rb on mica, feldspar, and total rock; Pb/U and Pb/Th on monazite; Pb/U on zircon).
Transvaal "System"	Quartzite, shale, dolomite, lava; 17,000 feet thick.
	Unconformity
Ventersdorp "System"	Lavas and some sediments; 11,000–14,000 feet thick. Northeastern South Africa. Uraninite 2,200(?) m.y. old by Pb207/Pb206.
Witwatersrand "System"	Quartzite, shale, conglomerate; 25,000 feet thick. Northeastern South Africa. Uraninite grains apparently 2,100 m.y. old, perhaps detrital and altered after deposition; new monazite $2,150 \pm 100$ m.y. old.
Dominion Reef "System"	Volcanics and some sediments, including arkose and gold-bearing conglomerate; closely associated with western part of Witwatersrand "System." At least 2,000 feet thick. Uraninite and monazite grains, apparently $3,050 \pm 100$ m.y. old, probably detrital.
	Great Unconformity
Crystalline Complex	Old granites, gray, widespread, intruding quartzites, schists, recrystallized lavas, etc.; sedimentary sequences locally more than 20,000 feet thick. An old granite near Johannesburg 3.2 billion years old by Sr/Rb whole-rock method. Other ages 2,800–3,100 m.y.

[a] This "system" and the others in this column are limited to Africa (and perhaps other southern continents); they are therefore unlike the Cambrian and other worldwide systems based on European type sequences.

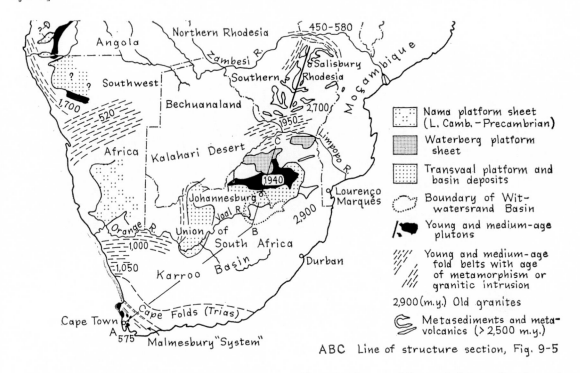

Fig. 9-4. *Structural diagram of southern Africa, showing the trend lines of deformed rocks and the areas of platform deposits, particularly those of Precambrian age. (Modified from L. O. Nico-laysen, Buddington Volume, Geol. Soc. Am., 1962.)*

Fig. 9-5. *Diagrammatic geologic section southwest-northeast through the Union of South Africa, more or less along the line ABC of Fig. 9-4.*

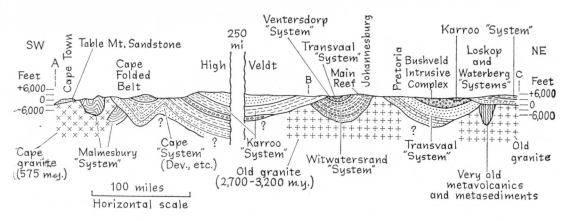

in the Transvaal area north of Johannesburg, by the moderately extensive volcanic extrusions and enormous plutonic intrusions of gabbro, red granite, and other rocks making up the Bushveld igneous complex, whose mean determined age of 1,940 m.y. is marked on Figure 9-4. The samples for the age-determinations of the Bushveld rocks (summarized in Table 9-1) were carefully selected after thorough field study. The Pb/Th ages for the monazite were very low, from 900 to 1,250 m.y., but this is usual, and the thorium ages

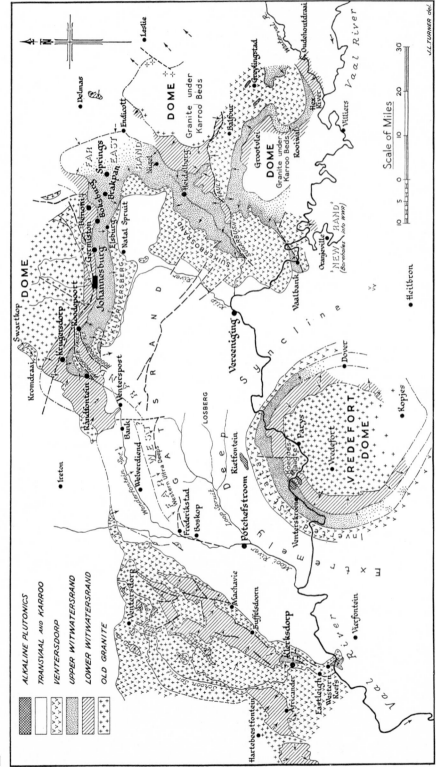

Fig. 9-6. *Geologic map of the Johannesburg-Vredefort area, South Africa. (From A. L. du Toit, The Geology of South Africa, Oliver & Boyd, Edinburgh, 1954.)*

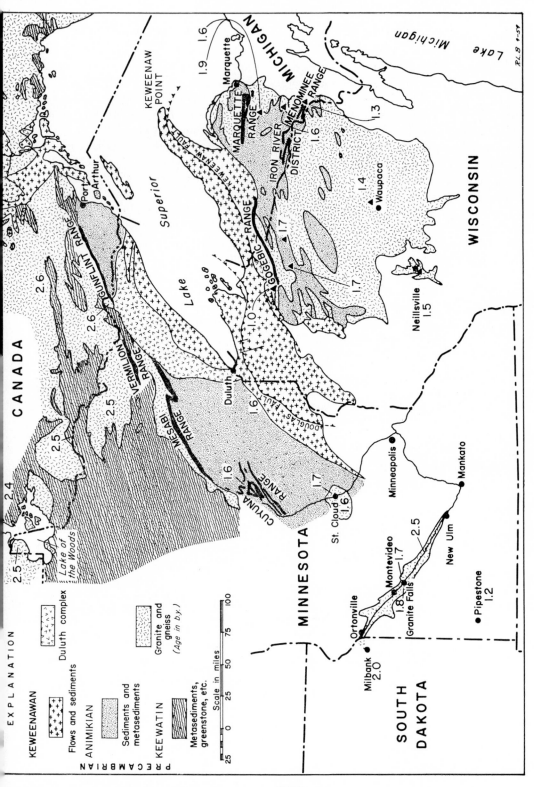

Fig. 9-7. *Geologic map of the Lake Superior region; Ar/K ages of rocks in billions of years. (Adapted from S. S. Goldich and others. Bull. 41, Minn. Geol. Survey, 1961.)*

were therefore ignored in the calculation of the 1,940 m.y. mean.

The best-known South African rocks are the thick basin deposits of the Witwatersrand "System" (Table 9-1). In Figure 9-4 the largely subsurface Witwatersrand Basin is outlined. The Witwatersrand rocks are largely hidden by younger series, as shown in Figure 9-6. At and near Johannesburg, the Main Reef, the gold-bearing quartz conglomerate somewhat above the middle of the thick Witwatersrand sequence, has yielded, by the lead-isotope methods, monazite and uraninite ages ranging from 2,000 to 2,200 m.y. The uraninite may have recrystallized from detrital grains, but the monazite was crystallized after deposition and gives a probable minimum age for this sedimentary series.

The widespread Crystalline Complex of southern Africa has yielded many ages between 2,600 and 3,200 m.y. One of these

was determined on the old granite at Johannesburg (Figs. 9-5 and 9-6). Others are marked on Figure 9-4. Probably the 3,050 m.y. ages on uraninite and monazite in the Dominion Reef "System" (Table 9-1) are on detrital grains and therefore further indications of Crystalline Complex ages.

In summary, the South African Precambrian is made up of a basement or Crystalline Complex of metasediments, metavolcanics, and granitic rocks, about three billion years in age, overlain unconformably by a sequence of at least six—and probably seven or eight— Precambrian "Systems," most of which are chiefly sedimentary, though two are chiefly volcanic.

b. Lake Superior Region

The Canadian Shield is the principal expanse of Precambrian rocks in North America (compare Fig. 9-1). It is mostly in Canada,

Fig. 9-8. *Structure section across Lake Superior. Compare Fig. 9-7. (After Leith, Lund, and Leith, Prof. Paper 184, U.S. Geological Survey, 1935.)*

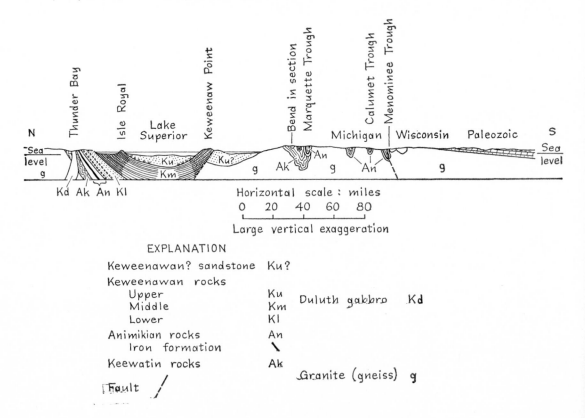

EXPLANATION

Keweenawan? sandstone   Ku?

Keweenawan rocks
    Upper   Ku   Duluth gabbro   Kd
    Middle   Km
    Lower   Kl

Animikian rocks   An
    Iron formation   \

Keewatin rocks   Ak

Fault   /   Granite (gneiss)   g

Fig. 9-9. *Geologic map showing "Archeozoic" metavolcanic and metasedimentary rocks north of Lake Superior. (After F. J. Pettijohn via Bernhard Kummel, op. cit.)*

north of the Great Lakes and the St. Lawrence River, but it extends south into the United States, notably on both sides of Lake Superior, in northeastern Minnesota, northern Wisconsin, and northwestern Michigan, as shown in a general way in Figure 9-2. The term "Lake Superior region," as here used, includes these parts of these states and also, to the north, southwestern Ontario as far northeast as the large Paleozoic outlier southwest of Hudson Bay (Fig. 9-2).

We shall follow one current usage in divid-

TABLE 9-2

Precambrian Column of the Lake Superior Region

Upper Cambrian	Sandstone, fossiliferous
	Unconformity
7. Keweenawan? (uppermost Precambrian or low Cambrian)	Sandstone, mostly red; no fossils. 4,000 feet thick. Mapped with the unquestioned Keweenawan in Figs. 9-7 and 9-10.
6. Duluth Gabbro and Red Granite	Intrusive at base of Keweenawan (5) and sending gabbroic dikes into Middle Keweenawan, Lower Keweenawan, and Animikian rocks. Probably older than the Upper Keweenawan rocks. The main mass, northwest of Lake Superior, and the dikes are 1,000–1,200 m.y. old by Ar/K (Fig. 9-11) and Sr/Rb.
5. Keweenawan	The Copper Series
C. Upper	Red and green feldspathic sandstone and shale; white quartz sandstone. 15,000 feet thick.
B. Middle	Basaltic and (rare) rhyolitic lavas; some conglomerates of rhyolitic pebbles; some sandstone. Native copper-ore deposits in conglomerate and in porous parts of some lava flows. 20,000 feet thick.
A. Lower	Sandstone and conglomerate. 400 feet thick.
	Unconformity
4. Granitic Intrusives	Pre-Keweenawan and post-Animikian. Widespread. In northeastern Wisconsin apparently 1,900 m.y. old by Pb/U methods; in Minnesota, 1,630–1,780 m.y. old by Ar/K and Sr/Rb.
3. Animikian	The Iron Series. Sometimes called Huronian, the type area being north of Lake Huron, but close time correlation to this area from the Lake Superior region is somewhat uncertain. Type Animikian at Thunder Bay, Ontario, but subdivisions clearest in Michigan.
C. Upper	Shale and slate, quartzite and graywacke, metavolcanics, and some iron formation. 10,000 or more feet thick, plus local volcanic piles several miles thick.
	Unconformity, in Michigan
B. Middle	Iron formation, with quartzite and slate at base. Up to 2,800 feet thick.
	Unconformity, in Michigan
A. Lower	In Michigan, dolomite underlain by quartzite and basal conglomerate. Up to 1,500 feet thick.
	Great unconformity
2. Granitic Intrusives	Widespread. Pre-Animikian, in part post-Keewatin (Algoman), in part mid-Keewatin (Laurentian). 2,400–2,600 m.y. old by Ar/K (Fig. 9-11) and Sr/Rb, 2,600 m.y. by U-Pb loss line (Fig. 9-12).
1. Keewatin	Pre-Animikian surface rocks, volcanic and sedimentary. Graywacke, conglomerate, iron formation, and metavolcanics (greenstones). 20,000 feet or more thick in several districts.

ing the stratified Precambrian rocks of the Lake Superior region into three sequences, Keewatin (oldest), Animikian, and Keweenawan. The name Keewatin comes from the Keewatin district in western Ontario, close to the Lake of the Woods on the international boundary, not from the Keewatin division of the Northwest Territories far to the north. Animikie is the Indian name for Thunder Bay on the north side of Lake Superior; flat-lying Animikian slaty shale is well exposed in the city of Port Arthur on the west side of Thunder Bay. The word Keweenawan is derived from Keweenaw Point, Michigan, on the southeast side of Lake Superior. The first two of these three localities are on the northwest side of the great Precambrian syncline whose axis lies in Lake Superior near its southeast shore, but Keweenaw Point (Figs. 9-7 and 9-8) is on the southeast side of the syncline. Animikian rocks are widespread on the syncline's southeast limb, where they overlie granite unconformably, but Keewatin surface rocks are rare on this limb. The southeast limb is complicated by faulting, unconformities, and notable pre-Keweenawan folding oblique to the main synclinal axis.

1. KEEWATIN. The Keewatin rocks are about half metavolcanics, half metasediments (Fig. 9-9). The metavolcanics are greenstones—that is, basalts with the pyroxene altered to the pale-green mineral chlorite. The metasediments are mostly graywacke and conglomerate, with some iron formation (to be described below), especially in the Vermilion district of northeastern Minnesota. Limestones and shales are almost unrepresented. Individual units are locally very thick. A conglomerate in Minnesota is 4,000 feet thick, one in Ontario 8,700 feet thick. The volcanic and

Fig. 9-10. *Geologic map of part of the Upper Peninsula of Michigan. (From H. L. James, Prof. Paper 314-C, U.S. Geological Survey, 1958.)*

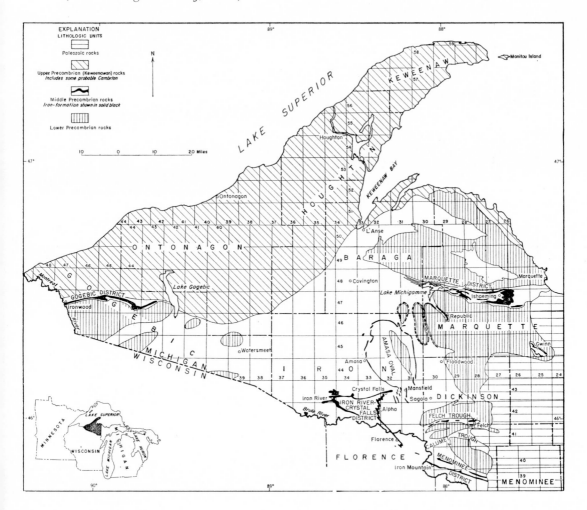

sedimentary units are interbedded. We can probably consider them, in a large view, as virtually contemporaneous. The graywackes are exceptionally dirty, the fine matrix making up about half of the volume. They show graded bedding and may well be the products of turbid flows (§ 4-9.b). In brief, the whole assemblage is typically eugeosynclinal.

At Rainy Lake, just north of the international boundary and halfway between Lake Superior and the Lake of the Woods (Fig. 9-7), the lowest rocks in the center of a Keewatin anticline are several thousand feet of metamorphosed sandstone and conglomerate —the Coutchiching series—that may be as old as any rocks in the Lake Superior region. These coarse clastic sedimentary rocks are rather high in quartz and in this as well as in other ways are similar to many widespread younger formations. The conclusion follows

that the conditions of weathering, erosion, transportation, and deposition in very early geologic times were at least roughly similar to those of later times. Some possible climatic differences will be discussed at the end of this chapter.

Between Rainy Lake and Lake Superior, especially in northern Minnesota, both the Keewatin and the granitic intrusives (No. 2 in Table 9-2) have been subdivided. An older granodiorite (Laurentian), 2,600 m.y. old, is intrusive into Coutchiching metasediments and some Keewatin volcanics, but is overlain unconformably by other Keewatin volcanic and sedimentary rocks (called the Knife Lake Series). Younger granites (Algoman), 2,400– 2,500 m.y. old, are much more widespread than the older ones and invade all the Keewatin surface rocks. In other parts of the Lake Superior region these subdivisions of the Kee-

Fig. 9-11. *Frequency distribution of 126 Ar/K ages, Precambrian of Minnesota and vicinity. (Data from S. S. Goldich and others, loc. cit.)*

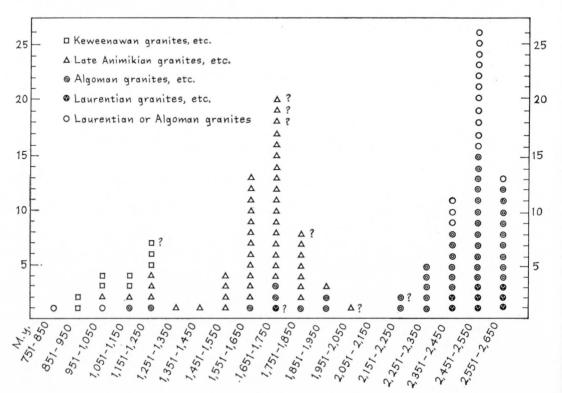

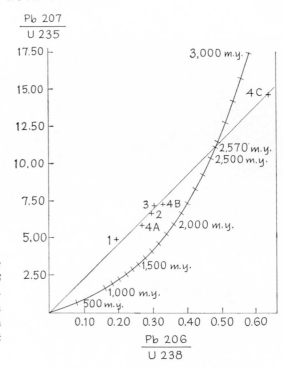

Fig. 9-12. *Early Precambrian lead ages and loss line, Lake Superior region. The Pb207/Pb206 mean age, 2,570 m.y., was made the intersection of the loss line and Concordia. (Data from G. L. Davis and others, Carnegie Institution Year Book, 1960; A. O. C. Nier; and Lamont Geological Observatory.)*

	$\dfrac{Pb206}{U238}$	$\dfrac{Pb207}{U235}$	$\dfrac{Pb207}{Pb206}$	$\dfrac{Pb208}{Th232}$
1. Coutchiching metasedimentary gneiss, Rainy Lake, Ontario. Zircon (Davis)	1,140	1,830	2,760	1,240
2. Gneiss, Black Rock, Michigan. Zircon (Davis)	1,710	2,100	2,510	1,300
3. Gneiss, Carney Lake, Michigan. Zircon (Davis)	1,735	2,160	2,590	1,240
4A. Pegmatite, Huron Claim, Manitoba. Uraninite (Nier)	1,564	1,985	2,475	1,273
4B. Pegmatite, Huron Claim, Manitoba. Uraninite (Lamont)	1,860	2,170	2,505	1,360
4C. Pegmatite, Huron Claim, Manitoba. Monazite (Nier)	3,217	2,839	2,590	1,827

watin and early granitic rocks cannot be made or are uncertain.

2. ANIMIKIAN. The Animikian rocks are predominantly sedimentary—largely shale that is extensively metamorphosed, in Minnesota and Michigan, into slate and schist. The Upper Animikian is exceptional in containing volcanics and some graywacke. The Middle Animikian is largely iron formation, and the Lower Animikian, in Michigan, mostly dolomite and quartzite. The Lower and Middle Animikian may well be platform and shallow-basin deposits. Eugeosynclinal conditions may have developed in the southern part of the region during the late Animikian.

3. IRON FORMATION. The iron formation is a chemical deposit, commonly made up of alternating thin layers of iron compounds and chert (Fig. 9-13). The chert was deposited as amorphous hydrous silica but now has crystallized into quartz whose grain size is a measure of the amount of metamorphism the rock has undergone. The coarser the grain the greater the metamorphism. The original iron-ore compounds were carbonate, oxide, silicate, and sulphide, with carbonate the commonest. Parallel belts (or successive sedimentary units) contained predominant sulphide, carbonate, and oxide, respectively, and these facies may have formed at different depths of water in a partially closed basin. In the

Fig. 9-13. *Photographs of banded iron formation, Iron River, Michigan. (From H. L. James,* BULLETIN, *Geol. Soc. Am., 1951.)*

ABOVE. *Sulphide facies (pyritic black slate) in a polished slab. The pyrite is pale in reflected light.*

BELOW. *Carbonate facies: chert, dark gray; ferrous carbonate, light gray.*

lowest part of the basin of deposition (Fig. 9-14.2), lack of oxygen may have favored the deposition of iron sulphide. In shallow water abundant oxygen may have favored the deposition of ferric oxide (originally ferric hydroxide). At intermediate depths the accumulation of ferrous carbonate may have prevailed. The iron and silica may have been brought into the basin by rivers that drained low, subtropical lands. The nearby lands must have been low, for the iron formation contains

little of the clay, silt, or sand produced by the erosion of mountainous or hilly terrains. The unusual climatic conditions necessary for the production of iron formation will be discussed at the end of this chapter.

Since deposition the mineral composition of the iron formation has changed somewhat. During Precambrian recrystallization, in part metamorphic, magnetite (Fe_3O_4) formed. Perhaps there was even earlier weathering of the first-formed ores, during partial exposure of the iron formation in Late Animikian time (Fig. 9-14.4). In later Precambrian time, through oxidation of the iron and leaching of the silicon, deposits of nearly pure soft iron oxide developed in the Lake Superior region, particularly in the Mesabi Iron Range northwest of Duluth (Minnesota). There the ore has been excavated by power shovels in open pits. This area has been the world's largest single source of iron; now, concentration of low-grade ores is supplementing the high-grade ores that are approaching exhaustion.

Exploration for iron ore in recent decades has been in part by geologic mapping, in part by the use of the magnetometer, sometimes, since 1945, by towing the instrument beneath an airplane. Some great new deposits have been found in the Canadian Shield, especially in Labrador, to take the place of fading Mesabi production.

For the stratigrapher and the historical geologist the great value of the thick Middle Animikian iron formation has been in its use as a horizon marker (Figs. 9-7 and 9-10). With its help the Animikian can be put in stratigraphic order and correlations made between the two limbs of the Lake Superior syncline. Note also how the symmetrical outcrop pattern of iron formation around the Michigan granite cores of anticlines (Fig. 9-10) indicates that these cores are unconformable beneath the Animikian rather than intrusive into that series.

4. POST-ANIMIKIAN DEFORMATION, PLUTONISM, AND METAMORPHISM. After the deposition of the Animikian sediments and

Fig. 9-14. *Depositional history of the Animikian (Huronian) iron formation of Michigan. (From H. L. James,* Economic Geology, *1954.)*

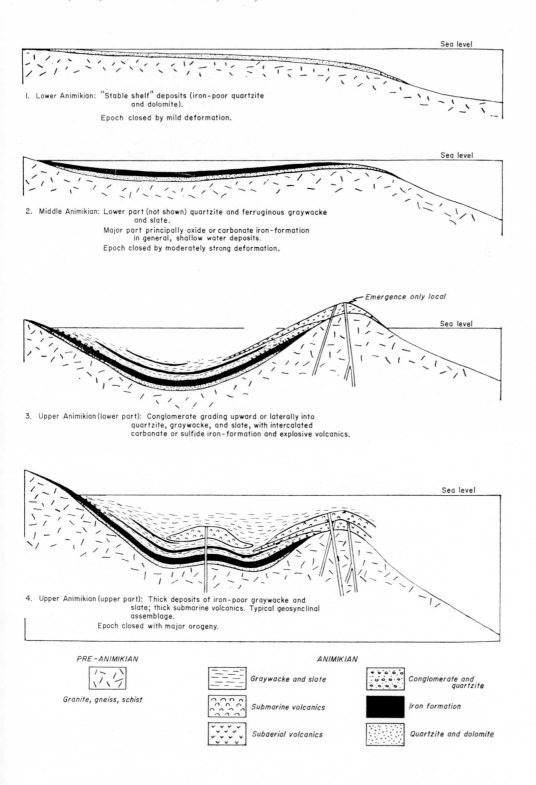

1. Lower Animikian: "Stable shelf" deposits (iron-poor quartzite and dolomite).

   Epoch closed by mild deformation.

2. Middle Animikian: Lower part (not shown) quartzite and ferruginous graywacke and slate.

   Major part principally oxide or carbonate iron-formation in general, shallow water deposits.

   Epoch closed by moderately strong deformation.

   — Emergence only local

3. Upper Animikian (lower part): Conglomerate grading upward or laterally into quartzite, graywacke, and slate, with intercalated carbonate or sulfide iron-formation and explosive volcanics.

4. Upper Animikian (upper part): Thick deposits of iron-poor graywacke and slate; thick submarine volcanics. Typical geosynclinal assemblage.

   Epoch closed with major orogeny.

   PRE-ANIMIKIAN

   Granite, gneiss, schist

   ANIMIKIAN

   Graywacke and slate

   Submarine volcanics

   Subaerial volcanics

   Conglomerate and quartzite

   Iron formation

   Quartzite and dolomite

before the deposition of the Keweenawan sediments and lavas, an east-west belt extending at least from the Cuyuna Iron Range, Minnesota, to the Marquette Range, Michigan (Fig. 9-7), was intensely deformed, invaded by granodiorite and granite that seem to be 1,900–1,600 m.y. (1.9–1.6 b.y.) old, and recrystallized by contact metamorphism in zones that extend for many miles beyond the edges of the present granitic outcrops. The sequence of events in central Minnesota is represented by Figure 9-15. The east-west belt of folding is called the Penokean belt.

The post-Animikian quartz plutonites do not all have the same composition or the same age. In east-central Minnesota, from the vicinity of St. Cloud northeast, two sets can be distinguished: the older gray and granodioritic, with Ar/K ages above 1,700 m.y. and averaging 1,760 m.y.; the younger pink or pinkish granite, at least half of the feldspar being orthoclase, with two 1,640 m.y. age-determinations.

Most of the Ar/K ages for this double period of plutonism in Minnesota merge into a late Animikian group with a single prominent peak on the age graph (Fig. 9-11),

centered at the 1,651–1,750 m.y. line. A slight secondary bulge at 1,151–1,250 m.y. represents samples from localities within the contact-metamorphic zones of Keweenawan plutons. In Michigan, Ar/K and Sr/Rb ages of metamorphosed Animikian slate, quartzite, and dolomite, and also of dikes intrusive into these rocks, are scattered from 2,000 to 1,100 m.y. The Michigan ages (not shown in Fig. 9-11) probably have a complicated explanation; we sweep them under the rug.

North of the closely folded belt, in northern Minnesota and Ontario (at Port Arthur, for example; Fig. 9-7), the Animikian is thin and unmetamorphosed, almost conformable with the Keweenawan, and dipping gently south. This area lacks post-Animikian, pre-Keweenawan granitic rocks. It may have been part of the continental platform of Animikian time, north of the east-west geosyncline.

It is worth noting that the pre-Animikian basement was present as the floor of the Animikian geosynclinal trough and is preserved in the cores of the Michigan anticlines (Fig. 9-10). The discordant Pb/U ages of these pre-Animikian rocks contributed to the 2.60 b.y. loss line (Fig. 9-12).

Fig. 9-15. *The Animikian in Minnesota. (Modified from S. S. Goldich and others,* loc. cit.)

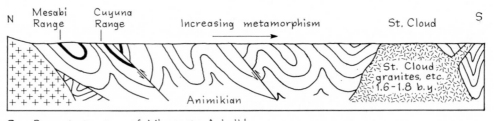

B. Present structure of Minnesota Animikian

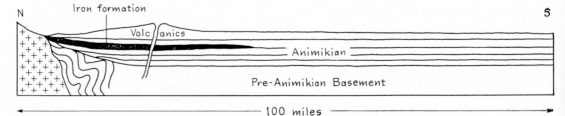

A. Deposition of Minnesota Animikian

5. KEWEENAWAN. The Keweenawan rocks are half sedimentary, half volcanic. The sedimentary rocks are mostly sandstones and conglomerates. Some of the sandstones are made up almost entirely of quartz grains; the rest, though moderately feldspathic, differ from most of the older sandstones by the small proportion of clayey matrix. The Middle Keweenawan basaltic rocks are close to the Duluth gabbro in composition and probably came from the same deep source.

6. KEWEENAWAN AND EARLIER GEOGRAPHIES. Between Animikian and Keweenawan times the general geography of the Lake Superior region underwent two fundamental changes.

The first change was in the pattern of structural deformation. From Keweenawan time on, the major structures have been large folds, in general with southwest-northeast axes. The outstanding feature is the great syncline, with a southwest-northeast axis beneath Lake Superior near its southeastern shore. The Keweenawan units crop out symmetrically about this axis (Fig. 9-7) and show by the junction of the two flanks at the southwest, northeast of Minneapolis, that the syncline has a northeast plunge. In the older Precambrian rocks the structures are differently oriented, smaller, and more numerous, as shown by the east-west belts of Keewatin rocks in western Ontario (Fig. 9-9), the complex Animikian structures of Figure 9-15, and the varied orientation of the contacts between Animikian and older rocks in Michigan (Fig. 9-10). As a result, the Keweenawan strata rest with great unconformity on different older rocks.

The second change, much less easily discovered, was in the direction of movement of the clastic sediments. The Animikian sandstones in Minnesota, Wisconsin, and Michigan show cross-bedding at many levels and many places, almost everywhere with cross-dips predominantly southeast (Ref. 4). The sand-depositing currents must therefore have moved southeast across the whole region (before the present complex structure developed, of course), carrying sediments from distant sources, probably in western Ontario, across the present site of Lake Superior. The Keweenawan cross-bedding, on the other hand, is toward Lake Superior.

The Middle Keweenawan lavas and the Duluth gabbro apparently came from a magma reservoir beneath Lake Superior. As the magma was discharged, the reservoir's roof no doubt sagged, aiding in the development of the synclinal structure. The extruded lavas piled up on the surface at the center of the synclinal basin and spread out laterally for tens of miles. Evidence of the directions of movement is found in old gas bubbles, now filled with minerals, at the bottoms of the flows: the bubbles, having been distorted, streak out in the direction of flow. The spread of the lavas southeast into Michigan reduced the area for accumulation of the gravel and sand being brought northwestward from the margin of the basin. Sediments and lavas, coming from opposite directions, were interbedded as a result of this interplay.

After all the Keweenawan lavas and sediments had been deposited and the Lake Superior syncline had developed approximately its present form, with dips flat near the center but up to 80° on the southeast limb, the copper ore was formed. Copper-bearing solutions, perhaps coming from a magmatic source, perhaps developed by subsurface concentration of copper from the Keweenawan lavas, moved upward along porous layers into a strip 35 miles long, centered on Houghton, Michigan. The ore mineral is native copper, and the ore has been obtained about half from filled cavities in the lava flows and half from the spaces between the pebbles in the principal conglomerate ore body, which is 5–10 feet thick and 18,000 feet long and extends 9,300 or more feet down the dip. The mined ore has been rich, up to 3 percent copper by weight.

9-4. *Precambrian Time Divisions*

With respect to Precambrian time-stratigraphic standards, the present moment is one of uncertainty. The best world standards may ultimately be found in Africa, but for the time being the units in the Lake Superior region may be taken as tentative standards. The three major stratigraphic divisions based on Lake Superior rocks are Keewatin, Animikian, and Keweenawan. Each is considered comparable in bulk and variety to all the Mesozoic or even all the Paleozoic systems. A fourth and latest Precambrian division corresponds to the Keweenawan-Cambrian lacuna of the Lake Superior region.

Each of the Precambrian divisions, except perhaps the last, somewhere includes plutonic as well as surface rocks. For example, the plutonic rocks of somewhat varied ages intrusive into and intimately mixed with the Keewatin surface rocks are placed in the Keewatin division unless they also invade Animikian rocks (or still younger rocks), in which case they are assigned to the youngest division of surface rocks that they invade.

The four tentative worldwide divisions of the Precambrian are defined in the following paragraphs.

a. *Keewatin and Approximately Contemporaneous Surface and Plutonic Rocks**

This time-stratigraphic unit includes the Keewatin rocks of the Lake Superior region and all other rocks, surface or plutonic, that formed previous to the deposition of the lowest Animikian surface rocks. The widespread 2,600 m.y. plutonic rocks are surely to be included with the Keewatin. So also are the somewhat younger plutonic rocks that invade the latest Keewatin and have ages down to perhaps 2,400 m.y.

* The *Archean* of the Geological Survey of Canada.

The rocks in Africa and Russia that appear to be the world's oldest are here called Keewatin, though they may ultimately be dated well enough to require a separate subdivision of the Precambrian. These very ancient rocks all seem to be metamorphosed surface rocks or pegmatites intrusive into such rocks. The oldest set of dates is for a group of mixed rocks, partly plutonic and partly metamorphic, in northwestern Russia; this set will be discussed briefly on a later page.

b. *Animikian and Approximately Contemporaneous Surface and Plutonic Rocks**

This time-stratigraphic unit includes the Animikian of the Lake Superior region, the post-Animikian and pre-Keweenawan granitic intrusives, and all other rocks that formed during approximately the same time. The range in years cannot yet be stated with much confidence. Animikian time includes the 1,600–1,800 m.y. Ar/K granitic ages in Minnesota (Fig. 9-11) and a 1,900? m.y. Pb/U age for a granodiorite in northeastern Wisconsin, as well as the earlier times of deposition of the Animikian sedimentary and volcanic rocks. The tentative time range is 1,500–2,400 m.y.

c. *Keweenawan and Approximately Contemporaneous Surface and Plutonic Rocks†*

This time-stratigraphic unit includes the Keweenawan of the Lake Superior region and all other rocks that formed during approximately the same time. The range in years is uncertain, but it apparently includes 1,000–1,200 m.y. (Fig. 9-11) and may reasonably be expanded to 900–1,500 m.y.

* The *Lower Proterozoic* of the Geological Survey of Canada.
† The *Middle Proterozoic* of the Geological Survey of Canada.

d. Keweenawan-Cambrian Lacuna*

The Precambrian time-stratigraphic framework based on the Lake Superior section has a large lacuna at the top, between the Keweenawan and the Cambrian—perhaps between 900 and 600 m.y. This lacuna appears to include the time of deposition of a great Eurasian sedimentary system, the Sinian, which was set up in China and has also been recognized in the U.S.S.R. Some rather doubtful glauconite ages for the Russian Sinian are between 600 and 800 m.y. With this lacuna filled, Precambrian time is conveniently divided into four parts, each with definite geological significance.

9-5. Precambrian Correlations

a. North America

1. CANADIAN SHIELD. Correlations between the Lake Superior standard section and the rocks of other areas must be made chiefly by the use of radiometric ages that indicate the times of crystallization of plutonic rocks. The most trustworthy ages are those derived from consistent groups of determinations. A group of concordant ages is not, however, enough. We must have some knowledge of the shape and extent of the body being dated. A rough guide is furnished by structural features such as the trends of deformed rock bodies. An area of consistent trends of similar rocks (illustrated in Fig. 9-9) may be called a structural province or subprovince. In Figure 9-16 the Canadian Shield is divided into such provinces and subprovinces.

Our Lake Superior sequence is to be found, in that figure, distributed among four provinces or subprovinces. The Keewatin area of east-west structural trends (Fig. 9-9) and

* The *Upper Proterozoic* of the Geological Survey of Canada.

2,300–2,600 m.y. plutonic ages lies in the Superior Province. The rest of the Lake Superior region is placed, from a Canadian point of view, in a Southern Province containing three subprovinces: flat Animikian (XIII), the Penokean belt of folded Animikian and older rocks (XII), and the Keweenawan syncline (XIV). The great southwest-northeast trending syncline, which seems to be reflected in the shape of Lake Superior, swings round to an east-west trend at the eastern end of the lake and disappears. In the other direction, on the northwestern side of the lake, east-west structural trends and 2,300–2,600 m.y. ages extend to Lake Winnipeg at the western edge of the Shield and north to the Nelson River, though at the north some anomalous younger ages are included. At the least, the Superior Province can be considered to include the full width of Precambrian exposures between Lake Winnipeg and the Hudson Bay Paleozoic outlier, shown in Figure 9-16, and to reach north almost as far as the Nelson River.

The Superior Province also extends east round the outlier and far to the northeast. The roughly east-west structural trends characteristic of the Keewatin rocks north of Lake Superior continue beyond James Bay to the sharply marked boundary of the Grenville Province, a line that is commonly called the Grenville Front. Up to this line, large masses of Keewatin-type metavolcanic and metasedimentary rocks are moderately frequent. Keewatin ages are known for associated quartz plutonites at many localities, even to the north beyond the latitude of 60°—a tribute to the enterprise of the Geological Survey of Canada. The plutonic ages and the consistent structural trends justify the labeling of the whole vast region as the Superior Province.

A small southern part of the Superior Province, in eastern Ontario northeast of Lake Huron and marked XI in Figure 9-16, is made up of the Cobalt district of rather flat-lying strata. In this district a single Ar/K age of 2,095 m.y. justifies provisional correlation with

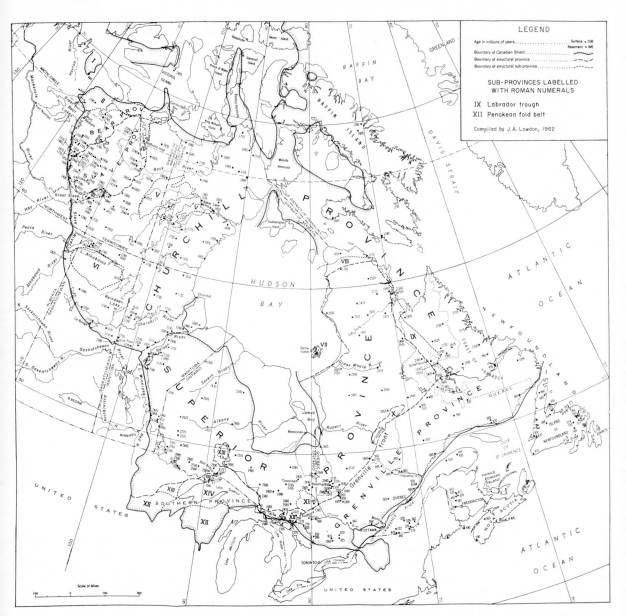

Fig. 9-16. *Map showing Ar/K ages of Precambrian rocks, provinces, and subprovinces in the Canadian Shield. (Adapted from J. A. Lowdon and others, Geol. Survey of Canada, 1963.)*

the Animikian group of rocks in the Port Arthur area north of Lake Superior. The eastern end of the Southern Province, in Ontario north of Lake Huron, contains a gently dipping sedimentary sequence whose basal conglomerate, near Blind River, bears rich uraninite ore that has furnished Pb207/Pb206 ages of 1,680 and 1,740 m.y. (J. A. Mair and others, 1960) The conglomerate is overlain by a slaty-sandy sequence, without iron formation, and lies with great unconformity on a largely volcanic basement complex that is probably Keewatin. The overlying sequence is bounded on the southeast by a great fault that separates it from plutonic rocks and probably from the Sudbury sedimentary-volcanic-plutonic complex, whose plutonic rocks have yielded somewhat doubtful Sr/Rb ages of 1,900 and 2,100 m.y. Both these parts of the Southern Province, and the Cobalt district as well, have structures and ages similar to those of Animikian rocks in the Lake Superior region.

The Grenville Front is no doubt a fault zone of great displacement, for immediately southeast of it the Grenville Province, of complicated but predominantly northeast-trending structure, contains rocks different in kind and in radiometric age from those to the northwest. The typical Grenville surface rocks are highly metamorphosed limestones and quartzites, which were deformed and invaded by plutonic rocks about one billion years old. The only significantly greater ages are very close to the Grenville Front. The forty-five Ar/K ages for rocks of the Grenville Province that

are shown in Figure 9-16 range from 440 to 1,645 m.y., with a mean of 960 m.y. Five concordant Pb206/U238 and Pb207/U235 ages (not shown in Fig. 9-16) range from 925 to 1,090 m.y., with a mean of 1,009 m.y. The concordant lead ages are the most reliable guides to the probable time of crystallization of the plutonic rocks; they suggest that the Ar/K ages are a little low. The numerous, widely distributed Ar/K ages, however, furnish the evidence that almost the whole Grenville Province is composed of rocks that crystallized or recrystallized during the same rather short time about one billion years ago.

Subsurface data (Fig. 9-17) have made possible the extension of the Grenville Province ages far to the south, beneath the Paleozoic cover, beyond Lakes Ontario and Erie. The wells from which the samples came are

Fig. 9-17. *Map of central North America, showing age zones similar to the provinces of Fig. 9-16; ages in b.y. (From G. R. Tilton and S. R. Hart,* Science, *vol. 140, 26 April 1963, p. 364, by permission of the American Association for the Advancement of Science.)*

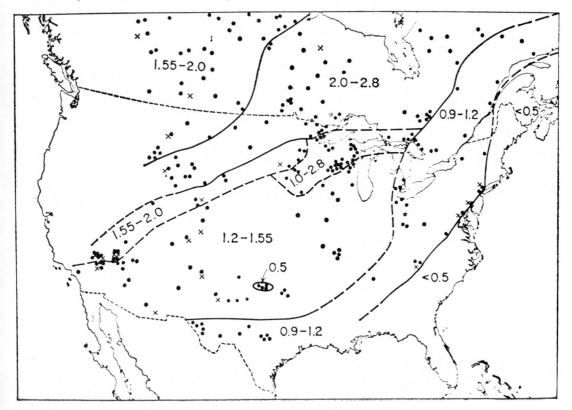

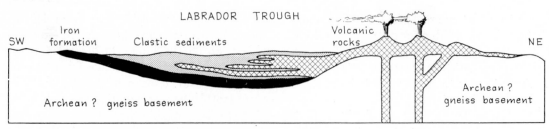

LABRADOR   TROUGH

A.   During a late stage in sedimentation

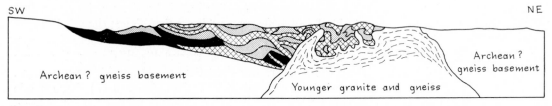

B.   Present

Fig. 9-18.   *Diagrammatic cross-section of the Labrador Trough during sedimentation and after folding. (After H. S. de Römer via T. H. Clark and C. W. Stearn.)*

rather closely spaced as far as south-central Ohio. Grenville ages even reappear southeast of the Paleozoic Appalachian Folded Belt, in New York, Maryland, North Carolina, and other states.

The age of the Grenville plutonics, at least, seems to be Keweenawan. Probably part of the Grenville sedimentary rocks are not much older than the plutonic rocks that have invaded them, for in younger and better-known folded belts (compare § 5-3 and § 6-3.b) the plutonites are not much younger than the youngest of the deformed and invaded surface rocks.

In the far northeast, at the Quebec-Labrador boundary, the Grenville Front is complicated by the apparently older structures of the southeast-trending Labrador Trough (IX of Fig. 9-16). The unmetamorphosed sedimentary rocks of this belt extend from northern Quebec to the southwest corner of Labrador (Fig. 9-18). "A thin group of quartzite, dolomite, and iron formation on the west side of this belt thickens eastward, and volcanic rocks become interbedded with the sedimentary rocks. The grade of metamorphism and deformation increases also until along the

eastern margin of the trough the sediments appear to pass into granite gneisses, although in places a fault may obscure the relationship." * The iron formation, now well known through commercial exploitation, is thick and typical, but time correlation with the Animikian iron formation is somewhat doubtful, especially as the greatest known age along the Labrador Trough, from an Ar/K ratio, is 1,590 m.y. The Labrador Trough may have been a combined mio- and eu-geosynclinal belt deformed at the end of Animikian time.

Enclosing Hudson Bay on the north is the Churchill Province, with 1,600–2,000 m.y. ages (Fig. 9-16). Beyond, near the northwest corner of the Canadian Shield, the small Slave Province repeats the 2,400–2,600 m.y. ages of the Superior Province. Apparently evidences of Superior ages were almost all obliterated from the Churchill Province by reheating during the period of Churchill plutonic activity; only a few were preserved, such as those of a 2,240 m.y. age west of Hudson Bay and a 2,390 m.y. age in Labrador.

* T. H. Clark and C. W. Stearn, *The Geological Evolution of North America* (1960), p. 265.

2. WESTERN UNITED STATES. The Grenville Front may continue southwest as far as western Texas, where a line extending east from El Paso separates 0.9–1.2 b.y. ages to the south from 1.2–1.55 b.y. ages to the north (Fig. 9-17). A narrow 1.55–2.0 b.y. belt extends from southern California through the Black Hills of South Dakota almost to Lake Superior. Just northwest of this narrow belt the Superior Province of very old rocks (2.0–2.8 b.y.) is represented by a branch reaching as far southwest as western Wyoming. In general, the boundaries between the Precambrian age belts of Figure 9-17 run from southwest to northeast.

A group of 0.5 b.y. quartz plutonite ages in southern Oklahoma, encircled by a solid line in Figure 9-17, represents the pre–Upper Cambrian platform complex of the region. The rocks would be considered Precambrian if the age determinations had not given such small figures. They are commonly called Cambrian and are so shown in Figure 8-15.

In the Grand Canyon, basement schists and gneisses have 1,350–1,550 m.y. Ar/K ages. An intrusive sheet in the wedge series (compare § 5-1.a) has yielded an unpublished Ar/K age of 1,100 m.y. This age suggests a late Keweenawan correlation for the wedge series. The metamorphism and plutonism of the Grand Canyon basement rocks apparently occurred in early Keweenawan time.

b. South Africa and Rhodesia

We shall consider here both the South African section described earlier in this chapter and the Rhodesian granitic and metamorphic rocks discussed in Chapter 8. The old granite around Johannesburg, with its probable 3 b.y. age, the Rhodesian granitic rocks 2,700 m.y. old, and the several belts of metamorphosed sedimentary and volcanic rocks invaded by the Rhodesian quartz plutonites may all belong to Keewatin time. The Dominion Reef "System" of South Africa is harder to place. Tentatively, its uraninite may be considered detrital and its age of about three billion years an upper limit for

the age of the surface-rock "System." Structurally, the Dominion Reef belongs with the Witwatersrand strata (compare Fig. 9-6). The Dominion Reef, Witwatersrand, Ventersdorp, and Transvaal "Systems," as well as the Bushveld plutonic complex, probably all belong in the 1,600–2,400 m.y. Animikian interval. The 1,950 m.y. metamorphosed folded belt along the Limpopo River (Fig. 9-4), north of the Witwatersrand and Transvaal basins (Fig. 9-5), contains sediments metamorphosed (and perhaps deposited) in Animikian time.

The Loskop and Waterberg platform strata are probably Keweenawan in age. The geosynclinal belt south of the lower Orange River (Fig. 9-4) was last metamorphosed in the same general part of Precambrian time. Some pre-Cape and probably post-Waterberg rocks of South Africa, notably the Malmesbury beds, may fall in the Keweenawan-Cambrian lacuna; others, including the upper part of the Nama platform sheet (Fig. 9-4), are rather surely Paleozoic.

c. Other Parts of the World

The third area with numerous Precambrian radiometric dates is in eastern Europe. This area has two parts, the Baltic Shield, where the Precambrian rocks are widely exposed at the surface, and the Russian platform to the southeast, in most parts of which the Precambrian is hidden beneath a thin Paleozoic cover. The ages of rocks of the Baltic Shield were given in § 8-3.f (compare Figs. 8-9 and 8-11). The most trustworthy and widespread dates were found to be approximately 1,650 m.y., 1,900 m.y., and 2,700 m.y. ago. The first two dates are no doubt Animikian, and the third is surely Keewatin. Among other, less well-established figures for rocks in the Baltic Shield are the 3,100–3,400 m.y. ages for mixed plutonic and metamorphic rocks on the northern side of the Kola Peninsula, U.S.S.R.

The Precambrian ages for the Russian platform are similar in a general way to those for the Baltic Shield, with the rather notable addition of 680–734 m.y. ages of glauconite, by the

Ar/K method, for the horizontal, unmetamorphosed Sinian sedimentary system.

In Australia, the Keewatin is represented by a 2,700 m.y. age (Fig. 8-13) from rocks that are probably widespread.

9-6. *Formation of Precambrian Continental Platforms*

Since almost all Precambrian age-determinations have been made on plutonic and metamorphic rocks, these ages are direct indicators of the times of consolidation of rigid rock masses, the very material of which continental platforms are composed. As a result, we can use these ages as evidence of the times of formation of the several parts of a continental platform.

Sediments and lavas were accumulating on platforms of subcontinental extent far back in Precambrian time. Around Johannesburg (Fig. 9-6) and elsewhere in southern and central Africa a platform with a flat surface, eroded on old granite, on schists that were originally sedimentary, and on metavolcanic rocks, began to be covered by the Dominion Reef and overlying surface series or by similar rock sequences in other areas, at an early date that may possibly have been as much as 2,700 m.y. ago. In North America the Animikian strata were deposited on a similar platform of crystalline rocks, about equally ancient. This platform was at least moderately extensive north of the Great Lakes and may have been very large, including almost all of the Shield northwest of the Grenville Front. In Michigan and Minnesota this platform was depressed to make the floor of the east-west Animikian geosynclinal trough that was later transformed into the Penokean fold belt. In Penokean (late Animikian) time, the Churchill and Bear Provinces (Fig. 9-16) seem also to have been consolidated by plutonism. Still later, at the end of Keweenawan time, the Grenville Province seems to have been added to the rigid Shield, as indicated by its billion-year ages. In Paleozoic time the southeastern part of the Grenville block was depressed to make the floor of the Appalachian miogeosyncline (compare Fig. 9-17). If the Grenville block extended still farther southeast, the radiogenic record of its age was obliterated in the late Paleozoic plutonism and metamorphism of the eugeosynclinal portion of the Appalachian belt.

9-7. *Precambrian Ore Deposits*

The most valuable substances taken from the rocks are fossil fuels, none of which are Precambrian, and metalliferous ores, the greater part of which are obtained from Precambrian rocks despite the fact that these rocks are exposed in but one-twelfth of the earth's land surface.

By far the largest tonnage of metalliferous ores is that exploited for iron. The world's largest group of iron-ore areas is in the Canadian Shield. Other major sources and reserves of Precambrian iron ores are in the Baltic Shield, especially in Sweden, in the Ukraine, in South Africa, and in the eastern South American platform, both in Brazil and in Venezuela. The commonest type of deposit is sedimentary iron formation, though some of the large phosphate-bearing magnetite (magnetic iron oxide) bodies, as at Kiruna in northern Sweden, probably separated out of igneous magma.

Half of the world's gold comes from the Witwatersrand quartz conglomerates near Johannesburg, South Africa. Some 70 percent of the world's nickel comes from a Precambrian gabbroic intrusion at Sudbury, Ontario. The world's production of uranium is largely, but far from entirely, derived from Precambrian rocks. Exact production figures are hard to come by. Considerable uranium is now produced from the Witwatersrand gold ores. Enormous reserves were discovered in the nineteen-fifties near Blind River, Ontario, in rocks of approximately Animikian age, in quartz-pebble conglomerate lenses near the base of the sequence. Much copper has been produced from Precambrian rocks, even though most of the world's present production and reserves are in younger rocks. The Kewee-naw Peninsula copper companies paid dividends of 300 million dollars before 1926, back in the days when dollars were worth more than they are now.

9-8. *Precambrian Life*

If the theory of evolution is true, as is strongly indicated by the whole history of life (to be developed in subsequent pages), the varied forms of animal life known from the Cambrian strata lead us to presuppose the existence of almost equally varied Precambrian forms. Amazingly enough, fossils have been found in only a few Precambrian formations; there they are numerous, but almost all are remains of the simple one-celled plants called algae.

Precambrian calcareous algae have been found in the Belt series of Montana (Fig. 9-19, Keweenawan?), in the Lower Animikian of Michigan (Ref. 5), in the iron formation of the Labrador Peninsula, and in many other parts of the world, always in strata of probably post-Keewatin age. Many make up reef-like structures, projecting above surrounding contemporaneous strata. In the modern world, similar algae are most prominent as important contributors to the coral reefs of tropic seas, though small limestone ridges and pyramids a few feet across also grow in other environments, including fresh water. In the rocks, coral and algal reefs, as far down as the lower Paleozoic, are everywhere marine. It is not unreasonable to consider the Precambrian algal reefs marine too. If the Animikian reefs were marine, perhaps other parts of the series, including the iron formation, were also deposited in sea water.

Some Precambrian fossils may not be algae. Those shown in Figure 9-20 are clearly the remains of microorganisms, but their relationships are uncertain. They were probably simple forms of life, but they cannot be called, with any confidence, algae or fungi or protozoans. Some larger Precambrian structures have been thought to represent coelenterates

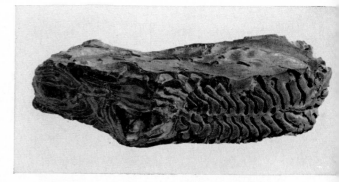

Fig. 9-19.   Newlandia major, *a calcareous alga from the Newland limestone of the Precambrian Belt series, 11 miles west of White Sulphur Springs, Montana. Specimen 8.7 inches long. (Peabody Museum, Yale University.)*

and other moderately complex animals; an example (Fig. 10-26) will be discussed in Chapter 10 in connection with similar Cambrian forms.

9-9. *Precambrian Climates*

Climates are defined in terms of atmospheric conditions: they may be warm or cold, wet or dry, seasonal or uniform. At the present time the earth is climatically zoned. Such zones may always have existed; or, on the other hand, the atmosphere may have been warm and moist over almost the whole earth at some times in the past.

Varied climatic conditions are the principal causes of the varied types of rock weathering now prevalent in different parts of the earth. In very cold or very dry climates little weathering takes place. In the moist tropics weathering is rapid. In cool moist climates the soil reaction becomes acid, and the products of the weathering of silicate rocks are aluminous-siliceous clay minerals, the other common elements having gone off in the drainage. In subtropical belts with alternate dry and very rainy seasons, aluminum hydroxide is the most stable residual product; iron and silicon go into solution in alternate seasons, but iron usually does not travel far; and the other elements

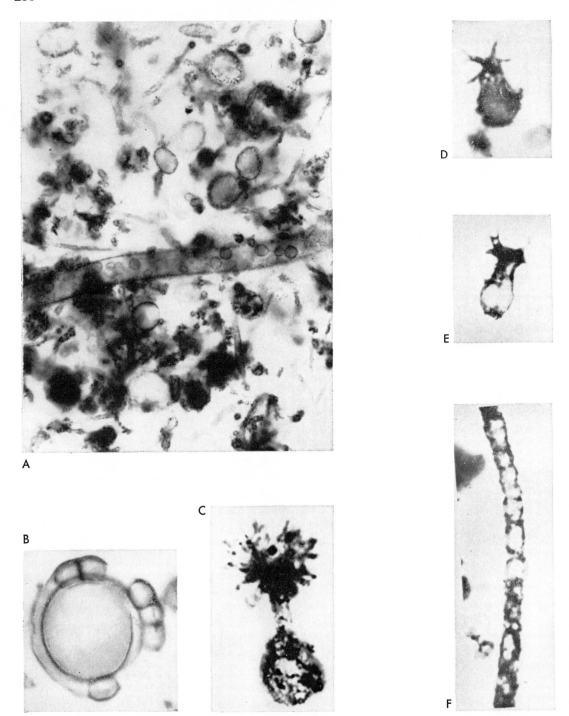

Fig. 9-20. *Microorganisms in chert of the Gunflint formation (Animikian), in southern Ontario north of Lake Superior: A, B, × 1,500; C, D, E, × 2,100; F, × 2,150. (Photomicrographs from E. S. Barghoorn, Harvard University, 1964.)*

are so soluble that they disappear from the areas undergoing surface weathering. As a result of these regional differences in weathering, the products of weathering available for transportation and deposition are correspondingly varied. Sedimentary deposits therefore vary with the climate, as has been emphasized in Chapter 4. In the subtropical regions with moist and dry seasons, for example, the stratified sediments include transported laterite (iron and aluminum hydroxides and oxides) or precipitated silicon hydroxide (consolidated as chert), rarely both together.

The most positive indicators of climate are the extremes among sediments. No Precambrian rock-salt deposits are known, and the few gypsum beds are very small. The combination of extreme aridity and interior basins was therefore probably rarer in the Precambrian than in later times. (Thick salt deposits are already present in the Cambrian, notably in Iran and central Asia.) Two other extreme assemblages are, however, widespread in the Precambrian.

One of these is the quartz-sand-clay-shale-limestone assemblage, which is also common in Paleozoic and Mesozoic platform deposits and was singled out in Chapter 4 as the typical platform facies, the probable result of stable structural conditions and prolonged weathering in a moist and no doubt at least moderately warm climate. This assemblage is well represented in several South African Precambrian "systems," in the metasedimentary rocks of the Grenville Province, in and near the Labrador Trough, and in the Lower Animikian of Michigan.

The other sedimentary assemblage indicating an extreme climatic condition is the iron formation. Its two principal constituents, chert and iron oxide or carbonate, are the two principal products of lateritic weathering and deposition in the moist tropics. Sheets of laterite, commonly with a hard protective crust above a soft main body of iron hydroxide (with or without aluminum hydroxide), are forming in many areas. At Conakry, in Guinea, a few degrees north of the equator, unusually pure lateritic iron ore constitutes a weathered zone 200 or 300 feet thick on a plutonic rock composed chiefly of olivine (ferrous magnesium silicate). More or less similar, recent residual laterite sheets are widely distributed from Cuba to the East Indies. Transported laterites have also accumulated in recent times, notably in India. Laterites are known at all levels in the geological column, but the abundance of iron formation in the Precambrian of the Canadian Shield, the Baltic Shield, South Africa, and elsewhere goes far beyond anything known in younger rocks. The Precambrian iron formation is not exactly like any sedimentary assemblage known to be forming today, particularly in its intermingling of chert and iron ore, but we need to modify the rule of uniformitarianism only a little to interpret the iron formation as a product of extreme and prolonged lateritic weathering over an extensive land area, with transportation of the laterite and dissolved silica to semi-enclosed basins conveniently distributed. Note one corollary: several parts of the Canadian Shield, Finland, and South Africa must have had subtropical or tropical climates in iron-formation time or times. Either the tropical belt was enormously expanded at that time, or the present continents were arranged differently.

The lateritic explanation of iron formation is not the only one that has been suggested. It has been pointed out that the oxygen of the atmosphere would be exhausted if only a small part of the ferrous (FeO) iron in the earth's crust were oxidized to the ferric (Fe_2O_3) state. Possibly the oxygen now in the atmosphere was all contained in the crust during Keewatin and Animikian times. The weathering and depositional conditions may then have been more favorable for the deposition of ferrous carbonate than at any later time. Evidence of the composition of Keewatin and Animikian atmospheres is uncertain or inadequate. The most pertinent evidence would be proof of oxidation during Animikian or earlier weathering. The soft red ferric oxide of the Mesabi and some other ores, however, seems to have developed in post-Animikian time, perhaps just before the Cambrian, when oxygen must have been present in air and sea, to support animal life. The available chemical analyses of gray-wackes, which contain both ferrous and ferric iron, are far too few to make significant any present comparison of the ferrous-ferric ratios in Animikian and later clastic sediments.

Still another extreme climate may have been represented in Precambrian times, though the evidence is rarely conclusive. Near Cobalt, Ontario, in a perhaps Animikian sequence, an unstratified conglomerate—up to 3,500 feet thick, with an abundant poorly sorted matrix (Fig. 9-21)—and overlying banded clays are somewhat similar to the boulder clay (till) and banded sandy silt-clay sequences of Pleistocene glacial deposits. These rocks have been considered evidence of Precambrian glaciation. But the conglomerate rests on an ancient soil rather than on a polished and striated rock surface, and the whole assemblage is similar to many alluvial fan deposits and banded lake clays formed in Cenozoic and Recent times in the semi-arid regions of the western United States and elsewhere. The alternative explanation—moderate aridity—seems more probable for this set of rocks and also for other supposed tillites in Precambrian sequences in many parts of the world, including China and South Australia. In Scandinavia, however, varved Precambrian sediments do lie on striated rock floors and contain boulders that may have been ice-rafted to their present positions; there Precambrian glaciation may really have occurred.

9-10. *Orders of Abstraction*

The iron formation and the Cobalt conglomerate make instructive exhibits in a consideration of the important distinctions between the

Fig. 9-21. *The Coleman conglomerate, Cobalt, Ontario. (From the Ontario Department of Mines.)*

orders of abstraction. The first order of abstraction used in this book is called stratigraphy and is represented by the classification of rocks into formations, such as the Animikian iron formation and the Cobalt conglomerate. The very naming of a formation and its representation on a map require generalization of the observed facts and deductions from them. Not every specimen of iron formation is like every other specimen. What is more, both the iron formation and the conglomerate are called sedimentary formations; their naming implies logical deductions from observed textures and compositions to a mode of origin. Nevertheless, this degree of abstraction merely sets off and names genetically a rather clean-cut rock body, easily recognized in the field by all observers. Moreover, the sedimentary origin of these rocks is not disputed by anyone. If, however, we use the rock as evidence of a historical event, such as glaciation or the prevalence of a subtropical climate in a particular region, the mental process carries us one step further away from observed reality. This is abtraction from an abstraction—that is, a second-order abstraction. It is only common caution to hold a second-order abstraction as a mere possibility—to be verified through the elaboration of imaginary models, to be checked in turn by more refined field observations and new laboratory studies.

The interpretation of the Animikian and other iron formations as products of lateritic, subtropical weathering leads us to third-order abstractions, such as drastic climatic changes since the Precambrian and great changes in the positions of the earth's poles or continents (compare Chap. 13). In working with such far-fetched ideas, we must not forget what a long limb we are out on. The long limb, however, is one of the most exhilarating features of the tree of knowledge. Not only is it fun to get out on, but a good shake may bring down fruit, not just from this branch but from others as well. If there is no fruit at all—no further insight into the nature of things, no new discoveries as side effects—then the limb may not be a living branch of science after all. That negative conclusion, if correct, is a good thing to know. The particular limb that is composed essentially of knowledge about Precambrian iron formations is probably going to be fruitful, but no one can yet be quite sure what the fruit will be. Much remains to be learned about the sedimentary iron formations in all parts of the world; perhaps special attention should be given to occurrences in Brazil, South Africa, and South Australia.

░░ | **PROBLEM**

It has been suggested that the continental platform of North America has grown by successive additions to a central nucleus. Use the ages summarized in Figs. 9-16 and 9-17 as bases for a discussion of this hypothesis. Try to locate a central nucleus and to work out a sequence of accretionary areas or belts. What evidence, if any, indicates that some parts of the North American platform collapsed or melted long after their first attainment of crystalline rigidity?

REFERENCES

1. G. L. Cumming and others: "Some Dates and Subdivisions of the Canadian Shield," PROCEEDINGS, Geol. Ass. Canada, vol. 7, pp. 27–79 (1955)

2. J. E. Gill and others: *The Proterozoic in Canada,* Special Pub. No. 2, Royal Society of Canada (1957)

3. S. S. Goldich and others: *The Precambrian Geology and Geochronology of Minnesota,* Bull. 41, Minnesota Geol. Sur. (1961)

4. F. J. Pettijohn: "Paleocurrents of Lake Superior Precambrian Quartzites," BULLETIN, Geol. Soc. Am., vol. 68, pp. 469–480 (1957)

5. H. L. James: "Sedimentary Facies of Iron-formation," ECONOMIC GEOLOGY, vol. 49, pp. 235–293 (1954)

6. H. L. James: *Stratigraphy of pre-Keweenawan Rocks in Parts of Northern Michigan,* Prof. Paper 314-C, U.S. Geol. Sur. (1958)

7. J. A. Lowdon and others: "Age Determinations by the Geological Survey of Canada," Paper 62-17, Geol. Sur. Canada, pp. 1–122 (1963)

8. A. L. du Toit: *The Geology of South Africa,* 3rd ed. (Oliver & Boyd, Edinburgh, 1954)

9. L. O. Nicolaysen: "Stratigraphic Interpretation of Age Measurements in Southern Africa," Buddington Volume, Geol. Soc. Am., pp. 569–598 (1962)

10. *Geological Map of the Union of South Africa,* *1 : 1,000,000* (Pretoria, 1955)

The Cambrian

THE GREATEST contrast between adjacent parts of the geologic column is that between Cambrian and Precambrian. The contrast is shown in its full extent in the Grand Canyon region, where it has two elements. First and more important, the Cambrian strata contain the oldest guide fossils of proved value for correlation. Second, the fossiliferous Cambrian formations overlap unconformably onto a Precambrian platform of complex structure. Similar clean-cut angular unconformities between Cambrian and Precambrian are present in many continental platform areas, but in large parts of some major geosynclines the first pre-Cambrian unconformity is hundreds or thousands of feet below the base of the fossiliferous Cambrian.

Cambrian advances onto several of the continental platforms and the abrupt appearance of the first Cambrian fauna are facts hard to explain. They are problems that can be discussed to advantage only after we gather a moderate store of knowledge concerning the fossils, the rocks, and the stratigraphic relations of the Cambrian in several regions.

10.1. Cambrian Occurrences and Guide Fossils

Beds containing Cambrian guide fossils, almost all of them trilobites, are known in the districts marked by small dots in Figure 10-1. Surface or subsurface Cambrian occurrences are extensive in most parts of North America and Eurasia, outside the Precambrian shield areas. Patches and strips of Cambrian are also widespread in northern and eastern Australia and in Tasmania. In addition, there are occurrences in Antarctica and in the Andean Belt of South America, as well as a notable strip in and near the Atlas Mountains of Morocco, and isolated bits at the head of the Red Sea, on some Arctic islands, and in New Zealand. Blocks of Cambrian rocks have also been dredged from the sea floor near Antarctica. Except for Morocco, no fossiliferous Cambrian is definitely known in the whole great expanse of Africa, and, outside the Andes, none in South America. In fact, Cambrian stratigraphy is practically confined to the northern hemisphere and Australia. We shall therefore discuss only the Cambrian stratigraphy of Europe, North America, eastern Asia, and Australia.

a. Northwestern Europe

The Cambrian in northern Wales, as restricted by Lapworth (§ 3-4.c.1) and as defined now by almost everyone, is not very fossiliferous. Sedgwick's lowest fossils of any stratigraphic value were probably in strata that we now call Ordovician. The first good guide fossil collected from the type Cambrian was probably a trilobite found by another stratigrapher in 1845. The stratigraphically useful specimens found since, mostly trilobites, are almost entirely in the Middle and Upper Cambrian. A few Lower Cambrian trilobites

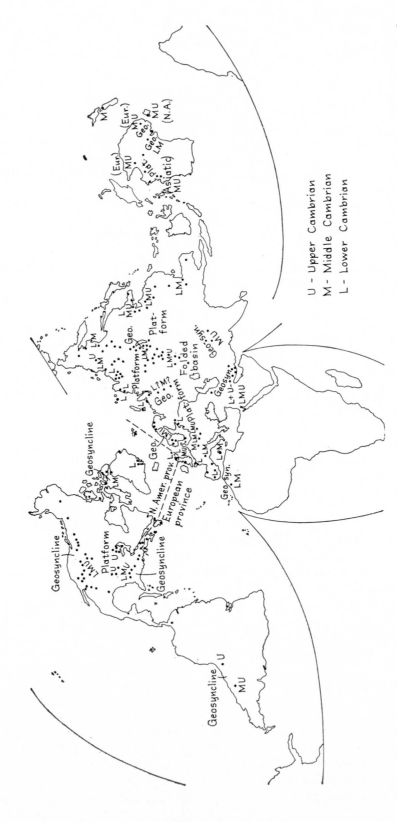

Fig. 10-1. *Map showing fossiliferous Cambrian localities of the world: Eur, N.A., Asiatic (in Australia), faunas of European, North American, and Asiatic affinities. (Data mostly from Ref. 3.)*

U – Upper Cambrian
M – Middle Cambrian
L – Lower Cambrian

Fig. 10-2. *Geologic sketch map of the Baltic region. 1, 2, eastern and western facies of the Cambrian–Silurian; 3, Eocambrian; 4, Norwegian Precambrian; 5, Precambrian of the Baltic Shield; 6, approximate limit of the Baltic Shield. (Adapted from Maurice Gignoux,* Stratigraphic Geology, *W. H. Freeman & Co., 1955.)*

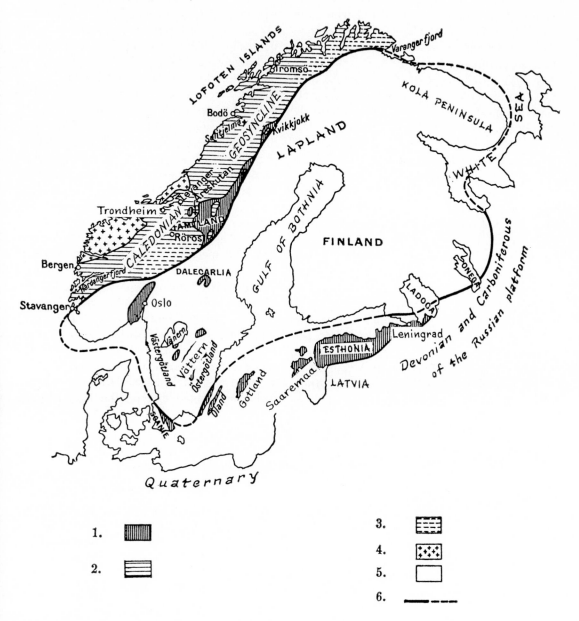

1.	▥	3.	▤
2.	▤	4.	✦
		5.	▢
		6.	▬ ▬ ▬

have been found in North Wales and the English county of Shropshire. But the British Cambrian has such complex structure and so few fossils that it has proved unsatisfactory as a standard for the world or even for north-western Europe. It is worth noting, however, that the North Wales Cambrian section, perhaps including some Precambrian, is 12,000–15,000 feet thick, mostly clastic, and now greatly deformed.

The European standard for the Cambrian is now considered to be in Scandinavia—around Oslo, Norway, and in southern Sweden. The Oslo Basin has provided a section with thirteen or more faunal zones, most of which are characterized by assemblages of trilobite species and each of which is named for a trilobite species, commonly one restricted to the zone. The best sequence of Cambrian strata near Oslo lies on the edge of the Baltic Shield platform (Fig. 10-2); it is some 400 feet thick, mostly shale, with conglomerate and sandstone at and near the base. The zones also extend northwest into the geosyncline that includes most of Norway and is on the strike of the Caledonian geosyncline of Wales and Scotland. All these Welsh, Scottish, and Norwegian geosynclinal strata were deformed at or before the beginning of Devonian time.

The Oslo Lower Cambrian includes four trilobite zones, with species of the genus *Holmia* (Fig. 10-3B) as guides for two. The Middle Cambrian is characterized from bottom to top by species of the genus *Paradoxides* (Fig. 10-3E). The Upper Cambrian has *Olenus* (Fig. 10-3O) at its base and closely related forms at higher levels, all belonging to the olenid subgroup of the ptychoparid group of trilobites (Fig. 10-4).

The Scandinavian Cambrian faunas are found throughout northwestern Europe, in Bohemia (Czechoslovakia), Poland, south-central France, the British Isles, and elsewhere. The trilobite members of the faunas fall largely into three groups, which here will be called olenellid-redlichiid, ptychoparid, and agnostid. *Holmia* and *Paradoxides* are olenellid-redlichiid. They have rounded heads, shaggy thoraxes, and very small pygidia (see § B-8 for terminology). *Olenus* is a ptychoparid (similar to *Ptychoparia* of the Middle Cambrian, Fig. 10-3I) with a well-defined pygidium of several segments and relatively small and slender eye ridges. The little eyeless agnostids (Fig. 10-3DJ) are very different, with heads and pygidia almost equal in size and only two or three thoracic segments between. Agnostids range through the Cambrian and Ordovician systems; a whole series of agnostid species make a succession of guides to zones and subzones of the Scandinavian Middle and Upper Cambrian.

Before leaving the European Cambrian, we take note of the great variations in its thickness, consolidation, and deformation. The rocks of the Caledonian (Scandinavian) geosyncline are thick, closely folded, and very well consolidated, but on the Baltic-Russian

Fig. 10-3. *Cambrian trilobites: C, F, Asiatic; B, E, I, European; D, J (and perhaps O), cosmopolitan; the others, North American. (From* Treatise on Invertebrate Paleontology, *courtesy Geological Society of America and University of Kansas Press.)*

NAME AND LOCALITY	GROUP (FIG. 10-4)	SUBSYSTEM
A. Olenellus thompsoni, *Vermont* ($\times$ 1.2)	*Olenellina*	*Lower Cambrian*
B. Holmia kjerulfi, *Norway* ($\times$ 0.5)	*Olenellina*	*Lower Cambrian*
C. Redlichia chinensis, *China* ($\times$ 1.3)	*Redlichiina*	*Lower Cambrian*
D. Lejopyge laevigata, *Sweden* ($\times$ 5.6)	*Agnostina*	*Middle Cambrian*
E. Paradoxides paradoxissimus, *Sweden* ($\times$ 0.5)	*Redlichiina*	*Middle Cambrian*
F. Blackwelderia sinensis, *China* ($\times$ 0.9)	*Ptychopariina*	*Middle Cambrian*
G. Elrathia kingi, *Utah* ($\times$ 0.7)	*Ptychopariina*	*Middle Cambrian*
H. Glossopleura boccar, *Montana* ($\times$ 0.7)	*Corynexochida*	*Middle Cambrian*
I. Ptychoparia striata, *Bohemia* ($\times$ 0.4)	*Ptychopariina*	*Middle Cambrian*
J. Glyptagnostus reticulatus, *Nevada* ($\times$ 5.8)	*Agnostina*	*Upper Cambrian*
K. Saukia acuta, *Wisconsin* ($\times$ 0.9)	*Ptychopariina*	*Upper Cambrian*
LM. Illaenurus quadratus, *Wisconsin* ($\times$ 1.1)	*Ptychopariina*	*Upper Cambrian*
N. Entomaspis radiatus, *Missouri* ($\times$ 5.5)	*Harpina*	*Upper Cambrian*
O. Olenus truncatus, *Sweden* ($\times$ 2.9)	*Ptychopariina*	*Upper Cambrian*

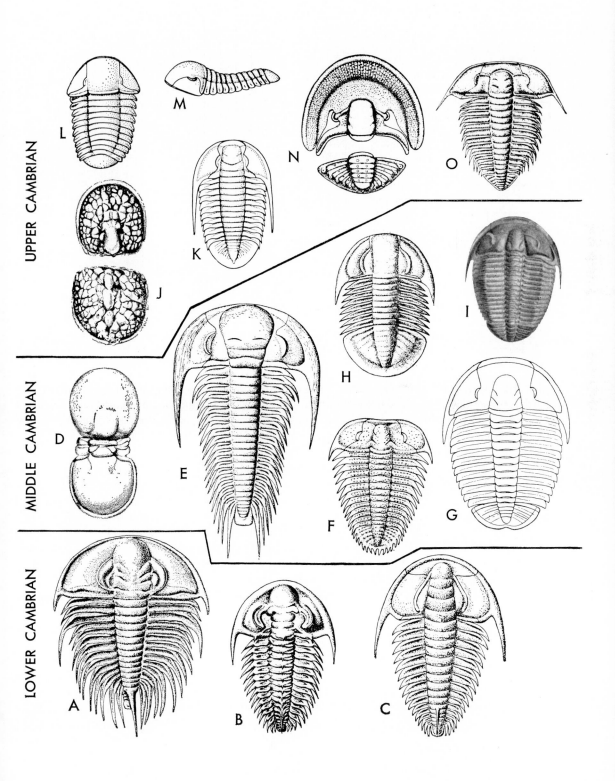

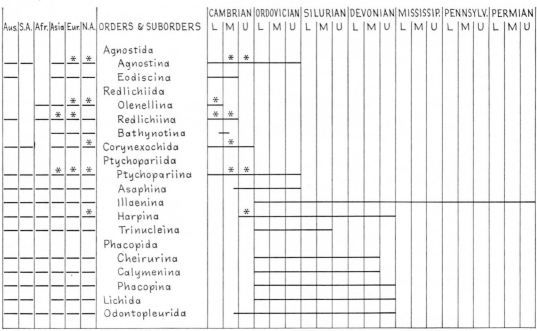

* Represented in Fig. 10-3; for example, a member of the Agnostina (the genus *Glyptagnostus*) in Fig. 10-3J

Fig. 10-4. *Geographic and stratigraphic distribution of trilobite taxa.* (*After* Treatise on Invertebrate Paleontology.)

platform the Cambrian is thin, flat-lying, and hardly consolidated at all. On the south side of the Gulf of Finland, from Esthonia to Leningrad (Fig. 10-2), the principal Cambrian unit is a Lower Cambrian blue clay 100–200 feet thick, as soft and uncompacted as any modern clay. It can never have had much of a cover of younger strata—probably not more than 3,000 feet, at most.

b. North America

In Figure 10-1 a dashed line crosses the Atlantic, from Britain to Newfoundland. South of the dashed line, in southeastern Newfoundland, on Cape Breton Island, near St. John (New Brunswick), and around Boston (Massachusetts), thick folded sequences contain Cambrian faunas of the European zones, though not all the zones are present and the Lower Cambrian contains no *Holmia*. Other European Lower Cambrian genera are found, so that *Holmia* is not greatly missed. At St.

John the section of the Cambrian shale, siltstone, and sandstone is 3,000 feet thick. In most places, unfossiliferous sandstone and conglomerate, up to 2,400 feet thick, underlie the fossiliferous Cambrian. On Cape Breton Island the Lower Cambrian overlaps unconformably northwest onto crystalline Precambrian rocks. The whole set of occurrences appears to be geosynclinal at the eastern edge of the continent, overlapping northwest onto a New Brunswick platform that is not obviously continuous with the main Canadian Shield. This eastern Cambrian geosynclinal sequence lacks volcanic rocks and contains the characteristic fossils of platform zones; it is apparently miogeosynclinal, though it became eugeosynclinal in the Devonian. Just across the New Brunswick platform to the northwest, only 150–200 miles away, the notably different Cambrian faunas of the North American province are found, in northwestern Newfoundland, on the Gaspé peninsula south of the St. Lawrence estuary, and extending southwestward from southern Quebec through Vermont and along most of the length of the folded Appalachians to eastern Tennessee and Georgia. (Compare § 6-3.b.)

Note especially, in Figure 10-1, the northern and eastern extension of the North American province to include the Lower Cambrian of both northwestern Scotland and the East Greenland geosyncline. *Olenellus* (Fig. 10-3A), the characteristic genus of the North American Lower Cambrian, is present in both areas. The barrier indicated by the dashed line must have been about as narrow in Britain as in Newfoundland. In northwestern Vermont, around St. Albans, the Lower and

Upper Cambrian contain faunas of the North American province, but a Middle Cambrian fauna is made up mostly of genera and even species known in the European province; this unit can be correlated with the upper part of the *Paradoxides* Scandinavian sequence, making it upper Middle Cambrian. This fauna also contains "members of genera (some as yet undescribed) which occur in contemporaneous beds in western North America, Asia, and Australia" (Ref. 12). The succession of faunas in northwestern Vermont—Lower Cambrian of the American province, Middle Cambrian containing a European-American mixture, and American Upper Cambrian—is encouraging for time correlation between provinces and

Fig. 10-5. *Cambrian stratigraphic diagram for southern Appalachian region. Faunas: T, uppermost Cambrian; F, median Upper Cambrian; D, lower Upper Cambrian; UM, upper Middle Cambrian; MM, middle Middle Cambrian; LM, lower Middle Cambrian; L, Lower Cambrian. (After John Rodgers, Ref. 3.)*

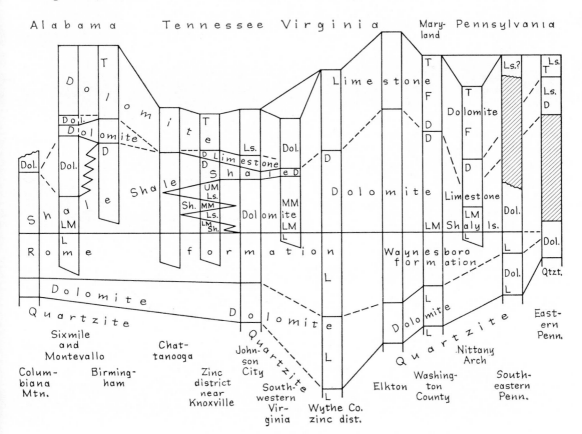

may lead to a better understanding of the nature of the New Brunswick barrier.

Over most of North America, west of New England and easternmost Canada, Cambrian faunas all belong to the North American province. In the main Appalachian geosyncline, from central Vermont south, two regions can be distinguished. As far south as northeastern Pennsylvania the Middle Cambrian is missing, the other Cambrian formations are rather thin, and the whole sequence lies unconformably on Precambrian rocks, mostly gneisses. In this northern Appalachian area the Lower Cambrian, commonly less than 1,000 feet thick, is made up of sandstone or graywacke, with *Olenellus* (Fig. 10-3A), overlain by dolomite; the Upper Cambrian, where present, is mostly dolomite.

In the southern Appalachian region, roughly south of Mason and Dixon's line, the Lower, Middle, and Upper Cambrian are all represented, in fossiliferous sections 3,000–6,000 feet thick, unconformably underlain by thick sequences of non-fossiliferous strata, mostly quartz-rich sandstones and rather siliceous volcanic rocks. In eastern Tennessee the underlying non-fossiliferous sequence, in one area 10,000 feet thick, in another perhaps 30,000 feet thick, includes considerable conglomerate and perhaps is interrupted by an unconformity. A typical fossiliferous Cambrian sequence (Fig. 10-5) begins with quartzite at the base, which is overlain successively by 1,000 feet of dolomite and 1,000 feet of red, green, and purple shale, all Lower Cambrian. The Middle Cambrian is some 2,000 feet thick, all dolomite or limestone in Virginia but half shale farther south. The Upper Cambrian is

Fig. 10-6. *Cambrian section, Kansas–Wisconsin; data from wells represented by vertical lines. (After Geologic Cross Section of the Central United States, Kansas Geol. Society, 1931.)*

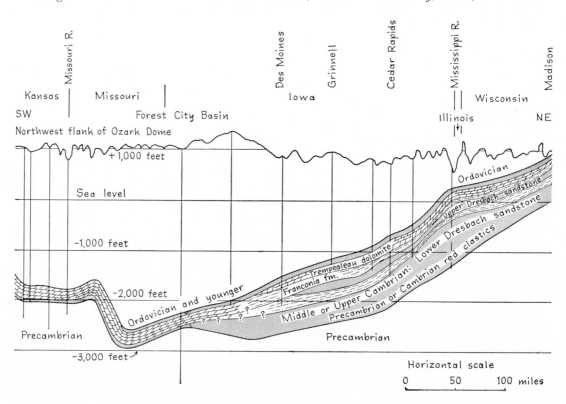

1,200–2,000 feet thick, everywhere limestone or dolomite. The Lower and Middle Cambrian are more largely silicoclastic on the northwest than on the southeast side of the geosyncline, indicating derivation of the clastic material from the central continental platform during Early and Middle Cambrian time.

On the main North American platform, the Lower and Middle Cambrian are almost completely missing. The Upper Cambrian is widespread south of the Great Lakes. In a belt across Minnesota and Wisconsin and extending east to the northern Adirondacks, the Upper Cambrian is mostly marine sandstone 1,000–1,500 feet thick, unconformable on varied Precambrian rocks that are commonly topped by a rubbly weathered zone indicative of prolonged subaerial decay. Farther southwest, south, southeast, or east, the Upper Cambrian gradually becomes mostly carbonate (Figs. 10-6 and 10-7), above a sandy basal unit unconformable on Precambrian granitic and other rocks. In general, the Upper Cambrian section is sandiest near the Canadian Shield and becomes almost completely carbonate a few hundred miles from the present margin of the Shield (at a much shorter distance in New York). The Shield appears to have been land in Late Cambrian time and the only major source of silicoclastic debris in all North America.

Changes in the trilobite faunas make possible the subdivision of the North American Cambrian into about fourteen zones: two Lower, five Middle, and seven Upper. Some of the trilobite guides are represented in Figure 10-3. *Olenellus* (A) is the best-known guide to the Lower Cambrian anywhere. *Holmia* (B), of the Scandinavian section, is a moderately close relative, placed in a different family of the same suborder. Note the similarities and dissimilarities in the central (axial) parts of the heads of *Olenellus* and *Holmia*. All known members of the suborder (Olenellina) are found in Lower Cambrian rocks, in most places in strata overlain by Middle Cambrian rocks containing different trilo-

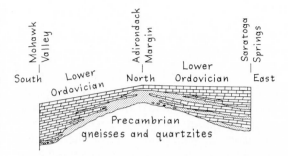

Fig. 10-7. *Upper Cambrian facies changes— from sandstone to carbonates—along the southern Adirondack border, New York.* (*After D. W. Fisher, Ref. 3.*)

bites, including species of the genus *Paradoxides* (E) in the European province and species of *Elrathia* (G) and *Glossopleura* (H) in the North American province. Note the prominent pygidia of the two North American Middle Cambrian guides and the short thoracic spines of *Elrathia*.

The North American Upper Cambrian is represented in Figure 10-3 by three genera. *Saukia* (K) is a guide to the uppermost Cambrian zone in the Lake Superior region and elsewhere. The other two genera (L-M and N), also from this uppermost zone, are introduced to give some idea of the varied forms present among the Upper Cambrian trilobites. The rather fantastic *Entomaspis* (N), a small form, is an early member of an Upper Cambrian–Devonian group. Late Cambrian was the time of climax for the trilobites, with 62 of 141 trilobite families represented.

The top of the Lower Cambrian is probably at about the same horizon in both the European and the North American province, for olenellids are Lower Cambrian guide fossils in both provinces. Agnostid guides to the highest Middle Cambrian zone of Scandinavia have recently been found by R. A. Robison, in Utah (Ref. 13), in a position that makes definite the long-suspected correlation of the American *Cedaria* zone with the lowest Upper Cambrian of the European Province.

c. Meaning of the North American–European Provincial Boundary

The greatest problem of Cambrian paleography is the nature of the boundary between the European and the North American province. Can it have been a narrow strip of low land extending right across the Atlantic Ocean? If so, how could it move back and forth across what is now northwestern Vermont, with only a single (Middle Cambrian) break in the narrow strip of land and even then only a slight and local mingling of the faunas? Can the barrier have been deep ocean? Not if the overlap northwestward onto it on Cape Breton Island is typical. Can it have been a facies difference, perhaps caused by variation in the depth of the sea? But the European province extends from the Caledonian geosyncline onto the Russian platform, and the North American province covers both the continental platform and several marginal geosynclines, as well as northwestern Scotland. No explanation of the provincial boundary yet proposed is adequate to explain all the evidence. We shall come back to this problem when we consider, in Chapter 13, possible changes in the positions of the earth's continents or climatic zones, or both.

d. Eastern Asia and Australia

The characteristic Lower Cambrian trilobite of eastern Asia and Australia, *Redlichia* (Fig. 10-3C), since it has the same general features as *Holmia* and *Olenellus*, has been placed in the same order but, chiefly because of differences in the structure of the head, in a different suborder, Redlichiina (Fig. 10-4). The geographic range of *Redlichia*, from Korea to Iran (with close relatives in Morocco) and from Australia to (perhaps) Siberia, suggests an Asiatic-Australian faunal province. If this suggestion is accepted, there were three rather sharply separated realms of marine life in Early Cambrian time: the North American realm with *Olenellus*, the European realm with *Holmia*, and the Asiatic-Australian realm with *Redlichia*.

In the East Asiatic rocks assigned to the Middle Cambrian, *Blackwelderia* (Fig. 10-3F) is a guide. This genus is limited to eastern Asia and Australia. In China and Korea almost all members of the faunas called Middle Cambrian are limited to the realm, but in northern and eastern Australia characteristic North American genera and equally characteristic European genera and species are present. In particular, the little Cambrian agnostids of northern and northeastern Australia are largely Scandinavian species that make possible correlations with Middle and Upper Cambrian Scandinavian zones (A. A. Öpik in Ref. 3). Some of the Middle Cambrian agnostids are in beds conformably above beds with *Redlichia*. *Redlichia* specimens were the first guide fossils noticed in these rocks, which were then called Lower Cambrian. Now the discovery of the agnostid species seems to require correlations of *Redlichia*-bearing Australian strata with the Middle Cambrian of Europe. As Europe is the type area for all horizons from the base of the Cambrian up, European correlations take precedence over Asiatic, and so *Redlichia* must occur in Middle Cambrian as well as in Lower Cambrian rocks. The next step will probably be a reexamination of the East Asiatic Middle and Lower Cambrian assignments. Some raising of horizons may extend *Redlichia* into the Middle Cambrian in eastern Asia as well as in Australia. The attempts to correlate eastern Asia and Australia with Europe give a good idea of the present degree of precision of interprovincial Cambrian correlations; they are the basis for the conclusion, stated near the end of Chapter 7, that worldwide Cambrian correlations are not yet much more precise than the division into Lower, Middle, and Upper.

10-2. The Top of the Cambrian

The British commonly make a shaly formation called the Tremadoc, 1,000–4,000 feet thick, the uppermost unit in the Cambrian. The Tremadoc contains a few characteristic trilobites and a distinctive dendroid graptolite (see § B-10) named *Dictyonema flabelli-forme*. The Tremadoc fauna also occurs in Scandinavia and elsewhere throughout the European faunal province, including New England and the Maritime Provinces of Canada. The trilobite fauna is abundant in Scandinavia and is rather closely related to that of the overlying Ordovician, though a few olenids are related to those of the underlying Upper Cambrian. In Britain the Tremadoc is conformable on the underlying Cambrian strata but lies unconformably beneath strata that are surely Ordovician, not only by original designation (Ref. 22) but also by subsequent usage.

For British local geologic history it is neater to include the Tremadoc in the Cambrian. In a description of the European Province and even more in any worldwide treatment, the Tremadoc is more conveniently called Lower Ordovician. Several forms of life, including the graptoloid graptolites (§ B-10), can then be said to have begun with the Ordovician. The one thing that must not be done is to use the latter classification and still cite the unconformity at the top of the Tremadoc in Britain as evidence of deformation between the Cambrian and Ordovician Periods. The British unconformity is not at the horizon of maximum faunal change in either the local British or the provincial European section.

10-3. *The Base of the Cambrian*

a. In Geosynclinal Belts

The Lower Cambrian in southern California, near the southern end of the Cordilleran geosyncline, has recently been studied rather throroughly. The geosynclinal deposits, which extend north and northeast from a point about 150 miles northeast of Los Angeles, are much thicker than those farther east, on the continental plate. A typical sequence of the eastern part of the miogeosyncline crops out in the Marble Mountains and adjacent areas in eastern California, on both sides of U.S. Highway 66. About 2,500 feet of fossiliferous Lower and Middle Cambrian strata lie unconformably on crystalline Precambrian rocks

that are partly quartz plutonite, partly metamorphosed sediments. The basal Cambrian unit is a quartz sandstone 500 feet thick, which is overlain successively by a thin shale and about 2,000 feet of carbonates. Fifty miles north of the Marble Mountains the crystalline basement and the fossiliferous Cambrian are separated by a California equivalent of the wedge series of the Grand Canyon. In the Basin Range country east of the Sierra Nevada, 150 miles northwest of the Marble Mountains, in the midst of the Paleozoic geosyncline, many thousands of feet of nonfossiliferous sandstone, shale, and dolomite underlie the lowest beds with Lower Cambrian guide fossils. The present Basin Range structure of this region has been represented in Figure 5-16; the thick Lower Cambrian and underlying strata are pictured in Figure 10-8; and a sample section is summarized in Figure 10-9. Olenellids are distributed through 6,700 feet of sandstone, shale, and limestone, which are conformably underlain by 3,800 feet of sandstone and dolomite, the latter only partially shown in Figure 10-9. The dolomite is underlain with apparent conformity by additional sediments 9,000 feet thick (largely mildly metamorphosed shale), but regional study shows that an unconformity is present at the base of the dolomite. Outside the area represented by this section, in eastern California and southwestern Nevada, the lowest olenellids are not found everywhere at the same lithologically determined horizon. All the observations, taken together, make a problem for the field geologist. Where shall he put the base of the Cambrian? Shall it be at the local base of olenellid-bearing strata (marked in Fig. 10-9), at the base of the lowest lithologic unit containing olenellids (also shown in Fig. 10-9), at the obscure unconformity below the dolomite (below the bottom of the figure), or at an obvious unconformity that cuts across the top of the crystalline complex and the California wedge series? All, or almost all, of these solutions have advocates. Perhaps the best choice is the ambiguous classification shown at the left of Figure 10-9, with a "Lower Cambrian or Precambrian" division extending from the local base of olenellid-bearing strata down to the first unconformity. Such an arrangement shows and emphasizes the relevant observed facts and suggests the increasing likelihood of Precambrian age as one proceeds downward beneath the lowest faunal zone.

The stratigraphic relations of the lowest Cambrian fauna in the California-Nevada area are typical for a geosynclinal occurrence. In the Atlas Mountains of Morocco, limestone 10,000 feet thick, in which calcareous algae of unknown stratigraphic significance are the only fossils, conformably underlies the beds containing the lowest Lower Cambrian guides. In Scandinavia, strata 4,000 feet thick, pre-dominantly clastic and including conglomerates that may be, at least in part, tillites, conformably underlie the beds with Lower Cambrian guide fossils.

Two general circumstances about the base of the Cambrian System should be kept in mind. First, its identification is uniquely difficult, so far as fossiliferous systems are concerned, because a conclusion based on the lowest occurrence of Lower Cambrian guide taxa cannot be checked against a conclusion based on the study of underlying guide taxa. Second, the Lower Cambrian guide taxa are different in the three principal faunal provinces, and especially different between the Oriental *Redlichia* province and the olenellid

Fig. 10-8. *Steeply dipping Lower Cambrian (and Precambrian) strata in eastern California, near the Nevada line; aerial view toward the southwest. The mountains in the foreground are about 15 miles southeast of Bishop, Inyo County, California; Sierra Nevada in distance. (Photograph by J. S. Shelton).*

provinces. No one can say with any confidence that the lowest *Olenellus* in California is at the same time horizon as the lowest *Redlichia* (or archaeocyathid) in Australia. These considerations are particularly important when one compares horizons based on fossil taxa with ages derived from radiometric data.

b. Cambrian Transgressions onto Continental Platforms

The continental platforms are blocks of Precambrian rocks (Fig. 9-1), of subcontinental extent, that have flat tops produced by erosion. Most platforms of the northern hemisphere, and the northeastern Australian platform, too, were extensively flooded by the sea at one time or another during the Cambrian. Large portions of the platform surfaces were then at or slightly below sea level, and they have remained fairly close to sea level ever since. Some platforms of the southern hemisphere were not overlain by stratified deposits until the late Paleozoic (§ 13-3.b), and the flatness of their tops may have been produced in post-Cambrian but pre-late Paleozoic, mostly pre-Carboniferous, time.

The flat-topped platforms of the northern hemisphere were covered by sedimentary blankets at somewhat varied times, ranging from Precambrian to post-Cambrian. The European (Baltic-Russian) platform has a flat erosion surface cut across Precambrian plutonic and metamorphic rocks. This surface is widely covered by Lower Cambrian beds, but the overlying Middle and Upper Cambrian strata are mostly limited to southern Scandinavia. In Russia the horizontal Precambrian Sinian System (§ 9-4.d), between the crystalline Precambrian basement and the Paleozoic succession, is widespread. On the Siberian platform Cambrian strata are varied, extensive (Fig. 10-1), and probably unusually thick. In eastern Siberia, two important units, both called Cambrian, are distinguished below the unit mapped as "Lower Cambrian." Age distinctions in Siberia are somewhat obscure and apparently are based largely on archaeocyathids (see below), but well-documented Lower Cambrian appears to be pres-

ent near Lake Baikal and elsewhere. In southeastern Asia and northern Australia the lowest horizontal beds, of unfossiliferous dolomite, perhaps Precambrian, are commonly overlain by Lower (and Middle?) Cambrian with

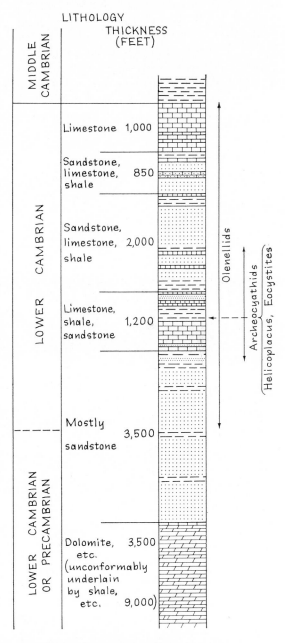

Fig. 10-9. *Columnar section of Lower Cambrian and underlying strata, Inyo County, California. (After C. A. Nelson,* BULLETIN, *Geol. Soc. Am., 1962.)*

Redlichia. In North America most of the central Precambrian platform, from the Canadian Shield south and west, carries a Cambrian cover that is commonly considered wholly Upper Cambrian.

Western North America as a whole appears to have been overlapped progressively by the advancing Cambrian sea and its deposits. On the Pacific side of the Cordillera, higher horizons extend farther and farther east, with two minor regressive exceptions, one each in the Middle and the Upper Cambrian. Three generalized shorelines, illustrating the progressive submergence, are shown in Figure 10-10. An Early Cambrian shoreline extended north-south through the west end of the Grand Canyon, near the Nevada-Arizona boundary line. A Middle Cambrian shoreline was 200 miles farther east, in Arizona near the New Mexico line. The Late Cambrian shore extended north-south through western New Mexico and Colorado. Farther north, in the Dakotas and Minnesota, a broad strait connected Pacific and Atlantic waters, separating a narrow southern midcontinental land mass from the larger land area of the Canadian Shield. In

Fig. 10-10. *Map of Early, Middle, and Late Cambrian shorelines in the western United States. (Generalized from Christina Lochman, Refs. 3 and 11.)*

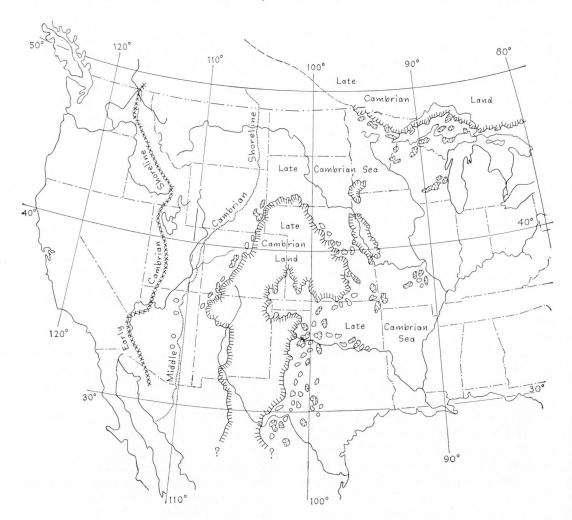

the Ordovician Period, the submergence of the North American platform became still more pronounced.

Some of the evidence of a platform land area that included most of North America in Early Cambrian time and then grew progressively smaller is negative: the absence of marine strata from the supposed land areas. But there is also abundant positive evidence, derived from the local sequences at hundreds of places, of progressive overlap. The Lower-Middle Cambrian overlap in the Grand Canyon has been described in § 5-1.b (see especially Fig. 5-6). The stratigraphic relations in southeastern Missouri are equally convincing for Upper Cambrian overlap. There the local relief on the surface of Precambrian rhyolite porphyry is 1,500 feet; the Upper Cambrian strata—basal sandstone overlain by dolomite that is shaly at some levels—overlap progressively onto porphyry islands (Fig. 10-10); locally derived conglomerate tongues extend out into the basal sandstone and higher shale for distances up to one mile from the island shores; and at some horizons dolomite beds lie directly on or abut against porphyry slopes of 5°–25°.

The almost continuously progressive overlap in North America is explained most simply by a slightly hesitant and vacillating eustatic rise of sea level during the whole of Cambrian time. This hypothesis, however, gains little if any support outside North America, as a study of the L, M, and U labels for particular Cambrian localities in Figure 10-1 will show. We might try to reconcile the Early Cambrian sedimentation on the European platform and its absence from the North American platform by postulating a lower general level for the European platform of that time. But then there must have been a local rise of the European platform to keep out the later Cambrian sea, or some more complicated history of sedimentation and erosion of the sort discussed in Chapter 5 for the hypothetical Grand Canyon Ordovician and Silurian. In any case, simple eustatic rise of sea level cannot be the whole explanation. One clumsy way out

would be to postulate slow and independent rise or fall for each platform; but it might be hard to find a plausible explanation for such widespread uniform rise or fall. One hypothesis suggests a subcrustal change of state from solid to liquid and back again; but a slow solidification of magma beneath all North America, the process taking 70 million years to reach completion, is hard to accept in the absence of any corroborative evidence. And so, having tried several simple explanations without success, we leave the Cambrian overlaps unexplained, at least for the time being.

Marine fossiliferous Cambrian is absent from the equatorial and southern platforms of Africa, eastern South America, western Australia, the peninsula of India, and—apparently—Arabia. Most of these platforms were so high or so upgoing during the early Paleozoic that they were not covered with sheets of sediments until Carboniferous time; then there began the Gondwana type of continental sedimentation, which will be discussed in Chapter 13.

10-4. *Precision of Cambrian Correlations*

Now, with some information at hand concerning the Cambrian System and its guide fossils in several parts of the world, we can discuss the precision of Cambrian time correlations, albeit somewhat more vaguely and generally than the Jurassic was treated in Chapter 7. For the Upper Jurassic of the North Atlantic region, the provincialism is great enough so that some British stages cannot be recognized in East Greenland or the Austro-Italian Alps, but the Austro-Italian guide ammonites can be used for correlations in most parts of the world. Provincialism prevails throughout the Cambrian System and makes many distant correlations vague or conflicting. We have discussed especially the Oriental *Redlichia* faunas, some of which cannot be assigned with confidence to either the Lower or the Middle Cambrian subsystem. In the Jurassic, some stages are brought into question in some places; in the Cambrian, some subsystem assignments are uncertain.

Recently, however, the prospects for precise Cambrian correlations between provinces have brightened. Several agnostid species, or sets of closely related species, have been found to have wide distribution at particular horizons. An Australian-Scandinavian correlation (Ref. 3) has been mentioned earlier in this chapter. Still more recent discoveries include the finding, in the United States, of Scandinavian guides to zones immediately below and above the Middle-Upper Cambrian boundary. Representatives of seven agnostid genera in Utah (Ref. 13) are very similar to Scandinavian upper Middle Cambrian guide species, including the one shown in Figure 10-3D, and the genus *Glyptagnostus* (Fig. 10-3J) of the lower Upper Cambrian has been found in eastern Nevada and elsewhere (Ref. 14). These discoveries, fortunately, confirm the previously doubtful correlations according to which the *Cedaria* zone of the North American Province has been considered lowest Upper Cambrian. *Glyptagnostus* is now known in Scandinavia, Great Britain, Alabama, Nevada, Tasmania, northeastern Australia, South Korea, northeastern Siberia, and northwestern Siberia (Ref. 14). Perhaps it and other agnostids were planktonic forms that were carried from continent to continent by currents.

The *Glyptagnostus* succession in North America is the basis for a line of reasoning that makes zones based on larger trilobites appear biofacial. The three lowest, generally recognized Upper Cambrian zones are named from the ptychoparioid genera *Cedaria*, *Crepicephalus*, and *Aphelaspis*. Using agnostids, one may recognize four horizons in this part of the section (Table 10-1). Three successive and slightly different *Glyptagnostus* populations have been distinguished by statistical treatment of measurements on many specimens (Ref. 14). The glyptagnostids have been found in east-central Nevada and northern Alabama. The first (lowest) *Glyptagnostus* population occurs with *Cedaria*, the second with *Aphelaspis*. No *Crepicephalus* fauna is present in these areas, and in Nevada the fossiliferous succession is continuous, without sign of unconformity, leaving no place for the *Crepicephalus* zone, even as a lacuna. The probable evolutionary continuity of the *Glyptagnostus* succession is attested by the intermediate statistical and other characteristics of the second population. Apparently the best set of correlations is the one shown in the table, with the horizons containing the first and second *Glyptagnostus* populations time-correlated with the lower and upper parts of the *Crepicephalus* zone. The latter occurs mostly in areas closer to the Canadian Shield, and this geographic distribution leads to the supposition that species of *Aphelaspis*, and possibly of *Cedaria*, represent offshore biofacies that may have lived in deeper water than the *Crepicephalus* biofacies. The

TABLE 10-1

Some Upper Cambrian Biofacies in North America

	OUTER FACIES	INTERMEDIATE FACIES	CENTRAL FACIES
Localities:	Nevada, Alabama	Missouri, Oklahoma	Minnesota, Wisconsin
Lithofacies:	Shale and silty limestone	Mostly dolomite	Sandstone
Horizons:			
Uppermost	*Glyptagnostus* population 3, *Aphelaspis*, etc.	*Aphelaspis* fauna	*Aphelaspis* fauna
Third	*Glyptagnostus* population 2, *Aphelaspis*, etc.	*Crepicephalus* fauna	*Crepicephalus* fauna
Second	*Glyptagnostus* population 1, *Cedaria*, etc.	*Crepicephalus* fauna	*Crepicephalus* fauna
Lowest	Pre-*Glyptagnostus*(?) fauna, with *Cedaria*	*Cedaria* fauna	*Cedaria* fauna

coordinated use of agnostids and ptychoparioid guide fossils seems necessary for provincial time correlations. A side effect of such correlations is the recognition of regional ecologic zones. The net result of this procedure, and of similar ones in other continents, may be world-wide correlations between subdivisions (stages) in the Middle and Upper Cambrian, even though most of the provincial guides have primarily biofacial significance.

10-5. Cambrian Climates

The Cambrian climates were apparently about like those of later times, with the production of weathering zones and sediments, in the Grand Canyon region and elsewhere, similar to those that are common in temperate and subtropical regions today. This conclusion, in Chapter 5, was based partly on data concerning present conditions that had been summarized in Chapter 4. There was, however, one notable change from the Precambrian: the preservation (and presumably the first extensive formation) of thick evaporite deposits. Soluble salts, mostly sodium chloride, are found in Iran and east-central Siberia, with anhydrite (calcium sulphate) also known in Arctic Canada. In Siberia, near Lake Baikal, salt (sodium chloride) at the base of the Middle Cambrian is 500 feet thick. Lower Cambrian potassium salts 600 m.y. old are also reported (§ 8-7.a). In Iran salt is associated with fossiliferous Cambrian sediments and Cambrian volcanics in the cores of anticlines. The salt also rises far above its stratigraphic level in piercement salt domes. The Cambrian ocean must have been salty, and some parts of Cambrian seas must have been evaporating pans, either because they were landlocked or because they were far inshore on broad, flat continental shelves. The Cambrian climate must have involved the existence of arid belts somewhat like those that exist today. The lack of salt beds in Precambrian rocks may indicate that abundant salt in the sea, or properly

Fig. 10-11. Brachiopods (Lingulella, Paterina, etc.) from the lower Bright Angel shale, Middle Cambrian of the Grand Canyon, Arizona. (Museum of Northern Arizona, Flagstaff; from J. S. Shelton, Geology Illustrated, W. H. Freeman & Co.)

shaped evaporating pans, or arid climates first appeared in the Cambrian.

10-6. Cambrian Life

a. Fossil remains

Cambrian plants are the simplest possible—they are all algae. Cambrian animals are surprisingly varied, all major phyla being represented except the Bryozoa and, perhaps, the Chordata (no vertebrates are known). The whole life record is marine.

By far the most abundant Cambrian fossils are trilobites and brachiopods. Trilobites, illustrated in Figure 10-3, furnish most of the guide fossils. Brachiopods, both Inarticulata and Articulata, are rather small and fairly numerous. A rock specimen from the Middle Cambrian of the Grand Canyon (Fig. 10-11) carries examples of a common type. The trilobite-brachiopod Cambrian faunas are very different from any fauna living today. Existing shellfish are mostly mollusks, whose commonest associates possessing hard parts are echinoderms, coelenterates, protozoans, sponges, and crustaceans, the last belonging to groups not very closely related to the trilobites.

Other Cambrian fossils (Table 10-2) are much rarer. They fall naturally into two groups, one represented by hard parts and widely distributed (Figs. 10-11–10-22), the other made up of impressions of soft animal bodies (Fig. 10-23) found at two localities: lowest Cambrian (or Precambrian) in South Australia, Middle Cambrian in British Columbia.

Minor Cambrian groups with hard parts include two that are rock-builders: algae and archaeocyathids. The cryptozoan algae (Fig.

10-12) are rather similar to the calcareous algae of the Precambrian (Fig. 9-19). They are locally prominent in the Upper Cambrian of eastern New York, as near Saratoga, and north of the Adirondacks in Canada. They occur as clusters of roughly globular, concentrically banded, concretion-like masses, each individual a foot or so across. The archaeocyathids (Fig. 10-13) were probably simple animals rather closely related to the sponges. The individual specimens are elongated, porous, double-walled, subcylindrical cups, commonly an inch or less in diameter and from two to four inches long. Several archaeocyathid subgroups are guides to the Lower Cambrian; other subgroups extend into the Middle Cambrian in Eurasia. Some Lower Cambrian sub-

TABLE 10-2

Cambrian Life

	LOWER CAMBRIAN	MIDDLE CAMBRIAN	UPPER CAMBRIAN
Protochordata?			
Dendroid graptolites			X
Arthropoda			
Trilobites—abundant	X	X	X
Ostracode crustaceans—rare	X (Glaessner)		
Other crustaceans—rare		X (Burgess shale)	
Onychophora—rare		X (Burgess shale)	
Annelida	X (Ediacara)	X (Burgess shale)	
"Scolithus"—common	X (worldwide)		
Echinodermata			
Primitive—rare	X	X	X
Mollusca			
Cephalopods—rare	?		X
Gastropods—rather rare	X	X	X
Polyplacophora—very rare			X
Monoplacophora—rare	X	X	
Brachiopoda			
Inarticulata—common	X (small)	X	X
Articulata—rather rare	X	X	X
Coelenterata—rare			
Sea-pen corals	? (Ediacara)		
Jellyfish	X (Ediacara)	X (Burgess shale)	
Hydrozoa?: stromatoporoids			?
Porifera			
Siliceous sponges—rather rare		X	X
Porifera?			
Archaeocyathids—common	X (great reefs)	?	
Protozoa			
Foraminifera	X		X
Algae			
Calcareous—not rare	X	X	X

Fig. 10-12. *Calcareous algae* (Cryptozoon), *Saratoga, New York; Upper Cambrian. (Photograph by E. J. Stein, courtesy of L. V. Rickard, New York Geological Survey.)*

groups are limited to one region, such as South Australia, but a few are cosmopolitan. In South Australia archaeocyathid reefs, each composed of many thousands of individuals, are distributed through several hundred feet of strata over a large area, measuring 400 miles from north to south.

The members of most other minor groups do not bulk large at any place, but they are important because they are the first of their kinds. The representatives of two phyla, echinoderms and mollusks, are especially interesting.

A few Middle Cambrian echinoderms have long been known, but the first usable or well-dated Lower Cambrian specimens were discovered by members of a University of California field class in 1962. A thorough search by experts yielded dozens of specimens, all found within about a mile of a highway across a desert range east of the Sierra Nevada. Some of the new forms were described and the others mentioned in the journal *Science* in May, 1963 (Ref. 15). The new species were assigned to the genera *Helicoplacus* (Fig.

Fig. 10-13. *Archaeocyathid* (Syringocnema), *South Australia; Lower Cambrian. 100 mm long. (From* Treatise on Invertebrate Paleontology, *courtesy Geological Society of America and University of Kansas Press.)*

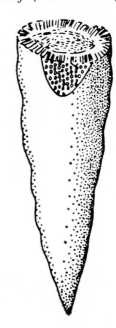

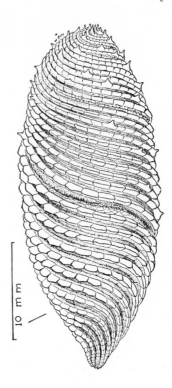

Fig. 10-14. *Coiled echinoderm* (Helicoplacus), *from 15 miles southeast of Bishop, California; Lower Cambrian.* (*From Ref. 15 by permission of the American Association for the Advancement of Science.*)
LEFT. *An expanded specimen, showing the mouth end; 18 mm across.*
RIGHT. *Reconstruction of partly retracted specimen.*

10-14) and *Eocystites* (Fig. 10-15), the former a new genus, the latter already known from the Middle Cambrian of the Grand Canyon and southern Nevada. The stratigraphic level in the Lower Cambrian, "2,500 feet above the base of the 6,700 feet of olenellid-bearing strata," is marked in Figure 10-9.

Eocystites resembles some Ordovician and other Paleozoic cystoids, the cystoids being the most generalized and primitive of the stemmed echinoderms (§ B-9.a), but none of the specimens of either Lower Cambrian genus shows any evidence of a stem. *Helicoplacus* is unique among echinoderms in its spindle-shaped body, made up of helically arranged plates, but its most amazing feature was the ability to expand and contract this body (compare the two parts of Fig. 10-14). As

Helicoplacus and *Eocystites* are the most ancient echinoderms yet discovered, were both free-living, and are morphologically widely separated from each other, the Precambrian ancestor of all the echinoderms (starfish, crinoids, sand-dollars, and all) may have been a globular, free-living form, already equipped with an external skeleton of calcareous plates. The Lower Cambrian discoveries increase somewhat the probability that the remains of a Precambrian ancestor will be found.

Two other primitive echinoderm groups, both with flat calyces, appear in the Middle Cambrian. The members of one of these groups, the edrioasteroids (Fig. 10-16), were somewhat like *Helicoplacus* but had ambulacral areas showing the well-marked five-fold symmetry of most later echinoderms. Both of the new Middle Cambrian groups were probably side branches from the main echinoderm stem; apparently they died out in the Middle Paleozoic, without leaving any descendants.

The Cambrian mollusks belong to four classes: monoplacophorans, polyplacophorans, gastropods, and cephalopods. Pelecypods have not been found below the Ordovician. Monoplacophorans (Fig. 10-17) have cap-shaped shells (A) somewhat like those of the gastropods called limpets, but their muscle scars, on the shell's inner surface (B), and the Recent

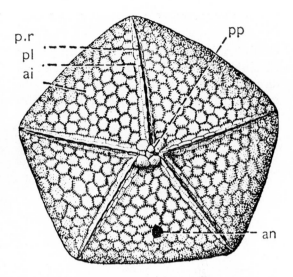

Fig. 10-16. *Edrioasteroid echinoderm* (Stromatocystis), *1.5 inches across, from Middle Cambrian of Bohemia: ai, interambulacral plates; an, anus; pl, lateral plates; pp, plates around mouth; p.r, cover plates.* (After F. A. Bather via Jean Piveteau, Traité de paléontologie, Masson, Paris, 1953.)

Fig. 10-15. *Cystid-like echinoderm* (Eocystites, *also called* Eocrinus), *from Bright Angel shale, Grand Canyon, Arizona; Middle Cambrian; calyx 1 inch across.* (From C. E. Resser, Carnegie Institution of Washington, 1945.)

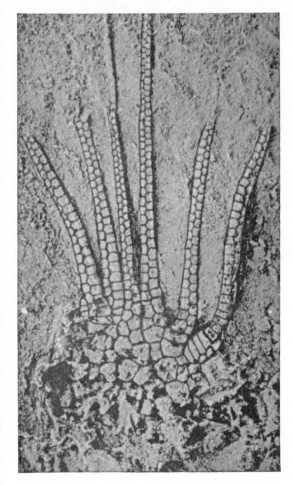

soft parts (C) are bilaterally symmetrical. The symmetry is similar to that of the polyplacophorans (chitons; Fig. 10-18), for a chiton has a straight body and bears a row of bilaterally symmetrical plaques on its back. Fossil monoplacophorans are known from the Lower Cambrian to the Devonian; in 1952 a species was found living at a depth of about 12,000 feet in the Pacific Ocean off Mexico (Ref. 18), later also off Peru. The chitons, with a range from the Upper Cambrian to the Recent, and the gastropods, with a range from the Lower Cambrian to the Recent, both have soft parts more or less analogous to those of the living monoplacophorans. Since modern gastropods have twisted figure-8 nervous systems that look as though they had been derived from a single bilaterally symmetrical loop, anatomists long ago postulated a bilaterally symmetrical ancestor, such as the monoplacophorans. Now the accumulating fossil evidence, including the symmetrical muscle scars (Fig. 10-17B) reported in 1954 (Ref. 17) as occurring on a lowest Middle Cambrian monoplacophoran, seems to justify the hypothesis. The Middle Cambrian form, however, or even its Lower Cambrian relative (Fig. 10-17A), cannot be directly ancestral to the gastropods, for liberty-cap gastropods (Fig. 10-19A) have also been found in the Lower Cambrian. A planospiral snail (Fig. 10-19BC) is known in the Middle Cambrian, and in the Upper Cambrian several types of typically coiled snails are present, including some with moderately high spires. Valves of true chitons have been

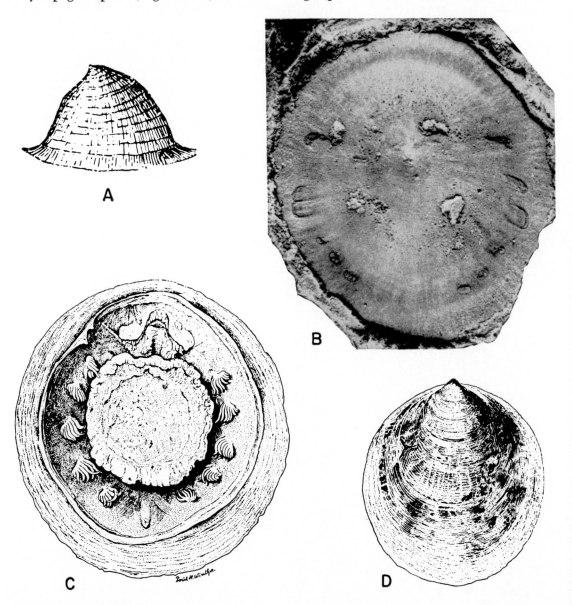

Fig. 10-17. *Monoplacophorans.*

AB. Scenella: A, *exterior, 0.5 inch high, from Lower Cambrian of Newfoundland (from Ref. 16.);* B, *interior, 0.6 inch across, with six pairs of muscle scars, from lower Middle Cambrian of British Columbia (from Ref. 17).*

CD. Neopilina, *dredged from the deep Pacific off Mexico: C, under side, showing bilateral symmetry; D, exterior of the single shell, 1.5 inches long. (From Ref. 18.)*

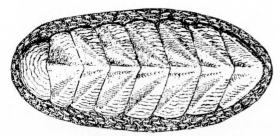

Fig. 10-18. *Polyplacophoran (chiton); Recent.* (*From Bernhard Kummel,* History of the Earth, *W. H. Freeman & Co., 1961.*)

Fig. 10-19. *Cambrian gastropods. (From Ref. 16.)*
A. *Liberty-cap gastropod* (Oelandia), *0.2 inch high, from Lower Cambrian of southeastern Newfoundland.*
BC. *Planospiral gastropod* (Coreospira), *from low Middle Cambrian of British Columbia.*

Fig. 10-20. *The straight nautiloid* Palaeoceras, *from uppermost Cambrian of central Texas. (From R. H. Flower, Bull. 40, New Mexico Bureau of Mines, 1954.)*
A. *Reconstruction, based on fragmentary specimens.*
B. *Internal mold of an upper segment, with faint indications of the latest septa.*
C. *Internal mold, corresponding to apical (lower) part of A, with septa retouched; 6.5 mm long.*

Fig. 10-21. *Molluscan(?)* Volborthella, *from Lower Cambrian of Tallin, Esthonia. At left, vertical section through* V. conica, 2.5 mm long; *at right, side and end views of internal molds of* V. tenuis, 3 and 2.5 mm long. (Photographs from O. H. Schindewolf.)

Fig. 10-22. *Very small brachiopod* (Angulotreta postapicalis), *from the* Cedaria *zone, lowest Upper Cambrian, central Texas. At left, natural size; at right,* × 13.6. (Redrawn from A. R. Palmer, JOURNAL OF PALEONTOLOGY, 1954.)
A. *Interior of brachial valve.*
B. *Exterior of pedicle valve, in profile.*

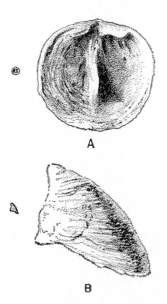

found in fairly late Upper Cambrian limestone in Missouri (Ref. 16).

A cephalopod from the Upper Cambrian of China is probably the oldest one known. It is a horn-shaped, chambered shell similar to some Chinese Ordovician forms. A straight, cylindrical cephalopod from the uppermost Cambrian of Texas (Fig. 10-20) has bulbous expansions of the siphuncle (§ B-7.c.2) similar to those of the Chinese forms. Tiny, straight, chambered shells (Fig. 10-21), found rarely in the Lower Cambrian, are resolutely rejected by some leading cephalopod specialists; for one thing, the supposed siphuncles are obscure. The affinities of these little shells are unknown.

Except for the trilobites, algae, and archaeocyathids, most Lower and Middle Cambrian fossils are small. The brachiopods of Figure 10-11 are typical. Much smaller brachiopods (Fig. 10-22) also occur.

b. Impressions of Animal Forms

The most remarkable Cambrian (and Precambrian?) fossils are the impressions of soft-bodied animals at two localities: lowest Cambrian (or Precambrian) at Ediacara, in South Australia, and Middle Cambrian in the Burgess shale high above the Canadian Pacific Railroad at Field, in easternmost British Columbia.

The Burgess shale locality was discovered in 1910 by Charles D. Walcott, director of the U.S. Geological Survey, who described from it more than a hundred species, including those shown in Figure 10-23, of algae, sponges, jellyfish, annelid worms (FHI), arthropods and arthropod-like forms (ABEG), and an onychophore (CD) that is the only fossil representative of a group whose rare living members seem intermediate between annelids and arthropods. Perfect trilobite specimens are present in the Burgess shale, but the fame of the locality comes from the hundreds of specimens that show anatomical details of other forms. Some of the most notable things are flattened algal tissues, sponge spicules and structures, the arrangement of worm bristles

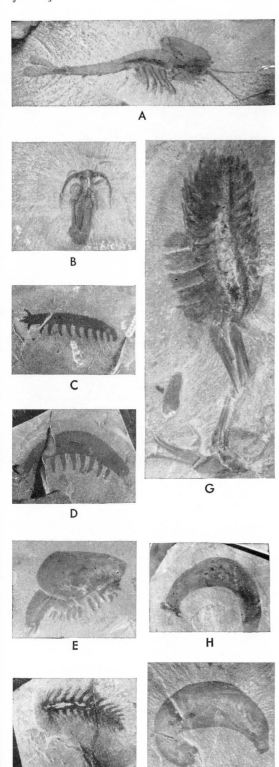

A

B

C

D

E

F

G

H

I

(F), and "shrimp" and onychophore append-ages (ACD).

The locality in the Ediacara Hills, 280 miles north of Adelaide, South Australia, has an ambiguous stratigraphic position. Unlike the Burgess shale, which is in the midst of a thick fossiliferous Cambrian sequence and contains Middle Cambrian guide trilobites, the Edia-cara occurrences include no established guide fossils and have none below them. A diagram of the Ediacara Hills structure (Fig. 10-24) shows the layer that contains the impressions of soft-bodied animals in sandstone about 500 feet stratigraphically below the lowest conventional Lower Cambrian fossils—ar-chaeocyathids and brachiopods. The impres-sions are in a very fine-grained layer so tight that the rock will not split to expose the fossils. All the specimens, of which 800 had been col-lected before 1962, have weathered out natu-rally. They include (Fig. 10-25) probable jellyfish (A), a probable sea-pen coelenterate called *Charnia* (B), several annelids (C), and flatworms(?) (D), as well as problematical forms of more uncertain affinities.

Not one of the soft-bodied forms from the Ediacara Hills can be assigned to any group of trilobites, brachiopods, or other type of animal or plant known from hard parts in Lower Cambrian strata. The soft-bodied fauna may therefore represent an unusual bi-ofacies that existed right up to the end of Early Cambrian time but apparently not into the time when the Burgess shale was de-

Fig. 10-23. *Middle Cambrian fossil impressions from Field, British Columbia. (Photographs by H. B. Whittington via Bernhard Kummel, op. cit.)*

A. Waptia, *a shrimp-like arthropod.*

B. Marrella, *a trilobite-like arthropod.*

C,D. Aysheaia, *an onychophore, perhaps close to the common ancestor of the arthropods and worms.*

E. Hymenocaris, *probably an arthropod.*

F. Canadia, *an annelid worm.*

G. Leanchoilia, *probably an arthropod.*

H,I. Ottoia (*two species*), *probably annelid worms.*

Fig. 10-24. *Cambrian (and Precambrian?) fossil beds in the Ediacara Hills, South Australia. About 150 feet of sandstone and 350 feet of dolomite are present between the two fossiliferous horizons. (After M. F. Glaessner, SCIENTIFIC AMERICAN, 1961.)*

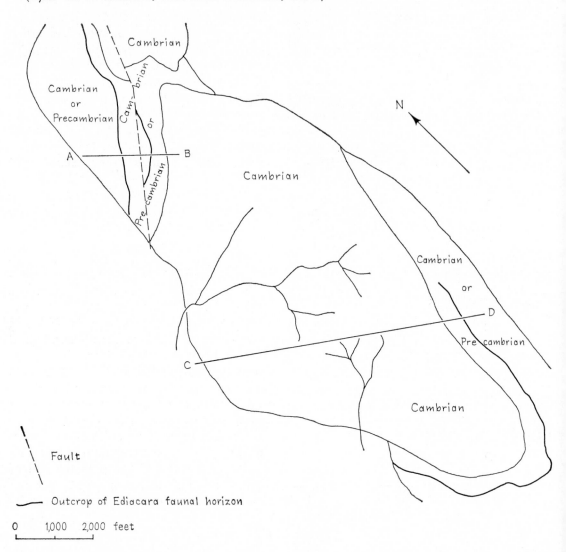

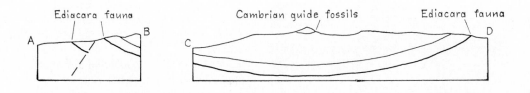

posited. On the other hand, the Ediacara
fauna may have become extinct before the
time of any Lower Cambrian trilobite, brachiopod, or archaeocyathid. It is best labeled,
so far as its Australian occurrence is concerned, "Lower Cambrian or Precambrian."

Some elements of the Ediacara fauna seem
to have been in existence far back in Precambrian time. The sea-pen(?) *Charnia* has
also been found in clearly Precambrian rocks
of the Charnwood Forest, England. Moreover,
at the very base of the Bass formation, the
lowest member of the wedge series in the
Grand Canyon Precambrian, numerous fossils
or pseudo fossils (Fig. 10-26), similar to the
Ediacara form *Spriggia*, have been collected
at a single locality. These two occurrences
suggest that the Ediacara fauna, or part of it,
existed in Precambrian time, though they
leave unsettled the question of the fauna's
persistence into Early Cambrian time.

c. Paucity of Early Cambrian Life

The Early Cambrian fauna, even including
that in the Ediacara sandstone, is more restricted than any later one. It is also an enormous advance over anything earlier. The most
complex forms that are even suspected of having existed earlier are coelenterates, which
may be contrasted with the brachiopods, mollusks, and annelids, and especially with the
trilobites, of the Early Cambrian. But all post–
Early Cambrian, and especially all post-Cambrian, faunas were much more varied and
much more advanced. Early Cambrian trilobites were spinier and less varied than
later trilobites. The oldest known brachiopods

A

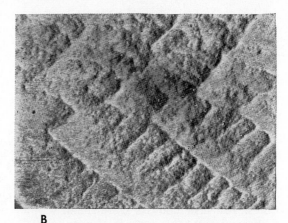

B

C

Fig. 10-25. *Fossil impressions from the Lower
Cambrian or Precambrian of the Ediacara Hills,
South Australia. (From M. F. Glaessner, loc.
cit.)*

A. Spriggia, *probably a jellyfish (coelenterate).*
B. Charnia, *probably a sea-pen, a kind of coral
(coelenterate).*
C. Spriggina, *an annelid worm (scale in mm).*
D. Dickinsonia, *a flatworm(?) similar to the
modern Spinther (scale in cm).*

D

Fig. 10-26. Spriggia(?), *from the lowest Bass limestone of the Precambrian wedge series in the Grand Canyon, Arizona. (From Raymond Alf Museum, Webb School, Claremont, California.)*

had the clumsiest of valve-closing mechanisms. The first mollusks were small, simple, and generalized, even if compared with the snails and nautiloids of the Late Cambrian. It may be that the only Early Cambrian arthropods were trilobites, though bivalved ostracode crustaceans have recently been reported. A little later in the Paleozoic several other major arthropod groups appeared. Finally, the Early Cambrian fauna included no graptolites, no fish, no other vertebrates.

If one compares Early Cambrian landscapes and seascapes with those of the present day, the contrast is extreme. On the land, there may have been almost no Early Cambrian life whatever, though weathering may already have been accelerated by bacteria and other extremely simple forms of life. Surely there were, on the land, no grasses, shrubs, or trees, nor even moss or lichens, and certainly no self-propelled animals. In the sea, there were no fish or whales or seals, no squids or other cephalopods, no crabs or lobsters, no clams,

no ordinary corals, very few foraminifers, and probably no diatoms.

d. Cause of Abrupt Appearance of Early Cambrian Fauna

The sudden appearance of the Early Cambrian fauna is one of the most obvious facts of stratigraphy and perhaps the hardest to explain. Many attempts have been made. W. K. Brooks of Johns Hopkins University, in 1894, emphasized the great and obvious differences that separate the trilobites, brachiopods, and other Early Cambrian groups from one another and their equally obvious relationships with animal groups living today: trilobites similar to living crustaceans, etc. He thought that the Cambrian forms must have had long and separate histories before Cambrian time. He postulated well-developed trilobites, brachiopods, etc., before the beginning of the Cambrian, all of them soft-bodied floaters or swimmers. He supposed that members of these groups successively discovered the bottom of the ocean, got into sharp competition with each other in this two-dimensional space, and finally acquired protective coverings at the time we call earliest Cambrian. Brooks's idea of the struggle for existence was somewhat naive.

An entirely different explanation was proposed by C. D. Walcott in 1910. He suggested that, in North America at least, the Precambrian sedimentary formations are non-marine. He thought that the fossiliferous strata we call Lower Cambrian in North America are the records of the first advances of the ocean upon this continent. If the implications of this hypothesis are followed out, we see that fossiliferous Precambrian strata should be sought beneath the oceans. As post-Cambrian deformation has been enormous around the continental margins, and as at least twice as much is now known about the marginal deformed belts as Walcott knew in 1910, the failure to discover, in Precambrian strata anywhere, possible ancestors of the Lower Cambrian trilobites and brachiopods, or even of the archaeocyathids, now makes the Walcott theory seem improbable. In Chapter 9, moreover, we found some evidence, perhaps not very convincing, that the Precambrian iron formations and their associated strata are of marine origin. It is possible, too, that all dolomite formations, including those of the Precambrian, are marine.

Other theorists have postulated the Precambrian development of trilobites, brachiopods, archaeocyathids, and primitive mollusks in environments where sediments are not usually deposited or preserved. The most obvious of such environments is the shore zone. An exceptionally well-exposed overlapping shore zone has been preserved, however, at the base of the Cambrian Tapeats sandstone in the Grand Canyon region (§ 5-1.b), and this zone is wholly barren of fossils, even though contemporaneous trilobites and brachiopods have been preserved not far away (compare Fig. 5-6). If animals evolved in this shore zone, their remains were not preserved there.

The geological record furnishes considerable evidence of varied tempo in evolution. Some paleontologists postulate a period of feverish evolutionary activity just before the Cambrian, the fossil remains of the hard parts of marine animals in the Lower Cambrian rocks having preserved the evidence of the varied animal evolution that had just occurred. The Ediacara and other recent discoveries of fossil animals below the typical Lower Cambrian trilobite fauna have, however, complicated the contrast between animal-rich and animal-free horizons. Moreover, the finding of agglutinated foraminifers (*Bathysiphon*, similar to Fig. B-4B), in the Lower Cambrian of Russia, emphasizes the haphazard way in which many kinds of fossils occur in the older rocks. These foraminifers may be the only ones known below the Upper Cambrian.

Though the Ediacara impressions give no indication of the concurrent existence of the ancestors of trilobites, brachiopods, archeocyathids, or even foraminifers, the stratigraphic interval between the two dissimilar faunas in the Ediacara Hills is surprisingly small to represent the time during which trilobites and brachiopods evolved. Perhaps the Ediacara impressions really do belong to a peculiar biofacies rarely preserved, which is irrelevant to any discussion of the evolution of the animals responsible for the production of the substances usually preserved as fossils.

Whatever one may think about changing tempo in evolution, one factor in the development of hard parts may have been that suggested by Charles Schuchert and Carl O. Dunbar (Ref. 7): "The development of actively predacious habits may have been the first great stimulus to the development of protective armor. It is not improbable that all Pre-Cambrian animals were herbivorous or scavenging, and that the development of the active carnivorous habit coincides with the great change" that resulted in the apparently sudden appearance of the Lower Cambrian faunas with easily preservable hard parts.

PROBLEMS

1. Write an essay on the New Brunswick–New England barrier. Define the problem, and treat it exhaustively; that is, consider all possibilities. See R. D. Hutchinson, "Cambrian stratigraphy, correlation, and paleogeography of eastern Canada," in Ref. 3.

2. Discuss the presence of Scandinavian agnostid zones in Australia as a biogeographic problem. How did the little blindies make the trip, and what held *Paradoxides* and *Redlichia* back? See A. A. Öpik, "Cambrian geology of the Northern Territory," in Ref. 3, and M. W. Johnson, "Plankton," in Ref. 3 of Chap. 2 of this book.

3. Is the Ediacara (South Australian) soft-bodied fauna Cambrian or Precambrian? Give reasons for your answer. Note any uncertainties about the base of the South Australian Cambrian, and consider the difficulties of determining the geologic ranges of soft-bodied organisms.

4. Using Table 10-1 as a starting point, discuss the application of the concepts of homotaxis and synchronism to the Upper Cambrian zones of North America. Compare the Upper Cambrian litho- and biofacies with those of the Lower and Middle Cambrian in the Grand Canyon (§ 5-1.b)

REFERENCES

Supplementary Reading

1. W. Charles Bell: "Cambrian," *McGraw-Hill Encyclopedia of Science and Technology* (New York, 1960)

2. M. F. Glaessner: "Pre-Cambrian Animals," SCIENTIFIC AMERICAN, March 1961, pp. 72–78

Background Material

3. John Rodgers and others: *El Sistema Cámbrico, su paleogeografía y el problema de su base*, 2 vols. (20th Int. Geol. Cong., México, 1956)

4. W. K. Brooks: "The Origin of the Oldest Fossils and the Discovery of the Bottom of the Ocean," JOURNAL OF GEOLOGY, vol. 2, pp. 455–479 (1894)

5. R. A. Daly: "Limeless Ocean of Pre-Cambrian Time," AMERICAN JOURNAL OF SCIENCE, 4th Series, vol. 23, pp. 93–115 (1907)

6. C. D. Walcott: "Abrupt Appearance of the Cambrian Fauna on the North American Continent," Smithsonian Misc. Coll., vol. 57, No. 1 (1910)

7. Charles Schuchert and C. O. Dunbar: *Historical Geology*, p. 142 (Wiley, New York, 1933)

8. C. L. Dake and Josiah Bridge: "Buried and Resurrected Hills of Central Ozarks," BULLETIN, Am. Ass. Petrol. Geol., vol. 16, pp. 629–652 (1932)

9. R. P. Sharp: "Ep-Archean and ep-Algonkian Erosion Surfaces, Grand Canyon, Arizona," BULLETIN, Geol. Soc. Am., vol. 51, pp. 1235–1270 (1940)

10. C. D. Walcott: "Cambrian Geology and Paleontology," Smithsonian Misc. Coll., vols. 53 (1908–1910), 57 (1910–1914), 64 (1914–1916), 67 (1917–1924), 75 (1924–1928)

11. Christina Lochman: "Paleoecology of the Cambrian in Montana and Wyoming," Memoir 67, Geol. Soc. Am., Part 2, pp. 117–162 (1957)

12. B. F. Howell: "How Should the Cambrian Epochs and Series be Delimited?" 21st Int. Geol. Cong., Part 8, pp. 37–39 (1960)

13. R. A. Robison, "Middle-Upper Cambrian Boundary in North America," BULLETIN, Geol. Soc. Am., vol. 75, pp. 987–994 (1964)

14. A. R. Palmer: "*Glyptagnostus* and Associated Trilobites in the United States," Prof. Paper 374-F, U.S. Geol. Sur. (1962)

15. J. W. Durham and K. E. Caster: "Helicoplacoidea: a New Class of Echinoderms," SCIENCE, vol. 140, pp. 820–822 (1963)

16. J. B. Knight: "Primitive Fossil Gastropods and Their Bearing on Gastropod Classification," Smithsonian Misc. Coll., vol. 117, No. 13 (1952)

17. Franco Rasetti: "Internal Shell Structures in the Middle Cambrian Gastropod *Scenella* and the Problematical Genus *Stenothecoides*," JOURNAL OF PALEONTOLOGY, vol. 28, pp. 59–66 (1954)

18. Henning Lemche: "A New Living Deep-sea Mollusc of the Cambro-Devonian Class Monoplacophora," NATURE, vol. 179, pp. 413–416 (1957)

19. C. A. Nelson: "Lower Cambrian–Precambrian Succession, White-Inyo Mountains, California," BULLETIN, Geol. Soc. Am., vol. 73, pp. 139–144 (1962)

The Cambrian of Wales

20. Adam Sedgwick: "On the Classification of the Fossiliferous Slates of North Wales, Cumberland, Westmoreland and Lancashire," QUARTERLY JOURNAL, Geol. Soc. London, vol. 3, pp. 133–164 (1847)

21. Adam Sedgwick: Preface to J. W. Salter's *Catalogue of Cambrian and Silurian Fossils* (Cambridge, England, 1873)

22. Charles Lapworth: "On the Tripartite Classification of the Lower Palaeozoic Rocks," GEOL. MAG. 1879, pp. 1–15

23. Bernard Smith and T. N. George: *British Regional Geology: North Wales*, 2nd ed. (Geological Survey, London, 1948)

24. C. J. Stubblefield: "Cambrian Palaeogeography in Britain," in Ref. 3

CHAPTER 11

The Rise of Vertebrates

VERTEBRATES are animals that have backbones. A backbone is a segmented axial column, which is composed of hard calcium phosphate bone, as in an adult man, or of less rigid organic cartilage, as in an adult shark. Vertebrates are included in a somewhat larger group, the Phylum Chordata, or the chordates —animals that at some stage of life possess a flexible axial rod called a notochord. In man and most other vertebrates the notochord is embryonic and is replaced at an early stage of life, commonly before birth, by the segmented bone or cartilage of the vertebral column, the true backbone. The non-vertebrate chordates are rare. Graptolites (§ B-10), if they really are hemichordates, are almost the only paleontological examples.

The living vertebrates can be divided into five classes (Fig. 11-1) by obvious features: (1) the fishes, which have gills; (2) the amphibians, such as frogs and salamanders, which really are amphibious; (3) the reptiles, which have scales; (4) the mammals, which have hair; (5) the birds, which have feathers. The fishes have fins and tails adapted for swimming. Adult forms of the other verte-brates have four limbs with leg structures adapted primarily for walking or running on land; these vertebrates are therefore called tetrapods. The bone patterns of fish fins are varied, but the bone pattern of a tetrapod limb is standardized, with one upper-limb bone, two lower-limb bones side by side, a group of small ankle bones, and five toes. Amphibians are fish-like in early life, when they live in water and breathe by gills, but their adult skeletons are typically tetrapodal (Fig. 11-2). In some groups, such as birds, whales, and horses, the standard tetrapodal limb-bone pattern is more or less modified, but it can still be recognized.

The known range of vertebrates is from the Early Ordovician to the present time. The Ordovician fossils, mostly found in western North America, are fragments of primitive fishes. The oldest known complete skeletons, also of primitive fishes, are from the Upper Silurian of northern Europe. From then on, the record is quite good. Some surprising details are known; the individual bone-sheathed arteries, veins, and nerves of some Early Devonian fishes have been named or numbered. The amphibians

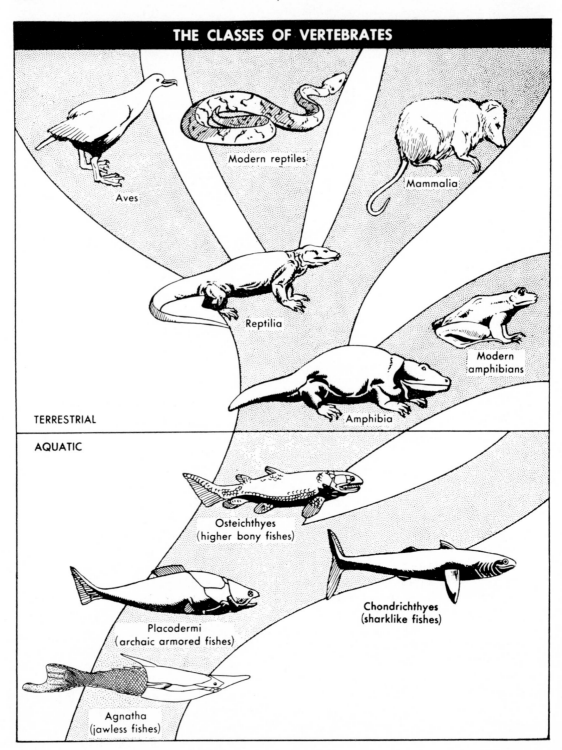

Fig. 11-1. *The classes of vertebrates.* (*Modified from Ref. 1.*)

Fig. 11-2. *A typical tetrapod skeleton:* Trematops milleri, *a Permian amphibian. Specimen 21 inches long. Shaded portion, restored.* (*From S. W. Williston,* JOURNAL OF GEOLOGY, *1909.*)

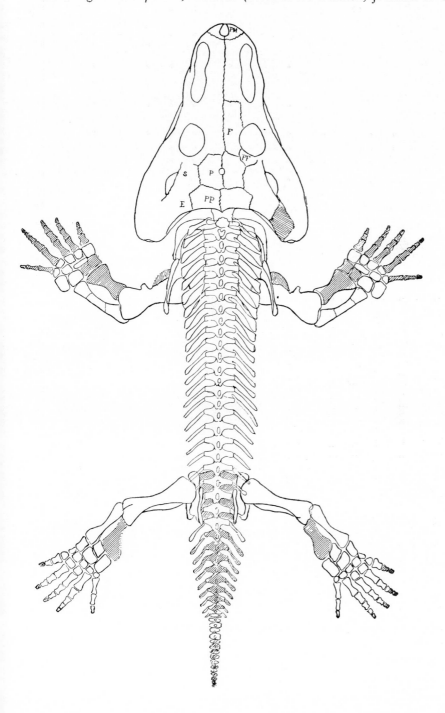

Vertebrates†

CLASS	GEOLOGIC RANGE												
	Ord.			Sil.			Devon.			Carb.	Perm.	Mes.	Cen.
	L	M	U	L	M	U	L	M	U				
Fishes													
I. Agnathans (Agnatha): primitive jawless fishes with sucking or similar simple mouths and pocket gills.													
A. Forms with one nostril.													
1. Osteostracans (Osteostraci): armored with head-thoracic dermal skeleton; eyes close together.						✳	✳	✳					
2. Anaspids (Anaspida): scaly or naked; fins; down-curved tails.						✳	✳						
3. Cyclostomes (Cyclostomata): naked; eel-like form.													Recent
B. Forms with two nostrils.													
1. Heterostracans (Heterostraci): heavy dermal armor; eyes far apart.	✳	✳	✳	✳	✳	✳	✳	✳					
2. Coelolepida: a minor group.						✳	✳						
II. Plate-skinned jawed fishes (Placodermi).													
A. Acanthodians (Acanthodii): paired fin spines; shark shape.						✳	✳	✳	✳	✳	✳		
B. Arthrodires (Arthrodira): heavy head and thoracic armor.						✳	✳	✳					
C. Antiarchs (Antiarchi): small; turtle-like shape and head paddles.						✳	✳	✳					
Less important groups.													
III. Sharks and their allies (Chondrichthyes): cartilaginous skeletons; bony teeth.									✳	✳	✳	✳	✳
IV. Bony fishes (Osteichthyes): internal skeleton, more or less ossified backbone.													
A. Crossopterygians (Crossopterygii): lobed fins.						✳	✳	✳		✳	✳	✳	Recent
B. Lungfishes (Dipnoi): thick scales; heavy teeth; lung-like bladders.						✳	✳	✳		✳	✳	✳	✳ Rec.
C. Enamel-skinned fishes (Palaeoniscoidea): large enameled scales; unsymmetrical tails.								✳		✳	✳	Rare	
D. Teleosts (Teleostei): bony vertebrae, ribs, fin-rays; flexible scales.												Jurassic—Recent	
Less important groups.													
Amphibians									✳	✳	✳	✳	✳
Reptiles										✳	✳	✳	✳
Birds												Jurassic—Recent	
Mammals												Jurassic—Recent	

TETRAPODS: VERTEBRATES HAVING FOUR LEGS, EACH LEG WITH A STANDARD BONE PATTERN

† Modified from A. S. Romer (Ref. 3).

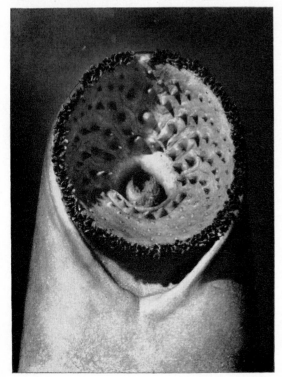

Fig. 11-3. *Models of the lamprey, a contemporary agnathan. (Courtesy of the American Museum of Natural History.)*
LEFT. *Lower side of head, showing the sucking funnel surrounding the mouth.*
ABOVE. *Lamprey (about 1/4 natural size) attached parasitically to a jawed fish (catfish).*

range from the latest Devonian to the present, the reptiles from the Carboniferous to the present, the mammals and the birds from the Jurassic to the present.

11-1. *The Four Classes of Fishes*

Fishes, the vertebrates that live and breathe in water throughout life, are now commonly divided into four classes, each a primary subdivision of the phylum Chordata (Table 11-1 and Fig. 11-1). The most primitive class, composed of jawless fishes, is the Agnatha; the others, all with hinged jaws, are the plate-skinned fishes (Placodermi, a highly varied group, but wholly Paleozoic), the sharks and

Fig. 11-4. *The osteostracan* Hemicyclaspis murchisoni, *from the lowest Devonian (Downtonian) of the English-Welsh border, about 2/3 natural size: C, tail fin;* D_2, *dorsal fin; d.cr, dorsal crest of trunk; dsf, dorsal "electric field"; orb, eye socket; Pec, pectoral fin. [From Ref. 17 with the permission of the Trustees of the British Museum (Natural History).]*

their allies (Chondrichthyes), all of which are marine and all of which have cartilaginous skeletons, and the higher bony fishes (Osteichthyes). The sharks and the bony fishes are familiar to us through their living examples. Most of the fishes living today, either in the sea or in fresh waters, belong to the Osteichthyes.

Most fish skeletons are composed of bone. Bone is a tissue made up largely of calcium phosphate; when it loses its organic content, the hard residue is more or less porous. The bony skeletons of fishes are partly internal but also include such external features as rigid scales. Most Paleozoic agnathans and all placoderms had extensive external (dermal) skeletons in the form of scales or plates; their internal skeletons were partially ossified, especially in the head region, where dermal and internal skeletons fused into armor.

a. The Agnatha

The jawless fishes (Fig. 11-1) lack hinged lower jaws and have rather simple mouth openings in the end of the snout or on the under side of the head. Living agnathans do not have gill slits like those of other fishes; their gills are in two rows of spherical pouches, on the sides of the throat, connected with the gut and with the surface by small tubes. The

agnathans are divided into two groups: those with a single central nostril and those with the usual double nostril. The single-nostriled group includes the living cyclostomes (round-mouthed ones), such as the lamprey (Fig. 11-3), which have cartilaginous skeletons. The lamprey has a long tongue-shaped structure, armed with horny spikes, that rasps off the skin and flesh of the fish to which the lamprey is parasitically attached and from which it sucks blood. All the known agnathans except the cyclostomes were Paleozoic, and there is no clear indication that any of the extinct forms were parasitic; they probably wriggled along sea or lake floors, either sucking up detritus or forcing it into their mouths by their forward movements.

Two Paleozoic (Silurian-Devonian) agnathan orders were single-nostriled. One of these, the Osteostraci (bone-shelled ones), had thin armor (Fig. 11-4) with the composition and structure of bone, even to canals, which were originally occupied by blood vessels, and tiny ovaloid **lacunae,** or cavities left by the decay of bone cells. The heaviest part of the armor was a plate over the head, but the rest of the animal's body was partially or completely covered by rather closely fitting scales. The other single-nostriled order, the Anaspida (shield-lackers), included forms with a few dermal plates and numerous scales in complex pattern (Fig. 11-5) and also some practically naked forms that have left impressions in the rocks (Fig. 11-6). Unlike any other fishes, the anaspids had down-tilted tails.

The agnathans with two nostrils include the armored Heterostraci (differently shelled; Fig. 11-7), which are known from the Lower Ordovician to the Upper Devonian. Their bony structure is so different from that of the Osteostraci or any other fishes (Fig. 11-8) that they were temporarily and mistakenly removed from the vertebrate phylum and placed with the cuttlefish cephalopods by a German paleontologist in 1847. T. H. Huxley, in 1858, put the evidence in order, chiefly through microscopical study (Fig. 11-8BC). The heterostracan plates are composed of calcium phosphate, the usual vertebrate skeletal material, and have the general laminar structure of most bone; but they lack lacunae and, despite their thickness, contain few canals for blood vessels or nerves. The general shape of the skeleton is similar to that of the osteostracans; and, long after Huxley's time, superb specimens (Fig. 11-7) with fish scales and fish tails, which showed conclusively that heterostracans should be classified as fishes, were discovered.

b. The Placodermi

The plate-skinned fishes include three principal orders, which can easily be distinguished: the acanthodians, the arthrodires

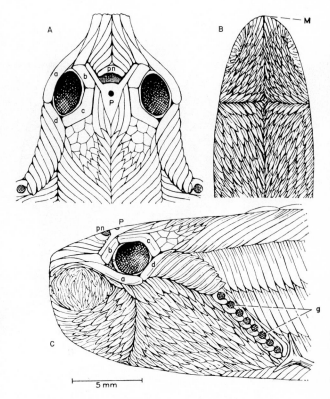

Fig. 11-5. *The little anaspid* Birkenia elegans, *from the Upper Silurian of the Lesmahagow area southeast of Glasgow, Scotland; reconstruction of head, viewed from above* (A), *from below* (B), *and from the side* (C): a, b, c, d, *plates around eye*; g, *pocket gills*; M, *probable mouth*; P, *Y-shaped pineal plate around medial eye*; pn, *prenasal plate*. (*Modified slightly from Anatol Heintz, Ref. 6.*)

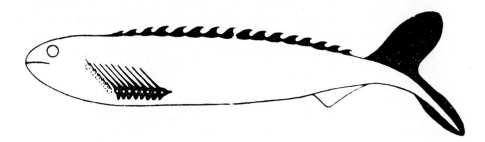

Fig. 11-6. *The anaspid* Lasanius problematicus, *reconstructed* (1.7/1) *on the evidence of 11 specimens from the Upper Silurian near Muirkirk, south of Glasgow, Scotland. The mouth is hypothetical. Note gill pouches, post-cephalic rods, and down-turned tail.* (*From F. R. Parrington, Ref. 6*).

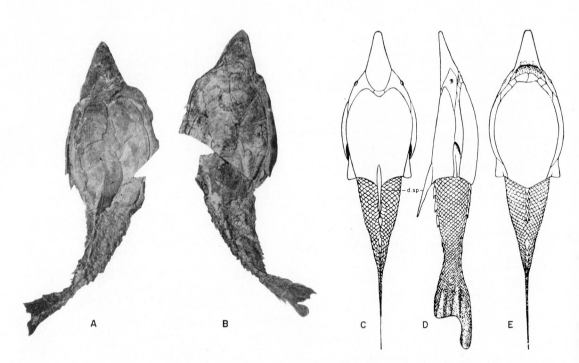

Fig. 11-7. *Heterostracan* Pteraspis rostrata, *from the Lower Old Red Sandstone, Welsh Border.*
(*From E. I. White, Philos. Trans. Roy. Soc. London, 1935.*)

A, B. *Upper, lower surface (specimen 7 inches long).*

C, D, E. *Restoration diagrams:* C, *from above;* D, *from the right side* (d.sp, *dorsal spine*);
E, *from below.*

(armored fishes), and the antiarchs. The acanthodians (Fig. 11-9) have rhomboid scales and sharp, paired fin spines. Their general shape is shark-like, but their internal structures are different from anything possessed by the sharks or their close relatives. They appeared at about the beginning of the Devonian and became extinct at the end of the Paleozoic. The arthrodires have closely fitted plates covering the head and, to the rear of a joint (Fig. 11-10), body armor that apparently covered from half to two-thirds of the soft parts. Some arthrodires are very large. Their first representatives are found in the Upper Silurian, they are common throughout the whole thickness of the Devonian, and then they disappear. The antiarchs (Fig. 11-11) are funny little flat fishes with shapes somewhat

like those of turtles or crustaceans. The external head and body armor is slightly jointed at the neck. The main carapace is rounded in outline, and there are two paddle-like head appendages. The antiarchs are limited to the Middle and Upper Devonian.

c. The Chondrichthyes

The sharks and their allies, which have cartilaginous internal skeletons, are represented in the rocks chiefly by teeth. The rare impressions of the whole body include superb specimens as old as the uppermost Devonian (Cleveland shale, Ohio; Fig. 11-12). Sharks' teeth are extremely common in some parts of the geologic record and are well distributed all the way from the Devonian to the Recent.

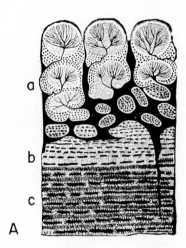

A

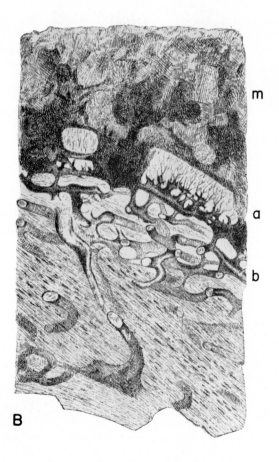

B

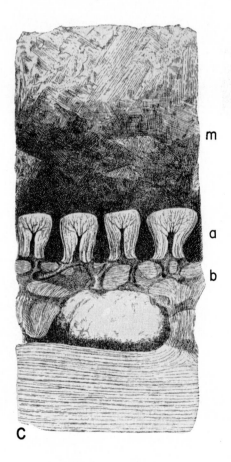

C

Fig. 11-8. *Bone structure of Devonian fishes, in section, greatly magnified: a, outer layer; b, layer with canals; c, layer with lacunae; m, matrix. (A from C. H. Pander via Eastman-Zittel Textbook of Paleontology, 1902; B and C from T. H. Huxley,* QUARTERLY JOURNAL, *Geol. Soc. London, 1858.)*
A. *A scale of the crossopterygian* Glyptolepis.
B. *The shield of the osteostracan* Cephalaspis.
C. *The shield of the heterostracan* Pteraspis.

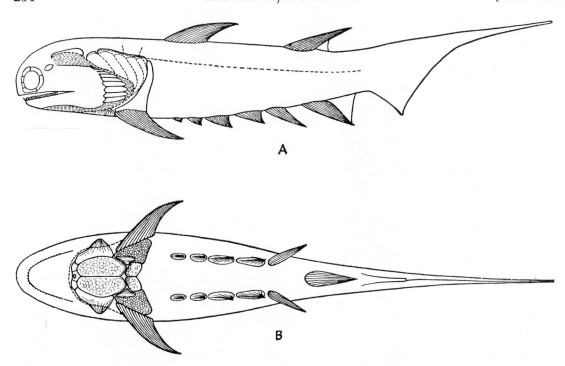

Fig. 11-9. *Reconstruction of the acanthodian* Climatius reticulatus (*not showing the pattern of the rhomboid scales covering the body*), *from the side* (A) *and from below* (B); *length 6 inches. Based on specimens from the Old Red Sandstone of Turin Hill, Forfarshire, southwest of Stonehaven, Scotland. Note the heavy shoulder girdle.* (*From D. M. S. Watson, Philos. Trans. Roy. Soc. London, 1937.*)

Fig. 11-10. *Model of* Dinichthys, *an arthrodire many feet long, from Upper Devonian shale, Cleveland, Ohio.* (*Courtesy of the American Museum of Natural History.*)

d. The Osteichthyes

The bony fishes include four groups of particular paleontological interest. Two of these, the crossopterygians and the dipnoans, have lobed fins; the other two, the palaeoniscoids (Paleozoic and Mesozoic) and the teleosts (Mesozoic and Cenozoic), have rayed fins.

The crossopterygians are lobe-finned bony fishes with moderately heavy scales. They include two genera now living deep in the Indian Ocean southeast of Africa. An example of one of these genera is shown in Figure 11-13. Otherwise the group is known only

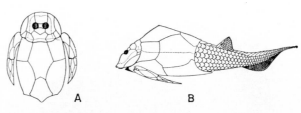

Fig. 11-11. Pterichthyodes milleri, *a Middle Devonian antiarch, Scotland, from above* (A) *and from the side* (B); × 1/3. (*Crown Copyright. Restoration after Professor D. M. S. Watson in* The Geology of the Orkneys, Memoirs of the Geological Survey of Great Britain, 1935. *Reproduced by permission of the Controller of Her Britannic Majesty's Stationery Office.*)

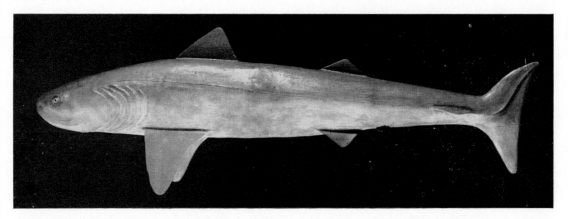

Fig. 11-12. Cladoselache fyleri, *a shark from the uppermost Devonian near Cleveland, Ohio: model based on nearly perfect specimen 22 inches long. (Courtesy of the American Museum of Natural History.)*

from Cretaceous and older rocks; its climax was in the Paleozoic, perhaps in the Devonian.

The dipnoans (Devonian–Recent) are close relatives of the crossopterygians. They take their name from the living lungfishes, inhabitants of swamps in Australia, Africa, and South America. The lungfishes have paired lung-like air-bladders, which enable them to survive droughts. The fossil dipnoans are recognized

Fig. 11-13. *Crossopterygian (coelacanth) fish brought into Grahamstown, South Africa, in 1953. (Photograph from Paul H. Dudley Sr.)*

Fig. 11-14. *The dipnoan* Dipterus valenciennesii *Sedgwick and Murchison, Middle Devonian, Achanarras, northeasternmost Scotland; 6 inches long. (Royal Scottish Museum, Edinburgh; photograph by Tom Scott, courtesy of Dr. C. D. Waterston.)*

by the peculiarities of their skeletons, especially the club-like fins, the heavy batteries of flat, plate-like teeth, and the bony scales of rhombic shape (Fig. 11-14).

The ray-finned Paleozoic Palaeoniscoidea (Fig. 11-15) had thick and shiny scales. They are sometimes called enamel-skinned fishes.

The teleosts have wholly ossified internal skeletons that include the vertebral column, numerous ribs, fin rays, and symmetrical tail assemblages; their scales are thin and more or less flexible. They include almost all the fishes living today and are mostly marine; a

Fig. 11-15. *The paleoniscoid* Palaeoniscus *of the Permian, 9 inches long. (Reprinted from Ref. 3 by permission of the University of Chicago Press. Copyright 1933 and 1945 by the University of Chicago.)*

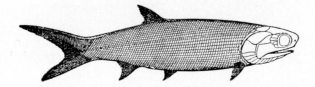

few kinds are restricted to fresh water. The fossil teleosts are also mostly marine. The teleost group appears first in the Jurassic and develops tremendously in the Cretaceous, gradually crowding out the early Mesozoic groups of advanced palaeoniscoid-like fishes. Today teleosts and sharks are almost the only fishes.

11-2. *Ordovician Fishes*

Although a continuous and well-documented record of complete fishes does not begin until we reach the Upper Silurian, with its agnathans in Scotland and on the island of Saaremaa (Oesel) in the eastern part of the Baltic Sea, fragmentary fish remains occur in the Ordovician. Bone fragments are abundant and widespread in the Middle and Upper Ordovician strata of western North America, and minute fragments of similar material have been found in the Lower Ordovician of Esthonia, just east of Saaremaa.

The ever-active C. D. Walcott, the Cambrian specialist, found numerous unmistakable bits of bone in the Middle Ordovician Harding sandstone near Canon City, Colorado (Fig. 11-16), and described two species in 1892. A piece of the fossiliferous rock is shown in Figure 11-17, and Walcott's best specimen, which is also the best ever found in the Ordovician, in Figure 11-18. The Canon City bone lacks lacunae and the smaller bone canals (see Fig. 11-8), as apparently do the millions of similar fragments in the American Ordovician; but they all have the calcium phosphate composition and the fundamental structures of bone, including cross-fibers and the dentine (dense bone, best developed in teeth) that makes up its prominent tubercles (Fig. 11-19). These last features are the particular characteristics of heterostracan bone, as emphasized by Huxley (Fig. 11-8C), and so the fragments must be from jawless fishes of the order Heterostraci.

The bone fragments are distributed through 65 feet of the 120-foot Harding sandstone, a marine formation that carries trilobites and nautiloids characteristic of the lower part of the North American Middle Ordovician. The bone bed has been followed for long distances in several parts of central Colorado (Fig. 11-16). A similar sandstone, 6–8 feet thick, with bone fragments of the same or similar heterostracan species, but lacking other fossils, lies conformably beneath a fossiliferous marine Middle-Upper Ordovician limestone in the Bighorn Mountains west of Buffalo, Wyoming (Fig. 11-16). At the top of this limestone, and hence in the Upper Ordovician, heterostracan bone fragments different enough to be assigned to a different species were discovered in 1951 and described in 1958 (Fig. 11-19). Similar fish remains of Middle or Late Ordovician age are also known elsewhere in the same general region, as far east as the Black Hills of South Dakota and almost as far north as the Canadian boundary (Fig. 11-16).

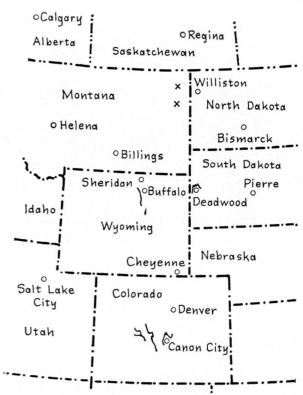

Fig. 11-16. *Map of a portion of west-central North America, showing the distribution of Ordovician formations carrying fish remains. (Based on Ref. 8; N. H. Darton, 1906; and other sources.)*

↘↗ Fish-bearing Ordovician outcrops

x} Region of subsurface Ordovician
x} cores with fish

Fig. 11-17. *Middle Ordovician Harding sandstone with fish fragments, from U.S. Highway 50, 5.5 miles west of Canon City, Colorado; almost natural size.*

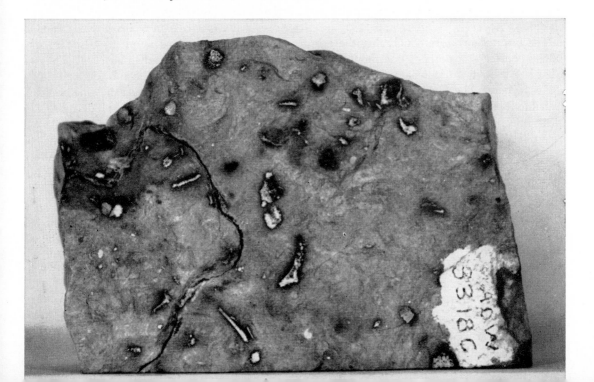

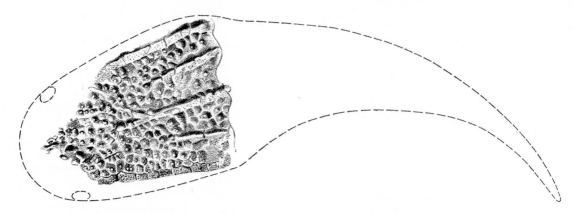

Fig. 11-18. *Shield of the heterostracan* Astraspis desiderata *Walcott, from the Harding Sandstone near Canon City, Colorado; 3 inches long. The possible shape of the animal is also shown. (Redrawn after Erik Jarvik, 1960.)*

Recently it has been shown (Ref. 8) that minute fossils in the Lower Ordovician of Esthonia, in the Baltic region just south of the Gulf of Finland, which have been problems since their discovery in 1889, are really tubercles broken from the plates of heterostracan jawless fishes similar to one of the kinds known from Colorado. The conclusion follows that this group of Ordovician animals had broad, perhaps worldwide, distribution.

11-3. *The Origin of Vertebrates*

Three questions arise concerning the origin of vertebrates—or, perhaps one should say, of chordates. First, from what? Second, when? Third, where? The first question is biological and has had uncertain answers. Many biologists now think that the phylum Echinodermata is the one most closely related to the Chordata, chiefly because echinoderm and hemichordate larvae are similar. No intermediate fossil forms are known, and neither the Ordovician vertebrates nor the graptolites have anything in common with the Cambrian and Ordovician echinoderms (compare Chap. 10). Annelid worms are similar to vertebrates in bilateral symmetry and in the elongation of the alimentary canal and other structures,

but these are very general characters, shared with the arthropods. In embryology and biochemistry annelids differ from chordates and echinoderms.

Vertebrates originated before or during the Early Ordovician, for moderately advanced vertebrates with complex bone structure are known in Middle Ordovician rocks. One might hazard the guess that some chordates existed during the Cambrian or even earlier.

The final question concerning vertebrate origin—where?—is the one discussed most vigorously. Americans have tended to favor fresh-water origin, Europeans marine. The Ordovician fish remains seem all to be in marine formations, at many places with associated marine conodonts, trilobites, nautiloids, etc. But the numerous pieces of bone are fragmentary. Americans have concluded that the dead fish or their bones were carried into the marine environment by streams. This question perhaps cannot yet be settled definitely, though some pertinent evidence is available. The bone fragments of the Harding sandstone occur in a thin platform formation that lacks local deltaic thickenings. The fragments are almost all angular; they are not rounded pebbles. They are much larger than the very fine sand grains of their matrix. They were not rolled down rivers to the sea. If the fish lived in fresh water, their bodies must have floated to the sea and broken up there. Some must have been carried far beyond any possible river mouths, for the Harding sandstone contains fragments of fish plates at many places in an area of 2,000 square miles in central Colorado. This sandstone is missing over a broad area of repeated uplift called Siouxia, between central Colorado on the south and the Wyoming-Dakota region on the north, but it may have covered Siouxia originally and been fishy throughout the whole region (compare Fig. 11-16). Some mid-Ordovician land probably existed in west-central North America, but just where it was is now difficult to say. The simpler hypothesis is that the Ordovician heterostracan fishes lived in the marine environment where they are found. In that case their poorly articulated external skeletons fell apart or were broken up after the deaths of the animals. One fact to keep in mind is the additonal Baltic Lower Ordovician occurrence. Worldwide distribution seems more easily explained if the animals were marine.

11-4. Mid-Paleozoic Fishes and Continental Formations

The Upper Silurian and Devonian fishes are numerous and varied, and they lived in varied environments. Upper Silurian occurrences were at least in part marine, but the fishes of the Old Red Sandstone surely lived in fresh water. Agnathans make up almost the whole of the Silurian assemblage, are common in the Lower Old Red, continue in greatly reduced numbers higher in the Old Red, and disappear from view at the top of the Devonian, though the boneless ancestors of the present-day lampreys must have lived on. Jawed fishes are common in the Lower Old Red and take over almost completely in the Middle and Upper Old Red. Lower, Middle, and Upper Old Red fish faunas are easily distinguishable; they provide the first sets of continental guide fossils. From the Devonian on there are two columns, one continental, the other marine, increasing the complexity and significance of the record and introducing a new complication in correlation.

a. Old Red Sandstone of Scotland

In Chapter 3 two British Devonian facies were distinguished, the marine Devonian of Devonshire and the continental Old Red Sandstone north of the Bristol Channel. In that

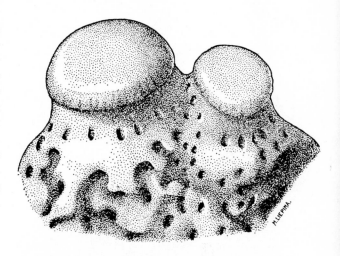

Fig. 11-19. *Pycnaspis splendens, an Upper Ordovician heterostracan found near Buffalo, Wyoming. (From Ref. 8.)*
ABOVE. *Detail of ornamentation, × 30.*
BELOW. *Section through tubercle, greatly magnified: d, dentine; c, canal.*

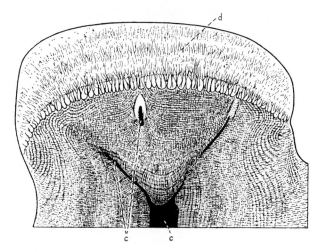

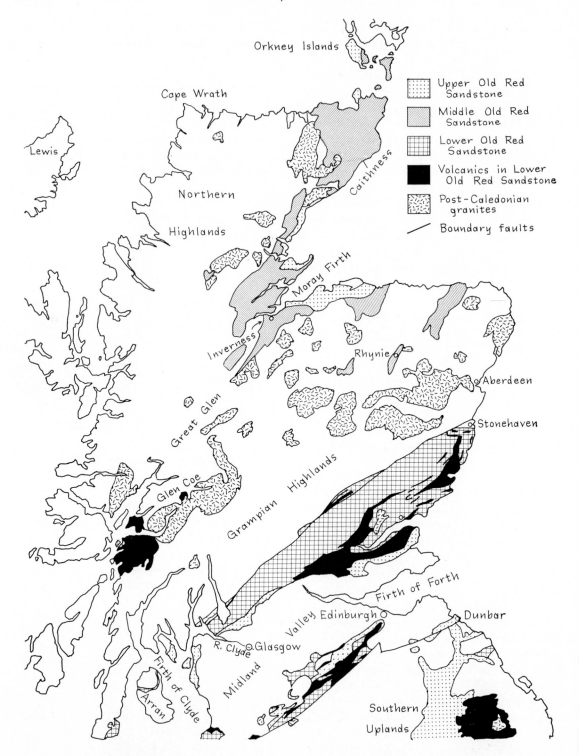

Fig. 11-20. *Geological map of Scotland, showing distribution of Old Red Sandstone and post-Caledonian granites. (After* Geological Map of Great Britain, *1948.)*

chapter, where discoveries made in England by Smith, Sedgwick, and Murchison were emphasized, the Old Red Sandstone described was that of Wales and the west-central border counties of England. Now we shall concentrate our attention on belts of Old Red Sandstone farther north, in Scotland, for it is there that most of the fish remains have been found.

Topographically, Scotland (Fig. 11-20) is divisible into four regions: (1) the Southern Uplands; (2) the Midland Valley, between the Firth of Clyde and the Firth of Forth, where most Scots live; (3) the Grampian Highlands, northwest of the Midland Valley, with a maximum altitude of 4,400 feet; (4) the Northern Highlands, still farther northwest, beyond the Great Glen and the Moray Firth.

The Old Red Sandstone of Scotland, shown by ruled and dotted patterns in Figure 11-20, is found in all the topographic regions but lies mostly in two more or less synclinal belts, each elongated southwest-northeast. One such belt, lying between boundary faults, includes almost the whole of the Midland Valley. The downfaulted mass has been eroded nearly to a flat surface, above which the more resistant rocks rise as low hills. Central outcrops of Carboniferous sediments and lavas are bounded by two marginal strips of Old Red Sandstone. On the southeastern side of the syncline, the narrow and interrupted Old Red outcrops extend northeast to Arthur's Seat in the city of Edinburgh and to Dunbar on the North Sea. This area is the site of historic Hutton discoveries: the intrusive sill in the Old Red at Arthur's Seat and the Silurian–Old Red unconformity at Siccar Point near Dunbar. On the northwestern side of the syncline, a broader band of Old Red outcrops extends from the mouth of the River Clyde to Stonehaven on the North Sea.

The second major Old Red belt lies between the Grampian and Northern Highlands. It underlies the northeast end of the Great Glen lowland and broadens greatly northeast, in a poorly defined syncline with a flank on each side of the Moray Firth. The synclinal axis,

if such it may be called, extends from the Great Glen into the Moray Firth, plunging northeast. Farther north, in Caithness and the Orkney Islands, the Old Red has a moderate northeasterly dip and overlies the schists and granites that are the surface rocks farther west and southwest.

The Scottish Old Red, tens of thousands of feet thick, is made up chiefly of sandstone, conglomerate, and other clastic rocks, with many thousands of feet of intercalated lavas, especially near the base. In the upland regions the Old Red lies with great unconformity on older rocks, which in the Southern Uplands are Ordovician and Silurian strata and in the Highlands are mostly early Paleozoic and Precambrian schist and gneiss, with many bodies of granite. The surfaces of unconformity are far from flat; in the Southern Uplands and elsewhere the Old Red fills well-defined valleys in the older rocks.

The Scottish Old Red is divided into three parts: Lower (L.O.R.), Middle (M.O.R.), and Upper (U.O.R.). Near Stonehaven (Fig. 11-21), the L.O.R. includes a conformable basal unit that is called Downtonian (lowest Devonian) because it contains a few agnathan fishes similar to some in the type Downtonian near Downton Castle on the English-Welsh Border. In the Pentland Hills southwest of Edinburgh the Downtonian was folded with the Silurian and unconformably overlain by higher beds of the L.O.R. The type Downtownian (in England) varies from brackish to non-marine; it grades downward into marine Silurian and laterally into lowest marine Devonian.

The Lower Old Red of Scotland is best developed in the Midland Valley, though some isolated areas are present farther northwest, on the west coast and in Glen Coe. In the Midland Valley the L.O.R. is made up of 15,000 feet of coarse conglomerates, red or brown sandstones, and red or varicolored shales, together with large additional thicknesses of interbedded andesite and basalt lavas and tuffs. Much of it is superbly exposed on the east coast south of Stonehaven. In this

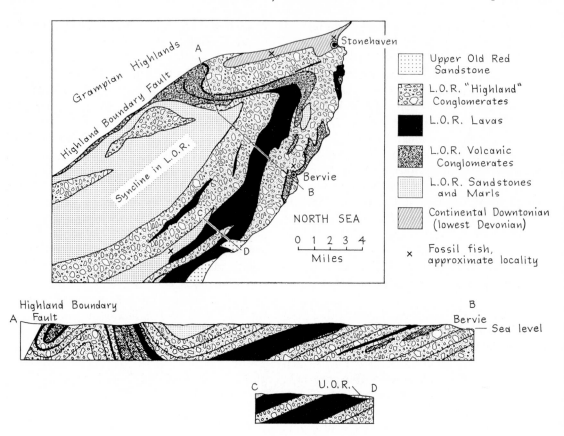

Fig. 11-21. *Geological map of Old Red Sandstone, including Downtonian, southwest of Stonehaven, Scotland. (After Ref. 10.)*

area, only one fish fauna has been found above the Downtonian, and it occurs at five or six levels, two of which are represented by locality crosses in Figure 11-21. Fish are distributed through 4,000 feet of the middle part of the L.O.R.

The Middle Old Red is limited to the Highland regions, in the northeastern part of the Great Glen and on both sides of the Moray Firth. About 20,000 feet thick, it includes 3,000 feet of barren red sandstone and breccia at the base (perhaps equivalent to part of the L.O.R.), 14,500 feet of interbedded pale sandstone, greenish-white mudstone, and dark-gray calcareous sandstone or sandy limestone with or without fish remains, and, at the top, 2,000 feet of soft red or yellow sandstone of U.O.R. type but with distinctive M.O.R. fish.

The Upper Old Red is present in all the Old Red areas of Scotland, from the Southern Uplands to the north coast (in Caithness) and the islands still farther north, lying unconformably, at one place or another, on almost every older Scottish rock unit, including the M.O.R. In the Midland Valley the U.O.R. is made up of 500–2,700 feet of red sandstone, chocolate-red or mottled shale, conglomerate, and sandy limestone, which, at the top, pass conformably into non-marine Carboniferous. Both in the Midland Valley and in the Highlands-Orkney-Shetland region the U.O.R. contains a characteristic fish fauna.

Southwest of Stonehaven (Fig. 11-21), the Lower Old Red was folded into a syncline and a narrow anticline (close to the Highland Boundary Fault), with dips of 25° common, and after the folding seems to have lost 8,000 feet of strata by local erosion before the U.O.R. was deposited. The unconformable overlap by the U.O.R. is shown near the North Sea (section CD of Fig. 11-21) and also, more spectacularly, in the city of Edinburgh. The folds trending southwest-northeast in the L.O.R. are evidence of the mild continuation into Old Red time of the Caledonian orogeny that produced similarly oriented but greater deformation in the pre-Devonian rocks.

Most of the conglomerates in the Lower Old Red of the Midland Valley are either accumulations of pebbles, cobbles, and boulders of pre-Devonian quartzites and other metamorphics (the "Highland" conglomerates of Fig. 11-21) or else volcanic conglomerates made up of fragments of nearly contemporaneous lavas. The M.O.R. and U.O.R. conglomerates and breccias, on the other hand, especially in the Highlands, are largely derived from granites that are younger than the Caledonian main folding and perhaps originated, in part, during L.O.R. time. In Glen Coe a granite invades lavas that overlie beds containing L.O.R. plants. One or more of the granite masses, however, must have solidified before L.O.R. time, for typical boulders of this type of granite occur in the L.O.R. "Highland" conglomerate just south of Stonehaven. The granite areas in the Highlands are numerous and extensive, as shown in Figure 11-20. The outcrops must represent rather shallow intrusives, for several masses were unroofed before they were covered unconformably by the M.O.R.

One of the most notable features of the Middle Old Red of Caithness (Fig. 11-20) is the persistent repetition of lithologic sequences that are commonly between thirty and seventy feet thick. The topmost member of each sequence is usually a fine-grained sediment with numerous mud cracks. This is overlain by the initial member of the next sequence, a black or dark-gray calcareous sandstone or sandy limestone that sometimes contains flattened fish skeletons (Fig. 11-14) and is therefore called a fish band. Occasionally, at about the

horizon of a fish band, there are nodular beds up to six feet thick, made up of rolled mud balls whose composition is the same as that of the underlying mudstone. The dark calcareous or nodular layer is succeeded by alternating mudstones and ripple-marked sandstones. Then the sequence ends in another bed of fine-grained sediment with mud cracks. In some sections a hundred or more such sequences occur, one right after another.

The principal animal fossils in such sequences, and everywhere else in the Old Red, are the numerous and varied fishes, many of which were apparently mud-burrowing detritus feeders. There are also many remains of land plants and one abundant invertebrate animal, a little bivalved crustacean (Fig. 11-22), similar to the living fresh- and brackish-water genus *Estheria*. This crustacean occurs in enormous numbers at some levels in the M.O.R. of northeastern Scotland and may be

Fig. 11-22. Asmusia (Eoestheria) membranacea, *a bivalved crustacean of the Middle Old Red of northeasternmost Scotland.* (*From T. R. Jones, Paleontographical Society, 1862.*) ABOVE. *A pair of valves;* × 4. BELOW. *On rock;* × 1.

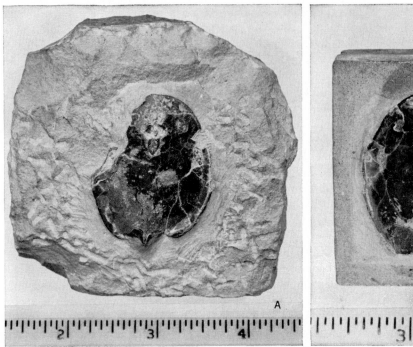

Fig. 11-23.   *The osteostracan* Tremataspis, *from the Upper Silurian of Saaremaa (Oesel) Island, Baltic Sea.*
A. T. milleri. (*Dartmouth College Museum.*)
B. T. mammillata. (*Dartmouth College Museum.*)
CDE. *A reconstruction of* T. milleri *by T. S. Westoll (Ref. 6): C, from above (carapace only, about 1.5 inches long); D, from below; E, from the side.*

the only invertebrate that has left recognizable remains in the Middle unit. In the L.O.R. of the Midland Valley, myriapods (thousand-legged worms) and eurypterids (Paleozoic water scorpions) have been found. It is the presence of land plants and of a few unmistakably non-marine animals, together with the complete absence of marine fossils, that is the basis for the consensus that the Old Red is non-marine.

The conditions of Old Red sedimentation may have been similar to present conditions in the Basin and Range region of western North America. The shallow Old Red lakes dried up frequently, as shown by the presence of mud cracks. The absence of salt accumulations, however, seems to require external drain-

age, probably to the nearest Devonian sea, a few hundred miles south or southeast. The massive accumulations of non-marine sediments, to a thickness of three or four miles in northern Scotland, must have been made possible by persistent subsidence. The relations of the northern and Midland Valley areas of deposition to each other will be discussed after consideration of the fish faunas.

b. Upper Silurian and Old Red Fishes

The Upper Silurian and Devonian fish faunas of Britain and other Atlantic-Arctic areas are all similar. Two age groups, however, can be distinguished, the earlier composed of Upper Silurian, Downtonian, and supra-

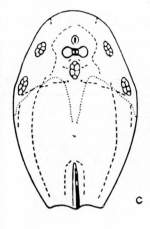

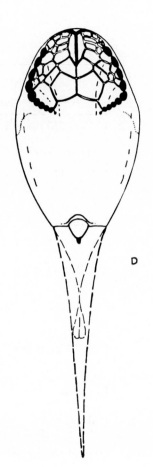

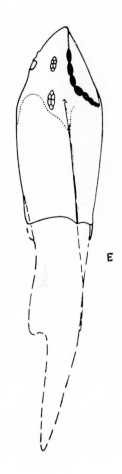

Downtonian Lower Old Red faunas, in which agnathans predominate, the later of Middle and Upper Old Red faunas, in which only a few rare agnathan species are known.

Perhaps the oldest well-preserved fishes are the small osteostracan agnathans found on the island of Saaremaa (Oesel) in the Baltic Sea south of the mouth of the Gulf of Finland. This island is now a Russian military base. Before 1939 its K_1 beds, low in the Upper Silurian, yielded thousands of examples of *Tremataspis* and other genera to several collectors, notably to the Dartmouth College biologist William Patten. On the upper side of *Tremataspis* (Fig. 11-23AC) one sees the single nostril and the closely spaced eye sockets characteristic of the osteostracans, as well as the small pineal opening between the eyes. The small mouth, on the lower side (D), is nearly terminal, is clearly jawless, and perhaps is a vertical rather than a horizontal slit. Some specimens have poorly preserved slender tails, but the details can only be guessed at (DE).

The uppermost Silurian (upper Ludlovian) and lowest Devonian (Downtonian) fish faunas (Table 11-2) are made up chiefly of osteostracans and anaspids, with a few heterostracans and very rare fragments of jawed fishes. The supra-Downtonian Lower Old Red faunas of the Scottish Midland Valley and the Welsh Borderland are predominantly osteostracan but also include numerous acan

TABLE 11-2 *

Devonian and Earlier Fi

MARINE STANDARD	GUIDE FISHES	BRITAIN
UPPER DEVONIAN		
Strunian (Carbonif.?)	*Remigolepis* (antiarch)	
Famennian	*Phyllolepis* (arthrodire) & *Bothriolepis* (antiarch)	U.O.R.
Frasnian	*Bothriolepis* & *Asterolepis* (antiarchs)	U.O.R.
MIDDLE DEVONIAN		
Givetian	*Asterolepis* & *Pterichthyodes* (antiarchs)	M.O.R.
Eifelian	?	
LOWER DEVONIAN		
Emsian	*Pteraspis dunensis* (heterostracan)	
Siegenian	*Cephalaspis* (osteostracan)	L.O.R. (main body
Gedinnian	*Cephalaspis* & *Hemicyclaspis* (osteostracans)	L.O.R. (main body and Downtonian
UPPER SILURIAN		
Ludlovian, Upper	Anaspids and cephalaspids	
Middle	Anaspids and heterostracans	Lesmahagow & Pentland H
Lower	*Tremataspis*	
MIDDLE SILURIAN Wenlockian		
LOWER SILURIAN Llandoverian		
UPPER ORDOVICIAN	Heterostracans	
MIDDLE ORDOVICIAN	Heterostracans	
LOWER ORDOVICIAN	Heterostracans	

* Compiled from Refs. 6, 8, 5, 9, and other sources. Based on local stratigraphic order and correlations by means of guide fishes or marine invertebrates or both.

U.O.R. = Upper Old Red Sandstone, M.O.R. = Middle Old Red Sandstone, L.O.R. = Lower Old Red Sandstone, Is. = Island, N.S.W. = New South Wales, cg = conglomerate, dol = dolomite, fm = formation, ls = limestone, sh = shale, ss = sandstone.

rmations in Homotaxial Arrangement

CANDINAVIA, ALTIC STATES N.W. RUSSIA	SPITSBERGEN	EAST GREENLAND	NORTH AMERICA	AUSTRALIA
		Mt. Celsius red ss, sh		?[a]
O.R." of Esthonia, Latia, & N.W. Russia		Cape Graah red ss	Cleveland sh, Ohio	Marine (N.S.W., Western Australia); lacustrine (Victoria)[a]
togor etc. f N.W. Russia			Escuminac, Gaspé, Quebec, Canada; Elbert fm, Colorado; central New York (many places)	?[a]
tic	Wijde Bay series	Canning ls		
	Gray Hoek series			Marine (N.S.W., Victoria): arthrodires
	Wood Bay series		Jefferson dol, northern Utah	
	Wood Bay series		Water Canyon fm, northern Utah	
	Red Bay series		Knoydart fm, Nova Scotia	
gerike, Norway				
beds, Oesel Is.			Vernon sh, New York; Bloomfield fm, Pa. Bloomburg fm, Pa.	
			Nerepis Hills, New Brunswick	
			Rose Hill sh, Perry Co., Pa.; Shawangunk cg, Orange Co., N. Y.[b]	
			Upper Bighorn ss, Wyoming	
			Harding ss, Colorado	
auconitic and, Esthonia				

[a] *Bothriolepis, Phyllolepis,* and *Remigolepis* associated in same formation (E. S. Hills, Ref. 6).
[b] May be higher in the Silurian.

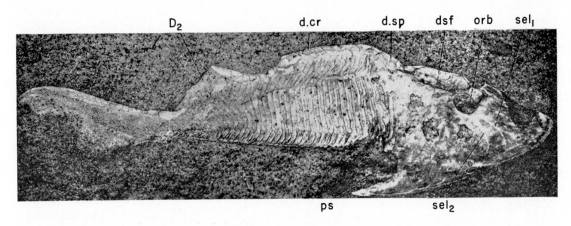

Fig. 11-24. *The osteostracan* Cephalaspis pagei, *from the Lower Old Red Sandstone of Forfarshire, Scotland* (*specimen 5 inches long*): D_2, *dorsal fin;* d.cr, *dorsal crest of trunk;* d.sp, *dorsal spine of head shield;* dsf, *dorsal "electric field";* orb, *eye socket;* sel_1, sel_2, *"electric" nerve canals;* ps, *sinus behind pectoral spine.* [*From Ref. 17 with the permission of the Trustees of the British Museum* (*Natural History*).]

thodian placoderms. The osteostracan *Cephalaspis* (Fig. 11-24) is common in both the Downtonian and the post-Downtonian parts of the L.O.R. *Hemicyclaspis* (Fig. 11-4), which is limited to the Downtonian, is similar but lacks the backward-pointing head-shield prongs of *Cephalaspis*. A sharp-spined L.O.R. acanthodian is shown in Figure 11-25.

The Middle and Upper Old Red faunas are characterized especially by antiarchs, which are the principal zone guides (Table 11-2). The short head paddles of the M.O.R. *Pter-*

ichthyodes are easily distinguished from the long paddles of the U.O.R. *Bothriolepis* (Fig. 11-26). Since the antiarchs are limited to Middle and Upper Devonian rocks and are rather widely distributed, they make fairly useful worldwide guides.

The other principal constituents of the Middle and Upper Old Red fish faunas are other kinds of placoderms: acanthodians and arthrodires. The great arthrodire *Dinichthys* (Fig. 11-10), which had head armor 10.5 feet long, may have been 30 feet long. A much

Fig. 11-25. Ischnacanthus gracilis, *an acanthodian 4 inches long, from the Lower Old Red Sandstone of Turin Hill, Forfarshire, Scotland.* (*From D. M. S. Watson, Philos. Trans. Roy. Soc. London, 1937.*)

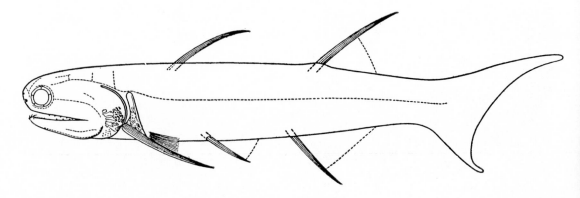

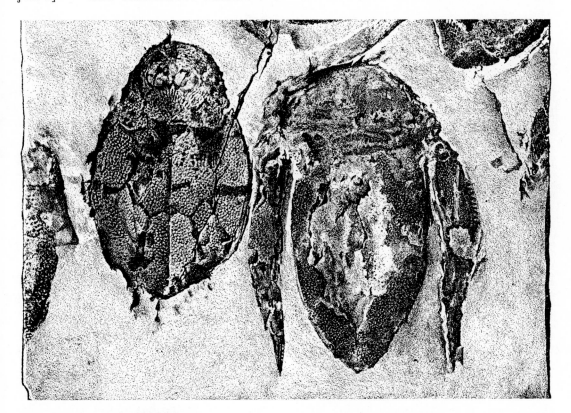

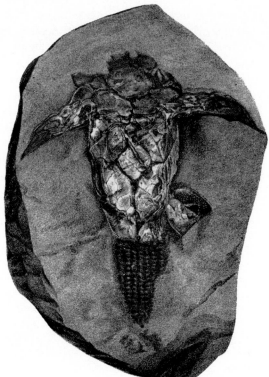

Fig. 11-26. *Devonian antiarchs.*

LEFT. Pterichthyodes productus, *from the Middle Old Red, northeastern Scotland. (From Ref. 11.)*

ABOVE. Bothriolepis hydrophila, *from the Upper Old Red, Dura Den, Fifeshire, Scotland. The 6-inch slab shows, on the right, the lower side of a shield with head paddles and, on the left, the upper side of one without paddles. (From Ref. 14.)*

Fig. 11-27. *The arthrodire* Coccosteus decipiens, *a specimen 13 inches long from the Middle Old Red, Orkney Islands, Scotland. (Crown Copyright. Restoration after Professor D. M. S. Watson in* The Geology of the Orkneys, Memoirs of the Geological Survey of Great Britain, *1935. Reproduced by permission of the Controller of Her Britannic Majesty's Stationery Office.)*

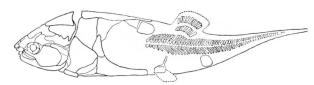

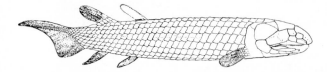

Fig. 11-28. *The crossopterygian Thursius pholidotus, a specimen 12 inches long from the Middle Old Red, Orkney Islands, Scotland. (Crown Copyright. Restoration after Professor D. M. S. Watson in* The Geology of the Orkneys, Memoirs of the Geological Survey of Great Britain, *1935. Reproduced by permission of the Controller of Her Britannic Majesty's Stationery Office.)*

smaller arthrodire of the M.O.R., described by Louis Agassiz in 1845, is shown in Figure 11-27. A notable new element in the Middle Old Red was provided by the lobe-finned crossopterygians (Fig. 11-28), the first bony fishes.

c. Anatomy of Mid-Paleozoic Agnathans

Scandinavian and British students of *Cephalaspis* and other Lower Devonian osteostracans made notable anatomical discoveries during the nineteen-twenties and nineteen-thirties. The principal breakthrough was made by E. A. Stensiö of Sweden, whose special technique was the making of drawings or photographs of serial sections of fossil specimens, some of which had been more or less freed from matrix before they were embedded in plaster for sectioning. Stensiö worked first with well-preserved material collected by Norwegians in Spitsbergen and later with equally good British specimens. His primary discovery was the absence of hinged lower jaws in *Cephalaspis* and similar forms. As a result of this work the class Agnatha, previously established for the cyclostomes, was greatly enlarged by the inclusion of previously known Paleozoic groups. Stensiö distinguished between an obvious dermal skeleton and an obscure associated internal skeleton, largely made up of bony coverings for nerves and blood vessels (Fig. 11-29). He named or numbered the canals for individual nerves, arteries, and veins in the head region, and showed

the complexity of the elongated central bone-sheathed cavity that had previously been called a brain cast. He described surface grooves that were probably the sites of sensory organs similar to the "lateral line" systems of lampreys and other modern fishes. Finally, he showed that the Downtonian cephalaspids had more elaborate and heavier internal skeletons than those higher in the Lower Old Red. Progressive loss of external armor also occurred, a change that is especially clear if the comparison is extended to include the solidly covered Late Silurian *Tremataspis* (Fig. 11-23).

The complexity of the cephalaspid anatomy can be taken as an indication that some Late Silurian and Early Devonian osteostracans were highly organized animals and were high on their particular (chordate) evolutionary ladder. Some of these agnathans may have been more sensitive to external stimuli than the jawed carnivores that destroyed them.

Imaginative and stimulating suggestions about the anatomy of Silurian and earlier fishes were made in 1946 by E. I. White of the British Museum, in connection with his study of a genus he called *Jamoytius* in memory of a fellow fossil-fisher named J. A. Moy-Thomas. *Jamoytius* was based on two fish-shaped specimens (Fig. 11-30), both of which are carbonaceous films on shaly flagstones, found in the Middle or Upper Silurian of the Lesmahagow inlier in the Midland Valley southeast of Glasgow. There is probably almost no hard skele-

Fig. 11-29. *Cast of the cranial cavity of the osteostracan* Kiaeraspis auchenaspidoides *(Downtonian of Spitsbergen), together with the eye sockets (Orb), the labyrinth cavities, and canals, seen from below, about 12/1: A.fa, facial artery; C.sem.post, posterior semicircular canal; Hy.s, anterior division of the cranial cavity, for the hypophyseal sac; Lsf, lateral sensory field; Sel$_{1-6}$, canals for nerves of the lateral "electric field"; Vest, vestibular division of the labyrinth cavity; V.ls$_{1-6}$, canals for superficial veins 1–6; V$_1$, V$_2$, I, III, V, VII–X, canals for nerves. Note the small size and slenderness of the central (cranial) cavity. (Redrawn from Ref. 16.)*

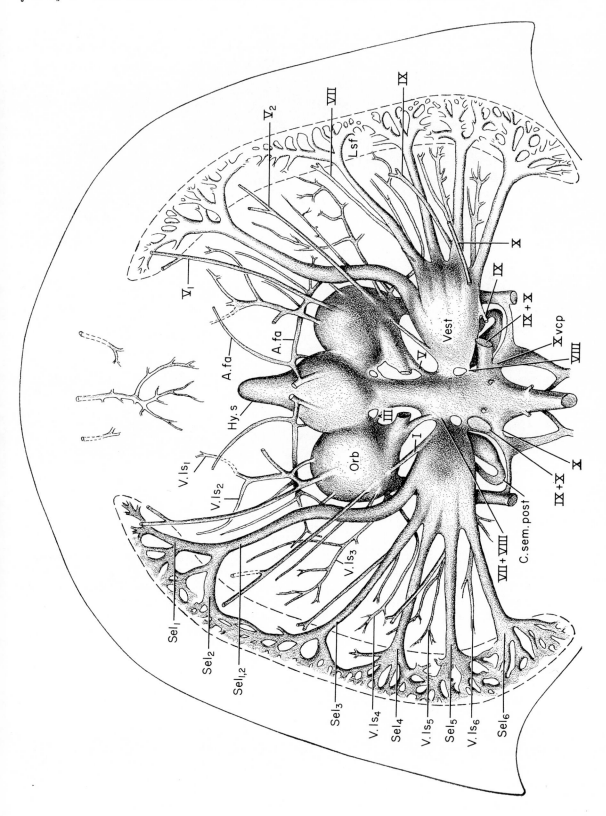

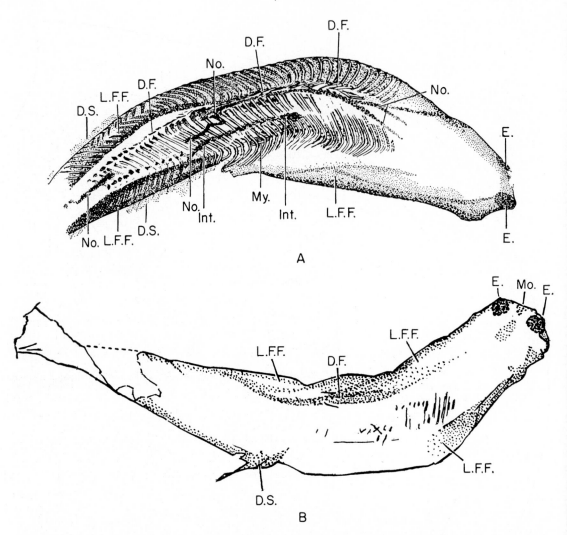

Fig. 11-30. *The two original specimens of* Jamoytius kerwoodi *(about 6–7 inches long), from the Middle or Upper Silurian of the Lesmahagow Hills southeast of Glasgow, Scotland: D.F., dorsal fin supports; D.S., displaced skin (or fin material); E., eye (though the central terminal spot in A is probably the mouth); Int., possibly the contents of the intestine; L.F.F., lateral fin-fold; Mo., mouth; My., exoskeletal structures or scales; No., notochord. (Adapted from E. I. White,* GEOL. MAG., *1946; see also Alexander Ritchie,* NATURE, *1960.)*

ton, just carbonized skin, eyes, notochord, scales, fin membranes, and the contents of a simple straight intestine. This animal was apparently the simplest of fishes, and its lack of hard parts makes a contrast to the typical cephalaspid, which was shield-covered and had more bone in Silurian than in later times. *Jamoytius* is perhaps the kind of primitive

ancestral fish to look for in Ordovician, Cambrian, or even Precambrian strata.

d. Jaws in the Devonian

The appearance of the jaw, at about the beginning of the Devonian Period, was one of the most notable events in the history of the vertebrates. Some Devonian jawed fishes had heavy teeth that could crush the woody parts of the newly developed swamp plants or even crack open shellfish; others had sharp spiky teeth that must have been useful for catching other fishes. The first group of jawed fishes to leave abundant remains, the acanthodians of the Lower Old Red Sandstone, had very sharply pointed teeth and were no doubt carnivores.

e. The Old Red of Scotland as the Continental Devonian Standard

The development of a continental Devonian standard based on the Scottish Old Red Sandstone was slow and hesitant, chiefly because most early workers did not distinguish a Middle Old Red. In the nineteenth century most Scottish geologists correlated the M.O.R. of northern Scotland with the L.O.R. Soon after 1900 the M.O.R. was established as a separate unit, chiefly because its fish fauna was so different from that of the L.O.R. of the Midland Valley. The relative ages of L.O.R. and M.O.R. were discovered in a roundabout way. First it was shown that the M.O.R. antiarchs and arthrodires were similar to those of the U.O.R. but that the L.O.R. agnathans were like those of the Downtonian, the latter being found both in Scotland and in the type section of the Welsh border. Second, the M.O.R. antiarchs and arthrodires were found in Spitsbergen in strata directly overlying beds with L.O.R. agnathans. Finally, a few good specimens of M.O.R. fishes were found in the Givetian (marine upper Middle Devonian) of the Rhineland and U.O.R. fishes in the type Famennian (marine Upper Devonian) of Belgium.

The Old Red Sandstone of Scotland, as now divided into three parts, appears to provide the best standard for the continental Devonian of the world. It includes an almost complete set of fossil-defined, continental time-stratigraphic units. In Greenland and elsewhere an additional *Remigolepis* (antiarch) zone (Table 11-2) is present at the top, between the *Phyllolepis* zone and the Carboniferous.

The roundabout way of establishing a standard continental Devonian fish sequence is perhaps less satisfactory than a single straightforward succession, but it finally does provide a standard that is mostly in one small area—Scotland—and so is preferable to a worldwide synthetic continental standard. A standard column that includes only the faunas of a single area is needed as a standard of reference in correlation problems, as we discovered in Chapter 10.

11-5. The Old Red Sandstone Continent

Rocks of Old Red Sandstone facies, whose principal fossils are fish and plants, are widely distributed in a large region that includes the northeastern Atlantic Ocean and an adjacent part of the Arctic Ocean (Fig. 11-31); from this region marine Devonian strata are almost completely missing. The Old Red is found in three southwest-northeast belts in the British Isles: (1) southern Ireland–southern Wales–Welsh border, (2) northern Ireland–Midland Valley of Scotland, and (3) a northern strip from the Moray Firth through Caithness to the Orkney and Shetland Islands. The northern strip is perhaps continued in Norway (crosses of Fig. 11-31). Great masses of Old Red crop out in east-central Greenland, in Spitsbergen (especially northwestern Vest Spitsbergen), and in New Brunswick and Gaspé. The similarities of the rocks and faunas in these areas have led to the hypothesis of a Devonian continent in the northernmost Atlantic-Arctic region.

Along the southwestern and southeastern margins of the Old Red region, continental and marine rocks are interfingered or interbedded. At the southwest there is a peninsula-like extension of the Old Red facies through eastern Canada into central New York State. There the Catskill formation of Old Red type is known to be Upper Devonian, for it grades westward into marine strata (§ 6-2). In northwestern Nova Scotia, perhaps near the center of this possible peninsula of the Old Red continent, the Lower Devonian red beds are un-

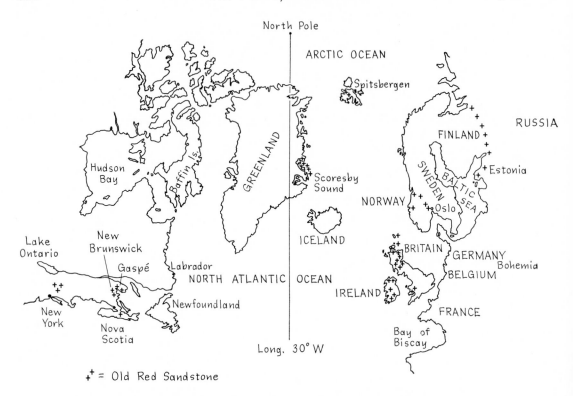

Fig. 11-31. *The region of the hypothetical Old Red Sandstone continent.*

conformable on the Silurian and contain osteostracan, heterostracan, and acanthodian fishes. On the northwestern side of the postulated peninsula, along what is today the southern side of the St. Lawrence estuary, in the Gaspé peninsula of Quebec and in northern New Brunswick, marine Lower Devonian sediments and thick volcanics unconformably overlie deformed Ordovician and Silurian rocks, mostly sedimentary, and are invaded by granitic rocks. The Lower Devonian is overlain by the Gaspé red and gray sandstones, 7,000–8,000 feet thick. Some beds in the Gaspé sandstones contain Middle Devonian marine fossils, but the rocks are probably mostly lagoonal and continental, as shown by the lithology, by plant remains, and by such fishes as *Cephalaspis* and *Climatius*. The best Devonian fish fauna in North America—an Upper Old Red assemblage—is in southern Gaspé, at a place called Escuminac.

Across the Atlantic, marine Devonian and continental Old Red are interbedded all the way from southern Ireland to Esthonia and the White Sea. In parts of this belt, as in Devonshire, Belgium, and Bohemia, the marine Devonian prevails; elsewhere, as in Esthonia, the facies is mostly Old Red. Even in the Dinant Basin of Belgium, now the type area for the marine Devonian, where the Middle Devonian limestones and the Upper Devonian shales are almost wholly marine, two sets of probably continental red or variegated shales are intercalated with the graywackes of the Lower Devonian, and there are some fishes (fresh-water?) at higher levels. When we consider the belt as a whole, the southeastern margin of the Old Red Sandstone continent is marked out with exceptional clearness.

If we take into account all the Devonian rocks in the northernmost Atlantic-Arctic region, the simplest explanation is a continuous

Old Red continental mass that extended from Scandinavia on the east to New York State and Gaspé on the west. This continent, if it really existed, may have collapsed piecemeal in the Mesozoic and Tertiary. No very great subsidence of the sea floor would be involved, for ocean depths between Greenland and Norway are largely less than 6,000 feet and almost everywhere less than 10,000 feet. Possibly Greenland and Norway were separated by continental drift, for the west coast of Norway and the northeast coast of Greenland (north of the East Greenland Old Red) are parallel to each other (Fig. 11-31), and both are made up of closely folded pre-Devonian rocks (Caledonides). Even Labrador and Greenland may have been separated by drift.

11-6. *Distribution of Devonian Fishes*

Most of the Devonian fishes that left well-preserved remains died in the Old Red Sandstone lakes of the North Atlantic region. The same kinds of fishes, however, also reached other parts of the world, including central Europe, central and western North America, eastern Asia, and even Australia (Table 11-2). Rather numerous good specimens have been found in marine beds, for example, in the Givetian (Middle Devonian) calcareous flagstones of the Rhineland, west of Bonn (Germany), and in the uppermost Devonian shale near Cleveland (Ohio). The Cleveland shale has yielded few fossils other than fish, but head shields of *Dinichthys* and other giant arthrodires occur at about the same horizon as primitive sharks (Fig. 11-12), which, like all other sharks, were rather certainly marine. Cleveland is more than a hundred miles west of the nearest Late Devonian shore, which was on the Catskill delta of central New York. *Dinichthys* either lived in the Cleveland sea or floated dead an amazing distance beyond the mouth of a Catskill river. Excellent specimens of Old Red fishes have also been found in the marine Devonian of the Cordilleran region—in, for example, a Utah dolomite. The

fish remains in bone beds in the marine Middle Devonian of central Ohio, however, are small, worn fragments, accompanied by the fragments of unmistakably marine organisms; the bits of bone may have come from Catskill rivers, though their abundance so far offshore is puzzling. The Australian Devonian fishes probably descended from pioneers that emigrated from the source area (in the northern hemisphere?) by sea. An Upper Devonian Australian fish fauna occurs in a shallow marine series in New South Wales and in lacustrine beds in Victoria. Even in Devonian times, apparently, and perhaps much earlier, some kinds of fishes could live both in fresh water and in the sea.

One of the puzzling problems presented by the distribution of fishes through strata of all ages is the complete absence of fish remains, even scales, from most marine formations. No doubt, ever since the appearance of carnivorous jawed fishes at about the beginning of the Devonian Period, most fishes have ended their lives as the prey of other fishes (compare Fig. 2-11). Little fishes may have been swallowed whole and thoroughly digested, but the very biggest fishes, such as *Dinichthys*, must have been eaten piecemeal. If they lived in the sea, why are their bones so rare in marine for-

Fig. 11-32. Ichthyostega, *a fish-like labyrinthodont (stegocephalian) amphibian, about 2 feet long, from the uppermost Devonian of East Greenland. (From Ref. 7, by permission of the American Association for the Advancement of Science.)*
A. *Skeleton.*
B. *Reconstruction of animal.*

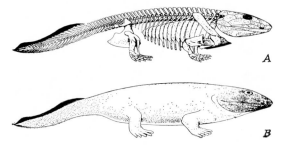

mations? The rarity of fish remains in marine rocks is made still more puzzling by an occasional exceptional marine formation, such as the Neogene Monterey shale of the California Coast Ranges, which contains fish scales everywhere and numerous fish specimens at some localities. Perhaps some of the places where that shale yields hundreds of complete fishes were the sites of volcanic catastrophes. Perhaps the primitive sharks of the Cleveland shale (Fig. 11-12) sank into a nearly lifeless, oxygen-free, closed depression in the sea floor, where there were no animals capable of eating

them and the impressions of their bacteria-transformed soft parts could be preserved. In general, bodies of fresh water appear to be better places to trap fishes, especially if they dry up occasionally. Lacustrine formations, from the Devonian up, commonly contain excellent fish faunas.

11-7. The Change from Fish to Tetrapod

Close relationships between Late Devonian fishes and amphibians have been demonstrated

Fig. 11-33. *Upper Devonian palates:* c.nt, *canal for notochord;* fe.exa, *opening for anterior external (incurrent) nostril;* fe.exch, *posterior nostril opening;* P, *parasphenoid bone;* Qu, *articular area for lower jaw;* sut, *boundary between anterior and posterior ossifications of brain case.* (*From Ref. 7, by permission of the American Association for the Advancement of Science.*)
A. *The osteolepid crossopterygian fish* Eusthenopteron, *Escuminac, Gaspé, Quebec.*
B. Ichthyostega, *East Greenland.*

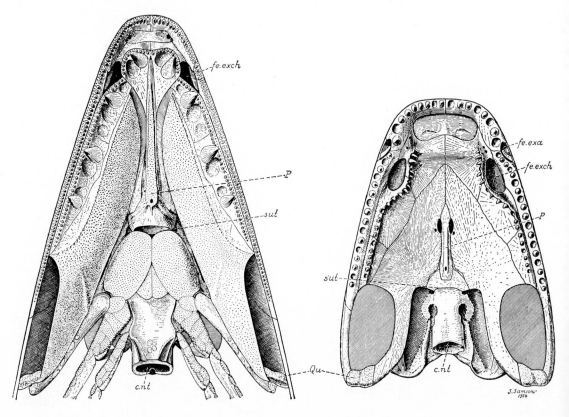

A   B

by the study of fossils found in East Greenland between 1928 and 1959. The Danes have made superb scientific use of Greenland's marginal rock exposures, and the *Meddelelser om Grønland*, now in more than 160 large volumes, contain one of the world's most important series of geological publications. The Danes entrusted the collection and study of the Devonian fishes to a group of Swedes. In 1932, G. Säve-Söderbergh, a 22-year-old student, published papers describing a new and very primitive amphibian—*Ichthyostega* (Fig. 11-32)—from a newly recognized uppermost Devonian zone in central East Greenland, north of Scoresby Sound (Fig. 11-31). The new zone (the *Remigolepis* zone of Table 11-2) was later correlated with the marine Strunian stage of the European continent, and the guide genus was found in New South Wales. Later expeditions to Greenland brought back much fine material, which enabled Säve-Söderbergh's assistant and successor, Erik Jarvik, to define a group of ichthyostegid amphibians, to describe a related crossopterygian fish from the same Greenland rocks, and to show the many close analogies between the bones of the ichthyostegids, still known only from East Greenland, and those of the Devonian crossopterygians of Greenland, Gaspé, and Scotland.

Ichthyostega is intermediate between certain Devonian fishes and the typical Stegocephalia, the principal group of Carboniferous-Permian amphibians. "Stegocephalian" means plate-headed, and *Ichthyostega* means fish-like stegocephalian. The animal represented in Figure 11-32 was indeed a plate-headed fish with four legs added. The model for the form, however, was not just a generalized fish but a particular kind of Devonian crossopterygian. The type of this crossopteryian group is *Osteolepis* (Fig. 11-35C), a Scottish Lower Devonian genus, but its members closest to *Ichthyostega* are found in the Upper Devonian of Gaspé and Greenland. The lower (palatal) sides of the skulls of the Gaspé fish and of *Ichthyostega* are similar in many details (Fig. 11-33). Note particularly the internal nostrils

(a feature of almost all tetrapods, but not found in most later fishes), the parasphenoid bone, and the large notochord canal. The labyrinthine patterns of the tooth structures are particularly similar (Fig. 11-34). These and other resemblances become overwhelming evidence of close relationship between these two forms, especially when the resemblances between the skull and tooth characters of *Ichthyostega* and the osteolepids are compared with the dissimilar characters of other Devonian fishes. Among tetrapods in general, the labyrinthodont tooth structure is so distinctive that the stegocephalians and their Triassic relatives are more accurately called labyrinthodonts. The ichthyostegan tail was wholly fish-like (Fig. 11-35), even to the little dermal fish bones (B), and closer to the tail of the Early Devonian *Osteolepis* (C) than to that of a Late Devonian crossopterygian (A).

The one new skeletal development in *Ichthyostega* was the replacement of paired fins by legs and feet. The similarities between whole sets of corresponding bones in a crossopterygian and in a primitive tetrapod (Fig.

Fig. 11-34. *Cross-sections of teeth of labyrinthodont type. (From A. Bystrow via Bernhard Kummel,* History of the Earth, *W. H. Freeman & Co., 1961.)*
A. *Crossopterygian fish* Eusthenopteron.
B. *Labyrinthodont amphibian* Benthosuchus.

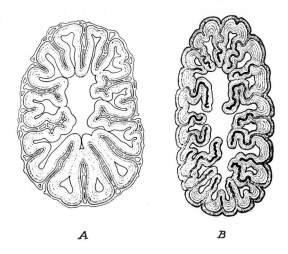

A   *B*

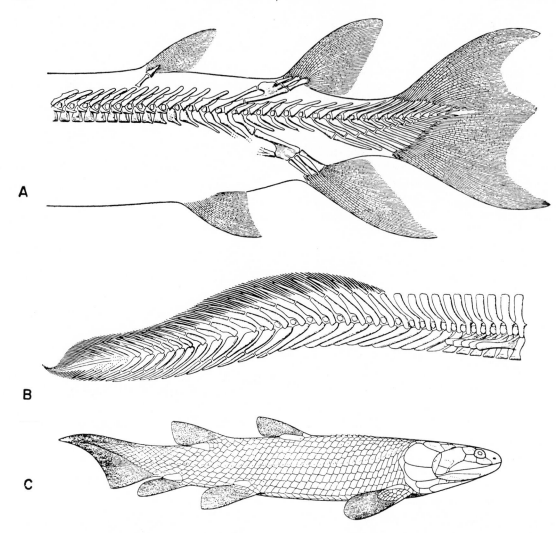

Fig. 11-35. *Ancestry of the fish-like tail of* Ichthyostega. (*From Erik Jarvik,* Meddelelser om Grøn-
land, *1952.*)
   A. *Tail of the crossopterygian* Eusthenopteron.
   B. *Tail (9 inches long) of* Ichthyostega.
   C. Osteolepis macrolepidotus *of Scotland, the crossopterygian at the beginning of the
line of descent from fish to amphibian.*

11-36) are close, but the new development
was nevertheless a startling one, as shown by
the combination of fish tail and walking foot
in *Ichthyostega* (Figs. 11-32 and 11-37). One
is left with a feeling of amazement that legs
actually did develop. Obviously, some stages
of the transformation are not yet known.

"The 'why' of tetrapod origin has been often
debated. Many of the earliest amphibians appear
to have been fairly large forms of carnivorous
habits, still spending a large portion of their time
in fresh-water pools. Alongside them lived their
close relatives, the crossopterygians, similar in
food habits and in many structural features and
differing markedly only in the lesser development

of the paired limbs. Why did the amphibians leave the water? Not to breathe air, for that could be done by merely coming to the surface of the pool. Not because they were driven out in search of food—they were carnivores for whom there was little food on land. Not to escape enemies, for they were among the largest of vertebrates found in the fresh waters from which they came.

"Their appearance on land seems to have resulted as an adaptation for remaining in the water.

"The earliest-known amphibians lived much the same sort of life as the related contemporary crossopterygians. Both lived normally in the same streams and pools, and both fed on the same fish food. As long as there was plenty of water, the crossopterygian probably was the better off of the two, for he was obviously the better swimmer— legs were in the way. The Devonian, during which land adaptations originated, was seemingly a time of seasonal droughts when life in fresh waters must have been difficult. Even then, if the water merely became stagnant and foul, the crossopterygian could come to the surface and breathe air as well as the amphibian. But if the water dried up altogether, the amphibian had the better of it. The fish, incapable of land locomotion, must stay in the mud and, if the water did not soon return, must die. But the amphibian, with his short and clumsy but effective limbs, could crawl out of the pool and walk overland (probably very slowly and painfully at first) and reach the next pool where water still remained.

"Once this process had begun, it is easy to see how a land fauna might eventually have been built up. Instead of seeking water immediately, the amphibian might linger on the banks and devour stranded fish. Some types might gradually

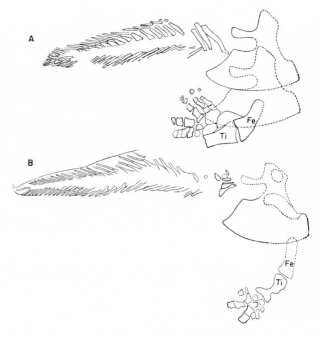

Fig. 11-37. *Association of hind foot and tail bones in two specimens of* Ichthyostega (A *and* B *each about 12 inches long) from the Upper Devonian of East Greenland:* Fe, *femur;* Ti, *tibia.* (*From Erik Jarvik,* Meddelelser om Grønland, *1952.*)

take to eating insects (primitive ones resembling cockroaches and dragon flies were already abundant) and, finally, plant food. The larger carnivores might take to eating their smaller amphibian relatives. Thus a true terrestrial fauna might be established." [*]

In the course of the Devonian, vertebrates had risen a long way. At the very beginning of the period, they had developed the lower jaw that made their whole bloody future possible, leading to the food cycle of Figure 2-11 and the similar terrestrial cycle envisioned by Romer. By the period's end they had come out on land—amphibians presaging the developments that we shall consider in Chapters 14, 15, and 16.

Fig. 11-36. *Devonian crossopterygian (left) and primitive amphibian (right) shoulder girdles:* cl, *clavicle;* icl, *interclavicle;* h, *humerus;* r, *radius;* u, *ulna;* sc, c, *fish bones preserved in primitive tetrapods.* (*From W. E. Swinton via Bernhard Kummel,* op. cit.)

[*] A. S. Romer, Ref. 3, pp. 140–141, reprinted by permission of the University of Chicago Press.

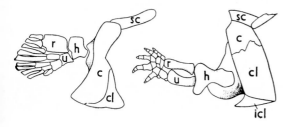

▨ | **REFERENCES**

Current

1. G. G. Simpson, C. S. Pittendrigh, and L. H. Tiffany: *Life: An Introduction to Biology*, 845 pages (Harcourt, Brace & World, Inc., New York, 1957)

2. A. S. Romer: *The Vertebrate Story*, 4th ed., 437 pages (University of Chicago Press, 1959)

3. A. S. Romer: *Vertebrate Paleontology*, 2nd ed., 687 pages (University of Chicago Press, 1945)

4. J. A. Moy-Thomas: *Paleozoic Fishes*, 149 pages (London and New York, 1939)

5. T. S. Westoll: "The Vertebrate-bearing Strata of Scotland," 18th Int. Geol. Cong., Part 11, pp. 5–20 (1951)

6. T. S. Westoll (editor): *Studies on Fossil Vertebrates*, 263 pages (The Athlone Press, University of London, 1958)

7. Erik Jarvik: "The Oldest Tetrapods and Their Forerunners," SCIENTIFIC MONTHLY, vol. 80, pp. 141–154 (1955)

8. Tor Ørvig: "*Pycnaspis splendens*, New Genus, New Species, a New Ostracoderm from the Upper Ordovician of North America," Proc. U.S. Nat. Mus., vol. 108, pp. 1–23 (1958)

9. Heinrich Bütler: *Das Old-Red Gebiet am Moskusoksefjord*, Med. o. Grønland, vol. 160, No. 5, 188 pages (1959)

10. *British Regional Geology: The Midland Valley of Scotland; The Northern Highlands* (Geol. Surv. and Museum, Edinburgh, 1948)

Classic

11. Louis Agassiz: *Recherches sur les poissons fossiles*, 5 vols., 1,420 pages and 369 plates; supplement, *Monographie des poissons fossiles du vieux grès rouge ou système Dévonien (Old Red Sandstone) des Iles Britanniques et de Russie*, 171 pages and 43 plates (Neuchâtel, 1833–1845)

12. Hugh Miller: *The Old Red Sandstone* (Edinburgh, 1841)

13. J. S. Newberry: *The Paleozoic Fishes of North America*, Monograph 16, U.S. Geol. Sur., 340 pages (1889)

14. E. R. Lankester and R. H. Traquair: *The Fishes of the Old Red Sandstone of Britain*, 134 pages and 31 plates (Palaeontographical Society, London, 1868–1914)

15. J. Kiaer: *The Downtonian Fauna of Norway: I, Anaspida*, Skr. vidensk. selsk. Oslo, math.-nat. Kl., 1, No. 6, 139 pages (1924)

16. E. A. Stensiö: *The Downtonian and Devonian Vertebrates of Spitsbergen: Family Cephalaspidae*, Norske statsunderstøttede Spitsbergen-ekspeditionen, XII, 391 pages and 112 plates (Norske Vidensk.-Akad., Oslo, 1927)

17. E. A. Stensiö: *The Cephalaspids of Great Britain*, 220 pages and 66 plates [British Museum (Nat. Hist.), London, 1932]

CHAPTER 12

The Rise of Land Floras

COMPLEX fresh-water and land plants developed about the time when fresh-water and land vertebrates were emerging. The oldest known continental flora, a rather primitive and restricted one, is Silurian. More varied and abundant floras appear in the Devonian and higher systems, the first climax, in the Upper Carboniferous (Pennsylvanian), being featured by the large primitive trees of the coal swamps.

In the previous chapter it was noted that the Devonian marks the beginning of a double standard in correlation, the new guides being fresh-water fishes. At the horizon of the Coal Measures, third and fourth sets of guides are added, the coal-swamp plants and the fresh-water pelecypods. Even the three kinds of non-marine guides, however, do not provide, for correlation, non-marine standards that are quite equal to those of the marine sequence.

12-1. The Structures of Plants

The plants living today vary greatly in structure, complexity, and habit. Marine plants, members of several groups united under the general designation "algae," are all rather simple. The largest and most complex of all algae are the kelps, which commonly grow attached to the sea bottom just offshore. The giant kelp of the California coast, which may be 150 feet long, consists of a fleshy brown stem with a holdfast or anchor at one end and leaf-like blades or bladed branches distributed along the stem at frequent intervals (Fig. 12-1). Unlike most other algae, the kelp is composed of many and varied cells. The loosely distributed, elongated cells in the center of the stem are different from those in the surrounding layer, which has radial structure, and equally different from the cubic surface cells, which form an epidermal layer that is commonly two cells thick. The reproductive organs are club-shaped cells on the surfaces of the blades. These cells subdivide into minute spores, and the spores develop into microscopic filaments that are male and female. The female filaments develop eggs; the male filaments produce sperm that swim to nearby eggs; the fertilized eggs that survive become kelp plants. The spore-producing and egg-producing "generations" (stages in the life cycle) alternate; as in most other plants, the egg-producing generation is insignificant in size. In kelp and other algae the reproductive processes are exceptionally simple, and the eggs are simple, small, and unprotected. Reproduction of this sort is effective in an aquatic environment.

Fig. 12-1. *Giant kelp of the southern California coast. The scale is 3 feet long. (Photograph by E. Yale Dawson, Natural History Museum, San Diego.)*

A land plant must get from the soil the water and nutrients used in photosynthesis and other physiological processes. For this and other reasons the circulation of sap, from the underground roots to the exposed parts of the plant and back, becomes necessary for a large plant. In addition to the differentiation into roots, stem, branches, and leaves, the plant develops specialized tissues and organs (Fig. 12-2). The tissues involved in sap circulation are the *xylem* and *phloem* (Figs. 12-2 and 12-3), which contain vertically elongated cells that become hollow. The sap moves upward through the inner tissue, the xylem, and downward through the outer tissue, the phloem. Cylindrical sheets of cells are added in the cambium, between xylem and

phloem (Fig. 12-2); annual rings are formed in this way.

Water and dissolved inorganic nutrients, of which there are many, enter the roots from the soil and rise through the xylem to the leaves. Photosynthesis of carbohydrates then takes place in the leaves, and the resulting heavier sap moves down through the phloem toward the roots. The water evaporated from the leaves or used in photosynthesis is immediately replaced by addition to the rising column of water through intake at the roots. The pull-up process operates through cell walls and is neither simply hydrostatic (balance of water and air columns) nor simply osmotic (equalization of concentrations of sap and

Fig. 12-2. *Segment of a dicotyledonous stem, with central pith, xylem, phloem, and cortex (bark). The cambium is the site of growth, where new rings of cells are added. (From H. J. Fuller and Z. B. Carothers,* The Plant World, *4th ed., Holt, Rinehart & Winston, Inc., New York, 1963.)*

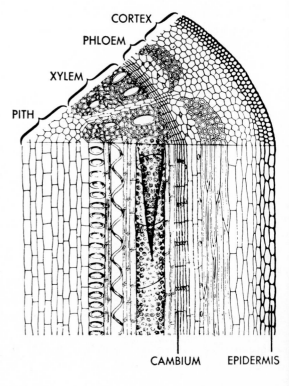

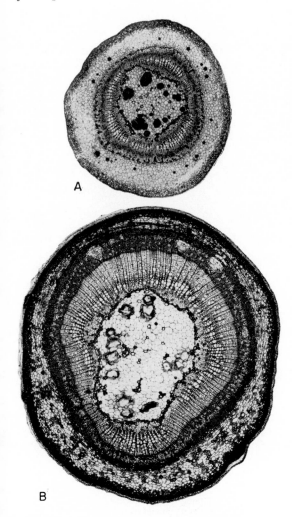

A

B

Fig. 12-3. *Cross-sections of very young linden (Tilia) stems. (From Katherine Esau,* Plant Anatomy, *John Wiley & Sons, New York, 1953.)*

A. *At end of primary growth.*

B. *After completion of first year's secondary growth.*

soil solution); the liquid column in a tall tree may cohere partly because each cell wall traversed adds support for the sap above it, partly through the mutual attraction of the sap particles.

The reproductive organs of land plants have developed in successive adaptations to a non-aqueous environment. In several lines

of descent, one of which led to the flowering plants, these organs finally came to produce seeds. A seed is made up of an embryo, a seed coat developed from the reproductive organ, and food-storage tissue. In the most successful plant group (the angiosperms, or flowering plants), the sperms are no longer mobile.

12-2. *Classification of Plants*

Plants are classified according to their tissues and organs. For living plants the primary emphasis is on the presence or absence of vascular tissues and the nature of the reproductive organs. A fundamental distinction is that between a naked embryo and one that has the protection of a seed coat (and therefore is properly called a seed). Recent and extinct forms are combined in a single general classification,* which is necessarily expanded to include wholly extinct groups:

Division Tracheophyta—vascular plants.
  Subdivision Pteropsida—seed-bearing plants and ferns.
    Class Angiospermophyta—angiosperms: flowering seed-plants.
      Monocotyledonae—monocotyledons: grasses, lilies, palms, etc. Triassic(?)–Recent.
      Dicotyledonae—dicotyledons: most flowering plants. Cretaceous–Recent.
    Class Coniferophyta—cone-bearing plants with naked seeds: conifers, ginkgos, Carboniferous *Cordaites*, etc. Devonian–Recent.
    Class Cycadophyta—loosely woody, heavy-leaved, with naked seeds: cycads, seed-ferns, etc. Devonian–Recent.
    Class Pterophyta—spore-bearing: ferns, etc. Late Devonian–Recent.
  Subdivision Sphenopsida—modern *Equisetum* (horsetail), Carboniferous *Calamites*, etc. Early Devonian–Recent.
  Subdivision Lycopsida—Paleozoic scale trees: *Lepidodendron*, etc.; Recent clubmosses and quillwort. Silurian–Recent.
  Subdivision Psilopsida—branching, vascular, almost leafless: Silurian and Devonian of Australia, Scotland, etc.; three Recent species.

* After Delevoryas (Ref. 1).

Fig. 12-4. *Horsetail* (Equisetum): L.S., *leaf sheath;* R., *rhizome (root-like stem)*; S., *sporangium (spore case)*. (*From Arthur Cronquist,* Introductory Botany, *Harper & Brothers, 1961.*)
A–E. Equisetum arvense: A, *fertile shoot* (× *1*); B, *sterile shoot* (× *1/4*); CDE, *enlarged details*.
F. Equisetum hiemale (× *1/4*).

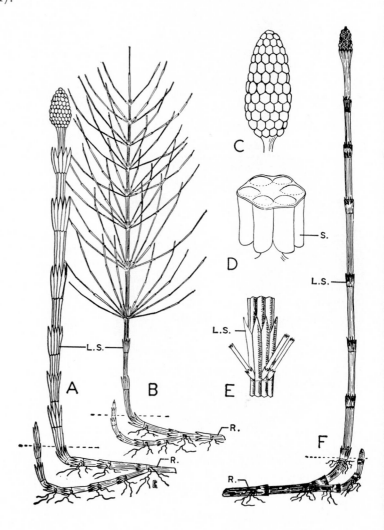

Division Bryophyta—mosses, liverworts, etc. Silurian–Recent.

Division Thallophyta*—simple plants, many of which are single-celled.

    Fungi—chlorophyll-free. Precambrian–Recent.

    Algae—green; blue-green; brown (seaweeds). Precambrian–Recent.

This moderately complex classification recognizes the great groups of plants that are

* Bacteria, not classified in this outline or elsewhere in this book, may be considered thallophytes.

still living and the relations of these groups to the extinct groups of the Paleozoic. The first division among living plants is between the vascular and the non-vascular forms. The non-vascular groups may, for our purposes, be classified as thallophytes (a most varied assemblage, but with few fossil representatives) and bryophytes. The Thallophyta are divided into the unpigmented Fungi and the mostly green or greenish Algae. The individuals are mostly small; many are single-celled and microscopic, though the algae also include the giant kelp of Figure 12-1. The second non-vascular division, the Bryophyta, includes mosses and similar simple and small multi-celled forms.

Most vascular plants are rooted on land. A few are rooted in subaqueous soil or float on water or hang in air, but the aqueous forms rise at least slightly into the air. The vessels that give the vascular plants their name are the tubes, previously described, that facilitate the movement of liquids.

Almost all living vascular plants may be divided into three major groups: (1) the horsetails, clubmosses, etc.: the Sphenopsida and Lycopsida; (2) ferns, cycads, conifers, etc.: the Pterophyta, Cycadophyta, and Coniferophyta; (3) the great assemblage of flowering plants (angiosperms): the Angiospermophyta. The angiosperms are divided into monocotyledons (grasses, lilies, palms, and the like) and dicotyledons (other flowering plants, including most non-coniferous trees and shrubs). One subdivision of the classification, the Psilopsida, is almost wholly Paleozoic; the three Recent species are rarities.

The fronded ferns and needle-leaved conifers are familiar plants, but horsetails, clubmosses, and cycads are less common. The living horsetails (Fig. 12-4), which are typical of the Sphenopsida, have conspicuous cone-shaped terminal spore cases. The plants are small and have corrugated stems. They secrete enough epidermal silica to feel harsh and justify the name "scouring rushes." The living clubmosses are typified by *Lycopodium* (Fig. 12-5), a shaggy little plant, not a moss at all, whose club-shaped spore cases yield the lycopodium powder of commerce. Some Carboniferous members of the Lycopsida were great trees. The Cycadophyta of the subdivision Pteropsida are typified by the living tropical and subtropical cycads, found as far north as Florida and Mexico. Cycads (Fig. 12-6) have short massive trunks, whorls of branches, and leaves like those of palm trees; they bear male and female seed cones.

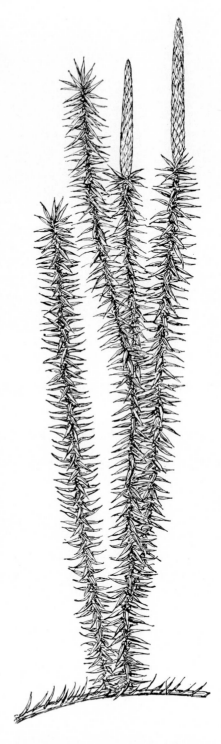

Fig. 12-5.　Lycopodium annotinum, *a club-moss, 5 inches long.* (*From Lyman Benson,* Plant Classification, *D. C. Heath & Co., 1957.*)

Fig. 12-6. *A cycad,* Cycas revoluta, *in cultivation in southern California.* (*From Lyman Benson, op. cit.*)
LEFT. *Whole plant.*
RIGHT. *Polliniferous cone surrounded by leaves.*

Fig. 12-7. Psilotum nudum, *slightly less than 1/2 natural size.* (*Photograph by E. N. Mitchell. From Arthur Cronquist,* Introductory Botany, *Harper & Brothers, 1961.*)

12-3. *Notable Events in the History of Plants*

Stratigraphically, four events are notable in the history of plants; (1) the first appearance of algae and fungi—in the Precambrian; (2) the appearance of multicellular land plants—possibly first, in very rudimentary form, in the Cambrian, and then, much more clearly developed, in the Late Silurian and the Devonian; (3) the proliferation of the great floras of the Carboniferous and Permian, with their ferns, giant horsetails, giant clubmosses, seed ferns, and primitive conifers; (4) the first appearance of unmistakable flowering plants—in the Early Cretaceous.

12-4. Pre-Silurian Plants

Banded incrustations and concentric structures called stromatolites, including *Cryptozoon* (Fig. 10-12), are common in some Precambrian and Cambrian limestones. They are more or less certainly attributed to deposition under the influence of blue-green or other algae. Some more complex Precambrian structures (Fig. 9-19) are certainly organic and probably algal.

Microorganisms whose remains are preserved in chert of the Gunflint Formation (Animikian) of southern Ontario, just north of Lake Superior, are in part of uncertain relationships (Fig. 9-20), in part definitely blue-green algae and fungi (Ref. 8). Some of the organic matter is preserved, either coalified or still brown and translucent under the microscope. The discovery of unquestionable plant material in rather early Precambrian rocks is one of the most important paleontological achievements of this century. Now it seems highly probable that thallophytes produced much of the rather widely distributed Precambrian carbon.

A few occurrences of Cambrian vascular plants have been reported but not proved. Structures similar to those of the modern clubmosses (Lycopsida), for example, were found in 1953 in eastern Siberia in strata that also contain trilobites considered to be Middle Cambrian. None of the Cambrian remains of supposedly higher plants has yet been supported by conclusive evidence of the nature of the plants.

Fig. 12-8. *Life cycle of* Psilotum: *E., egg; E.S., embryo sporophyte (asexual generation); S., sperm; Z, zygote (fertilized egg). The gametophyte (sexual) generation is represented twice, before and after the development of the embryo sporophyte. (From Arthur Cronquist,* Introductory Botany, *Harper & Brothers, 1961.)*

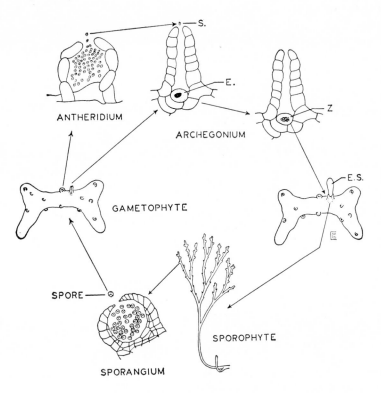

Fig. 12-9.   Rhynia, *from the Old Red Sandstone of Scotland,* × 0.7. (*From Lyman Benson, op. cit.*)

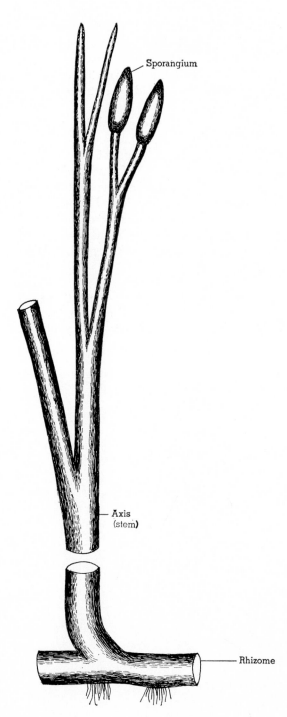

Fig. 12-10.   Archaeopteris, *an Upper Devonian fern-like plant, with fertile fronds, from Bear Island, Arctic Ocean; specimen 7 inches across.* (*After A. G. Nathorst via Walther Gothan and Hermann Weyland,* Lehrbuch der Paläobotanik, Akademie-Verlag, Berlin, 1954.)

12-5. Silurian and Devonian Psilopsida

Psilotum, a vascular plant without roots and almost without leaves (Fig. 12-7), is living today in tropical and subtropical regions of both hemispheres, ranging north as far as South Carolina. It has a simple life cycle, with a minute subterranean sexual generation (magnified in Fig. 12-8) that produces sperm and egg. The egg develops into the above-ground, spore-bearing plant. Primitive plants similar to *Psilotum* are known from Devonian and Silurian rocks. The first to be found was *Psilophyton* of the Gaspé (Quebec) Old Red Sandstone, described by John W. Dawson of McGill University in 1859. It was followed by *Rhynia* and related forms, reported in 1917 from the Scottish Old Red of the Southern Highlands (probably Middle Old Red). The cell structure of *Rhynia* (Fig. 12-9) was preserved in the replacing silica of the now cherty rock. During the nineteen-twenties, similar plants were found in the Upper Silurian and Lower Devonian of Australia, and now many Late Silurian and Early or Middle Devonian plants of the same general character are known from many parts of the world. Psilopsid plants may have been ancestral to all other vascular plants.

Some other Devonian plants were strikingly unlike the psilopsids. These others included both a late Middle Devonian giant fern and a rather large Late Devonian flora. The great tree fern was discovered in 1870 at Gilboa, forty miles southwest of Albany, New York. Fifty years later hundreds of standing stumps were found, some four feet in diameter, in the course of excavations for a dam. Now the site is mostly beneath a reservoir holding water for New York City.

The Late Devonian flora is made up largely of fern-like plants, such as *Archaeopteris* (Fig. 12-10), and rather small scale-tree lycopsids related to the Carboniferous *Lepidodendron*. This flora is similar to that of the Lower Carboniferous.

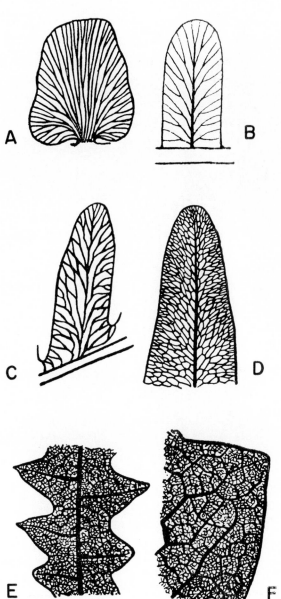

Fig. 12-11. *Shapes of fern-like leaves. (After Walther Gothan and Hermann Weyland,* op. cit.)

  A. *Sphenopterid form.*
  B. *Pecopterid form.*
  C. *Neuropterid form.*

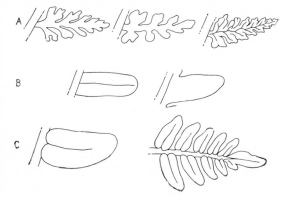

Fig. 12-12. *Veining of leaves. (From Walther Gothan and Hermann Weyland,* op. cit.)

  A. *Fan veining.*
  B. *Feather veining with midrib.*
  C. *Transition from feather veining to mesh veining.*
  D. *Simple mesh veining with midrib.*
  E. *Compound mesh veining.*
  F. *Complex mesh veining, as in the leaves of the tulip tree.*

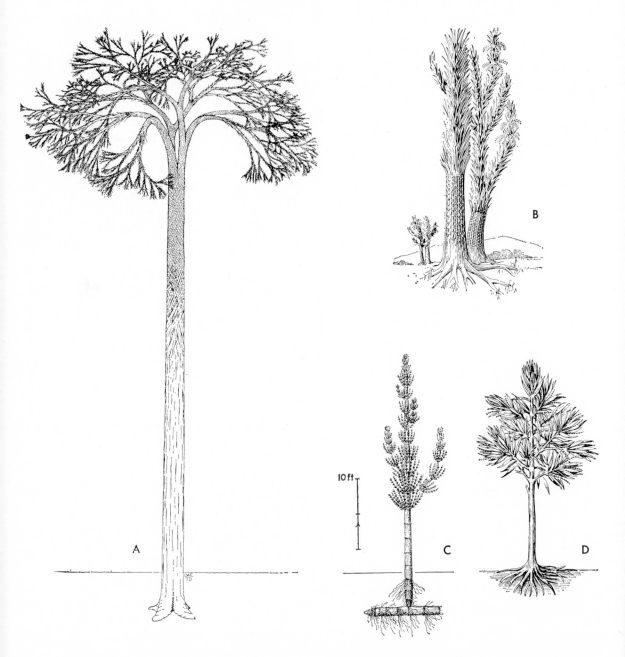

Fig. 12-13. *Carboniferous coal-swamp trees (30–100 feet high).* (A *from D. A. Eggert via Theodore Delevoryas, Ref. 1;* B *and* D *from C. O. Dunbar,* Historical Geology, *John Wiley & Sons, 1960;* C *from Arthur Cronquist, op. cit.)*

   A. Lepidodendron.   C. Calamites.

   B. Sigillaria.   D. Cordaites.

12-6. The Coal Flora

In Europe and eastern North America the most abundant and widespread fossil plants are those in Carboniferous rocks, at several horizons. The whole assemblage of these plants will be called the Coal Flora, though the workable coal beds are mostly Upper Carboniferous (Pennsylvanian). The commonest plant remains in the coal measures are fern-like leaves of varied form and veining (Figs. 12-11 and 12-12). Also common (Fig. 12-13) are the trunks, branches, and leaves of giant lycopsids, notably the scale-tree *Lepidodendron* (A) and the seal-tree *Sigillaria* (B), as well as sphenopsids such as *Calamites* (C) and conifer-like forms, notably *Cordaites* (D). Some of the fern-like leaves probably represent ancient ferns, but others, such as the neuropterid shown in Figure 12-14, carried seeds and are therefore assigned to the extinct group of seed-ferns (Devonian–Jurassic), which are members of the Cycadophyta. Some seed-ferns had stalks with primary wood, secondary wood, bark, and, beneath the bark, suggestions of vascular bundles similar to those of modern angiosperms. The inch-thick stem of the Carboniferous seed-fern of Figure 12-15 has structures superficially so similar to those of the linden (*Tilia*) that it is called *Heterangium tiliaeoides*. Flowering plants are unknown in these or other Paleozoic rocks. The largest plants of the coal swamps were *Lepidodendron*, *Sigillaria*, *Calamites*, and *Cordaites*, which varied in height from twenty to a hundred feet and were sometimes three or four feet thick at the base. Sandstone casts of *Lepidodendron* stumps and roots, in sandstone, are shown in Figure 12-16, and a composite picture of typical members of the Coal Flora in Figure 12-17. At the left and center are Late Carboniferous forms, including *Lepidodendron* (Ln), *Sigillaria* (Sg), and *Calamites* (Cal). At the right are Early Carboniferous forms, including *Astrocalamites* (As) and *Pitys* (Pt), the latter a coniferoid ancestor of *Cordaites*.

Fig. 12-14. Neuropteris heterophylla, *a Carboniferous seed-fern. (From D. H. Scott, Extinct Plants and Problems of Evolution, Macmillan and Co. Ltd., London, 1924.)*
ABOVE. *Varied foliage, some fronds still coiled.* BELOW. *At left, seeds on fronds; at right, a young frond.*

The eight Carboniferous sub-floras distinguished in central Europe (Table 12-1) are valid over a large area, which does not, however, include Britain. Common plant genera and a few of the guide species are listed in the right-hand column of the table. Comparison with the goniatite guide genera of the next column shows that the stratigraphic units based on plants are more numerous, especially in the Upper Carboniferous. Plants are especially important as horizon markers because

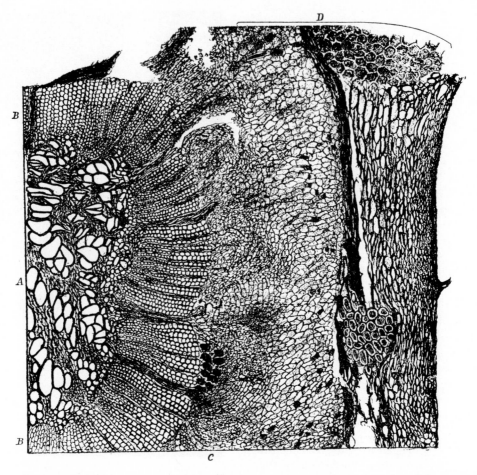

Fig. 12-15. Heterangium tiliaeoides, *a Carboniferous seed-fern from Halifax, Yorkshire, England;*
cross-section of stem (× 12): A, *axial wood;* B, *xylem;* C, *phloem (compare Fig. 12-3);* D, *bark.*
(Adapted from W. C. Williamson, Philos. Trans. Roy. Soc. London, 1887.)

the Upper Carboniferous is mostly continental and in many basins marine bands are lacking. The eight Carboniferous sub-floras fall into two groups: the two sub-floras below the principal floral change within the Carboniferous and the six above it. The great break (*Florensprung*) is a biostratigraphic lacuna between substages A and B of the Namurian, low in the Upper Carboniferous and perhaps at about the same horizon as the Mississippian-Pennsylvanian boundary in North America. Few species cross this break; below it, moreover, *Lepidodendron* is abundant but *Sigillaria* is almost completely absent. A second significant floral change occurs with the

beginning of the Stephanian: *Lepidodendron*, which had been on the wane, practically disappears, and typical *Sigillaria* is succeeded by subsigillarians. The Stephanian and Lower Permian floras are similar to each other, but the Upper Permian flora has a Mesozoic aspect. The three floral changes—one in the Namurian, the second between Wesphalian and Stephanian, the third mid-Permian—are great enough to be recognized in distant regions. If the paleobotany of the northern hemisphere alone is considered, the great floral break is in the middle of the Permian rather than at the end of the Paleozoic. This change in the floras has proved stratigraphi-

Fig. 12-16. *Natural sandstone casts of* Lepidodendron *stumps and roots, Victoria Park, Glasgow, Scotland. Note the nearly horizontal enclosing strata. (Photograph by Arthur Cronquist, 1964.)*

Fig. 12-17. *Panorama of a Carboniferous swamp: Cd., Cordaites; N., Neuropteris; Cal., Calamites; Sp., Sphenophyllum (vine-like); Ln., Lepidodendron; Sg., Sigillaria; As., Astrocalamites; Pt., Pitys. (From A. C. Seward,* Plant Life Through the Ages, *Cambridge University Press, 1931.)*

TABLE 12-1

Late Paleozoic Floras of Central Europe

SUBSYSTEM	STAGE AND SUBSTAGE	GONIATITES	PLANTS
Lower Permian			*Callipteris* (fern), *Walchia*, subsigillarians, *Sphenophyllum* (sphenopsid)
	Stephanian	*Schistoceras*	8. Pecopterids (with parallel-sided leaflets), subsigillarians
Upper Carboniferous	Westphalian D		7. *Neuropteris ovata* (broad-leaf seed-fern), *Sigillaria*, *Sphenopteris* (seed-fern)
	Westphalian C	*Gastrioceras*	6. *Neuropteris*, *Sigillaria*, *Sphenopteris*, *Sphenophyllum*
	Westphalian B		5. *Lepidodendron*, *Sigillaria*, *Sphenopteris*, *Neuropteris*, etc.
	Westphalian A		4. *Lepidodendron*, *Sigillaria*, *Lonchopteris rugosa* (mesh-veined fern)
	Namurian C	*Eumorphoceras* sp.	3. *Lepidodendron*, *Sigillaria*, *Calamites*, *Neuropteris* (seed-fern)
	Namurian B	*Reticuloceras*	
	Namurian A	*Eumorphoceras* sp.	Lacuna (*Florensprung*) 2. *Sphenopteris adiantoides* (seed-fern), *Asterocalamites*, *Lepidodendron*
Lower Carboniferous	Visean	*Glyphioceras* *Pericyclus*	1. *Lepidodendron*, *Asterocalamites*, etc.
	Tournaisian	*Gattendorfia*	Tournaisian flora similar to 1 above, but little known
Upper Devonian		*Wocklumeria*	*Archaeopteris-Cyclostigma* flora (fan-fern and lepidodendroid)

cally useful as far from Europe as southern Africa, as we shall find in Chapter 13.

The time of maximum coal development in Europe (Westphalian) is represented by Figure 12-18. Note the rudimentary development of the marine Tethys from Asia Minor to Morocco, the diverging Caspian and Uralian geosynclines to the northeast, the epicontinental Russian sea, the great expanses of land in Scandinavia, Spain, France, and southern Russia, containing small land-locked coal basins, and the important strip of coastal coal swamps extending from the British Isles through northwestern Germany to Poland.

12-7. *Fresh-water Pelecypods as Carboniferous Guide Fossils*

In Britain the coal plants have proved to be rather unsatisfactory guides to particular Car-

boniferous horizons, even between some adjacent coalfields, and stratigraphers have turned to fresh-water pelecypod faunas for guidance. The shells are extremely variable in form and sculpture, even within a single species (Fig. 12-19). As a result, statistical treatment of measurements, such as length and height, is necessary in the defining of guide species. The statistical distinction between two Scottish Lower Carboniferous species, one that of Figure 12-19, is shown in Figure 12-20. These two species are exceptionally distinct. Several score specimens must ordinarily be measured before a species can be identified; and, moreover, many species range through considerable thicknesses of strata. The complete assemblage of pelecypods, rather than one or two guide species, must usually be worked over before a horizon can be determined.

A stratigraphic classification based on statistical study of non-marine pelecypods has also been used to some extent in France, and the major distinctions can also be made in the Ruhr Basin of western Germany and even in the Donets Basin of southern Russia. Similar shells occur in the Pennsylvanian of eastern North America, but not much has yet been done with them statistically.

The demonstration of the value of pelecypods in British Carboniferous stratigraphy has been the greatest triumph of statistical paleontology. The method is probably not

Fig. 12-18. *Westphalian (Middle Pennsylvanian) paleogeography of Europe. (Adapted from Roland Brinkmann, Historische Geologie, 8th ed., Ferdinand Enke Verlag, Stuttgart, 1959.)*

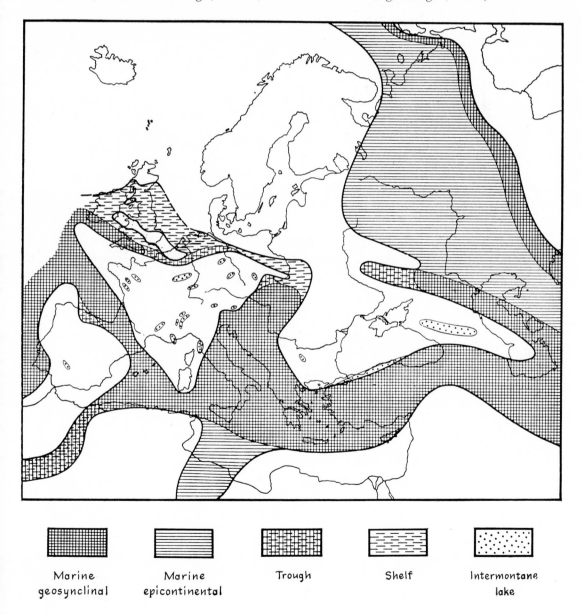

Marine geosynclinal   Marine epicontinental   Trough   Shelf   Intermontane lake

applicable, however, to interprovincial or overseas correlations.

12-8. *Environment of the Coal Flora*

Eastern North America and western Europe were as similar in the Carboniferous as in the Devonian. A marine Lower Carboniferous limestone, formed over large parts of each continent, grades into continental deposits, largely sandstone, near the shores of the northern part of the present North Atlantic. The Mississippian limestone of the American Midcontinent and Middle West becomes vari-colored sandstone in eastern Pennsylvania and southeastern New York. In East Greenland, the Lower Carboniferous is continental sand-stone containing some plant-bearing coaly beds. In northwestern Europe, the Carbonifer-ous limestone of the English Midlands be-comes shaly toward the north and non-marine in the Midland Valley of Scotland (compare Fig. 12-18).

The Upper Carboniferous is mostly con-tinental—the coal measures facies—through-out eastern North America and in most parts of northwestern and central Europe. The conditions of deposition were largely those of broad coastal plains, especially in America (Chap. 6), but there were also isolated lake and swamp basins within the continental up-lands, especially in Europe (Fig. 12-18) but probably also in North America (Nova Scotia).

The mountain-making rock deformations of the Devonian were continued, in somewhat different areas and orientations, throughout the Carboniferous and into at least mid-Per-mian time, when the main episode in the fold-ing of the Ural mountain chain took place, in the belt shown as a geosyncline in the north-east corner of Figure 12-18. Equally intense folding had occurred earlier, in pre-Carbonif-erous and mid-Carboniferous times, in France and western Germany, producing the upland area dotted with lake basins in Figure 12-18 and leading to unconformities of horizontal beds on vertical ones in eastern Germany and elsewhere.

A complex combination of circumstances seems to have made possible the accumulation of enormous quantities of plant residues, destined to form coal, in the North Atlantic region in Late Carboniferous time. One factor was mountain-making and the spreading of debris from the newly formed mountains in flat-topped sheets across interior basins and marginal (shelf) portions of the continental platforms, pushing back or keeping out the seas and producing flat floors for the coal swamps. A second factor was a favorable

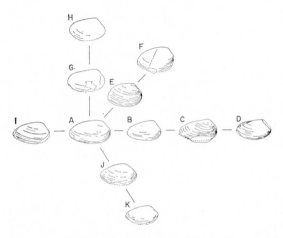

Fig. 12-19. *Variation in the fresh-water pelecy-pod* Carbonicola antiqua, *Lower Carboniferous, Fife Ness, Scotland. (From G. M. Bennison,* Palaeontology, *1960.)*

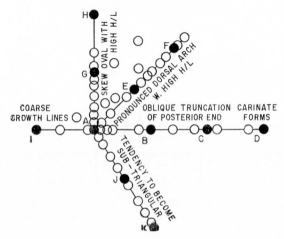

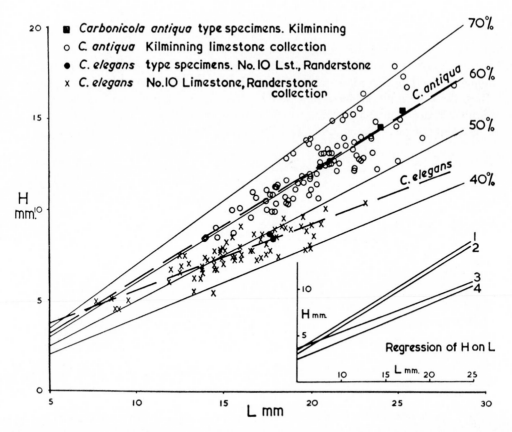

Fig. 12-20. *Height-length relations in* Carbonicola antiqua *and* C. elegans *at their type localities, Fife Ness, Scotland. (From G. M. Bennison, loc. cit.)*

climate for the production of lush vegetation. A third was the development of suitable plants, which apparently were not in existence before mid-Devonian time. The mountain-making and the climate produced conditions that favored the development of the coal plants, but they did not make such a development inevitable. Continental conditions existed as far back as the Cambrian (compare Chap. 10), and the Cambrian salt deposits are accompanied by barren formations that may have been non-marine. Probably Cambrian and Ordovician coal could not form in quantity, no matter how favorable the physical conditions, because appropriate plants did not yet exist.

12-9. *Indirect Evidences of Paleozoic Plant Life*

The principal Paleozoic floras represent the swamp facies. Other plant facies must have existed, especially in Late Carboniferous and Permian times. The rich late Paleozoic and Triassic amphibian and reptile faunas of Texas, South Africa, and southern South America, in particular, could not have flourished without moderately abundant vegetation, any more than a fox-and-rabbit fauna can exist without herbage for the rabbits to eat. What is more, the vegetation and the early land vertebrates probably were not limited to the basins of red-bed or other deposition;

they probably spread over the upland regions as well.

More generally, animal life cannot exist without plants to synthesize the organic fuel that animals eat. The abundant marine animals, from the Cambrian on, must have lived on widespread and flourishing marine plants, almost certainly algae. One curious fact in this connection is the absence of diatoms, the grass of the sea, from strata older than Jurassic. Some earlier food plants, however, must have been abundant. They may have been diatoms without hard parts, or they may have been other types of algae, perhaps members of the blue-green group that was in existence even before Cambrian time.

REFERENCES

1. Theodore Delevoryas: *Morphology and Evolution of Fossil Plants,* 189 pages (Holt, Rinehart & Winston, New York, 1962)

2. Walther Gothan and Hermann Weyland: *Lehrbuch der Paläobotanik,* 535 pages (Akademie-Verlag, Berlin, 1954)

3. Lyman Benson: *Plant Classification,* 688 pages (Heath, Boston, 1957)

4. Arthur Cronquist: *Introductory Botany,* 892 pages (Harper, New York, 1961)

5. A. C. Seward: *Plant Life Through the Ages,* 601 pages (Cambridge University Press, Cambridge, England, 1931)

6. D. H. Scott: *Extinct Plants and Problems of Evolution,* 240 pages (Macmillan, London, 1924)

7. Roland Brinkmann: *Geologic Evolution of Europe,* translated by J. E. Sanders, 161 pages (Enke, Stuttgart; Hafner, New York; 1960)

8. S. A. Tyler and E. S. Barghoorn: "Occurrence of Structurally Preserved Plants in pre-Cambrian Rocks of the Canadian Shield," SCIENCE, vol. 119, pp. 606–608 (1954)

9. E. S. Barghoorn and S. A. Tyler: "Microorganisms from the Gunflint Chert," SCIENCE, vol. 147, pp. 563–577 (1965)

10. G. M. Bennison: "Lower Carboniferous Non-marine Lamellibranchs from East Fife, Scotland," PALAEONTOLOGY, vol. 3, pp. 137–152 (1960)

CHAPTER 13

Gondwanaland

THE MOST eventful part of geologic history since the beginning of the Cambrian came near and at the end of the Paleozoic. Physical events included widespread mountain-making, less widespread granitic intrusions, exceptionally complete emergence of the continental platforms, glaciations in the southern hemisphere, and, in the northern hemisphere, the accumulation of coal beds and thick series of evaporites, the latter including the most soluble of sea salts. The outstanding event in marine biology was the extinction of many great groups of shallow-water animals. On land, the biological changes were much less notable.

13-1. *The Gondwana Problem*

The unusual late Paleozoic and early Mesozoic events are known primarily through the unusual rocks that were produced. Perhaps the most exceptional of these rocks are the Gondwana "System" and its correlatives. The type Gondwana sequence of tillite, plant-bearing beds, and other non-marine strata occurs in peninsular India. Correlative sequences are known in central and southern Africa, eastern South America, southeastern Australia, Antarctica, and some intervening islands. If all these places are considered together, as a single unit, they are called **Gondwanaland,** a term that becomes especially appropriate if the land masses were once united in a single supercontinent. The existence of such a supercontinent in late Paleozoic time is perhaps the most hotly argued question in historical geology.

a. The Gondwana Strata

The strata of the Gondwana "System" (which is not a system in the worldwide Cambrian–Pleistocene sense) lie almost horizontally on Precambrian gneisses in several basins in the north-central and northeastern parts of the Indian peninsula. They are divided into two parts: (1) the Lower Gondwanas, now considered late Paleozoic and Triassic, which include a basal boulder bed up to 100 feet thick and overlying beds containing almost all of India's coal; (2) the Upper Gondwanas, probably mostly Jurassic, which contain basaltic lavas near the top. The basal boulder bed, which is present almost everywhere, was described rather tentatively as a tillite in 1856, in the first volume of Memoirs of the Geological Survey of India. In 1875 a striated, ice-grooved pavement was discovered beneath the tillite west of Chanda, near the center of the peninsula, and this pavement is still the most conclusive evidence that the boulder bed is really glacial.

The coal measures have yielded a peculiar flora of ferns, typified by the net-leaved genera *Glossopteris,* with midribbed leaves (Fig. 13-

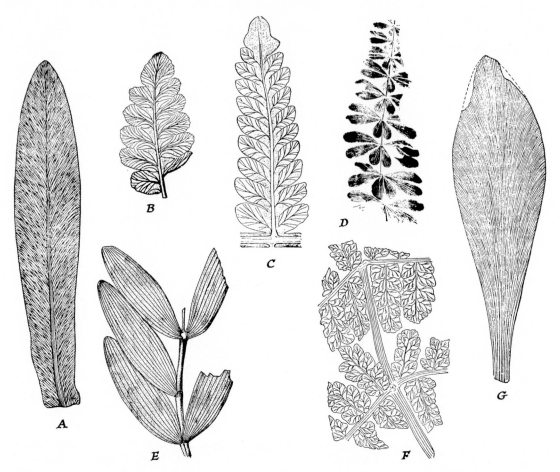

Fig. 13-1. *Typical members of the* Glossopteris *flora. (From E. A. N. Arber, British Museum, 1905, via Ref. 1.)*

    A. Glossopteris decipiens.   D. Sphenophyllum speciosum.

    B. Merianopteris major.   E. Schizoneura gondwanensis.

    C,F. Sphenopteris polymorpha.   G. Gangamopteris cyclopteroides.

1A), which was described in the eighteen-twenties, and *Gangamopteris* (Fig. 13-1G), a very similar form that lacks the midrib. The Lower Gondwana flora that includes species of these genera is called the *Glossopteris* flora. The first satisfactory description of *Glossopteris*, in 1828, included mention of specimens from India and Australia; in 1858 almost identical specimens were reported from South Africa. In all three regions, the basal beds of the *Glossopteris*-bearing sequence are widespread tillites overlying polished, grooved, and striated glacial pavements, which are especially extensive in several southeastern Australian states and in South Africa (Fig. 13-2). In Australia there are also higher glacial horizons; the tillites are interbedded with marine, fossiliferous Upper Carboniferous and Permian strata, with the highest tillites overlain unconformably by Triassic beds. In Southwest Africa the tillites are interbedded with marine strata whose crinoids, pelecypods, gastropods, and fish (Ref. 15) indicate Late Carboniferous age. The South African plant beds are mostly in the Ecca series of the Karroo "System" (Table 13-1). In 1929 the *Glossopteris* flora in the Ecca beds of Southern Rhodesia (Wankie coal measures) was found to be associated with members of the Coal Flora of the northern hemisphere (§ 12-6) and therefore probably of Carboniferous or Early Permian age (compare Table 12-1). Higher series in the Karroo sequence have yielded enormous numbers of reptile bones; these have been assigned to hundreds of species, some of which have close relatives in the Permian and Triassic faunas of northern continents.

b. The Hypothesis of a Supercontinent

Soon after the first correlation of *Glossopteris*-bearing and glacial formations across the Indian Ocean, several geologists suggested that southern Africa and peninsular India must have been connected by a land bridge in late Paleozoic time. In 1885 Eduard Suess of Vienna, in the final pages of the first volume of the worldwide stratigraphic synthesis that he called *The Face of the Earth*, applied the term Gondwanaland to a hypothetical late Paleozoic supercontinent that included southern and central Africa, Madagascar, and the Indian peninsula. Suess thought that Gondwanaland was separated from continental masses in the Eurasian region by an incipient Tethys. When the *Glossopteris* flora was found in southern Brazil, Suess added the Precambrian platform of eastern South America to Gondwanaland. Somewhat earlier he had included Australia, but in his last discussion of Gondwanaland he left this continent unmentioned, perhaps because the Precambrian platform of central and western Australia lacks a cover of continental formations of Gondwana age and type. In India, southern Africa, and South America, the Gondwana sediments and lavas are closely

Fig. 13-2. *Dwyka tillite on glaciated pavement, near Kimberley, South Africa. (Photograph by J. H. Wellington via Ref. 1.)*

TABLE 13-1

Gondwana Correlations: India — South Africa — South America

SYSTEM	SANTA CATARINA "SYSTEM," SOUTH AMERICA	KARROO "SYSTEM," SOUTHWEST AFRICA	KARROO "SYSTEM," UNION OF SOUTH AFRICA: KARROO BASIN	GONDWANA "SYSTEM," PENINSULAR INDIA
Jurassic	Baurú sandstone Serra Geral volcanics & sandstones; 3,000	Kaoko lavas; 2,100	Stormberg series Drakensberg lavas; 4,500	Upper Gondwanas Jabalpur series: sandstone & clay Rajmahal series: volcanics, etc. Mahadeva series: sandstone & clay
Triassic Upper Middle	Botucatú sandstone; 500 Santa Maria red marl & sandstone, reptiles; 265	Sandstone; 160	Cave sandstone (pale); 800 Red beds, reptiles; 1,600 Molteno beds: gray & blue shale, gray sandstone, no reptiles; 2,000 Beaufort series; 8,000 REPTILE ZONE Upper: red mudstone, sandstone 6. *Cynognathus* 5. *Procolophon*	Lower Gondwanas Panchet series: gray sandstone & red clay, amphibians & reptiles
Lower			Middle: red mudstone, sandstone 4. *Lystrosaurus*	
Permian Upper	Rio do Rasto group: maroon & gray shale, *Glossopteris* flora; 330	Sandstone; 330	Lower: yellow sandstone, blue-to-red shale, Upper: blue shale 3. *Cistecephalus* 2. *Endothiodon* 1. *Tapinocephalus* Ecca series; 10,500 Upper: blue shale	Damuda coal-bearing series: sandstone, shale & clay, coal, *Glossopteris* flora
Lower	Estrada Nova group: gray & black shales, etc., marine fossils; 700 Irati shale, *Mesosaurus*; 300	Shale, *Mesosaurus*; 190	Middle: coal measures, *Glossopteris* flora Lower: blue & green shales Dwyka series Upper: bituminous shale, *Mesosaurus*; 650	Talchir series: Talchir shale
Carboniferous Upper	Guatá group: sandstone, shale, coal, *Glossopteris*, marine *Eurydesma*; 600 Itararé tillites; 1,500	Coal measures, *Glossopteris*; 1,600 Tillite, *Eurydesma*	Lower: tillite; 2,500	Talchir tillite

Numbers represent thicknesses, in feet. In the Union of South Africa the thicknesses are approximate maxima, in part in the Cape geosyncline.

similar and lie unconformably on broad Pre-cambrian platforms. In all three regions continental faunas or floras, or both, range through the Permian and Triassic, at least. In all three regions thick lavas are present, which appear to be latest Triassic or Jurassic in age, though in India they are high in the Upper Gondwanas and probably very late Jurassic.

A hypothetical African-Indian land bridge might have skirted the northwest side of the Indian Ocean and included the Arabian Precambrian platform, but an African-American bridge would necessarily have extended across what is now the deep Atlantic. The appearance and disappearance of such a bridge seems incompatible with isostatic equilibrium, a principle well established in physical geology. A second defect of the land-bridge hypothesis appears when one attempts to explain the widespread tillites, which are probably interbedded with the marine Upper Carboniferous in South America and India as well as in Southwest Africa and Australia. Antarctica is also to be included, as tillites and an overlying *Glossopteris* flora have recently been found there (Ref. 16). The principal areas of glaciation were not just mountain valleys but were widespread and close to sea level. If one thinks of the continents as fixed in their present positions with respect to the earth's poles throughout their geological history, the Late Carboniferous glaciation extended from the South Pole to and beyond the equator (in India) at a time when the plants of the coal swamps flourished almost to the North Pole (in Spitsbergen) and northern regions were unglaciated.

c. The Hypothesis of Continental Drift

The distribution of glaciated areas might be improved by a shift of the poles. The best position for the South Pole seems to be halfway between Antarctica and Madagascar, but the glaciated regions of South America, India, and eastern Australia would still be within 10° of the equator. Considerations such as these have led to the formulation of another hypoth-esis, that of continental drift, proposed independently at least three times—first in the nineteenth century, second by the American F. B. Taylor in 1910, and third, in a greatly elaborated form, by the German Alfred Wegener in 1911, 1915, and later years. According to this hypothesis the Indian and South Atlantic Oceans were produced by the drifting apart of the continents that now surround them. Wegener proposed a complete geologic history of drift for all the continents, largely concentrated in Cenozoic time. This history proved to be incompatible with non-marine paleontology. Most Cenozoic land mammals are related to those that live in the same biological realm today. At present the northern continents make up one biologically homogeneous realm, **Holarctica,** to which Africa and tropical Asia are appendages. South and Central America make up a second realm, **Neogaea,** and New Guinea and Australia a third, **Notogaea.** The northwestern boundary of Notogaea winds through the East Indies; it is called Wallace's line because it was established by Alfred Russel Wallace in the course of his codiscovery with Darwin of the evidence for organic evolution. The fossil non-marine faunas of Australia, Africa, and South America, insofar as they are known (the Australian faunas are meager), are dissimilar as far back as the Cretaceous. These paleontological contrasts brought the Wegener drift hypothesis into disrepute among northern geologists, but it was accepted by most South American geologists and by many in other southern regions. In the late nineteen-fifties general interest in a drift hypothesis with a timetable different from Wegener's was aroused by new paleomagnetic data.

13-2. Paleomagnetism and Continental Drift

The earth is at present a magnetic dipole, with the field represented in Figure 13-3. The dipole axis (geomagnetic axis) is inclined 11.5° to the axis of rotation, with a north pole off the northwest coast of Greenland. Since

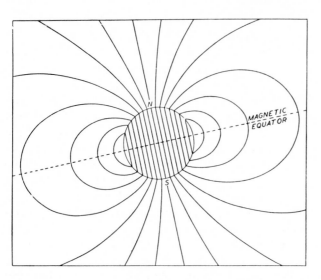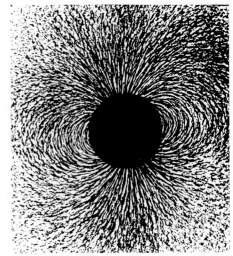

Fig. 13-3. *Lines of force of geomagnetic dipole. (From Sydney Chapman and Julius Bartels,* Geomagnetism, *Clarendon Press, Oxford, 1940.)*
LEFT. *Calculated.*
RIGHT. *Shown by iron filings in a magnetic field.*

there is also a complex non-dipole field of less intensity, the actual conditions are somewhat irregular. In the nineteen-sixties the north magnetic pole is near latitude 75° N., longitude 101° W., in the archipelago north of Canada, and the south magnetic pole is near latitude 70° S., longitude 148° E., at the edge of Antarctica, 1,300 miles from the point antipodal to the north magnetic pole. Lines of force, which are parallel to the earth's surface at the magnetic equator, become vertical at the magnetic pole. The actual magnetic poles have moved many degrees in the last few hundred years, if we may judge from the behavior of magnetic needles in such places as London, but no evidence has yet attested to historical movement of the dipole axis. If it does move, its mean position may be the axis of rotation.

At a particular place on the earth's surface the magnetic field tends to produce a characteristic orientation of a magnetic needle or other more or less free magnetic unit. The orientation is defined by a horizontal angle to geographic north, such as N. 10° E. or N. 30° W., which is called the **declination,** and an angle to the horizontal that is called the **inclination.** Inclination varies from 0° at the

magnetic equator to 90° at a magnetic pole. There is also a fairly regular distribution of magnetic intensity, which is more than twice as great at a pole as at the equator.

a. Paleomagnetism

Paleomagnetism is the magnetism of past times. It is known from the weak **remanent** (or permanent) **magnetism** that has persisted in some rocks. Since 1906 the orientations of the remanent magnetism of many lavas, red sandstones, and other rocks have been investigated. Since 1938, and especially since 1958, new instruments and improved laboratory procedures have made possible numerous fairly precise determinations.

The principal minerals that are significant in paleomagnetic determinations are magnetite (Fe_3O_4) in volcanic rocks and hematite (Fe_2O_3) in sedimentary rocks. The rocks, at their times of formation, became weakly magnetized, either by the rotation of magnetic grains into alignment with the earth's field, during sedimentation, or by preferred original alignment of newly formed grains, especially in igneous rocks, but probably also in hematite **formed in continental sediments soon after** their deposition. Even if the earth's field has later shifted or the continents have changed their positions, the weak but stable remanent magnetism can be ascertained.

Post-Eocene lavas and other rocks have been found to have magnetic orientations indicative of a magnetic dipole with an axis approximately the same as the present geographic axis. Pre-Cenozoic rocks, however, have different magnetic orientations.

After completion of a paleomagnetic study of, say, the Arizona Supai formation of Permian age, one may, assuming that the Permian magnetic field was that of a dipole, calculate the position of a *virtual* (or apparent) geomagnetic pole. The calculations are based on the mean orientation of the remanent magnetism in the Supai formation, as expressed by inclination and by declination with respect to the present geographic pole. The resulting virtual pole, in eastern Asia 50° from the present geographic North Pole, is shown in Figure 13-4 by the empty square labeled 53.

The other spot symbols (circles, squares, etc.) of Figure 13-4 represent virtual poles indicated by other formations in several continents. They are widely scattered and do not give a single position for the Permian pole. Each is merely the virtual pole derived from the study of one local formation. Note, however, that the virtual poles derived from the formations of a single continent are close together. The relations between virtual poles and the continents to which they pertain are most easily seen if the coordinates of the poles (as given, for example, in Ref. 9) are plotted on the National Geographic 16-inch or other erasable globe, but the plane projections of Figure 13-4 are moderately satisfactory.

b. Reversal of Poles

If a magnetic needle hangs free in the earth's present field, its south pole points north. Such an orientation is called normal. Paleomagnetic orientations, however, are likely to be reversed. Almost all the Permian orientations (Fig. 13-4) are reversed (open symbols). In the Triassic (Fig. 13-5), half of the orientations are normal (closed symbols), two are

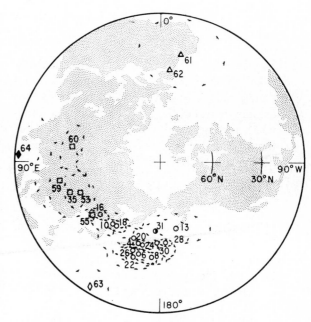

Fig. 13-4. *Virtual poles of Permian formations. Stippled: present positions of continents. Circles: poles of European formations; squares: North American; triangles: Australian; rhombs: African. Solid symbols: normal polarity; empty symbols: reversed polarity. (From Ref. 9.)*

Fig. 13-5. *Virtual poles of Triassic formations. (Same conventions and source as for Fig. 13-4.)*

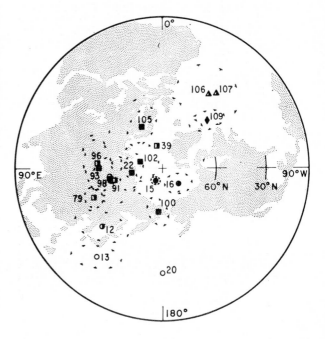

reversed, and the remaining formations provide examples of both reversed and normal orientation. Reversed remanent magnetism may be attributed to mineralogical causes in some rocks, but the preponderance of evidence, especially in the Pleistocene, indicates actual reversal of the earth's polarity—a somewhat startling conclusion that is important for theories of the origin of the earth's magnetic field, a subject beyond the scope of this book.

c. Precision of Paleomagnetic Determinations

The virtual pole of the Supai formation, No. 53 in Figure 13-4, was derived from the mean of many determinations of remanent declinations and inclinations. An oval of 95-percent confidence, calculated from the scatter in these determinations, is shown by a dashed line in the figure. The chances are 95 to 5 that an independent set of data would yield a mean that would plot inside this oval.

Most of the confidence ovals in Figures 13-4 and 13-5 are small, and the scatter of means for any one continent and period is, in the main, also small. The fourteen European circles of Figure 13-4, however, include four (Nos. 10, 13, 16, and 18) that are considerably northwest or northeast of the main group. These four formations are in the Esterel region of southeastern France and were involved in the mid-Cenozoic Alpine folding. Their orientations may not have been properly corrected for the effects of that unusually great deformation. (Additional paleomagnetic studies in the Pyrenees and Alps, made since Fig. 13-4 was prepared, show even greater scatter.) The remaining ten virtual Permian poles of the European group are close together in the North Pacific southwest of Bering Strait, in an oval 20° in maximum diameter, centered near latitude 43° N., longitude 170° E. The scatter is greater when all fourteen sets of European determinations are included, but the estimated mean for the continent and period is almost the same. The five virtual poles based on data from North American Permian formations (the squares of Fig. 13-4) are in eastern or central

Asia, within a triangle centered in western China near latitude 35° N., longitude 100° E. Only two sets of Permian determinations for Australia are available (the triangles of Fig. 13-4), but they are close together and probably structurally reliable, yielding a virtual north pole at the northwestern corner of Africa, close to latitude 33° N., longitude 9° W., and a virtual south pole northwest of New Zealand. Two sets of Kenya (East African) determinations, one Upper Permian, the other Lower Permian, can hardly be used because their poles (the marginal rhombs of Fig. 13-4) are far apart. Both Kenya localities are close to the Indian Ocean, far from the main bodies of the African Permian. More must be learned about the Kenya area and about late Paleozoic magnetic orientations elsewhere in Africa before the Kenya anomalies can be evaluated.

d. Paleomagnetic Data Bearing on Continental Drift

The virtual Permian magnetic poles of Figure 13-4 are all 40° or more from the present poles, and their longitudes are distributed through more than 180°, from the northwestern African poles based on Australian localities to the eastern Asiatic poles based on North American localities and the northwestern Pacific poles based on European localities. A wandering pole is not by itself an adequate explanation. Apparently the continents must have moved in relation to one another. Continental drift—each continent drifting on its own course with respect to the main mass of the earth and the poles of rotation remaining stationary—may be the whole explanation. If the continents have drifted, however, they have probably been propelled by deep internal currents that involved large portions of the earth's substance. Any such movements would probably be accompanied by at least some change in the positions of the magnetic and rotational axes.

Unfortunately, paleomagnetic data by themselves do not fix exactly the amount of possible continental drift. If no drift had occurred, the Permian poles for all the continents would coincide, and the single position for the Permian north pole would show the amount by which the pole had been displaced, with respect to all the continents, since Permian time. But, if we are forced to take relative continental displacement into account, the paleomagnetic data, by their very nature, become ambiguous. The Permian magnetic latitude of a Permian formation is determined by the paleomagnetic inclination. An inclination of 80° for a Permian formation north of Sydney, Australia, for example, yields, through the use of an appropriate formula, an angular distance of 19° to a Permian pole (Fig. 13-6). The rotation that has apparently occurred since the Permian is measured by the paleomagnetic declination (70° in the figure). The longitude, however, is not determinable from magnetic data. Longitudes are relative, and in the case under consideration we have nothing to refer to. We find this out if we move the virtual pole from the vicinity of New Zealand to its proper place at the geographic South Pole and take Australia along. The formation north of Sydney would then be 19° from the geographic South Pole, at some point on the parallel of latitude 71° S. (the dashed curve in the figure). The formation might be at longitude 151° E., directly south of its present position, as marked in the figure by a dotted meridian and by the dashed outline of Australia. This position was chosen according to the rule of minimum displacement, one expression of the rule of simplicity (§ 2-10), but the presence of another continent or some other geographical or geological reason might justify moving the formation—and Australia—to another longitudinal position.

e. A Paleomagnetically Controlled Drift Hypothesis

Paleomagnetic data are now dominant factors in any consideration of possible drift, but a satisfactory hypothesis must also take account of geographic and geologic evidence. Wegener and the other early drifters were impressed especially by the matching geography and geology on the two sides of the

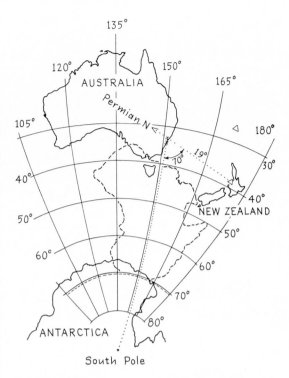

Fig. 13-6. *Virtual poles (triangles) of two Australian Permian formations, whose locations are marked by x's, with the observed angle of declination and the calculated polar distance (19°) for the more northern formation. A possible Permian position for Australia is shown in dashed outline.*

South Atlantic. Geographically, the sinuous east and west sides of this ocean are closely parallel, and the Mid-Atlantic Ridge, marked by the Azores and other volcanic islands, is similarly sinuous. Geologically, the Precambrian shields on both sides are overlain by Gondwana sequences. Now, with the paleomagnetic data for the successive periods as guides and restrainers, one can devise a historical hypothesis involving drift and including, with varying degrees of assurance, not only Africa and South America, but the other continents as well. One begins with the simplest possibility: the minimum continental displacements required by the geomagnetic poles calculated under the dipole assumption and illustrated in Figures 13-4 and 13-5. Two diagrams of the post-Carboniferous displacements (Fig. 13-7 for the southern units and Fig. 13-8 for the whole world) illustrate, in different ways, attempts to harmonize the varied evidence. In Figure 13-7 all the southern continents are gathered together in a Gondwanaland enveloping the Carboniferous South Pole. The partition of the supercontinent into the present continents (and the Indian subcontinent) is shown, as well as the break-up and the routes to the present continental positions. In Figure 13-8 the successive positions of central points in all the continents except Asia (represented by the Indian subcontinent) are shown more precisely. Since paleomagnetic data on the pre-Cretaceous rocks of peninsular India are lacking, the inclusion of that unit in the Carboniferous super-

Fig. 13-7. *Reconstruction of the Gondwana lands in Late Carboniferous time, according to Reinhard Maack (Ref. 12). Stippled: marine transgressions; arrows: later movements, mostly toward the north.*

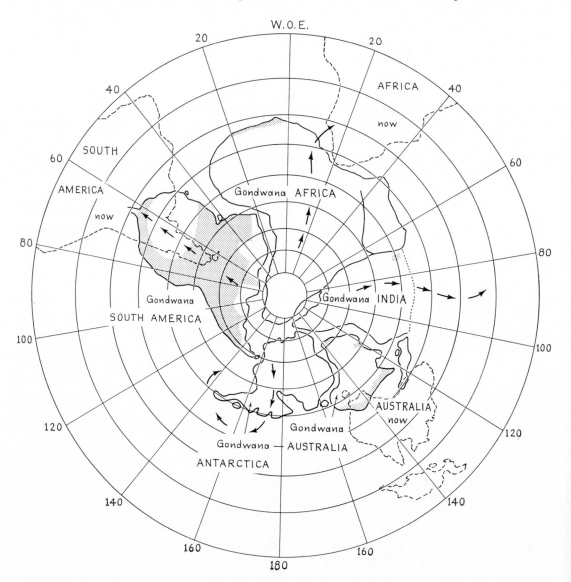

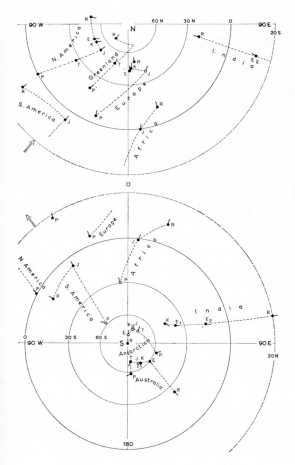

Fig. 13-8. *Postulated drift of continents, shown by the changes in position of the virtual pole of a central point in each continent, in stereographic projections of hemispheres having an overlap of 20°. Solid symbols are based on paleomagnetic data; tails point north. P, Permian; T, Triassic; J, Jurassic; K, Cretaceous; E, Eocene; R, present. (Adapted from Ref. 13.)*

supercontinent surrounding the South Pole, places its fragmentation in the Permian and Triassic, and puts in the Mesozoic the greater part of the drift to present positions by South America, North America, Africa, and Europe-Siberia. This timetable must now be tested at critical points by development of the late Paleozoic and early Mesozoic stratigraphic syntheses implied by the hypothesis and by comparison of the climatic and other characteristics of the syntheses with those appropriate to the postulated geographic positions of the continents. If we find discrepancies, we must consider the possibility that the Paleozoic and Mesozoic magnetic fields had nondipole components as great as, or greater than, those of today.

13-3. *Stratigraphic Tests of the Drift Hypothesis*

We can test the continental migrations suggested in Figures 13-7 and 13-8 by their paleoclimatological, paleontological, structural, and lithologic implications. The tests are especially fruitful when applied to the Gondwana rock sequences, for which the most useful standard is the Karroo "System" of South Africa.

a. *Karroo "System" of South Africa*

The main divisions of the Karroo are listed in Table 13-1, and a map of the Karroo outcrops is given in Figure 13-9. The Karroo rocks, originally, probably covered at least two-thirds of southern Africa. Their principal development is in an area lying northeast of the Cape of Good Hope and including both the east-west geosynclinal Cape folded belt and, north of the folded belt, the Karroo Basin at the southern edge of the African continental platform (horizontal strata of Figs. 13-10 and 13-11). The Karroo sequence is thickest at the south (column A of Fig. 13-9, in the northern part of the Cape geosyncline, and column B, in the Karroo Basin). The four divisions of the Karroo are separated primarily on lithologic grounds. The Dwyka series, at the base, is characterized by gray boulder clay

continent is justified only by its Gondwana geology. Paleomagnetic data place the Indian peninsula far south in the southern hemisphere during the Cretaceous and early Cenozoic (Fig. 13-8), probably not even close to the Tethyan east-west geosyncline that included northern India.

This new Gondwana hypothesis, based chiefly on consistent, recently published paleomagnetic data, begins with a Carboniferous

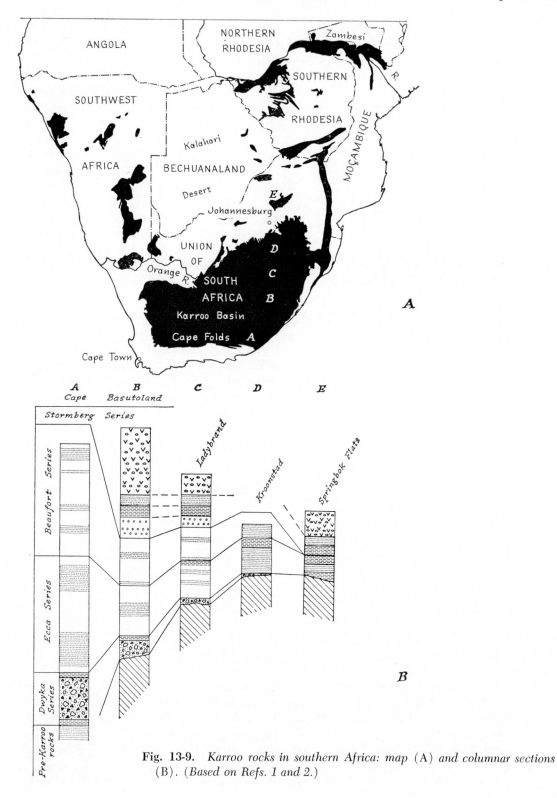

Fig. 13-9. *Karroo rocks in southern Africa: map* (A) *and columnar sections* (B). (*Based on Refs. 1 and 2.*)

Fig. 13-10. *Flat-lying Beaufort shale and sandstone in the east-west-trending, south-facing Nieuwveld escarpment west of Beaufort West, Cape Province, South Africa. (Photograph by J. H. Wellington, Johannesburg; courtesy of L. C. King, Durban, Natal.)*

Fig. 13-11. *Outlier of Beaufort shale and sandstone, capped by a basaltic sill, near Graaf-Reinet, east of Beaufort West, Cape Province, South Africa; looking southeast toward the Great Karroo Basin. (Photograph by J. H: Wellington, courtesy of L. C. King.)*

and shale, the Ecca by thick gray shale units and workable coal seams, the Beaufort by red and purple shales interbedded with light-colored sandstones, and the Stormberg by a fourfold sequence, from glittering white sandstone at the base, through red beds and gray sandstone to (at the top) thick basaltic lava flows (Fig. 13-9, column B).

In the geosyncline the Dwyka boulder clay (tillite), shale, and sandstone are 3,500 feet thick in some places, the overlying Ecca shale and sandstone are 10,000 or more feet thick, and the Beaufort variegated sandstone and shale series—source of hundreds of species of reptiles—is 8,000 feet thick. These lower divisions of the Karroo thin rapidly to the north, as shown in Figure 13-9, and the Dwyka and Beaufort disappear, so that in the north only the Ecca shales and the Stormberg sediments and volcanics make up the Karroo, or Gondwana, sequence. The Stormberg is very thick in the Basutoland portion of the Karroo Basin (column B), having 4,400 feet of sediments topped by 4,500 feet or more of basaltic lava. The Stormberg sediments are composed of the debris of the mountains formed by the Cape folding; they thin rapidly northward, and they become finer-grained in that direction. Probably the coarse debris of the thick Dwyka tillite of the geosyncline was derived from still farther south. Part of the thin Dwyka ground moraine in columns C and D, however, appears to have been brought in from

the north and northeast, as indicated by the striations of the sub-morainal pavement (Fig. 13-2) and by the stoss-and-lee form of the roche-moutonnée ridges in the striated rock floor.

The Karroo fossils are important, both for correlation and as indicators of habitat. In the Union of South Africa they are probably all continental or fresh-water, but in Southwest Africa two marine faunas are present in the Dwyka. The Upper Dwyka White Band, a bituminous black shale that weathers white, contains a little swimming reptile, *Mesosaurus* (Fig. 13-12), at many places, both in the Union and in Southwest Africa near the Atlantic coast. In Southwest Africa the Dwyka tillite is interbedded with shale containing the ubiquitous southern Carboniferous-Permian marine clam *Eurydesma* (Fig. 13-13) and is overlain by a shale sequence several thousand feet thick, all included in the Dwyka series. This shale carries marine gastropods, crinoid stems, and an Upper Carboniferous kind of fish (Ref. 15) near the base, coaly beds with *Glossopteris* at a higher level, and *Mesosaurus* at the top.

The Ecca shales and coal carry the *Glossopteris* flora, which in Southern Rhodesia, as previously noted, is associated with European genera that are Early Permian or older (see the floras of Table 12-1). The Beaufort contains six large reptilian faunas (Table 13-1), which make possible the correlation of

Fig. 13-12. Mesosaurus brasiliensis, *Brazil. A very similar species occurs in the South African Karroo. (From J. H. McGregor, courtesy of the American Museum of Natural History.)*

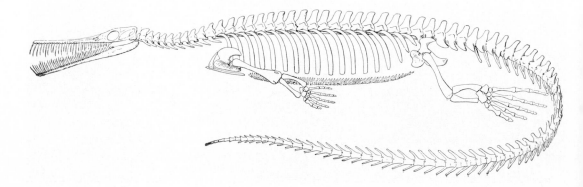

A   B   C

Fig. 13-13. Eurydesma playfordi, *a heavy-shelled pelecypod, from the Lower Permian of the Carnar-von Basin, Western Australia. (From J. M. Dickins, Geol. & Geophysics Bull. 41, Australian Bur. Min. Resources, 1957.)*
A. *Outside of a single valve, 50 mm high.*
B. *Edge view of a single valve, showing overhang of beak.*
C. *Side view of both valves.*

its lowest three faunal zones with the Upper Permian of Russia, of its fourth zone (Middle Beaufort) with the Lower Triassic of Russia, and of its fifth and sixth zones (Upper Beaufort) with northern-hemisphere Middle Triassic strata. In the Stormberg the lowest (Molteno) beds are barren, but the next two subdivisions (Red Beds and Cave Sandstone) carry Upper Triassic reptiles.

b. Comparison Between Karroo and South American Gondwanas

The stratigraphic and structural similarities between the Gondwana sequences and their geological environments in South Africa and South America are very striking, especially if the Gondwana sequence and structure in Southwest Africa, intermediate between those of South America and the Karroo Basin, are taken into account (Table 13-1 and Fig. 13-14). In the Paraná Basin of southern Brazil and adjacent countries, as in the Karroo Basin,

the Gondwana sequence begins with tillites, which are overlain successively by bituminous shale with *Mesosaurus*, shales and sandstones that in some areas carry the *Glossopteris* flora, varicolored sandstones and shales, white sandstones (clearly eolian in South America), and enormously thick and extensive lava flows near and at the top of the sequence. In southern Brazil and northern Uruguay, the tillites at and near the base of the sequence are overlain by and interbedded with banded siltstones and shales that are similar to those of the Pleistocene glacial sequence (§ 16-4.a).

The lithologic similarities between individual Karroo formations and the corresponding ones in South America are very close. The bituminous shales that carry *Mesosaurus* are alike in the two continents. The eolian Botucatú sandstone in Brazil is at least moderately close to the Cave Sandstone of Africa. The basaltic and other lavas at and near the tops of the sequences are alike on both sides of the

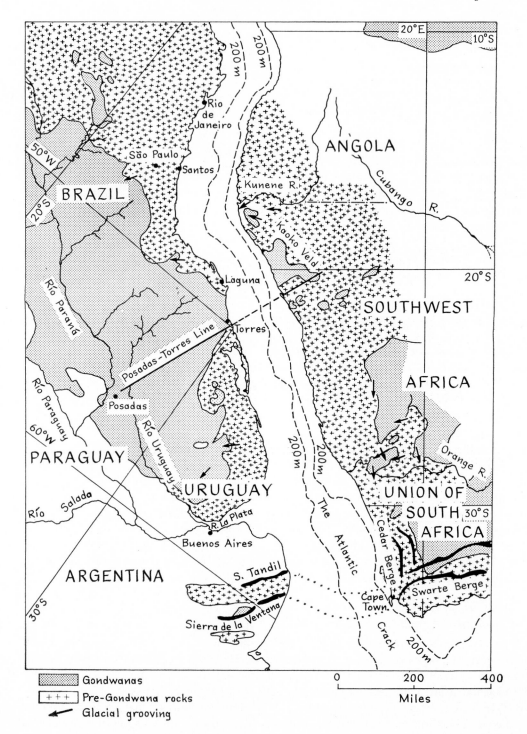

Fig. 13-14. *Fit between South American and South African Gondwana outcrops and structures; pattern of crosses: pre-Gondwana rocks. (After Reinhard Maack, Ref. 10, and Henno Martin, Ref. 5.)*

Atlantic. At other levels the variations between the continents are no greater than those within one continent.

Reptilian faunas are notable features of both the African and the South American sequences, but the large South American faunas apparently occur at Triassic horizons that are non-fossiliferous in South Africa. The Beaufort series, with its large Upper Permian–Middle Triassic faunas, is limited to the Karroo Basin and the Cape geosyncline; its reptiles are not known elsewhere in Africa or in South America. The Beaufort and its faunas are even missing from the northern part of the Union of South Africa (Fig. 13-9, column E) and from Southwest Africa (Table 13-1). If eastern South America and southwestern Africa are brought together (Fig. 13-14), the American area and the African Beaufort-free area fit nicely together. Both are northwest of a line connecting the river La Plata with the mouth of the Orange River. A principal South American source of Gondwana reptiles is the Middle or Upper Triassic Santa Maria formation of southern Brazil. The closest relatives of the Santa Maria reptiles are the moderately late Triassic forms of eastern Africa rather than those of the much nearer Middle Stormberg Red Beds (Upper Triassic) of the Karroo Basin. The Santa Maria red sandstone is therefore considered somewhat older than the Red Beds and is correlated with the barren Molteno white sandstone (Lower Stormberg) of the Karroo Basin (Table 13-1). Large reptilian faunas similar to those of the Santa Maria formation, and probably of about the same age, are found near Mendoza (Ref. 14), 1,500 miles southwest of southern Brazil, at the edge of the Argentinian Andes.

One of the most striking features shared by the African and South American Gondwanas is the *Mesosaurus* horizon, somewhat above the basal tillites. *Mesosaurus*, which occurs both as separated bones and as skeletons up to eighteen inches long, is known only in these areas; it does not even have close relatives elsewhere. In Africa it occurs in the White Band of the main Karroo area and also in shale or sandstone in two Karroo areas of Southwest Africa, one just north of the Orange River, the other much farther north in the Kaoko Veld (Fig. 13-14). In South America the Iratí bituminous shale, identical with the White Band and containing *Mesosaurus*, crops out all around the margin of the enormous Paraná Basin, in southern Brazil, Uruguay, Argentina, and Paraguay. The environment of *Mesosaurus* must be learned from its structure and associations. The form of the skeleton denotes a swimming animal. *Mesosaurus* is the only fossil in most occurrences, but a few crustaceans and insects have also been found in both the Karroo and the Paraná Basin. The insects are surely non-marine. Fossiliferous marine bands, however, occur close to or at the *Mesosaurus* horizon in the southwestern part of the Paraná Basin. Perhaps *Mesosaurus* was a surface swimmer of deep inland water bodies that had lifeless depths where bituminous mud accumulated. These water bodies may have been connected by one or more straits with a southern ocean, as the Black Sea is now connected with the Mediterranean. The lithology and distribution of the *Mesosaurus* strata are consistent with the hypothesis of two main bodies of fresh water, in the southern part of the main Karroo region and in the Paraná Basin. If the South Atlantic Ocean was a later development, the two basins may have been connected through bodies of fresh water in Southwest Africa. A barrier of some sort between the two main basins is indicated by slight differences between the *Mesosaurus* species of South Africa and that of Brazil, and by the assignment of the Paraná insects and crustaceans to different genera from those used for the Karroo forms (Ref. 5).

If Africa and South America are brought together on the 200-meter depth line, the Gondwana structures on the two sides of the Atlantic slot have the same trends and fit together surprisingly well. The rotation of South America shown in Figure 13-14 brings the gentle flexures and other structures of the South American Gondwanas into line with the African Gondwana structures that trend northeast all the way from Southwest Africa to the east African coast, northwest of a line that reaches the Atlantic at the mouth of the Orange River. A single example of these structures, called the Posadas-Torres line in South America, is marked on the figure. The Gondwana folds in eastern Argentina, south of the river La Plata, can be connected with the Cape folds in Africa. In the Cape folded belt, the Karroo overlies marine Devonian and other middle or early Paleozoic formations. Similar marine Devonian, with a similar fauna, occurs in a synclinal structure beneath the Gondwana beds of the Paraná Basin in Brazil and neighboring countries, but the Gondwana strata overlap eastward, hiding the Devonian.

The correspondence of Precambrian structures, when the two continents are brought

Fig. 13-15. *Fit between Precambrian structures of Africa and South America when the continents are brought together on the 2,000-meter depth line. (From Reinhard Pflug, NEUES JAHRBUCH FÜR GEOLOGIE UND PALÄONTOLOGIE, 1963.)*

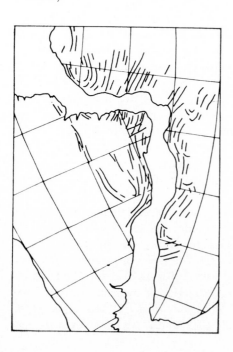

together on the 2,000-meter depth line, is shown in Figure 13-15. The structures compared are probably all those of early Precambrian rocks, unconformable beneath the horizontal Gondwana strata and some earlier Paleozoic rocks on both sides of the Atlantic. (The principal late Precambrian sedimentary series of east-central South Africa, described in § 9-3.a, do not extend to the west coast.) The Precambrian structures fit well from the mouth of the Amazon to latitude 30° S. in South America and the corresponding 20° S. in Africa. The structural swirl in Ghana and Liberia is continued on both sides of the Amazon. The Dahomey-Nigeria north-northeast trends are continued in the Brazilian bulge. From the Bight of Guinea south, the structures in both continents parallel the coast lines as far as latitude 20° S. in Africa. Farther south in Africa the Precambrian trend lines are varied and commonly almost perpendicular to the coast line; in South America the Precambrian is mostly hidden by younger rocks.

In both continents, the lowest Gondwana tillites lie on Precambrian crystalline rocks that were striated and deeply furrowed by glacial erosion. These features are well shown at five places in Uruguay and southern Brazil, including Itú, west of São Paulo, where the underlying rock is unweathered granite. Grooves and striations indicate ice movement from southeast to northwest. Glacially filled valleys in the Precambrian bedrock and structures in the glacial and fluvioglacial sediments point in the same general direction. In both the northern and the southern part of coastal Southwest Africa, numerous ridges, grooves, and striations in Precambrian bedrock beneath tillite indicate ice movements in directions varying from westward at the north to south-southeastward at the south. The composite picture for the juxtaposed continents, as shown by the arrows of Figure 13-14, is one of predominantly westward movement in both continents, perhaps from a single set of centers in the interior of Africa, previous to a separation of the African and South American continents. If late Carboniferous seas were as extensive in South America as the stippling of Figure 13-7 indicates, especially in the part of the continent closest to the pole, the tillites of eastern South America (un-stippled in the figure) must have been derived from local, Atlantic, or African sources. If they came from Africa, they might be expected to contain fragments of distinctive African rocks. Apparently they do. In particular, a violet quartzite that occurs in pre-Devonian formations in South-West Africa and South Africa seems to have representatives among the tillite boulders of southern Brazil. Mineralogically, texturally, and chemically, the boulders are like the supposed parent rock (Ref. 12).

The trans-Atlantic similarities between Gondwana rocks and fossils, pre-Gondwana rocks, Precambrian structures, glacial and other Gondwana structures, and post-Gondwana structures such as the Posadas-Torres Line seem to be about what one would expect if Africa and South America were parts of a single supercontinent up to the end of Gondwana time. Most of the supercontinent may have been undergoing erosion during most of the early and middle Paleozoic, but Gondwana continental sedimentation was widespread.

c. Drift and the Precambrian Iron Formation

The Precambrian iron formation (see § 9-3.b.3) is more similar to subtropical laterite than to any other sediment forming today. The presence of the iron formation at latitude 55° N., in Labrador, might be explained as the result of drift. The occurrences of the Precambrian iron formation in Brazil, South Africa, and Australia, however, at latitudes 20°–33° S., do not seem to call for much drift at any time. These southern lands are, nevertheless, just the ones that would be taken to the South Pole and back under the Gondwana drift hypothesis. Perhaps it would be simpler to consider the iron formation the product of weathering and deposition at a time or times when the climatic state was

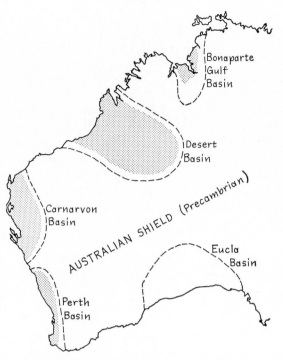

Fig. 13-16. *Structural map of the western part of Australia, showing Permian marine basin fillings (stippled). (After Kurt Teichert, Ref. 10.)*

quite different from what it is now; then drift might not have been necessary to bring the iron formation to Labrador.

13-4. An Australian Test of the Gondwana Hypothesis

Australia, unlike Africa, was partially covered by Permian epicontinental seas, which filled four marginal western and northwestern basins (Fig. 13-16). These basins may have been branches of a very narrow epicontinental marine belt crossing the supercontinent of Figure 13-7 or, more simply, branches of an Indian Ocean similar to the present one. If the latter explanation is the correct one, then, under the Gondwana hypothesis, Australia was separated from Africa at a very early date, long before the separation of Africa and South America.

a. Isolation of Australia

In its post-Gondwana history Australia has been the best example of a biologically isolated continent, and its isolation even continued after the recent arrival of the Bushmen. Some plants and animals came in from the north, but the biological changes were mostly climatically controlled. The unique Pleistocene and Recent flora is characterized by eucalyptus and acacia. In the Tertiary, the climate was warmer and more humid, and the forests were dominated by beech, conifers, and broad-leaved trees, which were somewhat more similar than the present dominant flora to the plants of northern continents. Today crocodiles are limited to northeastern Australia, but in the Pleistocene they lived much farther south, and in the Tertiary their range extended to the southern coast. Despite these floral and faunal changes, the normal eutherian mammals of northern lands (see Table 15-1, p. 398) seem never to have reached Australia and to have left the continent to more primitive egg-laying and marsupial (pouch-bearing) mammals such as the platypus and the kangaroo. The tropical cycads and some other cosmopolitan plants reached Australia in the early Mesozoic, but Mesozoic land reptiles of Karroo or any other type are almost unknown there; the very few fragmental reptilian remains are mostly dinosaurian (compare § 14-4.b.1). The Australian non-marine paleontological evidence is so scanty as to be inconclusive; it seems probable, nevertheless, that the land life of Australia was isolated from that of Africa and all the other continents almost continuously after the end of the Carboniferous-Permian ice ages, there being, during the Mesozoic, just enough connection with Asia to permit the incursion of such things as dinosaurs, crocodiles, marsupials, cycads, and flowering plants.

b. Paleomagnetic Data and the Floras

Careful paleomagnetic studies have recently been made of five eastern Australian tuffs and shallow intrusives (Ref. 17). The rocks are the Chocolate shales and Brisbane tuff (Triassic), the Gingenbullen dolerite (post-Triassic), and the Prospect and Tasmanian dolerites (Jurassic). Nearby poles are indicated, with small ovals of 95-percent confidence. The paleomagnetic data imply that Canberra, in southeastern Australia, was at latitude 68°–74° in Triassic and Jurassic times, with the pole very roughly in the present direction, some 60°–100° from the Permian direction (Fig. 13-6). The Triassic and Jurassic floras of eastern Australia, however, were probably all tropical or subtropical, in spite of the uncertainty of inferences based on floras lacking angiosperms and otherwise quite different from those of the present. A probably subtropical Triassic flora is found at about the latitude of Canberra; farther north by 7°–8°, in southeastern Queensland, at an indicated Triassic latitude of about 60°, the Triassic flora was probably tropical, for cycadophytes (compare Fig. 12-6) are abundant. The living cycadophytes are largely moist-tropical, but some of the Mesozoic forms, which have leaves with built-in protectors against water loss, may have been arid-subtropical.

Even if the uncertainties inherent in the use of extinct plants as guides to climate are taken into account, the Triassic floras of eastern Australia seem incompatible with the paleomagnetic data. Because of the tenor of the floral evidence, here and elsewhere, some paleobotanists have rejected all hypotheses of drift or polar migration. Such a rejection would not, of itself, solve the climatic problem. There would remain both the strange distribution of the *Glossopteris* flora, from latitude 85° S. to latitude 20° N., and the equally puzzling distribution of Gondwana glaciations.

Another treatment of the floral problem accepts very high Triassic and Jurassic latitudes for Australia and emphasizes the periodic warm climates that affected many parts of the world in the Paleozoic, Mesozoic, and early Cenozoic. The warm periods are indicated particularly by widespread tropical floras. One of the longer warm periods seems to have begun in the Triassic; cycadophytes may have flourished then within 30° of the geographic South Pole, almost at the Antarctic Circle. Under that hypothesis, however, it might be hard to explain the merely temperate Triassic floras found in high northern latitudes.

A third treatment accepts continental drift, approximate stability of the geographic poles, and minor non-dipolar elements in Paleozoic and Mesozoic magnetic orientations. We might even place a Triassic magnetic pole at latitude 70° S., south of eastern Australia, where it is now. By this rather special interpretation of the past in terms of the present, the Queensland cycadophyte flora would be placed at latitude 40°, or 13° south of its present position, and, considering the wide diffusion of Triassic warmth, not unreasonably close to the geographic South Pole.

One may test the last interpretation, to some extent, by taking into account all the paleomagnetic data for the Mesozoic of Australia. The inclinations seem to show that the latitude of Canberra varied somewhat erratically between 68° and 85° (Ref. 17; not greatly different from the implications of Fig. 13-8, based on earlier data); the pole direction varied, equally erratically, from southwest to south-southeast. These variations seem consistent with a stationary Mesozoic continent and a changing magnetic field. The concept is significantly different, however, from the model, based on historical records, that has commonly been used by the interpreters of paleomagnetic data. The historical changes in the orientation of the earth's magnetic field and in the probable positions of the magnetic poles seem to have been non-dipolar and to have been caused chiefly by erratic magnetic "noise." The changes have been rather rapid and should cancel out when periods greater than 10,000 years are considered. It is for this reason that most recent determinations of a formation's paleomagnetic orientation have been based on specimens from several horizons. Data from a single flow or from a single narrow intrusion are considered inadequate, but data from several flows or from a batholith that crystallized over a period of tens of thousands of years have been thought to eliminate the effects of non-dipolar or even cyclic dipolar wandering of the magnetic poles with respect to the pole of rotation. Now, perhaps, much longer periods of wandering should be taken into account.

13-5. *Holarctic Connections of Africa and South America*

If a south polar glaciated supercontinent existed in late Carboniferous time, its break-up and dispersal were rather rapid, so that by the Jurassic (Fig. 13-8) South America and Africa, perhaps still close together, had reached south temperate and equatorial latitudes. Africa, though it had been in a position to be widely glaciated during late Carboniferous time, was, from Middle Permian time on, in land communication with Russia and other parts of Holarctica, as shown by the way the reptiles got around. During the Cenozoic, South America was biologically isolated. A Neogaean mamalian fauna developed in its own way, becoming unlike the cosmopolitan faunas of Africa, Eurasia, and North America, though with occasional North American interchanges.

In the Paleozoic histories of the northern continents there is nothing as spectacular as the southern glaciation. A drift hypothesis, however, fits right in with some North Atlantic relationships. If Newfoundland and Britain were close neighbors in the Early Cambrian, the New Brunswick barrier (§ 10-1.c) really could have extended across Newfoundland and into Britain, separating a European province to the southeast from a North American province to the northwest. Such a barrier, short and wholly continental, is more credible than the trans-Atlantic facies boundary shown in Figure 10-1.

For the late Paleozoic, the North Atlantic "Old Red continent" becomes simpler and more compact if North America and northern Europe were closely joined. The similar fresh-

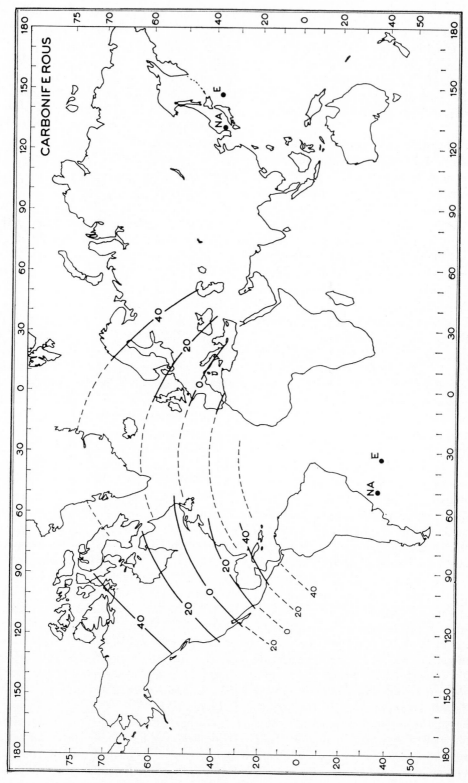

Fig. 13-17. *Carboniferous equator and parallels in North America and Europe, based on paleomagnetic data. (Adapted from D. van Hilten, Ref. 13.)*

water fishes (§ 11-6) and land plants (§ 12-6) are explained by the drift hypothesis, as are the lithologic similarities of some Devonian and almost all Carboniferous rocks. Figure 13-17 shows that the drift hypothesis places North America and Europe in the tropics, where vegetation is lush, at the time of coal-formation.

13-6. Significance of the Distribution of Evaporites

Cambrian and Ordovician evaporites are known from high latitudes, with gypsum in Arctic Canada and northeastern Greenland, only a few degrees from the North Pole, and Cambrian rock salt at latitude 70° N., in Siberia (Fig. 13-18). Today, however, in the northern hemisphere, where most of the land is, deposits of gypsum and rock salt are forming only in arid localities between the equator and 50° N.; the larger deposits are subtropical, being mostly between 20° and 35°. The far northern early Paleozoic evaporites may also have formed in subtropic latitudes, as indicated by certain paleomagnetic data, not given in this book.

The greatest of all known salt deposits are those of the Upper Permian, in Germany (52° N.) and in the western United States, notably in Kansas and New Mexico. According to the paleomagnetic implications of Figures 13-4 and 13-8, these salts were deposited in the subtropics, the German ones at 15°–20° N. and the American at 18°–35° S. Middle Pennsylvanian salts in Utah and Colorado were deposited at 5°–10° N., according to the generalized Carboniferous map of Figure 13-17. Silurian salt beds, now at 43° N. in Michigan and western New York (§ 6-2), may have had their origin, on rather doubtful paleomagnetic evidence, in the southern subtropics; and the Devonian salt beds of Saskatchewan, now at 50° N., may also have originated there.

No salt or gypsum deposits forming today are comparable in size to the great Paleozoic masses of salt and calcium sulphate. The

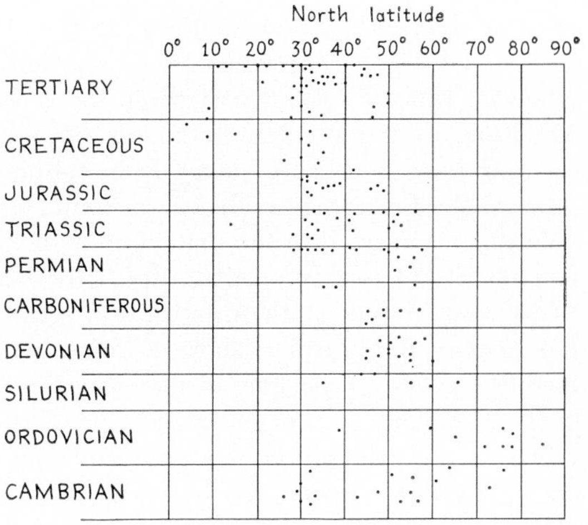

Fig. 13-18. *Evaporite deposits of the northern hemisphere, by age and latitude. (After Robert Green, Ref. 8.)*

Paleozoic evaporites probably formed through a dual system of water circulation: surface flow into the salt basin from the sea and deep flow of heavy brine back into the sea, giving the observed high proportions of anhydrite to rock salt in the Paleozoic evaporites. This difference from today's small evaporating basins would not, however, alter the requirements of aridity and strong solar heating, which are not likely to be attained at latitudes greater than 50°. Continental drift or wandering of the pole of rotation would help to explain the German and Saskatchewan salts and would be very nearly essential to an explanation of the Cambrian salts at 70° N. What is more, the detailed drift hypothesis of Figure 13-8, extended more doubtfully back to the beginning of the Paleozoic, seems to be consistent with almost all of the non-biological paleoclimatic data, as well as with the paleomagnetic data on which it was primarily based.

13-7. Historical Interpretation

a. The Gondwanaland Hypothesis

In this chapter we have considered a hypothesis of first importance. It now appears possible that two or more southern continents were joined in a late Paleozoic Gondwanaland that broke up rather rapidly in the early Mesozoic, as the present continents became separate units and drifted away from one another. The favorable evidence is found in paleomagnetism and in the matching of rocks and structures across oceans, especially between east-central South America and southern Africa (Fig. 13-14). There is some conflicting evidence, especially in the fossil floras of the Mesozoic. Paleomagnetic inferences are based on the assumption of a dominant magnetic dipole throughout the pertinent part of geologic history; this assumption is probably not entirely justified. What is more, the differentiation between the paleomagnetic effects of continental drift and those of a wandering of the magnetic poles has not yet been satisfactorily worked out. When the roles of wandering magnetic poles and changes in position of the earth's axis of rotation have been established, some difficulties may develop in connection with the earth's apparent rigidity. If some continents drifted away from one another, they were probably propelled by subcrustal convection currents. Such currents may have risen beneath the Mid-Atlantic Ridge and separated right and left to drive the New and Old Worlds to their present distances from each other. The origins and mechanisms of such enormous currents present difficult geophysical problems.

At present, if the varied and somewhat scanty data bearing on continental drift in general, and on the South Atlantic separation in particular, are all taken into account, only a tentative conclusion can be reached. Radiometric age data for the Precambrian of South America are almost wholly lacking, and paleomagnetic data for Africa are inadequate. These gaps in the evidence will probably be filled by 1970. A few score man-years of geologic mapping along the shores of southern Brazil and Southwest Africa, followed by thorough laboratory study of the rocks, may provide lithologic and structural evidence that will pass statistical tests. If the present suggestions of a Gondwana union between South America and southern Africa are confirmed, the possibility of continental drift will, of course, be settled, and the remaining problems will be of secondary importance.

b. The Complex Set of Late Paleozoic Events

The events of the late Paleozoic—mountain-making, granitic intrusion, continental emergence, deposition of evaporites and coal, and extinction of marine invertebrates—may have been related. Their chronology is nevertheless somewhat puzzling. One must distinguish sharply between two features of the physical history, one represented by unconformities, the other by lacunas in the sedimentary record. The principal unconformities in the geosynclines are records of folding, erosion, and the unconformable covering of earlier accumulations of sediments and volcanic rocks by new deposits. The lacunas on the continental platforms are evidence of the withdrawal of the seas, which was commonly followed by very slight erosion, and succeeded, often after a long interval, by further deposition. The platform unconformities, where they really exist, are sometimes discovered after the recognition of lacunas based on paleontological evidence.

The Carboniferous–Triassic orogenic belts, all marked by sharp folding and some by plutonism, are shown, along with the earlier Paleozoic Caledonian belts, in Figure 13-19. Late Paleozoic deformation began in the geosynclines in the Late Devonian and was probably almost ended in most places by mid-Permian time. In Britain and Norway, the type Caledonian belt was slightly reactivated after Carboniferous deposition, with a new and roughly parallel belt on its southeast side (not shown in the figure) marked by the line of English coal basins from Bristol north. The most celebrated late Paleozoic orogenic belts are the Appalachian (post-Pennsylvanian, perhaps late Permian or post-Permian), the central European (from mid-Carboniferous to mid-Permian), the Ural (Late Permian),

Fig. 13-19.   *Mid-Paleozoic (Caledonian) and Carboniferous–Triassic folded belts of the world. (After J. H. F. Umbgrove, 1947; from Ref. 1.)*

the Tasman, or East Australian (Late Carboniferous and Early Permian), and the Cape (mid-Triassic, post-Beaufort and pre-Stormberg; about the same age in eastern Argentina: Fig. 13-14). In Figure 13-19 the projection distorts Australia, where the Tasman folding has nearly north-south trends, and exaggerates the present separation of the Cape and South American folds that are connected in Figure 13-14. In general, the epicontinental seas disappeared from the platforms at about the same times that the geosynclinal belts became flooded and emergent, but the contemporaneity was rarely exact, and in South Africa the retreat of the sea, which occurred in the Devonian and involved only a small geosynclinal area anyway, long preceded the Cape folding. Considering the whole world, we see that the withdrawal of the seas from the continental platforms became marked at the beginning of Pennsylvanian time and was practically complete before the end of the Permian.

Several outstanding groups of shallow-water marine animals became extinct at the end of the Paleozoic. The great group of trilobites, which furnished the Cambrian guide fossils, shrank to a few genera after the end of the Devonian and disappeared completely at the end of the Permian. The rugose corals flourished from the Ordovician to the Permian; their most typical forms, the thick-walled, horn-shaped, solitary corals, were especially abundant in the Carboniferous and Permian; at the end of the Permian all rugose corals disappeared. Among the echinoderms, the camerate crinoids reached their peak in the American Mississippian but came to an end with the Permian, as did the bud-like blastoids and the Paleozoic groups of globular echinoids with more than ten rows of skeletal plates. Many large groups of brachiopods, including the typically Permian productids, did not survive the end of that period. Fusuline foraminifers, another leading Permian group, went out when the Triassic began. Finally, the Paleozoic goniatitic ammonoids were succeeded by the Triassic ceratites, and this change has been made the definition of the Permian-Triassic boundary. (This rule works well, in the main, though a very few goniatite and ceratite species transgress any boundary that can be drawn.) Though many great groups disappeared, almost at the same horizon, only a few new groups developed. As a result, the Lower Triassic marine faunas are made up of few species, with little variety. The change in marine organisms was not paralleled on land. Some insects, including the notable ones with two-foot wing spread, disappeared, but the dominant reptile groups survived into the Mesozoic with only moderate evolutionary changes.

One wonders in what ways the extraordinary events of the late Paleozoic were related. One element in the problem is the lack of exact contemporaneity. The principal evaporites in Europe and North America were Late Permian, considerably later than the northern coal measures or the southern glaciations. Even the latter may not have been exactly

contemporaneous with one another. Most northern coal measures were Pennsylvanian; some Australian glaciations were Permian, and all the southern glaciations may have been latest Pennsylvanian or Permian—a little late for most of the northern coals. The known differences in age and the remaining uncertainties in correlation make any simple interpretation in terms of climatic zones misleading. A second difficulty in such interpretation is the one-sided character of the zoning; there are, in particular, no northern glaciations to match those of the south.

Under the drift hypothesis, some of the difficulties disappear. There was no late Paleozoic glaciation around the North Pole because the northern hemisphere lacked high-latitude continental protuberances. The European and American Upper Carboniferous coals accumulated close to the equator, with the contemporaneous salt deposits subtropical, though they are now in Utah and Colorado (Fig. 13-18). In the Late Permian, after some drift toward the south by North America, not shared by Europe, German salts formed in the subtropics at 20° N., New Mexico and Kansas salts in the subtropics at 20° S.

The other late Paleozoic events may also be fitted into a drift hypothesis, with varying degrees of probability. The drifting apart of the Gondwana fragments may have been caused by the same deep-seated rearrangements of the earth's substance that caused basins to form, wrinkled geosynclinal belts into mountain ranges, and (somehow) caused the retreat of epicontinental seas. The gradual disappearance of shallow seas may have been disastrous for some forms of shallow-water marine life, and the broadened continental expanses may at first have favored the formation of tropical coal swamps and then, when the epicontinental seas had become greatly restricted, have favored an aridity and a circulation of concentrated and normal sea water that made possible the local accumulation of thick deposits of salt and anhydrite in subtropical regions. The increases in the sizes of the emergent continental expanses may even have led to broad snowfields at high (southern) latitudes, loss of heat from the earth by reflection of sunlight, and glaciation.

The uncertainty about continental drift can probably be endured by most people rather easily. For those closely concerned, the situation is a stimulating one that adds zest to the reading of pertinent periodicals and new books. Something decisive may appear at any time.

PROBLEM

Outline the geologic history of southern Africa in tabular form, beginning with the earliest Precambrian. Make use of the following summary statements, in addition to what has previously been given: some strips of marginal marine Cretaceous and Cenozoic sediments exist, but they are narrow and discontinuous; the central Kalahari Desert is covered by a thin mantle of non-marine Cenozoic deposits. What significance does the pre-Karroo history of Africa have for one's ideas about subcrustal movements of the earth's substance? What limitations, if any, does it put on eustatic changes of sea level? Has southern Africa, since Karroo time, risen with respect to sea level, sunk, remained constant, or oscillated? Is there any African evidence that oceanic areas have either increased or decreased during geologic time? Is there any suggestion that southern Africa may have been the central part of Gondwanaland?

REFERENCES

1. Bernhard Kummel: *History of the Earth,* Chap. 11 (Freeman, San Francisco, 1961)

2. A. L. du Toit: *The Geology of South Africa,* 3rd ed. (Oliver & Boyd, Edinburgh, 1954)

3. A. L. du Toit: *A Geological Comparison of South America with South Africa* (Carnegie Institution of Washington, 1927)

4. S. H. Haughton: *Gondwanaland and the Distribution of Early Reptiles,* Annexure, vol. 56, Geol. Soc. South Africa, 30 pages (1953)

5. Henno Martin: *The Hypothesis of Continental Drift in the Light of Recent Advances of Geological Knowledge in Brazil and in South West Africa,* Annexure, vol. 64, Geol. Soc. South Africa, 47 pages (1961)

6. A. L. Wegener: *The Origin of Continents and Oceans,* translation of 3rd ed. (Methuen, London, 1924)

7. S. K. Runcorn (editor): *Continental Drift* (Academic Press, New York, 1962)

8. A. E. M. Nairn (editor): *Descriptive Palaeoclimatology* (Interscience Publishers, New York, 1961); reviewed by A. G. Fischer, AM. JOUR. SCI., vol. 261, pp. 282–293 (1963)

9. Allan Cox and R. R. Doell: "Review of Paleomagnetism," BULLETIN, Geol. Soc. Am., vol. 71, pp. 645–768 (1960)

10. C. Teichert (editor): *Symposium sur les Séries de Gondwana* (19th Int. Geol. Cong., Algiers, 1952)

11. Comisión para la Correlación del Sistema Karroo (Gondwana), 20th Int. Geol. Cong., Mexico City, 256 pages (1958)

12. Reinhard Maack: "Zur Paläogeographie des Gondwanalandes," Report, 21st Int. Geol. Cong. (1960), Part 12, pp. 35–55

13. D. van Hilten: "Presentation of Paleomagnetic Data, Polar Wandering, and Continental Drift," AM. JOUR. SCI., vol. 260, pp. 401–426 (1962); discussed by G. W. Bain and E. R. Deutsch, vol. 261, pp. 186–200 (1963)

14. A. S. Romer: "Vertebrate-bearing Continental Triassic Strata in Mendoza Region, Argentina," BULLETIN, Geol. Soc. Am., vol. 71, pp. 1279–1294 (1960)

15. B. G. Gardiner: "*Namaichthys schroederi* Gürich and Other Palaeozoic Fishes from South Africa," PALAEONTOLOGY, vol. 5, pp. 9–21 (1962)

16. G. A. Doumani and W. E. Long: "The Ancient Life of the Antarctic," SCIENTIFIC AMERICAN, September 1962, pp. 169–184

17. E. Irving, W. A. Robertson, and P. M. Stott: "The Significance of the Palaeomagnetic Results from Mesozoic Rocks in Eastern Australia," JOUR. GEOPHYSICAL RESEARCH, vol. 68, pp. 2313–2317 (1963)

18. D. I. Axelrod: "Fossil floras suggest stable, not drifting, continents," JOUR. GEOPHYSICAL RESEARCH, vol. 68, pp. 3257–3263 (1963)

19. E. Irving: *Paleomagnetism and its Application to Geological and Geophysical Problems* (Wiley, New York, 1964)

CHAPTER 14

The Reptilian Heyday

THE FOUR-LIMBED vertebrates, or tetrapods, began modestly during the late Paleozoic and then, in the Mesozoic and Cenozoic, went through two tremendous outbursts during which highly varied forms developed, adapted to almost every possible way of life on the land, in the sea, and in the air. The first outburst, in the Mesozoic, was made up almost entirely of reptiles; the second, in the Cenozoic, of mammals and birds. In this chapter we shall consider the first outburst. We give our primary attention to the enormous variety of the Mesozoic reptiles and then take note of the beginnings of the birds and mammals, for both groups appeared in the mid-Mesozoic.

14-1. *Introduction*

The Mesozoic reptiles far surpassed in variety and interest the few survivors that live today. The list at the end of the chapter classifies the principal reptilian groups. Five subclasses and sixteen orders are distinguished. Only four orders have living representatives. But even this contrast does not adequately indicate the great difference between the Jurassic and Cretaceous reptilian faunas and that of the present. The Mesozoic reptiles were of all sizes, including the largest of land animals. They occupied almost every possible ecologic niche and were obviously the dominant animals of the time. In contrast, the turtles, snakes, lizards, crocodiles, and little New Zealand tuatera, the single living member of the Rhynchocephalia, are almost all obscure animals with positions in the economy of nature that are not very important or exhilarating compared with those of the mammals and the birds. One of the most striking things about the whole Mesozoic development of the reptiles is the increasing vigor and variety of most reptilian groups right up to the end of the Cretaceous and then the sudden disappearance of the outstanding groups before the Cenozoic began.

The heavy-bodied labyrinthodont (stegocephalian) amphibians, which had been surpassed in number and variety by similar heavy-bodied primitive reptiles during the Permian, were completely outclassed by the new types of reptiles that appeared during the Triassic and at the beginning of the Jurassic. The labyrinthodont group disappeared completely at the end of the Triassic, and amphibians have been unimportant ever since. The post-Triassic amphibians have been retiring types; most have been members of the two groups that include the frog and the salamander.

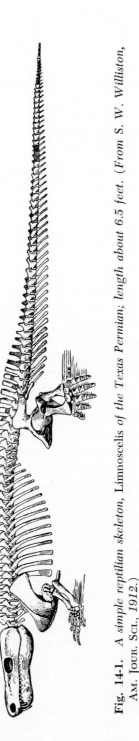

Fig. 14-1. *A simple reptilian skeleton, Limnoscelis of the Texas Permian; length about 6.5 feet. (From S. W. Williston, Am. Jour. Sci., 1912.)*

Even in the late Permian and earliest Triassic, the reptiles of South Africa were moderately varied, and some were large. Before the end of the Jurassic, reptiles were abundant almost everywhere; they occupied almost every possible niche on land, several groups had gone to sea, and one had taken to the air.

A modern reptile is an animal with a scaly skin. A Mesozoic reptile, however, is usually a more or less incomplete skeleton. Impressions of the skin are known, but they are very rare. Since scaliness is not a useful guide, one searches for clean-cut reptilian peculiarities in the skeleton. A primitive reptilian skeleton is shown in Figure 14-1. Reptiles have much more highly developed bony girdles at the shoulders and the hips than amphibians do, and these girdles have characteristic numbers and arrangements of bones. A reptilian skull is made up of a fairly constant number of bones, in a characteristic arrangement. The bones of the mouth region, and the teeth, are particularly useful for distinguishing reptiles from amphibians and from mammals.

From three to seven bones, closely interlocked, make up each side of the lower jaw of a reptile (Fig. 14-2). Since the lower jaw of a mammal has but one bone on each side, a lower jaw is enough to show whether the animal was a reptile or a mammal. Reptilian teeth are somewhat similar to those of amphibians but quite different from those of mammals. Reptilian teeth are not well rooted, but fit loosely into vague sockets; they are easily lost and as easily replaced. In a mammal, the second and last set of teeth occupy deep sockets in the jaw bones. A single fossil tooth is often enough for the distinction between mammal and reptile.

14-2. Classification of Reptiles

The best guides to differences among reptiles are found in the skulls. The primary features are the number and arrangement of openings in the temporal region, behind the eye sockets. Five types of skull are distinguished (Fig. 14-3); these can be gathered

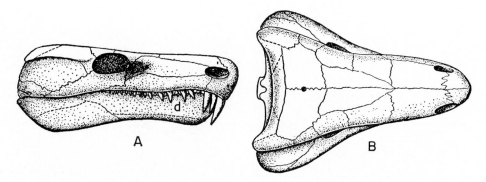

Fig. 14-2. *A simple reptilian skull,* Limnoscelis *of the Texas Permian; length about 10 inches.* (*After S. W. Williston, 1911. Reprinted from Ref. 4 by permission of the University of Chicago Press. Copyright 1933 and 1945 by the University of Chicago.*)
   A. *Side view. Note the dentary* (d) *and three other bones of the lower jaw.*
   B. *View from above.*

Fig. 14-3. *Five types of reptilian skulls: synapsid, parapsid, anapsid, euryapsid, and diapsid.* (*From Ref. 1, courtesy of the American Museum of Natural History.*)

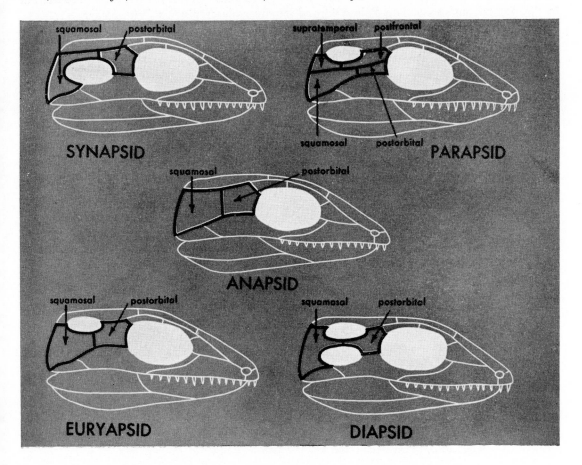

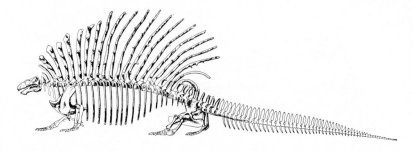

Fig. 14-4. *A Texas Permian pelycosaur* (Edaphosaurus), *with spiny, sail-like ridge. (Courtesy of the American Museum of Natural History.)*

into three more arbitrary groups: that with no temporal opening (anapsid), those with one temporal opening (synapsid, parapsid, and euryapsid), and that with two temporal openings (diapsid).

The reptiles with no temporal openings (anapsids) include both the turtles, which have flourished moderately from the Triassic to the present, and some late Paleozoic and Triassic forms (the cotylosaurs, p. 394; typical skeleton, Fig. 14-1) that are not at all like turtles.

Reptiles with a single temporal opening include the synapsid order Therapsida, which led to the mammals, and several important aquatic orders, notably the parapsid ichthyosaurs, which were fish-like, and the euryapsid plesiosaurs, which were box-bodied.

The synapsid reptiles are limited to the Pennsylvanian, Permian, and Triassic. Of the two orders, the pelycosaurs (Pennsylvanian–Permian) are the more primitive. They are

known chiefly from Texas and other parts of the mid-continent of North America. They included some bizarre types, such as a rather heavily built herbivore with a sail-like ridge (Fig. 14-4). The therapsids (Permian-Triassic), which are especially abundant in South Africa, developed from pelycosaurs; they included heavily built herbivores and somewhat more agile carnivores (Fig. 14-5).

The aquatic mesosaurs and ichthyosaurs are both parapsids, with a single highly placed temporal opening, as shown in Figure 14-3. The probably fresh-water mesosaurs of the late Paleozoic (Fig. 14-6; compare Fig. 13-12) look somewhat like very small crocodiles but had hind limbs so paddle-like that life on shore must have been difficult. Their South African–South American distribution was discussed in Chapter 13. The much later ichthyosaurs (from mid-Triassic to Late Cretaceous) are found in marine formations in almost all parts of the world. A Lower Jurassic example,

Fig. 14-5. Cynognathus, *a mammal-like therapsid reptile of the South African Triassic; length 7 or 8 feet. (Courtesy of the American Museum of Natural History.)*

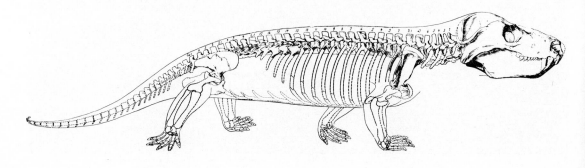

with carbonized skin preserved, is shown in Figure 14-7. The ichthyosaurs, in their perfect and fish-like adaptation to marine navigation, are similar to the mammalian porpoises of the Cenozoic.

The euryapsids, the third subclass with one temporal opening, include the marine plesiosaurs of the Jurassic (Fig. 14-8) and Cretaceous and also somewhat similar Triassic forms, most of which are less perfectly adapted to aquatic life. The typical plesiosaur (left side of Fig. 14-8) was described by the early nineteenth-century cleric and paleontologist William Buckland as a snake threaded through a turtle.

Reptiles with two temporal openings are all members of the subclass Diapsida, which contains eight orders. The first three, small and rare or early and rare, are of minor importance.

The next two orders, the Saurischia and the Ornithischia, share the name "dinosaur." They include the largest land animals of the Jurassic and Cretaceous (or any other period) and were so unlike each other that the general term "dinosaur" can be justified only by usage, which developed because the big bones typical of the two orders occur in rocks of the same systems. Actually, though some dino-

Fig. 14-6.　Mesosaurus brasiliensis, *as restored by J. H. McGregor; total length about 16 inches. (Reprinted from Ref. 2 by permission of the University of Chicago Press. Copyright 1914 by the University of Chicago.)*

Fig. 14-7.　Ichthyosaurus quadriscissus *with skin, 5.5 feet long, from the Lower Jurassic, Holzmaden, southwestern Germany. (Courtesy of the American Museum of Natural History.)*

saurs were massive beasts, others were almost as daintily built as birds.

The next order is made up of the pterosaurs, the fragile flying reptiles of the Jurassic and Cretaceous. They were somewhat like bats, with membranous wings.

The seventh order is composed of crocodiles and similar animals, some of which lived as long ago as the Late Triassic. Crocodiles of considerable variety, including some sea-going types, were at least as abundant in the Mesozoic as they have been in later times.

The final order, the Squamata, includes not only the snakes and lizards, but also the mosasaurs, the largest and strangest lizard-like animals that ever lived. The mosasaurs had a short but varied and successful oceanic career in the Late Cretaceous. They developed paddle-like limbs and powerful swimming tails.

The variety and development of reptiles during the Mesozoic will be illustrated chiefly by examples from seven orders—three made up of forms with one temporal opening, the others with two. The first three orders are the land-living therapsids and the aquatic ichthyosaurs and plesiosaurs; the other four are the land-living saurischian and ornithischian dinosaurs, the flying pterosaurs (pterodactyls), and the aquatic mosasaurs of the order Squamata (p. 394). The three aquatic groups will be considered first.

14-3. Water Reptiles of the Mesozoic

The water reptiles of the Mesozoic include plesiosaurs, ichthyosaurs, mosasaurs, mesosaurs, turtles, crocodiles, and several other groups. Of these we pick three marine groups

Fig. 14-8. *Restoration of plesiosaurs of the European Lower Jurassic: at left,* Plesiosaurus guilelmi, *long-necked and short-headed; at right,* Thaumatosaurus victor, *short-necked and long-headed. (Courtesy of the American Museum of Natural History.)*

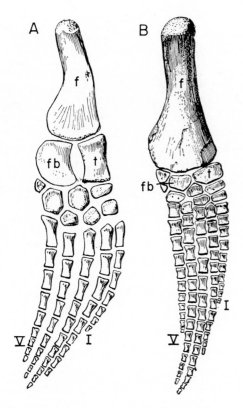

Fig. 14-9. *Right hind paddles of plesiosaurs:* f, *femur;* fb, *fibula;* t, *tibia;* I, *first digit;* V, *fifth digit. (Adapted from Ref. 2 by permission of the University of Chicago Press. Copyright 1914 by the University of Chicago.)*

A. Thaumatosaurus *of the German Lower Jurassic.*

B. Trinacromerum *of the Kansas Upper Cretaceous.*

most world-wide distribution. None has yet been found in the rocks of South America, but there is good reason to expect that sooner or later some will be discovered in the widespread marine Cretaceous strata of that continent. Plesiosaurs are especially well known from the European Jurassic and Cretaceous and from the Upper Cretaceous of Kansas. One of their most interesting features is the more fin-like appearance of the paddles of later forms. The foot and ankle bones became more numerous and the leg bones shorter, so that broad, many-boned, streamlined paddles developed. In the Upper Cretaceous forms the limb bones give only slight indications of derivation from the leg bones of land tetrapods. A comparison of Early Jurassic and Late Cretaceous paddles (Fig. 14-9), however, shows that the transformation from a typical tetrapod leg did occur. The plesiosaurs are found in shales and limestones and in chalky rocks that suggest that the animals lived in open epicontinental seas, but they must have on occasion either clambered out on the beach or stuck their noses into gravel beds on the bottom of the sea, for the box-like skeletons contain numerous stomach stones (Fig. 14-10), each a half inch or an inch in diameter—round pebbles of durable rocks that became polished

Fig. 14-10. *Pebbles from the stomach of a plesiosaur. (Courtesy of the American Museum of Natural History.)*

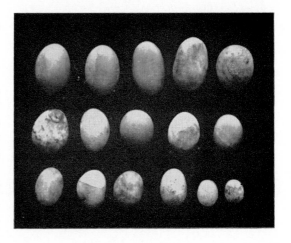

for special mention: the plesiosaurs, the ichthyosaurs, and the mosasaurs.

a. Plesiosaurs

Bones of plesiosaurs are abundant in Jurassic and Cretaceous rocks of many regions. Several complete specimens were found in the Oxford Clay at Peterborough and are now exhibited in the British Museum. Such fine specimens are rare, but even a few bones enable the specialist to tell not only that he has a plesiosaur but just what genus of plesiosaur is represented. The plesiosaurs had al-

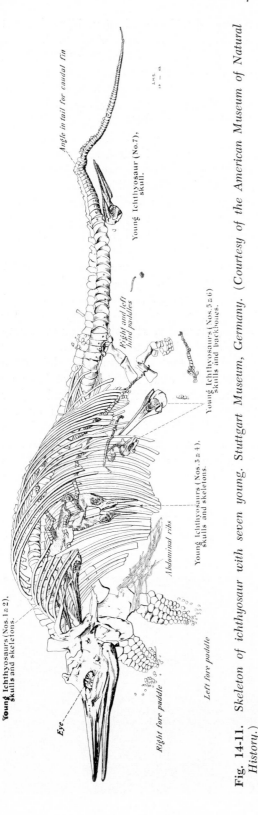

Fig. 14-11. *Skeleton of ichthyosaur with seven young. Stuttgart Museum, Germany. (Courtesy of the American Museum of Natural History.)*

in the course of their long use as gizzard stones to grind up food swallowed hurriedly and whole.

b. Ichthyosaurs

Among the best and most completely preserved of all fossils are specimens of ichthyosaurs from the Lower Jurassic of Germany and England. In some examples the complete skeleton in undisturbed articulation, together with impressions of the skin, ligaments, and muscles, and such odds and ends as stomach contents, have been preserved. One specimen in the museum at Stuttgart, Germany, contains the remains of more than two hundred belemnites that were in the animal's stomach—a meal without any variety whatever. Another specimen (Fig. 14-11) has seven little ichthyosaurs in or near it, probably unborn young, though they may have been the food of a cannibalistic adult. Most reptiles lay eggs, but the habit of bearing the young alive would have been a valuable adaptation to life on the high seas (Fig. 14-12). Other marine reptiles, such as the turtle, go ashore and bury their eggs in the sand. Eggs of the size that reptiles lay would almost all be eaten if they were just left in the waters of the open sea; they would have little chance to perpetuate the race.

In Figures 14-7 and 14-11 one sees that the row of ichthyosaur tail bones was marked by a sharp angle, that the tail was vertical, and that the small bones at the end went only into the lower fluke. This is a very unusual arrangement. The earliest-found skeletons did not show impressions of the soft parts, but some were so perfectly preserved that the fluked tail was predicted.

The ichthyosaurs range from the Middle Triassic almost to the end of the Cretaceous. The Triassic forms were primitive, with the paddle-like limbs only moderately well developed and with very clear differentiation of the upper and lower limb bones from the ankle and foot bones. Even the earliest Jurassic forms, however, had fish-like paddles (Figs. 14-7 and 14-11). An even more striking difference is in the tail. The Middle Triassic forms had very poorly developed flukes and long, nearly straight tails. Perfect flukes appeared first in the earliest Jurassic forms and were continued almost unchanged through the rest of the Jurassic and Cretaceous.

Ichthyosaur remains are widespread, in Europe, North America, India, Australia, New Zealand, the islands of the East Indies, and even Patagonia. The animals were truly cosmopolitan, as might be expected from their fish-like form. It must have been easy for them to move about all over the world. Since they make excellent guide fossils where they are found, their rarity in most places is a stratigraphic misfortune. The Cretaceous rocks of a whole region, such as far western North America, may yield two or three examples—in contrast to the uncountable millions of invertebrates in the same set of strata.

The ichthyosaurs may have been the marine descendants of fresh-water mesosaurs. The mesosaurs, however, occur at the very beginning of the record of the aquatic reptiles, and there is a long gap between their disappearance at the beginning of the Permian and the appearance of the ichthyosaurs in the mid-Triassic.

c. Mosasaurs

The third and last group of Mesozoic water reptiles to be mentioned here is composed of the Late Cretaceous mosasaurs, also found all over the world. These giant water lizards, members of the order Squamata, were up to twenty feet long. They are divided into only a few genera, but the species are numerous. The succession shows a considerable development, all between the early part of the Late Cretaceous and the end of the same period. Regional variations are also notable, the species in western Kansas and California, for example, being different from one another and from those in England and Belgium.

A composite mosasaur skeleton, reconstructed from specimens found in central California, is shown in Figure 14-13. The skeleton is very lizard-like. For one thing, the bones of

Fig. 14-12. *Ichthyosaur and young.* (*Courtesy of the American Museum of Natural History.*)

the jaws and the bones with which the lower jaw articulates are loosely connected with each other so that the animal could greatly distend mouth and throat in the process of swallowing its prey.

The long and loosely articulated mosasaur skeletons are not ordinarily found in such symmetrical order as the ichthyosaurs and some plesiosaurs. Usually just a few bones, or perhaps only a single bone, are found at one place. The customary disintegration of skeletons and the great number of local species of mosasaurs suggest that these animals may have spent their whole lives in shallow waters near shore. They may even have laid eggs instead

Fig. 14-13. Kolposaurus, *a mosasaur 33 feet long, found high in the Cretaceous of west-central California. (From C. L. Camp, Univ. California Memoirs, 1942.)*

of having their young born alive and may have gone up rivers to lay these eggs in safe places. This also would explain the fact that immature examples of mosasaurs are unknown.

One of the most famous of all fossils is the original mosasaur, which was found near the Maas River at Maastricht, Holland, in 1780. It was discovered in an underground stone quarry beneath St. Peter's Mount, almost under a fort occupied successively by Austrian and other foreign soldiers. A doctor connected with the garrison paid the workmen to give him fine fossils. When the four-foot skull represented in Figure 14-14 was uncovered in 1780, this doctor obtained it. No sooner had he got it nicely prepared for exhibition than it was taken away from him by a canon of the cathedral, who owned the overlying ground immediately adjacent to the fort. This brought up a nice point in the Roman law that prevailed in the region and led to a celebrated lawsuit, which the doctor finally lost to the canon. In 1795 a French Republican army laid siege to the city and bombarded St. Peter's fort, but strangely spared the adjacent building in which the canon had exhibited his prize skull. This led the canon to suspect that the French wanted the skull as a trophy, and so he hid it across the river in the city. When the French finally captured the city, a French scientist named St. Fond persuaded the army "representative of the French people" to offer 600 bottles of fine wine for the skull. The next day a dozen French grenadiers delivered the skull undamaged and claimed the reward. The skull was carted off to Paris, where St. Fond wrote a big book about it, illustrated by fine woodcuts, including the one reproduced here. A few years later the celebrated French naturalist Cuvier, the founder of comparative anatomy, reached the conclusion that the mosasaur, instead of being a crocodile, as St. Fond and others had supposed, was really a member of a new group closely related to the lizards. There were never any other lizards equal to these giant sea lizards of the latest Mesozoic.

Fig. 14-14. *The original mosasaur being removed from the Upper Cretaceous chalk at Maastricht, Holland. (From Ref. 8.)*

14-4. *Land Reptiles of the Mesozoic*

The principal groups of Mesozoic land reptiles are the therapsids and the two dinosaur orders. The therapsids are limited to the Permian and the Triassic and are best developed in South Africa. Dinosaur bones are widely distributed in Mesozoic rocks, are highly varied, and in some places are (or were) extremely abundant.

a. Therapsids

Bones of therapsids, the reptiles closest to the mammals, are particularly numerous in the Beaufort beds of the Karroo sequence in the Union of South Africa (Table 13-1). They include the remains of herbivores as big as bears (Fig. 14-15) and carnivores varying in size from animals no bigger than a rat to those as big as large wolves. Some of the Upper Beaufort (Lower Triassic) carnivores are especially mammal-like. The high stance, jaw structure, and differentiated teeth of *Cynognathus* (Figs. 14-5 and 14-16) are almost as mammalian as reptilian. The fore legs are longer than the hind legs, and the articu-

lations of the bones show that the legs were erect and held the animal well off the ground. The lower jaw (Fig. 14-17C), though still made up of three or more bones and connected with the skull through intermediate bones in reptilian fashion, was mostly a single bone, in which the teeth were rooted in a way approaching that of mammals.

b. *Dinosaurs*

The Saurischia and the Ornithischia, especially because of their enormous sizes, are perhaps the most notable animals that are known exclusively from fossil remains. Several kinds of dinosaurs were larger than any nondinosaurian land animals that ever lived.

1. INTRODUCTION. Dinosaur remains are mostly bones and footprints. Impressions of the skin are extremely rare. The areas where dinosaur remains have been found in abundance are rather few, but some are large. One includes a great part of the Rocky Mountain region of North America, extending from Utah and Colorado on the south through Wyoming and Montana to Alberta. This area is by far

Fig. 14-15. Ceratocephalus, *a herbivorous therapsid 14 feet long, from the Permian* Tapinocephalus *zone of the Beaufort beds, Union of South Africa. (From Friedrich von Huene, 1931.)*
ABOVE. *Complete skeleton.*
BELOW. *Landscape with three reptiles.*

the world's greatest source of dinosaur material. The number of bones that have come from it is almost unbelievably large; some are still stored unstudied. Many complete or nearly complete skeletons have been found. The most fossiliferous strata are uppermost Jurassic and Cretaceous, representing rather well the last half of dinosaurian history. The great period of dinosaur-collecting in North America began soon after the completion of the first transcontinental railroad in 1869 and continued for at least forty years. When one sees the breath-taking exhibits of the American Museum of Natural History in New York, the Peabody Museum in New Haven, the National Museum in Washington, or any one of a dozen other museums in the United States and Canada, one should think not only of the great beasts in their native swamps but also of gangs of hardy men racing across the continent to newly found paleontological bonanzas, where they worked fast to get the heavy bones safely encased and shipped before hostile Indians or rival collectors could interfere (Ref. 6).

A second important region for dinosaur remains, and the one first exploited, is in western and central Europe. Several fine skeletons have

Fig. 14-16. Cynognathus, *a carnivorous therapsid from the Upper Beaufort (Lower Triassic) of South Africa; skulls about 18 inches long. (Courtesy of the American Museum of Natural History.)*

Fig. 14-17. *Jaws of synapsid reptiles: d, dentary. (Reprinted from Ref. 4 by permission of the University of Chicago Press. Copyright 1933 and 1945 by the University of Chicago.)*
   A. *The pelycosaur* Dimetrodon, *from the Lower Permian of North America.*
   B. *The primitive therapsid carnivore* Cynarioides, *from the Upper Permian of South Africa.*
   C. *The advanced therapsid carnivore* Cynognathus, *from the Lower Triassic of South Africa.*

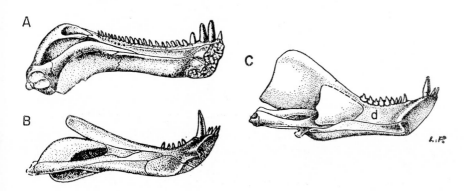

been found in Belgium. The British occurrences are scattered, and few if any whole skeletons have been found; nevertheless, about a hundred species of British dinosaurs are known, with ages ranging from Triassic to latest Cretaceous. Other notable dinosaur areas, from which many nearly complete skeletons have been obtained, are Mongolia and eastern Africa. In general, the dinosaurs occur in considerable abundance all round the world, mostly in the northern hemisphere but also in tropical eastern Africa and even, rarely, in South Africa and Australia.

The two dinosaurian orders are not very similar to each other. The skeletons show many consistent differences, those in the pelvic girdle being particularly useful. The saurischian pelvis is represented in Figure 14-18AB, the ornithischian in C–F. The saurischian pubis makes a broad angle with the ischium,

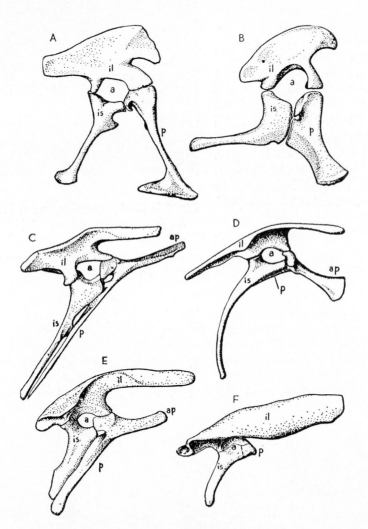

Fig. 14-18.   *Saurischian and ornithischian pelvic girdles:* il, *ilium;* a, *hip socket;* is, *ischium;* p, *pubis;* ap, *anterior process of pubis. (Reprinted from Ref. 4 by permission of the University of Chicago Press. Copyright 1933 and 1945 by the University of Chicago.)*
SAURISCHIAN: A, *theropodan;* B, *sauropodan.*
ORNITHISCHIAN: C, *ornithopodan;* D, *ceratopsian;* E, *stegosaurian;* F, *ankylosaurian.*

Fig. 14-19. *Skeleton of* Ornitholestes, *an Upper Jurassic theropod dinosaur about 6 feet long.* (*Courtesy of the American Museum of Natural History.*)

but the two bones are side by side in the Ornithischia. The meaning of the figure becomes clear when a particular drawing (Fig. 14-18A) is compared with a photograph of a closely related genus, the saurischian skeleton represented in Figure 14-19.

2. THE SAURISCHIA. These are divided into two strikingly different suborders. The *theropods,* which flourished throughout the Mesozoic, were mostly carnivorous bipeds. The *sauropods,* large herbivorous quadrupeds, are limited to the Jurassic and the Cretaceous, though precursors are known among the theropods of the Upper Triassic in Europe, North America, and Africa.

The theropods are typified by the Late Jurassic form shown in Figure 14-19. Much earlier similar forms are known from a few skeletons and many tracks (Fig. 14-20) in the Triassic sandstones of the eastern United States. The tracks show that the animals

moved about on two feet, putting one foot in front of the other and leaving a single line of prints, which are three-toed, like those of birds. The three-fold prints correspond nicely to the three toes of the theropod foot.

Late in the Cretaceous the theropods became gigantic. *Tyrannosaurus* (Fig. 14-21) was the largest of all land carnivores, fifty feet long from the tip of its nose to the end of its tail and, as it stood up on its hind legs, in its usual stance, probably twenty feet high. The teeth lack the differentiation that would be shown by a mammalian carnivore, but they must have been effective in seizing prey and tearing off chunks of flesh. The theropods no doubt fed largely upon sauropods.

The herbivorous *sauropods* had short fore legs but used all four feet in walking. The short fore legs may mean that the big sauropods had bipedal ancestors. The largest sauropods, such as *Brontosaurus* of the uppermost Jurassic of western North America (Figs. 14-

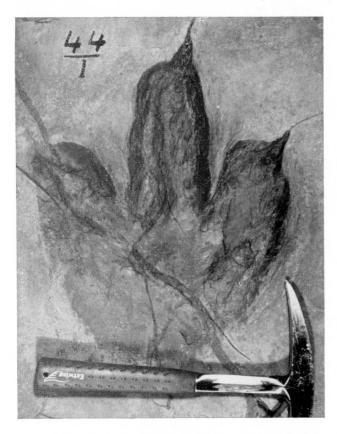

Fig. 14-20. *Footprints of theropod dinosaurs in the Triassic sandstone (brownstone) near Amherst, Mass. (Photographs from R. M. Foose, Amherst College.)*
LEFT. *Print of a large dinosaur. The geologist's pick gives the scale.*
RIGHT. *Sets of steps of a small dinosaur, which lead to the conclusion of bipedal stance and make possible estimates of height. The scale is 15 inches long.*

22 and 14-23), were the largest of all land animals. They grew up to eighty-seven feet long and must have weighed as much as forty tons. Their footprints are as large as small washtubs. Perhaps they were amphibious. Their remains are found in muddy organic formations that may represent old swamp deposits, and their footprints (Fig. 14-22) show the prints of all four feet but lack associated impressions of the tail. Perhaps the heavy tail was partially supported by the shallow water of a swampy environment.

3. THE ORNITHISCHIA. These, the dinosaurs with bird-like pelvic girdles (Fig. 14-18), are divided into four suborders, markedly different from one another. The most widespread and longest-lived suborder was that of the ornithopods, or *duck-billed dinosaurs*, whose remains are known from rocks of Middle Jurassic–Late Cretaceous ages in Europe, North America, Africa, and eastern Asia. They reached their culmination in the late Cretaceous of Europe and western America. Since they had no teeth in the front part of the jaw, it seems probable that they lived in swampy places where they cropped the abundant vegetation with the horny, bill-like front parts of their jaws. The Cretaceous duck-bill *Trachodon* is represented in Figures 14-24 and

14-25. Here again is an animal with very short front legs. Those legs were strong enough for use in walking, but in that position the animal really stuck up behind.

The other three groups of the Ornithischia (p. 394) have rather short ranges. The stegosaurs lived from the Early Jurassic to the Early Cretaceous, with a maximum in the Late Jurassic; the ankylosaurs were chiefly Early Cretaceous, but survived into the Late Cretaceous; and the ceratopsians are known only from Upper Cretaceous rocks. Like the duckbills, most of these animals were very large.

The *stegosaurs* had the unusual arched shape shown in Figures 14-26 and 14-27. The animal was characterized by its small head, tremendous curving vertebral column armored with great triangular plates, and tail with four spikes. The whole animal was twenty-five or thirty feet long and probably weighed ten tons. The brain was exceptionally small, even for a dinosaur—not much bigger than a walnut, and perhaps one-twentieth the size of the group of nerve ganglia just above the pelvic girdle. This curious arrangement of nerve centers was the butt of Bert Leston Taylor's well-known jingle:

> Behold the mighty dinosaur,
>   Famous in prehistoric lore,

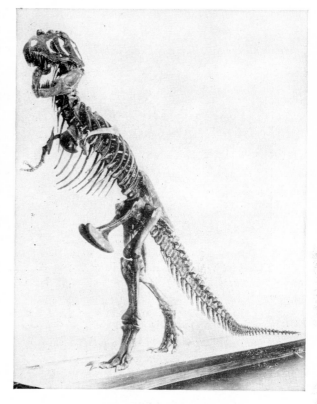

Fig. 14-21.   Tyrannosaurus rex, *a gigantic Upper Cretaceous theropod dinosaur of western North America. (Courtesy of the American Museum of Natural History.)*

Fig. 14-22.   *Skeleton of* Brontosaurus, *70 feet long, from the Upper Jurassic of western North America, mounted above tracks found in Texas. (Courtesy of the American Museum of Natural History.)*

Fig. 14-23.   Brontosaurus. (*Painting by Charles R. Knight; courtesy of the American Museum of Natural History.*)

Fig. 14-24.   Trachodon mirabilis, *a Late Cretaceous duck-billed dinosaur of western North America, 30 feet long. (Courtesy of the American Museum of Natural History.)*

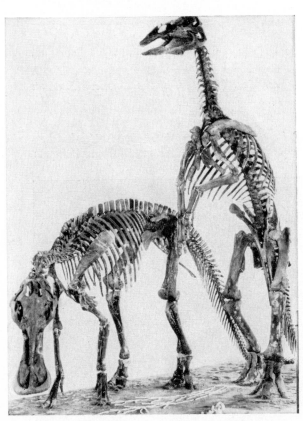

Not only for his power and strength
   But for his intellectual length.
You will observe by these remains
   The creature had two sets of brains—
One in his head (the usual place),
   The other at his spinal base.
Thus he could reason "A priori"
   As well as "A posteriori."
No problem bothered him a bit;
   He made both head and tail of it.
So wise was he, so wise and solemn,
   Each thought filled just a spinal column.
If one brain found the pressure strong,
   It passed a few ideas along.
If something slipped his forward mind,
   'Twas rescued by the one behind,
And if in error he was caught,
   He had a saving afterthought.
As he thought twice before he spoke,
   He had no judgment to revoke.
Thus he could think without congestion
   Upon both sides of every question.
Oh, gaze upon this model beast,
   Defunct ten million years at least.*

An *ankylosaur* of the Early Cretaceous was built like an armored tank. Skull and back were covered by heavy bony plates (Fig. 14-29). The large plates in a row on each side ended in sharp spikes. This monster was no doubt clumsy, but it must have been hard to crack.

* First published in the Chicago Tribune.

Fig. 14-25. Trachodon. (*Painting by Charles R. Knight; courtesy of the American Museum of Natural History.*)

Fig. 14-26. *Skeleton of Stegosaurus, 18 feet long, from the Upper Jurassic of western North America. (Courtesy of the American Museum of Natural History.)*

The last ornithischian group, and in many ways the most interesting, was made up of the great *ceratopsians* of the Late Cretaceous, animals which ranged from the size of small oxen to giants thirty feet long, the biggest ones coming at the very end of Cretaceous time. As shown in Figure 14-28, the last of the ceratopsians had three horns and, at the back of the skull, an enormous frill three or four feet across. The whole giant skull was balanced on the short neck. These plant-eaters were no doubt also effective fighters, having swords and bucklers. The first dinosaur eggs found (Fig. 14-30) were those of ceratopsians; they were discovered in the lowest Upper Cretaceous rocks of Mongolia in 1922 by an expedition of the American Museum of Natural History.

Fig. 14-27. Stegosaurus, *with a background of cycads and other plants. (Painting by Charles R. Knight; courtesy of the American Museum of Natural History.)*

Fig. 14-28. Triceratops prorsus, *18 feet long, one of the last of the horned dinosaurs, from the Lance formation, uppermost Cretaceous, Niobrara County, Wyoming. (U.S. National Museum, courtesy of the Smithsonian Institution.)*

Fig. 14-29. *Model of* Palaeoscincus, *a Lower Cretaceous ankylosaur of western North America.* (*Courtesy of the American Museum of Natural History.*)

Fig. 14-30. *The small and primitive* Protoceratops, *with eggs, from the Cretaceous of Mongolia.* (*Courtesy of the American Museum of Natural History.*)

Fig. 14-31. *A Late Cretaceous landscape in western North America: the great carnivore* Tyranno-saurus *and the horned herbivore* Triceratops, *with a background of dense vegetation. (Painting by Charles R. Knight; courtesy of the American Museum of Natural History.)*

Fig. 14-32. *Restored skeleton of* Rhamphorhynchus phyllurus, *a pterosaur from the Upper Jurassic of Germany; skull 5 inches long. (Courtesy of the American Museum of Natural History.)*

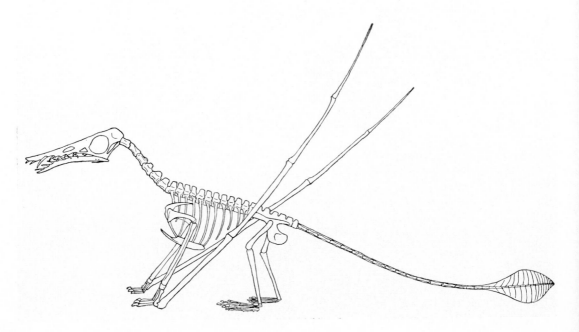

The food of the big herbivores, the ceratopsians and all the rest, must have been lowland plants, especially those growing in swamps. Since flowering plants first appeared in the Cretaceous and the very greatest of the dinosaurs had lived in the Jurassic, there cannot be any causal connection between the appearance of the flowering plants and the development of the giant herbivorous dinosaurs. The somewhat more primitive plants that were abundant in the Paleozoic and continued through the Mesozoic were no doubt sufficiently luxuriant to furnish enough food for the great dinosaurs of the Mesozoic swamps and plains. One concept of a Late Cretaceous landscape is shown in Figure 14-31—the gigantic *Triceratops* and *Tyrannosaurus* in the foreground, and lush vegetation, including a cycad-like tree, in the background.

14-5. *Flying Reptiles of the Mesozoic*

The *pterosaurs*, or flying reptiles, were rather closely related to the dinosaurs, but were much smaller and considerably rarer. Instead of occurring in continental or swamp formations, they are found chiefly in marine limestones or shales. This suggests that the animals were fish-eaters, rather than night-flying land animals like their analogues, the mammalian bats. A typical Late Jurassic pterosaur (Figs. 14-32 and 14-33) was about eighteen inches long and had a very light skeleton, the larger bones being hollow. The wings were membranes supported by the fourth (and last) toes of the front limbs. Some occurrences suggest that these membranes could be folded, as can those of the bat. Cuvier recognized the pterosaurs as reptiles by the characteristics of the head and other bones. This was one of the early triumphs of comparative anatomy.

Pterosaurs range in size from animals as small as sparrows to giants (in the Upper Cretaceous Kansas chalk) that had a wingspread of twenty-five feet. They are known from the beginning of the Jurassic to the end of the Cretaceous, and, as in most other groups, by far their largest representatives were the Cretaceous forms. Pterosaurs have been found chiefly in Europe, but also in the Cretaceous of western America and in Africa. Hundreds of fragmentary specimens were found more than a hundred years ago, some as early as 1780 in the Upper Jurassic limestone quarries at Solnhofen in Bavaria.

Fig. 14-33.   *A representation of the flying* Rhamphorhynchus. (*Courtesy of the American Museum of Natural History.*)

14-6. *Mesozoic Birds*

The earliest birds appeared a little later than the flying reptiles and were themselves rather reptilian. They were especially close to such diapsids as the dinosaurs and the pterosaurs, though the latter were not in any sense intermediate between reptiles and birds. Birds fly in a different way.

The oldest known birds are two rather similar skeletons, each about the size of a crow, from the very fine-grained Upper Jurassic

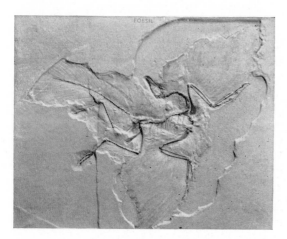

Fig. 14-34. Archaeopteryx, *a primitive bird from the Upper Jurassic of Solnhofen, Bavaria, Germany: above, the fossil; below, the restoration. (Courtesy of the American Museum of Natural History.)*

limestone quarried at Solnhofen, Bavaria. One, *Archaeopteryx* (Fig. 14-34), is in the British Museum, the other in Berlin. The jaws carry teeth, and the fore limbs end in claws; the skeletons are so similar to those of some diapsids that they might be called reptilian were it not for the associated feathers, especially along the wings and tail. An *Archaeopteryx* is represented in Figure 14-35 in the claws of a contemporary theropod dinosaur (the *Ornitholestes* of Fig. 14-19).

In the Cretaceous the birds showed considerable development. Giant divers found in the Upper Cretaceous of western Kansas are three feet long (Fig. 14-36).

14-7. *Mesozoic Mammals*

The fossils in Mesozoic rocks that are assigned to the Mammalia represent small animals and occur in strata ranging in age from Middle Jurassic to latest Cretaceous. The specimens are mostly teeth, lower jaws, parts of skulls, and a few limb bones.

The oldest mammalian fossils are tiny jaws an inch or so long, found a few miles northwest of Oxford, England, in the Stonesfield "Slate." This rock is a fine-grained limy sandstone bed, six feet thick, in marine oolitic limestone of Middle Jurassic age. The first jaw was collected about 1764, but it was not properly classified for a hundred years. The real discovery came in 1812 or 1814, when a stonemason sold two specimens to an Oxford student, who carried them to Professor William Buckland, the first Oxford paleontologist. Buckland's classification of these specimens was long disputed, but in 1838 their mammalian character was confirmed in a study by Sir Richard Owen. A single bone makes up one whole side of the lower jaw, and the teeth are well rooted (Fig. 14-37). The first two genera represented in the figure have slender cheek teeth with three cusps in line and are called *triconodont;* a third Stonesfield genus has broader cheek teeth, also three-cusped, and is called *trituberculate.* Molar, premolar, canine, and incisor teeth can be dis-

Fig. 14-35. *An* Archaeopteryx *seized by* Ornitholestes, *a contemporaneous theropod dinosaur. (Courtesy of the American Museum of Natural History.)*

tinguished. These jaws and teeth give one a definite concept of primitive mammalian mouth structures.

Nineteen species of small mammals were obtained as the result of long collecting in the fresh-water Purbeck formation of the uppermost Jurassic in the south of England. Similar mammals have also been found in the Upper Jurassic of North America and Africa. Mammals are commoner in the Upper Cretaceous, and in the uppermost Cretaceous of the Rocky Mountain region, in northern Colorado, Wyoming, and Montana, they are truly abundant. The members of one group, the *multituberculates*, appear to have been the first herbivorous mammals; some were as large as woodchucks. The first *marsupials* appeared, moderately close relatives of the living opos-

Fig. 14-36. Hesperornis regalis, *a toothed diver 3 feet high, from the Upper Cretaceous of Kansas. (Courtesy of the American Museum of Natural History.)*

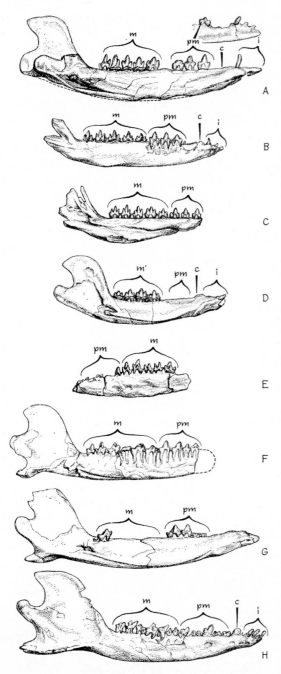

Fig. 14-37. *Lower jaws (about 1 inch long) of mammals from the Middle Jurassic Stonesfield "Slate" near Oxford, England: m, molars; pm, premolars; c, canine; i, incisors. (Redrawn from E. S. Goodrich, 1894.)*

TRICONODONTS: A, B, C, Amphilestes; D, Phascolotherium.

TRITUBERCULATES: E, F, G, H, Amphitherium.

sums. There were also eutherian mammals (see § 15-3), little *insectivores* somewhat similar to the living shrews and moles.

Thus by the end of the Cretaceous both the pouch-bearing and the more modern types of mammals were in existence. It must be emphasized, however, that all the Mesozoic mammals were insignificant in the sense that individuals were very small, compared with the reptiles, and extremely rare, until almost the end of the era, if one may judge by the rarity of specimens in comparison with the abundance of reptilian bones.

It may be noted again that the earliest mammals are clearly related in a general way to the Late Triassic mammal-like therapsid reptiles. The relationships are not close, though an inch-long mammalian humerus from Stonesfield has some similarity to the much larger humerus of *Cynognathus*, the South African Triassic therapsid. In general, it seems clear that the therapsid reptiles must have been rather closely related to the common ancestors of the various Mesozoic mammalian groups and that the differences between the therapsids and the latter must be, in part, a corollary of the long barren sequence that includes the Lower Jurassic.

14-8. *Extinction of the Great Reptilian Groups at the End of the Cretaceous*

The dinosaurs, the pterosaurs, the ichthyosaurs, the plesiosaurs, and the mosasaurs all flourished almost to the end of the Cretaceous, and then they all suddenly disappeared, just as the ammonites did at almost the same time. The duck-billed and ceratopsian dinosaurs apparently outlived, by a little, the other dinosaurian groups; but, since localities where vertebrate remains are found are rare, and the chances are against preservation of all the different types of animals living at any particular time, the differences between the times of extinction of the various groups of reptiles should not be emphasized. The differences may be more apparent than real. All that we can say is that at about the same time, approximately at the end of the Mesozoic, there was an end to the groups of vertebrates that had been the characteristic and dominant features of the life of the Mesozoic, on the land, in the sea, and in the air. Still other groups, which had contributed to the greater variety of Mesozoic reptiles, had disappeared earlier. We have mentioned that the therapsids dropped out at the end of the Triassic. Several minor groups, not listed in this book, had disappeared at various times during the Mesozoic or even earlier. Even if one takes these earlier extinctions into account, the mass disappearances at about the end of the Cretaceous are amazingly coincidental.

What can have caused the disappearance of so many and such varied animals at approximately the same time in the earth's history? Many explanations have been suggested, especially for the extinction of the dinosaurs, and four will be mentioned here.

(1) The climate may have become unfavorable. No extensive Cretaceous glaciation has been demonstrated, but the climate at the period's end may have grown colder.

(2) The reptiles may have been displaced by mammals. But the mammals did not, at the very beginning of the Cenozoic, expand immediately into highly varied and effective groups that could take the places of the ceratopsians and *Tyrannosaurus*, to say nothing of plesiosaurs and mosasaurs. It was not direct mammalian competition that ousted the great reptiles. The reptiles apparently disappeared, in fact, before the mammals began their great development. There may, however, have been a relation to the rise of the mammals in one rather curious way. Possibly the little mammals learned to suck reptilian eggs. This would explain the disappearance of the egg-laying dinosaurs, but it could not explain the disappearance of such a group as the ichthyosaurs, whose young were born alive.

(3) A possible cause of extinction is giantism. This is suggested primarily by the fact that in many extinct animal groups the last members were exceptionally large. This was strikingly true of several groups of Late Cretaceous reptiles, including several kinds of dinosaurs, the mosasaurs, and the flying reptiles. But it is not the giants alone that were extinguished. The giants came on the scene, and then they and all the smaller forms disappeared at once. This fact suggests an idea related to giantism—deterioration and then extinction as natural periods in the history of a group as of an individual. Perhaps a group of organisms goes through an early period when the animals are small and simple, then a period of developing variety, together with increase of size, and, finally, various grotesque manifestations including giant size. This also seems to fit the dinosaurs as a descriptive fact, and it is perhaps true of some other reptilian groups. It would be incautious, however, to conclude that, because this sort of thing has happened several times in geologic history, a group must, by inherent necessity, disappear soon after it has reached its maximum in variety and in size of individuals.

(4) A very easy answer would be that diseases caused by virulent micro-organisms affected many groups of reptiles late in the Cretaceous. The few kinds of reptiles that survived the epidemics may have been those that managed to develop resistance to the diseases. This is, unfortunately, pure speculation. Knowledge of prehistoric diseases is almost limited to bone diseases, especially arthritic disorders, and the latest Mesozoic reptiles are not known to have been exceptionally arthritic. But, as a last resort, one might conclude that all the highly varied reptiles of the uppermost Cretaceous were carried off by a series of related epidemics.

One thing seems almost certain. The story of the reptiles, unlike that of the mammals, was nearly completed long ago. We can see clearly their origin in rather simple forms in the late Paleozoic, their development into enormous variety by Triassic and Early Jurassic times, their apex in the Late Jurassic and the Cretaceous, their sudden drop to insignificance at the end of the Cretaceous, and the long obscure survival of a few forms to the present.

▨ THE CLASS REPTILIA

Subclass Anapsida (anapsids)—reptiles with a solid skull roof
  Order Cotylosauria (cotylosaurs)—primitive reptiles (*Limnoscelis,* etc.); Penn-sylvanian–Triassic
  Order Chelonia—turtles; Permian–Recent
Subclass Synapsida (synapsids)—one low temporal opening
  Order Pelycosauria (pelycosaurs)—cotylosaur-like; Pennsylvanian-Permian
  Order Therapsida (therapsids)—between pelycosaurs and mammals; Permian-Trias-sic
Subclass Parapsida (parapsids)—high temporal opening; aquatic
  Order Mesosauria (mesosaurs)—moderately adapted to water life; late Pennsylvanian
  Order Ichthyosauria (ichthyosaurs)—fish-like; marine; Triassic–Cretaceous
Subclass Euryapsida (euryapsids)—one high temporal opening; aquatic
  Order Protorosauria—pre-plesiosaurs; Permian–Jurassic
  Order Sauropterygia—plesiosaurs, etc.; Triassic–Cretaceous
Subclass Diapsida (diapsids)—two temporal openings
  Order Eosuchia—primitive diapsids; Permian–Jurassic
  Order Rhynchocephalia—small, persisting diapsids of the land; Triassic–Recent
  Order Thecodontia—early diapsids of land and fresh water; Triassic
  Order Saurischia—dinosaurs with saurian pelvis; Triassic–Cretaceous
    Suborder Theropoda (theropods)—bipeds; Triassic–Cretaceous
    Suborder Sauropoda (sauropods)—quadrupeds; Jurassic-Cretaceous
  Order Ornithischia—dinosaurs with bird-like pelvis; Jurassic-Cretaceous
    Suborder Ornithopoda (ornithopods)—duck-billed dinosaurs; Jurassic-Cretaceous
    Suborder Stegosauria (stegosaurs)—armored hump-backs; Lower Jurassic–Lower Cretaceous
    Suborder Ankylosauria (ankylosaurs)—armored, tank-like; Cretaceous
    Suborder Ceratopsia (ceratopsians)—horned dinosaurs; Upper Cretaceous
  Order Pterosauria (pterosaurs)—flying reptiles; Jurassic-Cretaceous
  Order Crocodilia—crocodiles, etc.; Triassic–Recent
  Order Squamata—lizards, snakes, mosasaurs; Cretaceous–Recent

▨ REFERENCES

1. E. H. Colbert: *The Dinosaur Book,* 2nd ed., 156 pages (American Museum of Natural History, New York, 1951)

2. S. W. Williston: *Water Reptiles of the Past and Present,* 251 pages (University of Chicago Press, 1914)

3. H. G. Seeley: *Dragons of the Air,* 239 pages (Methuen, London, 1901)

4. A. S. Romer: *Vertebrate Paleontology,* 2nd ed., 687 pages (University of Chicago Press, 1945)

5. G. G. Simpson: *A Catalogue of the Mesozoic Mammalia in the Geological Department of the British Museum,* 215 pages (London, 1928)

6. C. H. Sternberg: *The Life of a Fossil Hunter,* 286 pages (Holt, New York, 1909; Jensen, San Diego, 1931)

7. C. H. Sternberg: *Hunting Dinosaurs in the Bad Lands of the Red Deer River, Alberta, Canada,* 261 pages (San Diego, 1932)

8. Barthélemy Faujas de Saint-Fond: *Histoire naturelle de la montagne de St. Pierre de Maestricht,* 263 pages [Paris, An 7 (1798 or 1799)]

CHAPTER 15

The Age of Mammals

MAMMALS have been the outstanding animals since the beginning of the Paleogene, even though they have been forced to struggle for their lives against insects and other pests or rivals. Not only are mammals the biggest Cenozoic animals, but, on land, they are and have been very numerous. Mammals are distinguished by many special features. The living forms have hairy skins and suckle their young. These distinctions are not helpful in paleontology, but the skeletal characteristics of mammals are fortunately adequate.

15-1. *The Mammalian Skeleton*

The typical mammalian skeleton has a definite number and arrangement of bones, except in the tail. Each bone has a name and can usually be recognized rather easily by its shape and position. The frontal bone of the dog skull (Fig. 15-1), for example, has obvious analogues in the horse and in man. Many of the mammalian bones are recognizable in reptiles and in amphibians, but in these other tetrapods the number is both greater and more variable.

In most reptiles the long limb bones (Fig. 15-2, left) lengthen by ossification in the cartilage at the joints, and the animal may grow throughout life, albeit slowly in old age. In mammals and a few reptiles, mostly lizards,

the ends of the bones, called **epiphyses, are** dense bone, which provides excellent bearing surfaces; the joints are smooth, hard, and lubricated. Growth occurs in cartilage between epiphyses and shaft (Fig. 15-2, center, right); when this cartilage is ossified, growth ceases and the junction between epiphysis and shaft gradually becomes obliterated. A long bone with a recognizable epiphysis is almost certainly that of a mammal, probably a rather young one. The long bones of mammals (and

Fig. 15-1. *Skull of wolf*, Canis occidentalis, *side view:* Ex.O, *exoccipital;* Fr, *frontal;* L, *lachrymal;* M, *inferior maxillary, or mandible;* Ma, *malar;* Mx, *maxillary;* O.S, *orbitosphenoid;* Pa, *parietal;* Pl, *palatine;* P.Mx, *premaxillary;* S.O, *supraoccipital;* Sq, *squamosal;* Ty, *tympanic (auditory bulla);* Zyg, *zygomatic process of squamosal. (From Ref. 1.)*

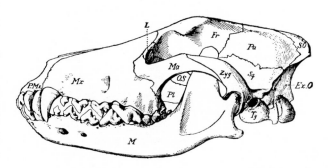

birds) are hollow (Fig. 15-2, right), but those of reptiles and amphibians are solid.

In all reptiles, even the most mammal-like, each side of the lower jaw is made up of several bones, but in mammals there is only one bone on each side (Fig. 15-1; see Fig. 14-17 for a reptilian jaw). Some of the reptilian bones that make up the back part of the lower jaw or were close by in the skull have, in mammals, been reduced in size and transferred in position so that they have become ear bones. This well-demonstrated transformation is one of the most amazing developments in the history of the vertebrate skeleton and provides one of the most satisfactory distinctions between reptiles and mammals.

Practically all mammals have the same head bones, and apparently all early mammals had the primitive tetrapod limbs: one upper leg bone, two lower leg bones, ankle bones, and five-toed feet. In many groups this primitive condition has been changed through a progressive reduction in the number of toe and ankle bones. In the foot of the horse only a

Fig. 15-2. *Reptilian and mammalian long bones.* (*Drawings by R. M. Alf.*)
LEFT. *Femur of turtle,* × *0.55.*
CENTER. *Femur of porcupine,* × *0.55.*
RIGHT. *Distal end of radius of domestic pig, showing a separated epiphysis, and cross-section of the hollow shaft,* × *0.7.*

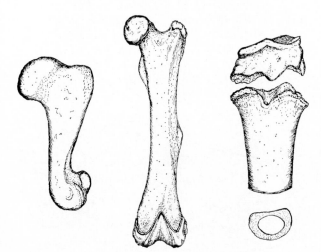

single row of functional bones remains, the middle toe having been enormously enlarged and strengthened.

The parts of the mammalian skeleton most useful in classification are the teeth. The mammalian tooth is complexly developed, with internal close-grained bone (dentine), a smooth enameled surface, and definite roots. In most mammals the teeth occur in two successive sets: (1) milk, or primary; (2) permanent. A single fossil tooth is ordinarily enough to tell a collector whether he has a part of a mammal or of some other vertebrate. If the collector knows teeth at all well, he can place his find in a particular mammalian family, genus, or even species.

The typical mammal has forty-four permanent teeth, eleven on each side, above and below. (Some opossums and other primitives have extra teeth.) There are three incisors (biting teeth) on each side of each jaw, twelve altogether; then the long, tearing canines, one on each side, above and below; then four scissorlike premolars on each side of each jaw; and at the back three broad-topped grinding teeth (molars) on each side, above and below. The distinctive features of the different kinds of teeth are best seen in the more generalized mammals. The dog is a good example (Figs. 15-1 and 15-3), though here there is not quite a full set of teeth. The dog lacks the hindmost upper molars and has only forty-two teeth altogether. The full set of forty-four teeth is described by the standard dental formula as

$$\frac{3\text{-}1\text{-}4\text{-}3}{3\text{-}1\text{-}4\text{-}3}$$

—that is, three incisors, one canine, four premolars, and three molars on each side above and below. The dental formulas of most living groups have been reduced from that of the primitive state in one way or another. Man, for example, has but thirty-two teeth:

$$\frac{2\text{-}1\text{-}2\text{-}3}{2\text{-}1\text{-}2\text{-}3}$$

—that is, two incisors, one canine, two premolars and three molars on each side above and

Fig. 15-3. *Skull of wolf from above (left) and from below (right):* B.O, *basioccipital;* BS, *basisphenoid;* PS, *presphenoid; other letters as in Fig. 15-1. (From Ref. 1.)*

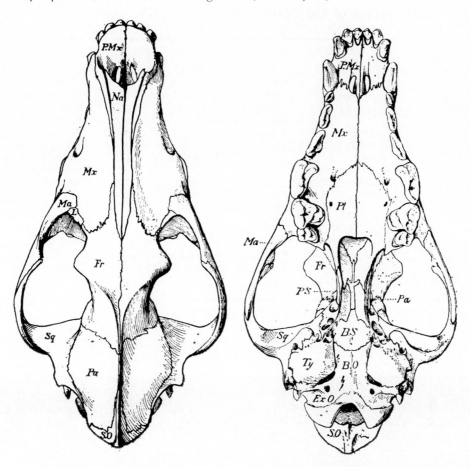

below. If, in addition to the dental formula, the number and arrangement of the cusps and other features of the individual teeth are given, the result is a handy guide to the principal groups of mammals and even to many subdivisions of those groups.

15-2. *Classification of Mammals*

The class Mammalia is divided into many orders. Several orders are primitive Mesozoic groups that are either unknown in the Cenozoic or represented by only a few survivors in the Paleocene (Table 3-4). Several other orders, including one that is represented in the present fauna, are so unimportant throughout their history that they are not worth our attention. If these early or rare orders are omitted from consideration, the fourteen orders listed in Table 15-1 remain. Some of these orders require further definition or comment.

The egg-laying mammals, the monotremes, are extremely rare and are unimportant except for the fact of their existence. Two living animals, the duck-billed platypus and the spiny, ant-eating echidna of Australia and New Guinea, are included here. The continued existence of these egg-layers in Notogaea (see § 13-4.a) was no doubt made possible by the absence of eutherian rivals for their ecologic niche.

TABLE 15-1

Classification of the Mammalia*

SUBCLASS OR INFRACLASS	ORDER	EXAMPLES	RANGE [a]
Prototheria	Monotremata	Australian platypus and echidna	Pleistocene–Recent
Metatheria	Marsupialia	Opossum, kangaroo, etc.	Cretaceous–Recent
Eutheria		Placental mammals	
Clawed	Insectivora	Shrews, etc.	Cretaceous–Recent
	Chiroptera	Bats	Eocene–Recent
	Carnivora	Dogs, cats, bears, seals, etc.	Paleocene–Recent
	Edentata	Sloths, etc.	Paleocene–Recent
	Rodentia	Rats, squirrels, beavers, etc.	Paleocene–Recent
Nail-bearing	Primates	Lemurs, lorises, monkeys, apes, men	Paleocene–Recent
Fish-like	Cetacea	Whales and porpoises	Eocene–Recent
Hoofed	Condylarthra	Primitive ungulates	Paleocene-Eocene, Miocene
	Notoungulata	South American ungulates	Paleocene–Pleistocene
	Proboscidea	Elephants, etc.	Eocene–Recent
	Perissodactyla	Odd-toed ungulates: horses, etc.	Eocene–Recent
	Artiodactyla	Even-toed ungulates: cattle, etc.	Eocene–Recent

[a] See Table 3-4 for subdivisions of the Cenozoic.

* Omitting the rarer orders, most of which are Mesozoic and Paleogene.

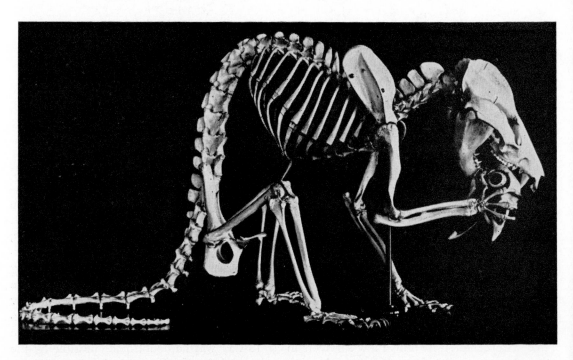

Fig. 15-4. *Skeleton of opossum,* Didelphis marsupialis, *with chicken's head in mouth. (Courtesy of the American Museum of Natural History.)*

The second group in Table 15-1 is made up of the pouch-bearers, or marsupials, whose young are born immature and carried by the mother in an abdominal pouch, or marsupium, until they are mature enough to take care of themselves. This group includes the opossums of South and North America, the kangaroos of Australia, and many other forms. Opossum and kangaroo skeletons are shown in Figures 15-4 and 15-5. The kangaroos are herbivorous; the opossums are omnivorous, with a preference for meat. In addition to these two fairly well-known types, and many other plant-eating animals, there have been, in the geologic past, a considerable number of meat-eating marsupials, especially in South America. The history of the marsupials displayed early vigor and variety in the late Mesozoic and then gradual disappearance from all parts of the world except Australia, South America, and southern North America.

Among the other groups three will barely be mentioned. The Cetacea (whales and porpoises) and the Chiroptera (bats) are of interest as mammals that have developed fishlike forms for life in the open sea or have learned to fly effectively, thus more or less equaling the Mesozoic record of the reptiles in these respects. The Rodentia, including squirrels, rats, mice, beavers, and many other common animals, make up one of the largest, most varied, and geologically most important mammalian groups. Unfortunately we do not have space for more than a mention of this complex order, which has flourished throughout the Cenozoic and whose study offers one of the most interesting possibilities for the development of useful mammalian guide fossils for continental Cenozoic rocks.

We shall give more attention to the carnivores, the edentates, and the great group of hoofed mammals, or ungulates. The carnivores make up the principal carnivorous or meat-eating group among all the mammals. Carnivores are prominent in the Recent fauna, including dogs, cats, bears, raccoons, skunks, weasels, the ocean-going seals, and several other groups. They are characterized by the

Fig. 15-5. *Skeleton of kangaroo,* Macropus. (*Courtesy of the American Museum of Natural History.*)

prominence of the cutting, biting, and tearing teeth, especially the tearing teeth at the corner of the jaw, the canines. The dog's dentition shown in Figures 15-1 and 15-3 may be considered primitive, for it includes a nearly full set of teeth with all the functional types represented, even to the grinding or molar teeth in the back of the jaw. The cats, on the

Fig. 15-6. *Skull of lion,* Felis leo. (*Courtesy of the American Museum of Natural History.*)

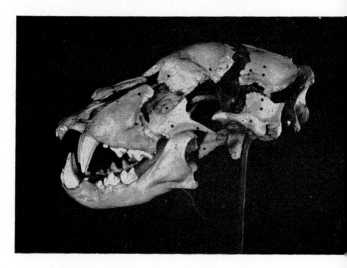

Fig. 15-7. Skeleton of Glossotherium, a South American mylodont ground sloth. (Courtesy of the American Museum of Natural History.)

Fig. 15-8. Skeleton of a condylarth, Phenacodus primaevus, from the Eocene of western North America. (Courtesy of the American Museum of Natural History.)

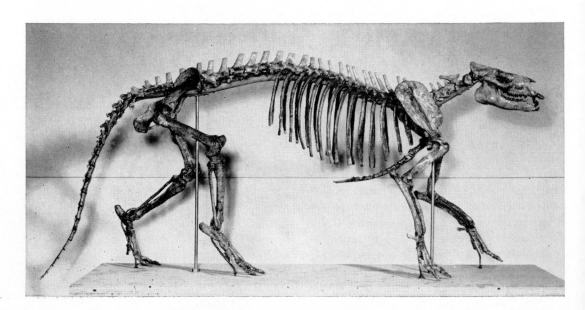

other hand, have developed a tearing and slicing dentition without grinding molars, so that the jaws have become very short, as shown in the skull of the lion (Fig. 15-6). The lower and upper cheek teeth of a cat-like animal slide past each other like the two halves of shears. Dogs, of course, can eat many different kinds of food, and can even grind up small bones, but lions, tigers, and other cats are flesh-eaters, slicing up their meat and swallowing it without grinding.

Not all meat-eaters are members of the order Carnivora, and a few of the Carnivora are not meat-eaters. Some extinct South American meat-eating animals, with teeth specialized for this purpose, were clearly members of the marsupial group, and the modern giant panda of Tibet is a vegetarian member of the Carnivora.

The edentates, or the toothless ones, are among the strangest and most specialized of mammals. Teeth either are absent or are rudimentary columnar cheek teeth without any enamel. The typical edentate is a sloth, either the small modern tree sloth or the giant prehistoric ground sloth. The ground sloth (Fig. 15-7) had a small cylindrical brain case; some species had well-developed armor consisting of small bony nodules in the skin. It was a dull and slow-moving South American animal, the culminating member of a varied group, who managed to get into North America in the Pliocene, but became extinct in both continents at the end of the Pleistocene.

The largest of all mammalian groups is the ungulate, characterized by the presence of hooves on the toes. Ungulates are herbivores; some eat foliage, more crop grass. An abundance of the right type of plants is essential to their welfare. Five ungulate orders are to be mentioned, two extinct and three that have living representatives. An early ancestral order of ungulates is that called the condylarths (Table 15-1). These animals had the feet and stance of a carnivore (Fig. 15-8); but they also had cheek teeth specialized for grinding (shown in plan in Fig. 15-9), and, even when they had five toes, there was a little hoof at

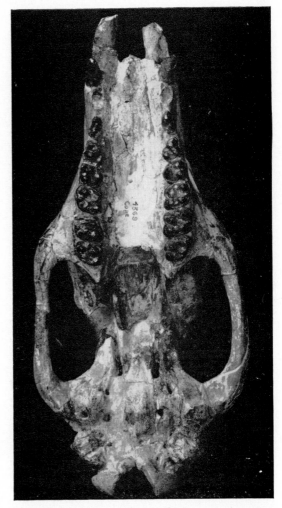

Fig. 15-9. *Skull of the condylarth* Phenacodus primaevus, *seen from below. (Courtesy of the American Museum of Natural History.)*

the end of each toe. Surely these are ungulates, but equally surely they must be considered primitive, carnivore-like ungulates. Most condylarths were restricted to the Paleocene and the Eocene (Table 3-4), but a late Miocene relic has been found in Colombia. The condylarths are the ancestral hoofed mammals.

A second extinct order, the Notoungulata, has a longer history. The order is made up chiefly of numerous Eocene and later forms in Patagonia and elsewhere in South America, but its earliest representative is in the Upper Paleocene of Mongolia, and it includes a single form in the Lower Eocene of western North America. Notoungulates are distinguished by many features, including the tooth patterns. Some had claws, and none were very well hoofed. Some developed superficial resemblances to northern mammals; one large, heavy-legged form was somewhat like a rhinoceros. The South American notoungulates, despite freedom from competition with the more advanced northern orders, declined sharply at the end of the Miocene and became extinct in the Pleistocene, the final blow perhaps being given by an invasion of North American ungulates.

The three living groups of ungulates, the proboscideans, the perissodactyls, and the artiodactyls, may be distinguished by their hooves. The elephants and other proboscideans have always walked on five-toed horny pads. In most perissodactyls the body weight is borne either by single toes, as in the modern horse, or by three toes on each foot, as in many of the horse's ancestors. Most artiodactyls put their weight on two toes and two hooves; common examples are cattle, sheep, and camels. The pigs have four functional toes, two main ones. There are also five-toed artiodactyls, and the first horses had four toes on the front feet. In general, perissodactyls are odd-toed, artiodactyls even-toed.

15-3. *Cenozoic Mammals of the Heartland*

For almost every mammalian order an eventful history is recorded in the rocks. Almost all can be traced back to ancestral representatives in Middle Paleogene (Eocene) or older rocks. The monotremes, however, though the most primitive order, are known only from the Pleistocene and Recent of Australasia. Monotremes may, nevertheless, be closely related to one or more of the Mesozoic orders not included in our list. The marsupials of the Cretaceous were as widespread as any other order, but since the Eocene they have

been almost entirely Australian or South American.

The higher, or eutherian, mammals are practically the only ones that have been present in Eurasia, Africa, or North America since the beginning of the Eocene. The further discussion in this chapter will be restricted almost entirely to these higher mammals and to their occurrence in these three continents, which together make up the mammalian heartland.

The primitive eutherians include the condylarths (Fig. 15-8) and several orders that are not listed in Table 15-1. These orders developed in the Paleocene and are known best from western North America. Several of the orders disappeared during the Eocene or Oligocene. Some of the last primitive eutherians apparently were about as large as small bears.

All the more advanced orders except the bats, the whales, and the more modern ungulates were represented by one or more ancestral types in the Paleocene. The early carnivores, for example, can be subdivided into several groups. One was a primitive generalized group that flourished in the Paleocene and Eocene. It was then gradually replaced by the much more varied modern types, such as the primitive cats, the primitive dogs, and so forth. Almost from the start there were two kinds of cats, the saber-tooth variety and the true cats. The canines in the saber-tooth group were very long and very thin, especially those in the upper jaw (Fig. 15-10), which could be thrust downward like daggers into the prey. The saber-tooth cats became extinct in the late Pleistocene. Apparently they were doing very well indeed up to the very end, and it is a little mysterious that only lions, tigers, and the various other true cats have lived on into our modern world.

Primates are especially interesting to us because we belong to that group. Fossil primates are somewhat rare, except in the Lower Eocene, and the specimens known are mostly small fragments. Apparently most primates were tropical tree-dwelling animals and seldom contributed their remains to the sedi-

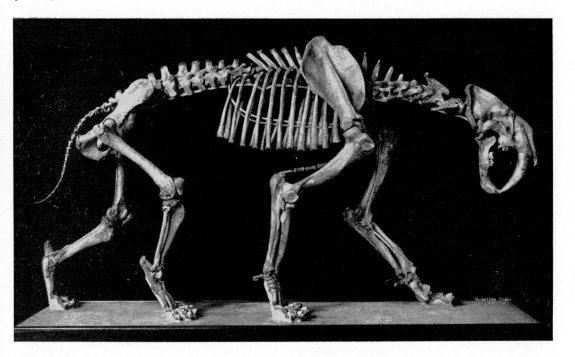

Fig. 15-10.   *Skeleton of the giant South American saber-tooth* Smilodon bonaerensis, *from Argentina. (Courtesy of the American Museum of Natural History.)*

ments that have been preserved for our study. Primates may be divided into three groups: (1) The small, squirrel-size lemurs and lorises, which live today in the East Indies and Madagascar and various other places around the Indian Ocean, run around on all fours; but their skulls, teeth, and toes are rather similar to our own. (2) The tarsioids have a modern, nocturnal and arboreal representative, which, with its big staring eyes, is shown in Figure 15-11. The lemurs and tarsioids are very common fossils in the Eocene, but are rare at higher levels in the rocks. The tarsioids are fairly close, anatomically, to the group of higher primates that includes man. (3) This group includes (a) the New World monkeys, such as the little spider monkeys; (b) the Old World monkeys, which differ from the New World forms in their teeth and other skeletal features; (c) the great apes, such as the gorilla, and man. Group 3 is known from the Oligocene of Egypt right up to the present, mostly by isolated teeth or jaw fragments, but

Fig. 15-11.   *Skeleton of the small primate* Tarsius. *(Courtesy of the American Museum of Natural History.)*

rarely by skulls. Almost all the Neogene fossil primates are limited to the Old World. A few New World Neogene monkeys are known, notably in Patagonia and Colombia.

15-4. *Cenozoic Ungulates*

The best-known and most interesting animals of the age of mammals, especially in the heartland, are the ungulates, primarily the brontotheres, camels, elephants, and horses. We shall concentrate our attention on these four groups.

a. Brontotheres

The brontotheres (also called titanotheres) are limited to the Paleogene. They are found first in Eocene rocks and became extinct before the Oligocene ended. They were perissodactyl ungulates with four or three toes, remote relatives of the horses. The teeth were sometimes large and heavy, but always primitive and apparently not very effective. The short-crowned cheek teeth were rarely worn down to the roots, a fact suggesting that they were not used in grinding up siliceous or dirty fodder. The brains were extremely small compared with the sizes of the animals. Near the end of their career the brontotheres developed into giants eight feet high at the shoulder. These later brontotheres had pairs of horns (Fig. 15-12).

The brontotheres flourished in western America, particularly in South Dakota, Nebraska, and Wyoming, though their range extended west to California. Their remains are common in Mongolia and have also been found in Burma and in Europe. The locally abundant bones of gigantic brontotheres in the Rocky Mountain region indicate that this

Fig. 15-12. *The large brontothere* Brontotherium, *from Oligocene tuff of the Rocky Mountain region. (Painting by Charles R. Knight; courtesy of the American Museum of Natural History.)*

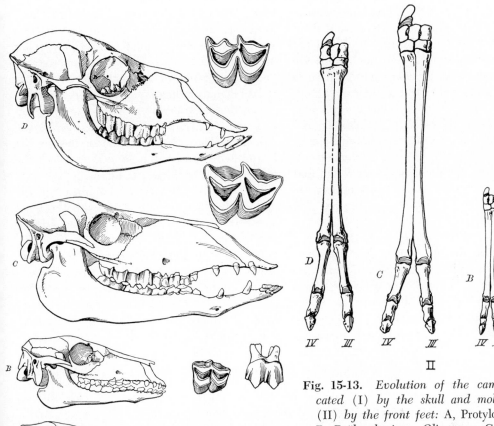

Fig. 15-13. *Evolution of the camels, as indicated* (I) *by the skull and molar teeth and* (II) *by the front feet:* A, Protylopus, *Eocene;* B, Poëbrotherium, *Oligocene;* C, Procamelus, *Upper Miocene; all from western North America.* D, Lama huanacus, *the living guanaco of South America. (From Ref. 1.)*

animal marked a climax among the Paleogene browsing animals. Apparently these were the largest common and widespread animals of the time. If we may judge by their rather inefficient teeth, they must have lived on lush vegetation, and their sudden extinction before the Paleogene's end may have been connected with the disappearance of favorite types of food. The disappearance of the brontotheres is but one of several Late Paleogene extinctions, both in Asia and in America, particularly of groups of exceptionally large animals.

b. Camels

The camels belong to the even-toed or artiodactyl group of ungulates. Like their relatives,

the cattle, deer, and sheep, they developed highly specialized feet and also teeth with the characteristic crescent or double-crescent enamel pattern that most artiodactyls have (Fig. 15-13). Camels produced effective long-crowned cheek teeth approximately at the end of the Paleogene, at the time when grasses appeared. Long-crowned teeth developed in about the same way at about the same time in the horse and other groups; in place of the short-crowned tooth with definite anchored roots, there evolved a tooth with a much longer crown and a delayed development of the root system, so that the permanent tooth could keep pushing up out of the jaw as it was added to below and as it was worn off above. The teeth also invariably became covered by external, calcium phosphate **cement**, which coated the tops of the teeth and filled the deep pits produced by down-folds of the enameled tooth surface. Some such folds are several inches deep. A characteristic pattern of wear is produced, shown in the camel teeth of Figure 15-13, here producing crescent-shaped enamel ridges. The result, for the camels and for other groups with long-crowned cheek teeth, was an efficient grinding apparatus capable of handling rough and dirty food. The gritty food was not necessarily grass; modern camels browse on bushes and thorn trees.

The history of the camel extends from the Eocene to the Recent. The earlier history is known only from North America, to which the group seems to have been restricted until about the end of the Pliocene. The living forms are the true camels of southwestern Asia and North Africa, with their humps, and the llamas of the Andes of South America,

with their heavy covering of long hair. Both these developments are probably late adaptations of these two marginal forms. These relics at the very extremes of the maximum Neogene geographic range of the camel group are not to be taken as indicating any close relation between the Sahara-Arabian region and the Andes—as, for instance, by a bridge across the Atlantic. The wide separation of these relics is quite obviously due to extinction of the group in most of the heartland.

In North America camels flourished to the end of the Pleistocene. Along with the main line, with its long-crowned teeth and grazing habits, there was also, right into the late Neogene, the browsing giraffe camel, *Alticamelus*, whose diet of clean food, presumably the foliage of trees, is demonstrated by its short-crowned teeth. The extinction of all the camels in North America at the end of the Pleistocene was perhaps due to the development there of an unfavorable habitat. When Lieutenant

Fig. 15-14.   *The Warren mastodon, a specimen of* Mammut americanus *found in the Pleistocene of New York State. (Courtesy of the American Museum of Natural History.)*

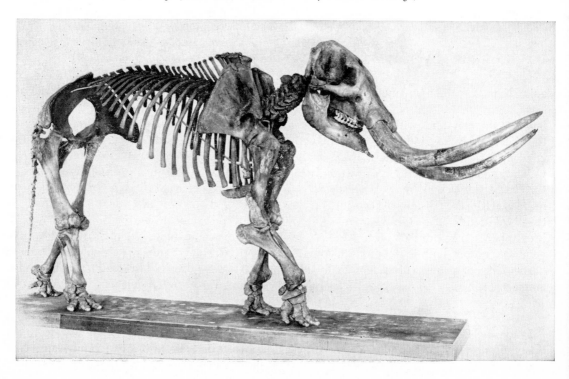

Beale brought his seventy-six camels to the Southwest in 1857 and then, harassed by mule-skinners and the confusion that preceded the Civil War, had to turn many of them loose, the freed camels survived but did not multiply as freed horses did.

c. Elephant and Mastodon

The proboscideans, typified by the living elephants, have a history that extends from the Eocene to the present. They have been practically limited to Africa, Eurasia, and North America, although they did invade South America during Pleistocene time. At one time or another proboscideans have ranged over all of the heartland continents. They are first known from the Eocene of Egypt, but most of their history is best documented in Europe, Asia, and North America.

The elephants have developed massive columnar legs and almost equally columnar five-toed feet with pads, as shown in Figure 15-14. Their heads and teeth underwent extraordinary changes just lately, in the Pleistocene (Fig. 15-15). Most members of the group, including the Pleistocene mastodon (Fig. 15-14), got along with short-crowned teeth, which no doubt were adequate for browsing purposes as long as the animals were able to tear loose masses of highgrowing swale vegetation or the more succulent branches of trees. The elephants proper (*Elephas*, etc.), however, developed, early in the Pleistocene, long-crowned teeth of a peculiar laminated type (Fig. 15-15A).

Moeritherium, of the Egyptian Eocene (Fig. 15-15F), was a small and rather primitive generalized mammal, though its dentition already included the broad flat grinding cheek teeth characteristic of proboscideans, as well as long incisors, the future tusks. This development went a little farther in *Palaeomastodon*, of the Egyptian Oligocene, in which there were four clean-cut tusks, two in the upper jaw and two in the lower jaw. In the wide-ranging *Gomphotherium*, of the Miocene (Fig. 15-15D), found all over Europe and North America, these tusks became two or

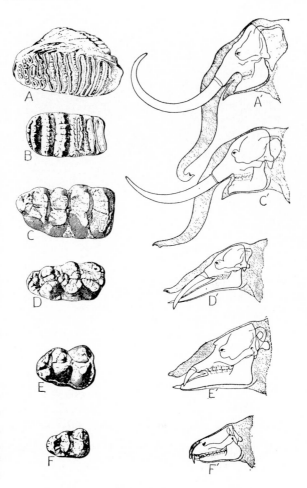

Fig. 15-15. *Evolution of the head and molar teeth of mastodons and elephants.* (*Courtesy of the American Museum of Natural History.*)
FF'. Moeritherium, *Eocene of Egypt.*
EE'. Palaeomastodon, *Oligocene of Egypt.*
DD'. Gomphotherium, *Miocene.*
CC'. *Mastodon* (Mammut), *Pleistocene.*
B. Stegodon, *Pliocene.*
AA'. Elephas, *Pleistocene.*

three feet long, and the front part of the skull was correspondingly elongated. The mastodon (*Mammut*) of the late Neogene and Pleistocene of Europe and North America (Fig. 15-15C) lost the lower tusks completely. Its whole jaw was considerably shorter, and the two tusks of the upper jaw became curving, massive rods twelve feet long, teeth unequaled

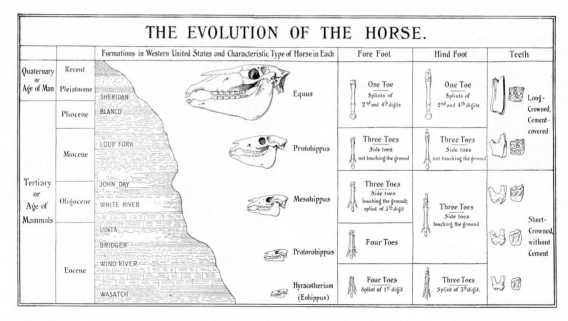

THE EVOLUTION OF THE HORSE.

		Formations in Western United States and Characteristic Type of Horse in Each	Fore Foot	Hind Foot	Teeth
Quaternary or Age of Man	Recent				
	Pleistocene	SHERIDAN — Equus	One Toe — Splints of 2nd and 4th digits	One Toe — Splints of 2nd and 4th digits	Long-Crowned, Cement-covered
	Pliocene	BLANCO			
Tertiary or Age of Mammals	Miocene	LOUP FORK — Protohippus	Three Toes — Side toes not touching the ground	Three Toes — Side toes not touching the ground	
	Oligocene	JOHN DAY — WHITE RIVER — Mesohippus	Three Toes — Side toes touching the ground; splint of 5th digit	Three Toes — Side toes touching the ground	Short-Crowned, without Cement
	Eocene	UINTA — BRIDGER — Protorohippus	Four Toes		
		WIND RIVER — WASATCH — Hyracotherium (Eohippus)	Four Toes — Splint of 1st digit	Three Toes — Splint of 5th digit.	

Fig. 15-16. *Evolution of the horse. (A diagram prepared in 1902; courtesy of the American Museum of Natural History.)*

Fig. 15-17. *Chewing surfaces of upper cheek teeth of horses. (After W. D. Matthew; courtesy of the American Museum of Natural History.)*
A. Orohippus, *Middle Eocene.*
B. Epihippus, *Upper Eocene.*
C. Parahippus, *Lower Miocene.*
D. Merychippus, *Middle Miocene.*
E. Equus, *Pleistocene...*

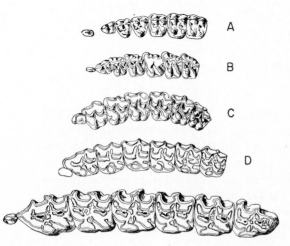

by any other animal except its relatives the elephants.

The elephants proper, *Elephas* etc., appeared in the latest Neogene, flourished in the Pleistocene of Eurasia, Africa, and North America, and have lived on in Africa and southern Asia. These are the most interesting of the proboscideans, especially because of their variety and their associations during the Pleistocene. The Pleistocene giants were the largest of all land mammals, up to fourteen feet high at the shoulder, with single cheek teeth a foot high, a foot long, and three or four inches thick. As shown in Figure 15-15A, these long-crowned teeth developed with long thin infolds of enamel, producing through wear as many as twenty-four enamel ridges in a single tooth, which made an exceptionally efficient ridged grinding surface. One of the most curious features of the elephant's dentition is an arrangement by which there are only one or two functional grinding cheek teeth on each side of each jaw at any one time. The teeth come in obliquely from the rear and gradually push out the old teeth.

The members of the proboscidean group got bigger and more varied epoch by epoch, up to the Pleistocene. The Neogene four-tuskers may have dug roots and tubers. Long-crowned teeth appeared very late, no doubt marking a change to a somewhat gritty diet. The group has now apparently passed its peak, as shown both by slight reduction in maximum size and by the great restriction of its geographic range.

d. Horses

The last of the four groups of ungulates to which we are giving special attention is the large one culminating in the horse and the zebra. This is probably the best-known family of fossil mammals. Animals that can properly be called horses in the broad sense are known from the Eocene to the Pleistocene in North America, from the Eocene to the Recent in Africa and Eurasia, and in the Pleistocene of South America. Now they have been spread over the world by man.

The earlier forms had short-crowned teeth. Long crowns appeared early in the Neogene, just as the grasslands were spreading. The development of the horse is shown in barest outline in Figure 15-16. The earliest horse, commonly called eohippus, is known from the Eocene of Europe and western North America. Eohippus was a whippet-sized animal, with four front toes and three rear toes, with short-crowned teeth differentiated in the primitive mammalian fashion, but with the canines already on the way to suppression and with the cheek teeth showing the first suggestions of the typical horsey pattern of bumps and furrows. The further development of the equine cheek-tooth pattern is shown in Figure 15-17. The two rows of teeth at the top of the diagram are Eocene; they are short-crowned teeth of small animals. The middle row represents, with change of scale, a much larger animal, the *Parahippus* of the Miocene. It was still a browser, as shown by its short-crowned teeth. The fourth member of the series is the Miocene *Merychippus*, of about the same size as *Parahippus* but with long-crowned teeth,

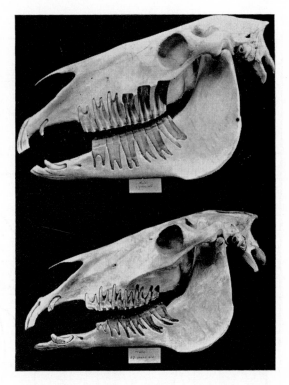

Fig. 15-18. *Above: skull of modern horse* (Equus) *eight years old, prepared to show cheek teeth, which have been worn down somewhat; below: skull of horse twenty-seven years old, with cheek teeth almost worn away. (Courtesy of the American Museum of Natural History.)*

which have complicated enamel ridges rising above softer internal dentine and external cement. The final horse is *Equus*, of the Pleistocene and Recent. Its teeth are shown in plan at the bottom of Figure 15-17 and in side view in Figure 15-18.

The history of the horse is known much better in western North America than anywhere else in the world, millions of teeth and other bones being present in the continental sediments of the whole region from the Dakotas and Nebraska west. But the horse became extinct in America in the latest Pleistocene and was reintroduced by the Spaniards. The horse had migrated from North to South America in latest Neogene or earliest Pleistocene time, but it had become extinct there just

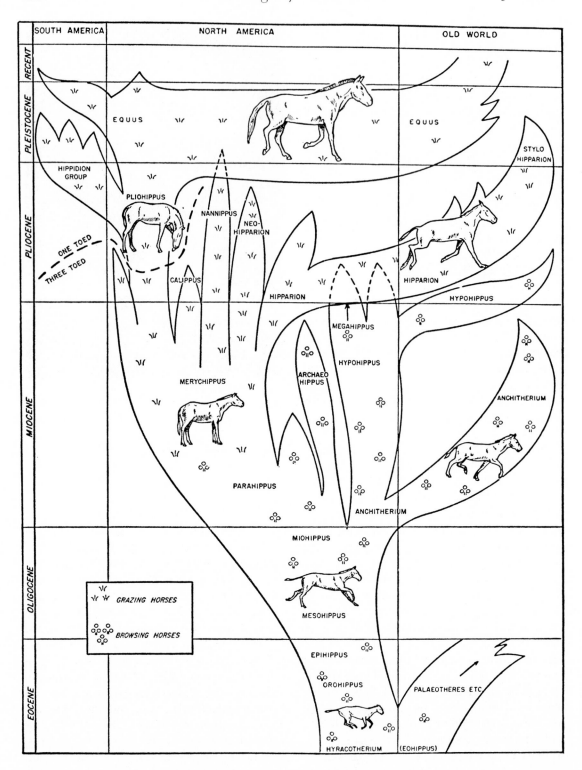

Fig. 15-19. *The lineages of the horse family, with restorations to scale.* (From *Horses* by G. G. Simpson. Copyright 1951 by Oxford University Press, Inc. Reprinted by permission.)

as in North America. When reintroduced by the Spaniards, horses soon went wild and became so common that every Indian warrior of the plains region rode one. Probably the Pleistocene extinction was due, not to unfavorable climate or food supply, but to epidemic disease or other catastrophe.

The complete succession of fossil remains, especially the rapidly changing and easily distinguished teeth, makes horses the perfect guide fossils for the formations that contain them. They are also the most satisfying of all examples of evolution.

15-5. *Evolution of the Horse*

The lineage and geographic distribution of the horse are shown in Figure 15-19. The origin in North America or Europe is shown, the spread all over Eurasia and North America, repeated extinctions in the Old World, the final expansion into South America, and the favorite foods of the various types. It will be noted that the leaf-eaters did not go out of existence with the appearance of *Merychippus*. During the Miocene there were two types of horses, those with long-crowned teeth, which ate grass, and those with short-crowned teeth, which were browsers. The browser *Hypohippus* did not finally become extinct in the Old World until late in the Neogene. The development of the skulls of the successive horses is shown in Figure 15-16. Note the persistence of the characteristic sinuous or rounded enamel pattern, which is contrasted with the sharper, arcuate forms of the camels and other artiodactyls. Note also the flowing W shape developed in the enamel patterns on the inner edge of the upper cheek teeth in the horses (Fig. 15-17), which are contrasted with the double crescents of the camels. It is easy, at a glance, to tell a fossil horse tooth from a fossil camel tooth. Note also in Figure 15-16 the striking change in proportion in the various parts of the skull and lower jaw, the tremendous deepening of the cheek region to take care of the growing battery of grinding teeth.

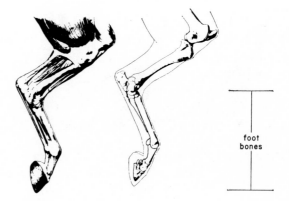

Fig. 15-20. *Hind leg of modern horse.* (*Redrawn after the American Museum of Natural History.*)
LEFT. *With muscles and ligaments.*
RIGHT. *Skeleton.*

At the same time that these changes were taking place, a notable change was occurring in the brains of the horses. Among the most striking features in the later horses are the larger and more corrugated brain case and a change of shape that allows the front lobes of the brain to be proportionally much larger in *Equus* than in eohippus. Eohippus was not only primitive but dull, whereas the modern horse is not only bigger and a more efficient feeder but also, if one may judge by the character of the brain alone, a brighter animal.

One of the most remarkable changes that have taken place in any animal in the course of its development is the transformation in the horse's feet. The obvious changes are the loss of all but the middle toe and that toe's great elongation (Figs. 15-16 and 15-20). The most notable change, however, is not that from a four- or three-toed to a one-toed foot, which is really a rather unimportant late change, but that from a pad-footed to a spring-footed state, shown in Figure 15-21. The little eohippus with its four toes probably had springy pads somewhat like a dog's and was probably an efficient runner. Its foot action has been described by G. G. Simpson: [*]

[*] From *Horses*, by G. G. Simpson, pp. 193, 197. Copyright 1951 by Oxford University Press, Inc. Reprinted by permission.

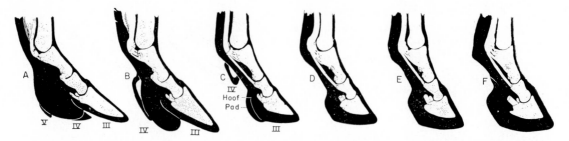

Fig. 15-21. *Evolution of the horse's hoof, not to scale;* III, IV, *and* V: *third, fourth, and fifth digits.*
(Modified slightly from C. L. Camp and Natasha Smith, Univ. California Memoirs, 1942.)

A. *Eohippus* (Hyracotherium), *Eocene.*	D. Pliohippus, *Pliocene.*
B. Mesohippus, *Oligocene.*	E. Equus, *Pleistocene.*
C. Merychippus, *Miocene.*	F. Equus (*modern horse, zebra*), *Recent.*

"Relatively slow-moving animals, like bears or men, often set their heels and (if they are four-footed) their wrists on the ground when they walk. Most of the faster animals have increased the effective length of the leg where it counts most, at the lower end, because their heels and wrists are held well up off the ground and the weight falls at the end of the long bones corresponding to those of the palm (metacarpal bones) and instep (metatarsals) of man. This had already happened in eohippus, in which the wrist (corresponding with the 'knee' of *Equus*) and the heel (corresponding with the hock) were permanently raised. Eohippus bore its weight on the ends of the four metacarpals of the forefoot (one of which survives as the shank in *Equus*) and the other three metatarsals of the hindfoot (one of which is the cannon bone in *Equus*). Below the ends of these bones and between and behind the toes was a heavy, flexible but tough pad or cushion. As each foot took off for a stride, it rolled up from the pad onto the toes and gave a final thrust from the small hooves on the ends of the toes. As the foot came down at the end of the stride, it landed on the cushion. You can see almost exactly how the mechanism worked by looking at the foot of the next friendly dog you chance to meet. The only obvious difference is that a dog has claws where eohippus had little hooves. In fact, except for not being hooked, even the hooves of eohippus were as much like a dog's claws as like the radically different hoof of *Equus*."

But in *Merychippus* the ligaments at the back of the footbones, larger and stronger and more complex, became parts of a spring mechanism. When the animal landed on one foot, the middle toe was strongly flexed by the impact, stretching the elastic ligaments on the back side of the foot. As the weight moved forward and the foot came back into position to take off on the next stride, the ligament snapped back like a rubber band and literally bounced the animal forward. This spring makes for remarkably fast action in horses of increasing weight and is different from anything that could have occurred in earlier pad-footed types. The modern horse is thrown forward by a spring that was set as soon as the forethrust hoof struck the ground.

The development of the horse has been notable and is well documented. The various types of horses are accurately placed in a well-known stratigraphic succession (Fig. 15-16). The skeletons or partial skeletons of thousands upon thousands of horses from many different levels make an almost continuous record. We know that the horses were transformed from little animals about as big as dogs to the large horses of Pleistocene and Recent time. We know that their teeth and skulls went through changes that enabled them to crop grass effectively for moderately long lives. We know that their feet developed a spring mechanism that made them especially effective runners with notably quick starts. We know that, unlike those of the brontotheres, their brains also developed, so that they became unusually alert and intelligent animals. Here is a superb example of useful transformations, changes that produced an animal superior, by any standard, to the initial form. Here we have material for the study of evolution. This material has given rise to varied ideas as to the way in which the transformations, the evolution, occurred. One of the most interesting theories that have come from the study of horses is called **orthogenesis**. The idea is well expressed in a jingle:

> Said the little Eohippus,
> "I am going to be a horse
> And on my middle finger-nails
> To run my earthly course."

That is to say, there was something preordained about the transformation from the original five-toed mammal to the very different horse with its single elongated toe on each leg. The orthogenetic interpretation is that the animal's feet and teeth went through a whole series of transformations that were not of much good to the intermediate forms and became really valuable only in the final product (*Equus*). It appears now that this idea is not justified by the facts. The little eohippus was a pretty effective animal in its own forest sphere, even a good runner. The animals of intermediate size, which moved on three toes, may have found the extra toes extremely handy. Those toes were off the ground at the beginning of the stride, but in the earlier spring-footed forms, in particular, the side toes may have decreased the shock of landing on the single main toe as the spring went into action. As the foot was flexed in the setting of the spring, the side toes must have touched the ground, even hard ground, and have been real support to the animal, preventing sprains, which are the plague of the modern horse, even with its much stronger toe and ligaments. Even after the one-toed *Pliohippus* developed (Fig. 15-19), the three-toed line persisted for millions of years and apparently got along just about as well as the one-toed. The one-toed group has survived, and the three-toed forms have disappeared; but it does not appear that the three-toed condition was ever much of a handicap, and it may, under some circumstances, have been a real advantage. A somewhat similar conclusion can be reached with regard to the teeth. From the very start, the presence of cement, and even a slightly longer-crowned tooth with the opportunity for continued growth after adolescence, must have been useful to an animal that was eating a little grass along with leaves and shrubbery. The transformation to the grass-eating habit may have gone along with the development of longer-crowned teeth and been made possible by changes in the teeth. In other words, there does not seem to be any justification whatever for the idea that the horses during the middle part of their development were not helped in the struggle for existence by their intermediate state with regard to feet and teeth. It was not necessary to wait for advantage until the present (final?) state had been reached. Now that we know the difference between the pad-footed and spring-footed mechanisms, it is hard to remember that the feet of the earlier horses looked so ineffective that they led to the idea of orthogenesis.

15-6. *Résumé of the Mammals*

In this chapter we have presented brief summaries of the histories of a few groups of hoofed mammals. Other groups have had, in a general way, a similar history. The great number, the great variety, and the dominance in size of the varied groups of mammals make the Cenozoic the age of mammals, even though, among smaller animals, insects were also very effective during this same period. The age of mammals may be far from over, despite all the damage that man has done to himself and to other mammals and all that he may do in the future. Already the mammals have had an eventful history, mostly on land, and mostly on the great continents. In this chapter we have considered chiefly the central area made up of North America, Eurasia, and Africa. In these continents the mammals have reached three successive climaxes of development—in the early Paleogene, in the latest Paleogene, and in the Pleistocene. At each climax, some group or groups of mammals reached a maximum in size as well as a maximum in variety, and then the whole group disappeared either from the whole earth or from the major part of its previous living space. Primitive mammals not described in this book came to an end in the early Paleogene. Brontotheres and several other groups ended their careers in the late Paleogene. The giant ground sloths, the saber-tooth cats, and some other groups became extinct in the Pleistocene.

REFERENCES

1. W. B. Scott: *A History of Land Mammals in the Western Hemisphere,* 2nd ed., 786 pages (The Macmillan Co. and The American Philosophical Society, New York, 1937); reprint (Hafner, New York, 1962)

2. G. G. Simpson: *Life of the Past,* 198 pages (Yale University Press, New Haven, 1953)

3. A. S. Romer: *Vertebrate Paleontology,* 2nd ed., 687 pages (University of Chicago Press, 1945)

4. G. G. Simpson: *Horses,* 247 pages (Oxford University Press, New York, 1951)

5. W. D. Matthew and S. H. Chubb: *Evolution of the Horse,* Guide Leaflet No. 36, 67 pages (Am. Mus. Nat. Hist., New York, 1927)

6. C. L. Camp and Natasha Smith: "Phylogeny and Functions of the Digital Ligaments of the Horse," Memoirs, University of California, vol. 13, pp. 69–124 (1942)

7. H. F. Osborn: *The Titanotheres of Ancient Wyoming, Dakota, and Nebraska,* Monograph 55, U.S. Geol. Sur., 2 vols., 701 and 953 pages (1929)

CHAPTER 16

The Pleistocene

THE PLEISTOCENE (also called Quaternary) is the youngest geological system. Its sediments and lavas have exceptional significance; in addition, much happened during Pleistocene time to the exposed portions of older systems. The most unusual events were several widespread glaciations.

The Pleistocene is important in human affairs. It was then that most soils acquired their characteristic features. Soil conditions are commonly dominant factors in plant growth; man and other animals live, directly or indirectly, on plants. In the United States, the miracles of the midwestern corn belt are performed on superior, mostly limestone-glacial soils, the wheat of eastern Washington is grown on periglacial Palouse (loess) soils, and the highly productive irrigated lands of California are mostly Pleistocene and later alluvium. Soils, mantle rock, and landslides, developed during the Pleistocene, are important factors in the stability of foundations for buildings, roads, bridges, and dams. Ground water aquifers are usually Pleistocene deposits. Most of human prehistory occurred during the Pleistocene; prehistoric men and their cultures are dated by stratigraphic and geochemical methods.

16-1. *Pleistocene Deposits*

Pleistocene deposits are rather thin in most places, but they occur almost everywhere. They may make up only a few feet of red clay in the central Pacific Ocean, but they thicken to tens or hundreds of feet of mostly coarser sediments near shore. On land, clastic Pleistocene sediments vary from a few feet to hundreds of feet on deltas, in flat-floored stream valleys, and on stream terraces; they become thousands of feet thick in the tectonic basins of the mountainous regions that border the Pacific Ocean and constitute the east-west Alpine-Himalayan belt. Notable members of the Pleistocene System are the local tuffs and lavas that make up such volcanic piles as Vesuvius and Etna. The most unusual and distinctive of all Pleistocene accumulations, however, are those deposited by glacial ice, glacial outwash streams, and periglacial wind storms over large parts of the northern continents—surface layers that covered almost everything and in many areas can still be followed as a continuous cover, up hill and down dale.

In general, the Pleistocene is continental in land areas and marine beneath present seas, but at the margins of continents and islands some continental formations extend beneath the sea and some marine sediments are present on land. On many shores marine Pleistocene terrace deposits rise tier on tier to elevations of hundreds of feet.

a. Shallow Marine Deposits

The marine sequences now called Pleistocene were named Newer Pliocene by Lyell in 1833, with a type area in southeastern Sicily.

In 1839 Lyell designated these strata as Pleistocene; the new name and its definition were soon generally accepted, but the definition was later given up by its author. After the recognition of continental glaciation about 1840, emphasis shifted to continental deposits, and a non-stratigraphic notion—that the Pleistocene was the *time* of continent-wide glaciations—became widespread and was accepted by Lyell. Finally the International Geological Congress of 1948, fortunately for geologists who work outside the glaciated regions, redefined the base of the Pleistocene System in terms similar to those first used by Lyell, but in a marine sequence on the southern Italian mainland instead of in Sicily.

Lyell, in 1833, reported that 95 percent of the molluscan species known from his type deposits were still living—mostly near the type areas, in Mediterranean waters. All over the world, marine coastal deposits with 90 percent or more of their molluscan species Recent are usually considered Pleistocene, at least tentatively. The tediousness and uncertainty of the percentage method, however, have led almost everywhere to the use of guide species for subdivision of the section and for regional correlations. The Pleistocene strata of Sicily and the Italian mainland have, by the use of such guides, been divided into three stages whose faunas differ chiefly in their temperature facies. Similar distinctions have been made elsewhere. The base of the marine Pleistocene, marked by the disappearance of Pliocene guides, is commonly better marked than the divisions within the Pleistocene.

b. Continental Deposits

Terrace deposits along the upper courses of the Arno and Po rivers of northern Italy contain no marine shells but do yield occasional fresh-water shells and also teeth and other bones of rather modern mammals, notably cattle, submodern horses, and elephants with long-crowned cheek teeth. Teeth of the same species of elephant have been found in marine Lower Pleistocene deposits not far away, notably along the lower course of the Arno River. The continental deposits of the upper Arno (Fig. 16-1; also Fig. 1-3) and Po are therefore correlated with the marine Lower Pleistocene; they are placed in the *Villafranchian Stage,* with type locality at Villafranca, near Asti, in the upper Po valley (Fig. 16-2). The mammalian assemblage is from horizons high in the stage and is called the *Upper Villafranchian* fauna. The lower Villafranchian may be Pliocene. Faunas of Villafranchian type have been found at many places in Eurasia, Africa, and North America, notably in central France, Holland, England, several parts of east-central Europe, Spain, Morocco, Algeria, Tunisia, Tanganyika, northwestern India, northwestern Texas, and southwestern Kansas. The formations that contain such faunas are usually considered Lower Pleistocene, especially if appropriate species of cattle, horse, and elephant mark the fauna as Upper Villafranchian.

Fig. 16-1. *Horizontally stratified (and vertically rilled) Upper Villafranchian strata, mostly stream sand and gravel; near the top, thin dark lake beds containing the fresh-water clam Unio. The whole section corresponds to the lower part of the horizontal strata in the foreground of Fig. 1-3. Terranova, upper Arno Valley, 25 miles southeast of Florence, Italy. (Photograph by Augusto Azzaroli, University of Florence.)*

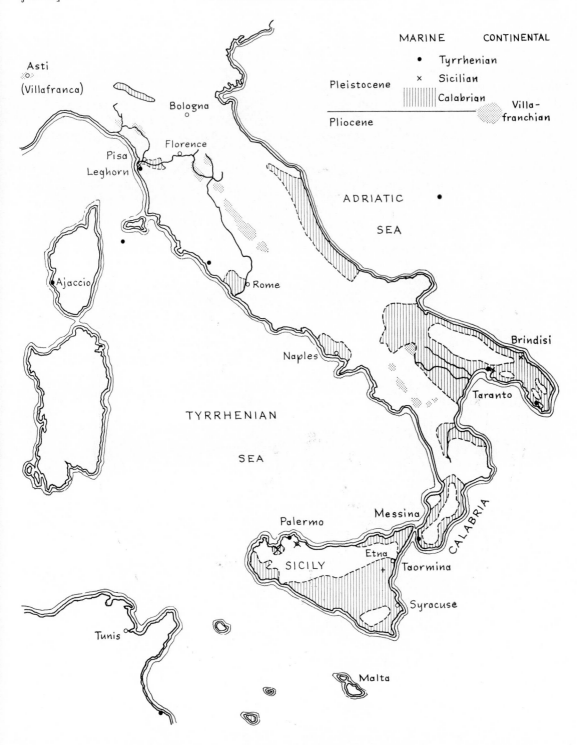

Fig. 16-2. *Map of Italy, showing marine and continental Pleistocene sediments. (After Maurice Gi-gnoux, 1913.)*

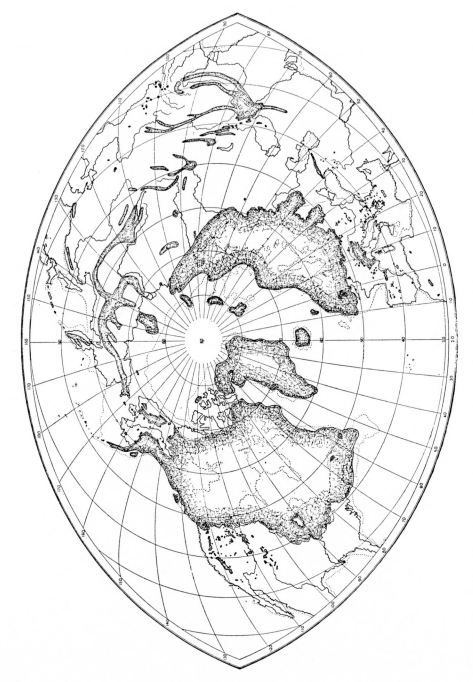

Fig. 16-3. *Map showing areas of Pleistocene glaciation in the northern hemisphere. (From Ernst Antevs,* Bulletin, *Geol. Soc. Am., 1929.)*

Higher horizons in the continental Pleistocene, in Europe and elsewhere, have commonly yielded two mammalian faunas that can be distinguished locally as Middle and Upper Pleistocene.

c. Pleistocene and Recent

Some geologists consider all post-Pliocene deposits Pleistocene. According to a more common usage, the one followed in this book, post-Pliocene deposits are divided into two parts: a major Pleistocene division and a minor, overlying Recent division. A Recent-Pleistocene contact, however, cannot be followed far by stratigraphic or paleontological methods. It has therefore become convenient to call Recent all sediments formed during approximately the last 11,000 years, reserving the term Pleistocene for earlier post-Pliocene deposits. The justification of this boundary is the rather abrupt change that occurred in the strata of high and middle northern latitudes some 10,500–11,500 years ago, a change apparently connected with an equally sudden warming of the climate. The method of dating this change will be described later.

d. Glaciation

The principal areas of probably Pleistocene continental glaciation in the northern hemisphere, now mostly free from ice, are shown in Figure 16-3. Northern Europe was covered by ice sheets that extended south as far as London, Leipzig, Warsaw, and Kiev, almost reaching Volgograd (Stalingrad). In addition, masses of ice reached northward from the Alps and coalesced to form piedmont glaciers on the Bavarian plains, so that only a narrow corridor in southern Germany remained ice-free, between the northern and the Alpine glaciers. In North America, continental glaciation extended as far south as the Missouri and Ohio rivers, northernmost Pennsylvania, and Long Island. Alpine glaciers many miles long were present in the Cordillera as far south as the Front Range of Colorado and the Sierra Nevada of California.

In both northern Europe and northern North America, the late geologic section is made up of several tills, with intervening loess (wind-deposited silt) or clay and sand. At some places the interglacial deposits contain the remains of subtropical plants or animals, indicating interglacial climates warmer than the present climate of the region.

A prime problem of Pleistocene stratigraphy is correlation between glaciated and unglaciated regions. Since no Villafranchian fauna has been found in a section that includes a complete sequence of glacial deposits, this fauna cannot be assigned, with much confidence, either an interglacial or a preglacial

Fig. 16-4. *Structure section, Palos Verdes Hills, California, from the top of San Pedro Hill eastward to Second Street in San Pedro. (Data from W. P. Woodring and others, U.S. Geological Survey, 1946.)*

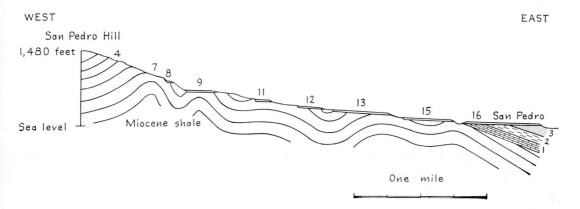

position. Indirect evidence involving northern Italy, Holland, and England indicates, as we shall see, that the earliest European glaciation was probably Pleistocene. The Upper Villafranchian, however, may be wholly preglacial, preglacial and early glacial, or wholly interglacial.

e. Complex Marine Pleistocene Sequences

In at least two regions, the type area in southern Italy and coastal southern California, the marine Pleistocene is exceptionally thick and complex. At San Pedro, on the southwest edge of the Los Angeles Basin, the section is divided by sharp unconformity. In Figure 16-4 the Pleistocene sedimentary units (and a few terraces that have been denuded of sediments) are designated by numbers between and including 1 and 16, No. 1 being the oldest and No. 16 probably the youngest. The three oldest sedimentary units—a marl, a silt, and a sand—have been tilted 10°–20°. The whole mass of Miocene strata to the left must have been tilted along with these three units, and both Miocene and Lower Pleistocene eroded somewhat, before the thirteen later units were deposited on terraces of San Pedro Hill (the highest of the Palos Verdes Hills). The numbering indicates the age sequence exactly if, as seems likely, in late Pleistocene time the Palos Verdes Hills rose above the Los Angeles plain step by step, without downward reversals of movement.

Folding of the earlier Pleistocene sediments is, in California, limited chiefly to the margins of the sedimentary basins. In the center of the Los Angeles Basin the uppermost two or three thousand feet of sediments are considered Pleistocene, in part marine but grading laterally into non-marine sands and silts. The beds are nearly horizontal and grade downward into Pliocene strata that are missing from Figure 16-4 and are represented there only by the unconformity between the Miocene and the lowest Pleistocene unit.

The Pleistocene sediments of the Los Angeles Basin contain many million seashells,

assigned to species at least 90 percent of which are Recent. A few of these species are found all round the world in northern latitudes, but almost none occur in the Mediterranean Recent or Pleistocene faunas. Correlation with the type Pleistocene is therefore carried out almost entirely by the percentage method and is very vague. At San Pedro four slightly different molluscan faunas can be distinguished, in units 1, 2, 3, and 15-16. The fauna of unit 2 is colder than the others, perhaps because it lived in deeper water. The 15-16 fauna is perhaps the warmest of all. Eight of the higher terraces (among units 4–14) have relatively small specialized beach or rock faunas of uncertain temperature facies. Only the fauna of unit 2 is appreciably colder than the one living near shore in southern California today; even it includes only one or two species that today are limited to far northern waters. Detailed correlations between the marine Pleistocene of southern California and that of other parts of the Pacific coast of North America are impossible, to say nothing of stage-by-stage correlations with Europe.

In Sicily and on the southern Italian mainland, the Calabrian, the lowest of the three Pleistocene units, is made up of hundreds of feet of gravel, sand, clay, and limestone, horizontal or slightly folded (so that it rises to 1,800 feet above sea level in Sicily); it contains a molluscan fauna similar to that living in the Mediterranean today, plus rather rare northern invaders. The second unit, called the Sicilian, and the third, called the Tyrrhenian, are rather thin and occur mostly on terraces, commonly up to 300 feet above the sea for the Sicilian, rarely as high as 700 feet. The Sicilian

Fig. 16-5. *Pleistocene lakes of the southwestern United States: DV, Death Valley; GSL, Great Salt Lake; LB, Lake Bonneville; LM, Lake Manix; SL, Searles Lake. (Base map copyrighted by Jeppesen and Co., Denver, 1962. Pleistocene lakes, gray, perhaps not all contemporaneous, from J. S. Shelton, using data from many sources, including J. H. Feth, Prof. Paper 424-B, U.S. Geological Survey, 1961.)*

contains a cold fauna and the Tyrrhenian (on low terraces) a warm fauna that includes a dozen or more species now found only in the tropical Atlantic.

Sharp angular unconformities within the Pleistocene are not limited to California but occur also in Tunisia, East Africa, and West Pakistan.

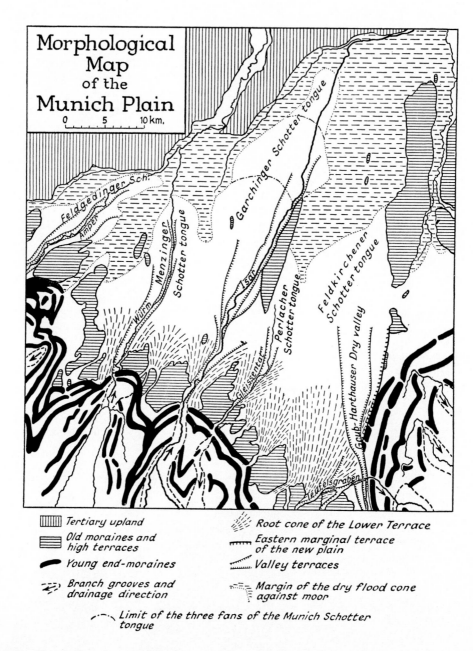

Morphological Map of the Munich Plain

0   5   10 km.

|||||| Tertiary upland

≡ Old moraines and high terraces

▬ Young end-moraines

⇢ Branch grooves and drainage direction

⫽ Root cone of the Lower Terrace

⚍ Eastern marginal terrace of the new plain

⚍ Valley terraces

⚍ Margin of the dry flood cone against moor

⌒ Limit of the three fans of the Munich Schotter tongue

Fig. 16-6.   *Morphological map of the Munich plain (Bavaria), showing Würm and earlier Pleistocene moraines and outwash. (From Ref. 3.)*

f. Pleistocene Lake Beds of the Great Basin

The closed basins of the western United States contained many large lakes during parts of the Pleistocene (Fig. 16-5). The Great Salt Lake had a much larger predecessor, which even overflowed northward into the Snake-Columbia drainage system. This Pleistocene water body is called Lake Bonneville. Two sets of high-level Bonneville terrace deposits are present along the fronts of the Wasatch and other ranges near Salt Lake City. In the basins of northwestern Utah the lake beds are hundreds of feet thick. Lake Bonneville dried up completely at least once during the Pleistocene; the salt deposit then formed was covered and protected by later mud and sand. Other complex lacustrine sequences occur elsewhere in the southwestern United States. Pleistocene species of elephants, camels, horses, and other mammals have been found in the lake beds and in associated alluvial deposits.

g. Glacial and Interglacial Deposits

In Bavaria four sets of moraines have been found, corresponding to four advances of glaciers from the Alps. The four tills have been named Günz (the earliest), Mindel, Riss, and Würm (the latest, Fig. 16-6). Note that the initials of the names are in alphabetical order. North of the four sets of moraines are four corresponding sets of outwash gravels occurring as terraces along valleys cut below the level of the earlier outwash plains. Three sets of interglacial loess and other sediments are also present. In northern Germany, beyond the ice-free corridor, three sets of glacial tills are present (not four as in the Alps), and all

TABLE 16-1

Pleistocene Correlations

NORTH SIDE OF ALPS (BAVARIA)	NORTHERN GERMANY	U.S. MIDDLE WEST
Würm moraines and Lower Terrace Gravels	Weichsel till and non-glacial interbeds	Wisconsin till and non-glacial interbeds
Schieferkohlen of Riss-Würm Interglacial Stage	Eem Beds (interglacial)	Sangamon loess and other interglacial sediments
Riss moraines and Upper Terrace Gravels	Saale till	Illinoian till
Höttinger breccia of Mindel-Riss Interglacial Stage	Holstein lake beds and other interglacial sediments	Yarmouth loess and other interglacial sediments
Mindel moraines and Younger Sheet Gravels (*Deckenschotter*)	Elster till	Kansan till
?	——	Aftonian loess and other interglacial sediments
Günz moraines and Older Sheet Gravels (*Deckenschotter*)	——	Nebraskan till

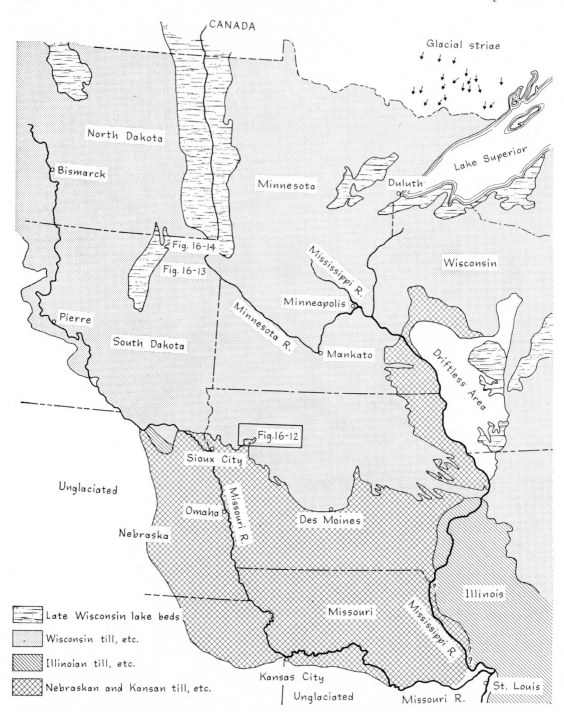

Fig. 16-7. *Pleistocene glacial units west of the Great Lakes. (Based on maps by R. F. Flint, Geol. Soc. Am., 1949 and 1959.)*

EARLY WISCONSIN	SAND / TILL AND VARVED CLAY
SANGAMON ?	SCARBOROUGH CLAY / DON BEDS
? ILLINOIAN	TILL
ORDOVICIAN	SHALY LIMESTONE

Fig. 16-8. *Don Valley glacial (Early Wisconsin and ?Illinoian) and interglacial (Sangamon?) beds, Toronto, Canada. (Photograph by A. K. Watt, Ontario Water Resources Commission; column from T. H. Clark and C. W. Stearn,* The Geological Evolution of North America, *Ronald Press, New York, 1960.)*

three contain boulders of Scandinavian origin. These tills are separated from one another in many sections by interglacial sediments, the lower being fresh-water, with flora and fauna somewhat cooler than those of the present, the upper being in part fresh-water, in part marine, with faunas slightly warmer than those of the present (Table 16-1). Outside the glaciated areas, in both Germany and northern France, loess was widespread. The Pleistocene section in northern Germany is shown by wells to be about 1,000 feet thick.

In the American Middle West the Pleistocene glacial deposits are mostly less than 200 feet thick, commonly much less, but a boring in central Ohio went through almost 800 feet of glacial drift and one in upper Michigan 1,200 feet. The midwestern tills are divided into four age groups: Nebraskan (the oldest), Kansan, Illinoian, and Wisconsin. Intervening loess and other interglacial materials are called Aftonian (the oldest), Yarmouth, and Sangamon. Possible correlations with Europe are shown in Table 16-1. The younger tills, especially the Wisconsin, are in general less extensive and project southward onto the older

drift in a series of lobes (Fig. 16-7). The Nebraskan and the Kansan are widespread west of the Mississippi, and the Illinoian covers a broad expanse east of the river. In southwestern Wisconsin, between the Nebraskan-Kansan tills to the west and the Illinoian to the southeast, an unglaciated driftless area is marked by integrated stream systems, with a few river gorges hundreds of feet deep, making a marked contrast to the surrounding glacial landscapes. Apparently the main areas of Nebraskan-Kansan and Illinoian drift mark the sites of gigantic southward-reaching glacial lobes on both sides of the driftless area.

At many places in central North America three units (for example, two tills with intervening clay or sand or loess) are exposed in a single section. One of the best-known of these sequences is in the Don Valley near Toronto (Fig. 16-8). There the interglacial clays contain leaves of papaw and osage orange, warm-temperate plants now living hundreds of miles to the south.

The correlations suggested in Table 16-1 are far from certain and at best are not likely to

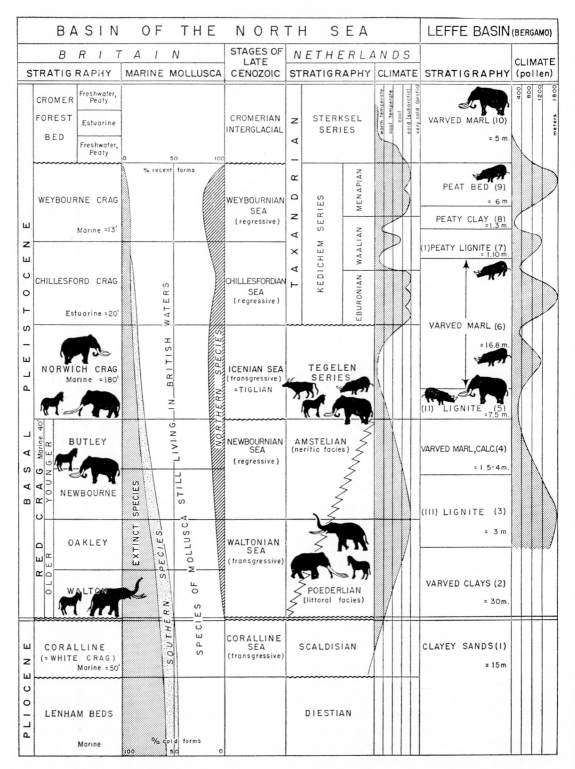

Fig. 16-9. *Villafranchian correlations: Italy, Holland, England. (From Ref. 18 by permission of the author and the American Association for the Advancement of Science.)*

be exact, but they now seem to be the most probable. The early Alpine glaciations, typified by the Günz in Bavaria, may have been both mild and local and may have been earlier than any north-European continental ice sheet. Early tills and outwash gravels (*Deckenschotter*) are known all along the northern side of the Alps, from Bavaria west, and extend southwest to the vicinity of Grenoble, France. Perhaps these glacial and periglacial deposits should be correlated with lake and swamp deposits south of the Alps, including those near Bergamo, Italy, which at three levels contain pollen of trees now living 4,700 feet higher in the Alps, and which at four other levels yield the pollen of warmer vegetation and the mammals of the Villafranchian fauna (Fig. 16-9). By this interpretation the Villafranchian mammals are characteristic of the warmer phases of a long period of early mild and local (Günz and other) glaciation. These mammals are also found in the probably later (post-Günz) Cromer Forest Bed of the eastern English coast, where they are associated with an elephant species that is usually found higher in the section. The three successive British tills are all younger than the Cromer Forest Bed and probably should be correlated with the three glaciations of northern Germany. In North America, the complete Pleistocene sequence in southwestern Kansas, which begins with beds containing a probably Villafranchian fauna, is hundreds of miles southwest of the sequence along the Missouri River that includes the Nebraskan till; correlations between the two sequences are uncertain.

h. Oceanic Pleistocene Sediments

The sequences immediately beneath the ocean floor are studied in cores up to fifty feet long. One objective is a standard oceanic Pleistocene column, with planktonic microorganisms as guide fossils. Experience has shown that the floors of deep basins are to be avoided, partly because the calcium carbonate of the plankton is likely to dissolve before reaching the bottom and partly because microfossils of varied ages become mingled in the turbid flows

that enter the basins as slumps from the basin walls. The localities most favorable for column-making are in the tropics, on submarine plateaus and broad ridges, including the Mid-Atlantic Ridge, 10,000–12,000 feet below the surface and far from land. Two cores made up of calcareous clays, from the mid-Atlantic at the equator, are represented in Figure 16-10AB, and two from the Caribbean in CD. Fairly consistent changes in microfossils occur at corresponding depths. A foot or so below the sea floor the planktonic foraminiferal fauna of the region is underlain by a cooler facies. The transition occurs at a horizon found to be 10,000–13,000 years old by a method to be described later; this horizon is taken as the top of the Pleistocene. Several feet lower, the facies suddenly changes back to warm; other changes occur at lower horizons, and some long cores, perhaps including D, may contain beds representing two cold and two warm Pleistocene stages. A generalization of the Atlantic-Caribbean column is given in EF, in which twenty-five meters (eighty-two feet) of calcareous clay contain six faunal zones (u–z) that may represent time from the Riss to the Recent, inclusive. The data on *Globorotalia menardii* (A–D) were supplemented by those on other species, but, even so, the climatic inferences are not wholly consistent with the paleotemperatures indicated by the ratios of oxygen isotopes in the foraminiferal shells (Ref. 12). The generalizations of both E and F must therefore be considered tentative.

Probably no single core represents the whole Pleistocene; the earlier part of the Pleistocene record must therefore be sought in cores whose upper portions are marked by one or more lacunas. About a dozen such cores show a marked change in microfossils—the disappearance of *Discoaster* (§ B-1.b) and several species of planktonic foraminifers—at a single horizon in the Atlantic and within a few feet of one another (thirty or forty feet below the sea floor) in the tropical Pacific (Ref. 11). The uppermost discoasters are tentatively considered to lie just below the base of the Pleistocene, though correlation has not yet been obtained with the type Lower Pleistocene

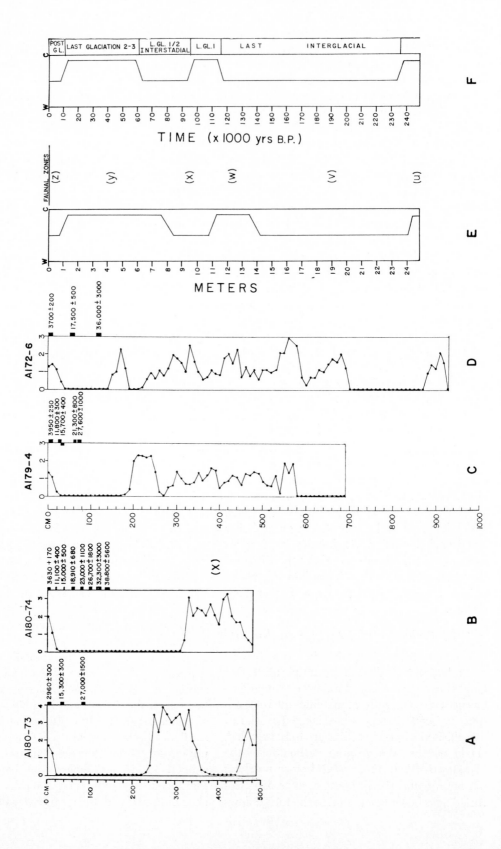

Fig. 16-10. *Distribution of the warm-water planktonic foraminifer* Globorotalia menardii *in cores from the floor of the mid-Atlantic on the equator (AB) and from the Caribbean south of Hispaniola (CD). A zero (0) indicates the absence of the species; 1, 2, 3, and 4 are points in the measurement of its quantitative abundance. Solid rectangles mark the depth range of samples used for radiocarbon dating, and the numbers to the right of the rectangles show the age in years B. P.; ±, analytical uncertainty. E is a generalized column, in meters, with six faunal zones (u–z) based on planktonic foraminifers: three (v, x, and z) with the present temperature facies, three (u, w, and y) colder. F is an extrapolation of the radiocarbon time scale to 240,000 years and a tentative correlation with glacial and interglacial stages and substages (stadia): W, warm; C, cold; Post Gl., Recent; L. Gl. 1, first substage of last (Würm) glaciation. Points near the right sides of A–D represent abundant warm-water foraminifers, but vertical lines at the right sides of E and F mark cold stages. (Adapted from D. B. Ericson, Maurice Ewing, Goesta Wollin, and B. C. Heezen, in* BULLETIN, *Geol. Soc. Am., 1961.)*

(Calabrian) in southern Italy, where *Discoaster* is rare and redeposition has made interpretation difficult (Refs. 10 and 11).

In general, correlations between the deep-sea, shallow marine, glacial, and extra-glacial continental facies of the Pleistocene are still difficult and uncertain.

16-2. Geomorphic Features of Pleistocene Age

The details of most landscapes are the results of erosion and deposition during Pleistocene and later times, though the major plains, plateaus, and mountain ranges were in existence when the period began. The canyons of the Sierra Nevada attained their present depth and form during the Pleistocene. The U-shaped valleys and cirque depressions (Fig. 16-11) may well have been initiated in the early Pleistocene, but the presence of lakes indicates renewed glacial activity in Wisconsin time, probably late Wisconsin. Most river, lake, and marine terraces were Pleistocene develop-

Fig. 16-11. *Mountain glaciation in the Sierra Nevada: Mount Whitney from the northeast; cirques with glacial lakes in the foreground. (Photograph by J. S. Shelton.)*

ments, and on Californian and some other coasts the marine terraces were formed rather late in the Pleistocene (Fig. 16-4). Niagara Gorge is actually a post-Pleistocene development.

a. Pleistocene Features in the Middle West

After each glacial stage, new stream systems slowly developed. The degree to which the new systems cover the ground is a measure of the age of the landscape. Unfilled lake basins and uneroded terminal moraines are almost all Wisconsin and were commonly formed rather late in the stage. Early Wisconsin moraines are almost as minutely dissected as those of the earlier Pleistocene stages; an example from Iowa is represented in Figure 16-12. A little farther north, in southwestern Minnesota and eastern South Dakota, a landscape of late Wisconsin glaciation is characterized by lakes and undrained swales (Fig. 16-13). Still farther north, in Ontario and Quebec, numerous lakes in lowland bedrock are no doubt evidences of erosion in late

Wisconsin time, erosion that is also indicated by the grooves and striations represented by arrows in the upper right corner of Figure 16-7.

In some basins of the North American lowland preglacial exits were temporarily filled with glacial ice, which caused the formation of very large lakes. Some of the late Wisconsin and post-Wisconsin lakes have been given names. Lake Chicago formed in the southern part of the Lake Michigan basin while the northern part of the basin was still ice-filled; its high-level shores are marked by terraces. Somewhat later Lake Algonquin, as shown by its shore lines, covered most of the present Lake Michigan and Lake Huron basins, but was still ice-dammed on the north. The largest lake of all was Lake Agassiz, farther west, in the Red River valley of Minnesota and the Dakotas (Fig. 16-7) and reaching far north into Canada, beyond the present Lake Winnipeg. This lake was larger than all the present Great Lakes taken together. Its outlet during much of its history was a broad channel (Fig. 16-14) that led southeast through the valley

Fig. 16-12. *Contrast in drainage patterns on early and late Wisconsin tills, northwestern Iowa. See Fig. 16-7 for location of area. (Adapted from R. V. Ruhe, American Jour. Sci., 1952.)*

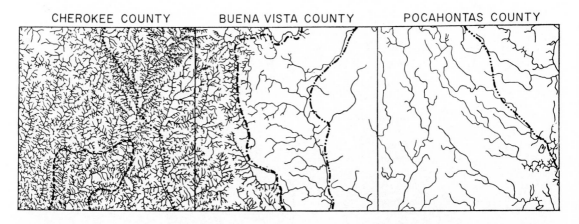

CHEROKEE COUNTY   BUENA VISTA COUNTY   POCAHONTAS COUNTY

LEGEND

Southwest edge of youngest Wisconsin till.

West edges of underlying, slightly older Wisconsin tills.

Boundaries of outcrops of earlier Wisconsin till sheets.

Fig. 16-13. *Air view of a Wisconsin moraine forty miles east of Aberdeen, South Dakota. (Photograph by J. S. Shelton.)*

Fig. 16-14. *Outlet of the Pleistocene Lake Agassiz, looking southeast, downstream. (From J. S. Shelton, Geology Illustrated, W. H. Freeman & Co.)*

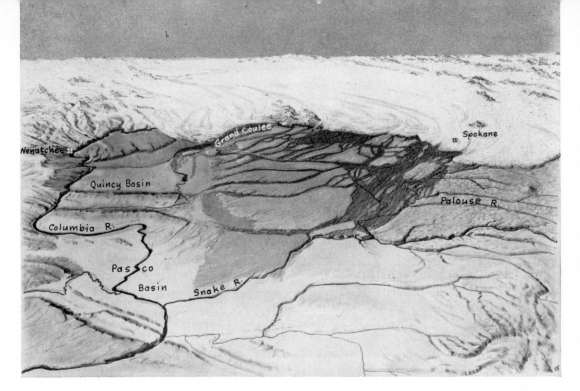

Fig. 16-15. *Diagrammatic sketch of eastern Washington, showing, in combination, both the maximum advance of the late Pleistocene ice sheet and the channeled scablands developed during glacial retreat. (Drawing by Hal Shelton after map by J. H. Bretz and others,* BULLETIN, *Geol. Soc. Am., 1956.)*

Fig. 16-16. *Scabland channel cut through rounded Palouse topography near Ewan, Washington (south of Spokane); aerial view east-northeast. (From J. S. Shelton,* Geology Illustrated, *W. H. Freeman & Co.)*

of the Minnesota River to the newly developing Mississippi River. The rapid lowering or
emptying of the late glacial lakes when the ice
barriers were breached, as when the developing Great Lakes found new outlets, first into
the Hudson drainage system and then into the
St. Lawrence, must have caused extraordinary
erosion and giant depositional features. The
effects of such floods have not been recognized
with certainty in these places or elsewhere in
northeastern North America, though a possible
relic of flood erosion is preserved in potholes
fifteen feet across, high above the Mohawk
River at Little Falls, New York.

b. The Channeled Scablands of Eastern Washington

Perhaps the clearest record of a catastrophic
discharge of lake waters is preserved in arid
southeastern Washington. The water came
from the late Pleistocene Lake Missoula of
northwestern Montana, which was bounded
along part of its northwestern side by glacial
ice. When the ice melted northward to expose
a pass through the mountains northeast of
Spokane, the water of Lake Missoula, suddenly
released southwestward in the general direction of the lower Columbia River, scoured
away much of the earlier Pleistocene loess (the
Palouse soil) in the region represented in
Figure 16-15. The flood spread over the site
of Spokane (at the upper right) and across
the basalt plateau in the center of the map to
dump its gravel, sand, and silt in the Quincy
and Pasco basins at the southwest, where the
great installations of the Atomic Energy Commission now are. A typical scoured scabland
channel south of Spokane is shown in Figure
16-16. Note the contrast between the rough
surface of the eroded basalt in the channel
and the soft contours of the Palouse lands on
both sides. Downstream this channel must
have been occupied by a torrent 200 feet deep,
which not only scoured away all the Palouse
soil up to 200 feet above the valley floor but
also broke over a divide 200 feet high and
spilled into the Snake River valley to the south.
A similar flood in the gorge of the Columbia
River itself is indicated by giant ripples, 200–
300 feet from crest to crest (Fig. 16-17), at a

Fig. 16-17. *Giant ripples in coarse sediments beside the Columbia River; aerial view upstream at Trinidad, near Wenatchee, Washington, with low lighting from left. (From J. S. Shelton,* Geology Illustrated, *W. H. Freeman & Co.)*

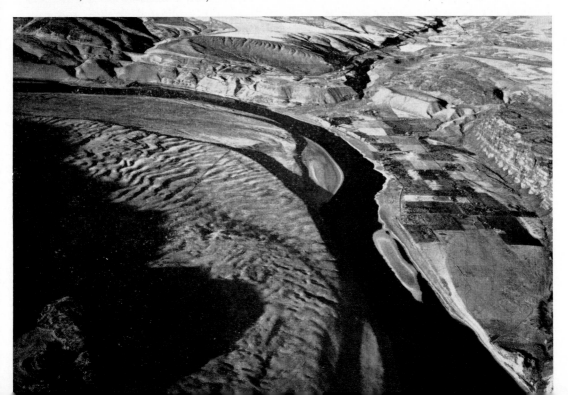

Fig. 16-18. *Dry Falls in the Grand Coulee, Washington.* (*From J. S. Shelton*, Geology Illustrated, W. H. Freeman & Co.)

point near Wenatchee in the northwestern part of the map. A single Spokane flood may have lasted only a few weeks. A longer continued outpouring of glacial floodwaters is indicated by the dry gorge, a thousand feet deep, called the Grand Coulee (at the upper left of Fig. 16-15; air view, Fig. 16-18), which must have been eroded out while the Columbia's flood was going this way during a much longer period, perhaps for hundreds or even thousands of years. Perhaps during all this time the Columbia gorge, where the river now flows, was ice-dammed. When the glacier melted, the Columbia River returned to the present gorge, forced that way by the high rock barrier at the head of the Grand Coulee, upstream from the Coulee's 417-foot-high Dry Falls.

The story just told has been pieced together from a great mass of evidence. The contrast between the three topographies—the till left by the glacier; the unglaciated, softly rounded Palouse hills; and the rough, channeled scablands—is apparent from the air. On the ground, it can be seen that the Palouse soil and other materials removed from the north-

eastern part of the area, near Spokane, have been deposited in the southwestern basins.

Much patient work has gone into the study of the Palouse soil. It has uniform grain size and lacks bedding or other structure; these are the characteristic features of wind-deposited loess. In some sections an earlier, weathered, somewhat consolidated Palouse soil can be distinguished from a later, fresher, looser material. Perhaps there were two periods of loess-formation. Both periods were probably Pleistocene, and of course both occurred before the beginning of the Spokane flood.

16-3. *Changes in Drainage Due to Pleistocene Glaciation*

After the ice sheets had covered northern North America and Europe, dumped till and outwash, and retreated, new drainage lines formed that did not everywhere coincide with preglacial valleys. In the north-central United States the preglacial Upper Missouri, Upper Mississippi, and Teays outlets (Fig. 16-19) were filled with glacial deposits so thick, extensive, and high that after the ice retreated these rivers were diverted to new courses. The Upper Missouri was diverted from a course toward Hudson Bay to one toward the Lower Mississippi; the Upper Mississippi turned from a course through central Illinois to its present position (the Illinois River follows part of the old course); and the old Mississippi tributary called Teays mostly disappeared, its Kanawha (West Virginia) headwaters being taken over by the Ohio, which had previously been a short stream but now developed into a great river along the southern edge of the glaciated region. The lower part of the Missouri also follows fairly closely the southern edge of the early Pleistocene glacial deposits (Fig. 16-7). The present Ohio and Missouri are practically new rivers. To the north, the Great Lakes developed on the sites of preglacial valleys, in part as a result of the deformation that will be described on a later page.

Fig. 16-19. *Preglacial drainage in central North America. The postglacial course of the Missouri River is dotted from central North Dakota to the Nebraska line. Parts of the postglacial Missouri, Mississippi, and Ohio Rivers are shown as sinuous state boundaries. (From "Bedrock Topography and Pleistocene Glacial Lobes in Central United States" by Leland Horberg and R. C. Anderson,* JOURNAL OF GEOLOGY, *by permission of the University of Chicago Press. Copyright 1956 by the University of Chicago.)*

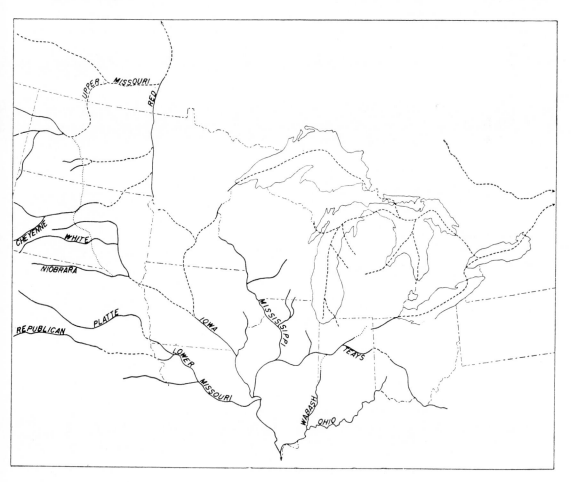

16-4. *Dating of Pleistocene Horizons*

a. *Radiocarbon Dating*

The uppermost Pleistocene and the overlying sediments can be dated by radiocarbon, or carbon 14, which occurs in atmospheric, fresh-water, and oceanic carbon dioxide and in wood, peat, shells, and other substances derived rather recently from those carbon dioxide reservoirs. The carbon in lower Pleistocene and older rocks (limestone, coal, etc.) contains no determinable amount of C14, but is made up of the other carbon isotopes, C12 (98.9 percent) and C13 (1.1 percent). Carbon 14, even in the atmosphere, where it is most abundant, is present as a mere trace and must be determined by a delicate method involving the use of a Geiger counter.

Carbon 14 forms continuously in the upper atmosphere, through the bombardment of nitrogen 14 by cosmic rays. It emits beta rays (high-speed electrons) and reverts, with a half-life of about 5,570 years,* to nitrogen 14 again. Radiocarbon from the upper atmosphere mingles rapidly with the rest of the atmosphere and spreads more slowly through fresh and oceanic waters. Wood, getting its carbon from the air, reflects closely the atmospheric content of carbon 14, but newly formed seashells, especially on coasts where upwelling of deep ocean water prevails, may give apparent radiocarbon ages of several hundred years, and newly developed fresh-water shells may give apparent ages up to 3,000 years. Since 1900 the atmosphere has been contaminated appreciably by inert carbon dioxide from fossil fuels containing practically no carbon 14. Since 1952 the testing of nuclear bombs has abnormally increased the amount of carbon 14 in the atmosphere. But wood from parts of oaks or other trees formed slightly before 1900 makes a satisfactory standard for comparison with earlier wood or shells. (A specially pre-

pared carbon compound is still better.) Wood, shells, or other materials that started with normal amounts of radiocarbon lose almost all of it in 50,000–60,000 years, and the minute amount remaining is ordinarily indeterminable.

Radiocarbon ages are usually given in years B.P. (before the present; more precisely, before A.D. 1950, a date chosen by a Cambridge conference in 1962). Years B.C. can be obtained by subtracting 1,950.

Thousands of samples have been dated by radiocarbon since 1950. Some of the most instructive and encouraging results have come from Egyptian mummies and other specimens whose age in years is known from independent evidence. Here, however, we limit ourselves to Pleistocene, and perhaps slightly later, horizons.

The approximate end of mid-latitude glaciation—and of the Pleistocene—has been dated scores of times, and the range of variation is indicated in Table 16-2. Some ages in the table are replicates on the same sample (Nos. 3A–E, 6AB, 7A–C, 9AB). The results are moderately encouraging, with the exception of 9A, in which a gross error must be involved. Apparently analytical errors are usually not over 6 percent, here ±600 years. Systematic errors, due to abnormally high or low content of radiocarbon, may be the result of carbon replacement, perhaps long after the first formation of the substance. Wood, whose elements are locked in complex organic structures, is likely to retain its original carbon and to show changes by obvious signs of decay. Charcoal is reliable under favorable circumstances, since elemental carbon at ordinary temperatures is one of the most inert of substances; the times of wood formation and of charring, however, may not have been the same, and the wood may have altered before it was charred. Some insoluble carbon gives too low an age (Ref. 8, vol. 5, p. 164). Dates based on peat appear to be reliable; compare No. 10C in Table 16-2 with the other members of the 10A–J series. Pollen mud (gyttja) gives about the same age as associated wood (Table

---

* The number is almost surely a little low, but is still used as the basis for radiocarbon ages; it is likely to be increased soon to 5,730 years, raising the radiocarbon ages given in this chapter by about 3 percent.

T A B L E 16-2

Radiocarbon Dates for the End of Glaciation*

SAMPLE NUMBER	ANALYSIS NUMBER	MATERIAL	AGE IN YEARS B.P.	GEOLOGIC POSITION	LOCALITY
1	T-53	Pollen-rich peat	10,720 ± 240	End-glacial lake	Troms, northern Norway
2	T-50	Shells	10,500 ± 400	End-glacial marine terrace	Ruds Vedby, Zealand, Denmark
3A	K-101bis	Wood from peaty mud	11,090 ± 240	End-glacial, Younger Dryas/Alleröd	" " "
3B	BM-19	Same wood	11,333 ± 200	"	" "
3C	St-18	"	10,200 ± 300	"	" "
3D	U-20	"	10,830 ± 130	"	" "
3E	U-75	"	10,680 ± 130	"	" "
4A	B-16	Wood	10,200 ± 200	End-glacial	Near Bern, Switzerland
4B	Pi-6	Same wood	10,178 ± 400		
5	Q-279	Moss-peat	11,205 ± 120	Late glacial	Lincolnshire, England
6A	Q-207	"	11,011 ± 230	"	Durham, England
6B	C-444	Same moss-peat	10,851 ± 630	"	
7A	Q-2	Moss-peat	11,071 ± 180	"	Cornwall, England
7B	C-341	Same moss-peat	9,861 ± 500	"	" "
7C	GL-27	" "	9,728 ± 140	"	
8	Y-526	Wood	11,480 ± 160	Post-glacial	Columbus, Ohio
9A	C-419	"	6,401 ± 230	Late glacial	Near Appleton, Wisconsin
9B	Y-488	Same wood	11,280 ± 100	"	
10A	C-308	Spruce wood	10,877 ± 740	Beneath very late Wisconsin till	Two Creeks, Manitowoc Co., Wisconsin
10B	C-365	Tree root	11,437 ± 770	"	" "
10C	C-366	Peat matrix of C-365	11,097 ± 600	"	" "
10D	C-536	Spruce wood	12,168 ± 1500	"	" "
10E	C-537	Peat matrix of C-536	11,442 ± 640	"	" "
10F	W-42	Wood, weathered?	11,350 ± 120	"	" "
10G	W-83	Wood	11,410 ± 180	"	" "
10H	Y-227	Spruce wood	11,130 ± 350	"	" "
10I	M-343	Inner part of log	10,400 ± 600	"	" "
10J	M-342	Outer part of same log	10,700 ± 600	"	" "
11	Y-391	Wood fragments	11,570 ± 260	In silt of Lake Iroquois	Hamilton, Ontario
12	I(AGS)10	Sedge-peat	10,820 ± 420	Late glacial marine terrace	Munday Creek, Alaska

The mean, omitting No. 9A, is 10,918.
Ages are based on a half-life of 5,570 years and are therefore probably about 300 years low.

* The samples numbered 6B, 7B, 9A, and 10A–E are from Ref. 7; 10F and 10G are from H. E. Suess, *Science* (1952); 10H is from R. S. Preston *et al.*, *Science* (1953); 10I and 10J are from H. R. Crane. *Science* (1956); the others are from Ref. 8, vols. 1 and 2.

16-3, Nos. 28A–C). Raw data from shells are suspect; original shell carbon low in C14 has already been mentioned; later replacements may either increase or decrease the amount of C14 without producing obvious changes in the gross features of the shells. Nevertheless, shells commonly give about the same ages as contemporaneous plant remains (Table 16-2, Nos. 1 and 2).

The samples in Table 16-2 came from North American or European sediments thought to be approximately end-glacial. From this table we may conclude that the ice sheets of the last glaciation withdrew from Denmark, England, and the United States some 11,000 years ago. We may even take this approximate date as the end of Pleistocene time; that is, a geological event may be dated within a thousand years or so—geologically very close tolerance.

One sample in Table 16-2, No. 8, is post-glacial but gives an age above 11,000 years B.P. The locality, Columbus, Ohio, is rather far south. The age may mean that the last continental glacier had retreated northward beyond Columbus slightly more than 11,000 years ago, even though it persisted for many centuries farther north in the United States. Post-glacial radiocarbon dates farther north are almost all less than 10,000 years B.P.

A check on these radiocarbon dates and their significance is furnished by a combination of two other methods of study. One method is the analysis of the kinds of pollen present in bog deposits and other sediments. In near-glacial layers, the pollen is mostly from conifers; in more temperate layers, it is mostly from hardwoods. The pollen grains are facies fossils and, used judiciously, make possible correlations and the determination of *relative* ages. The second method is the counting of annual layers, called varves, in Swedish and other lake sediments. Varves, through the work of Gerard de Geer of Sweden, between 1904 and 1910, furnished the first method of determining absolute ages. Varves, moraines, and pollen analysis indicate that the Scandinavian glacier retreated across the Baltic 13,000–14,000 years ago (Fig. 16-20) and that

TABLE 16-3

Late Pleistocene Radiocarbon Dates *

SAMPLE NUMBER	ANALYSIS NUMBER	MATERIAL	AGE IN YEARS B.P.	GEOLOGIC POSITION	LOCALITY
1	UCLA-120	Wood from well	9,650 ± 150	About 150 feet subsea	Terminal Is., Long Beach, Calif.
2	B-16	Log	10,200 ± 200	Würm-retreat peat, top of Paleolithic	Seeberg, Switzerland
3	L-399D	Bone carbonate	9,580 ± 500	Paleolithic: middle Magdalenian	Grotte de la Garenne, France
4	A-386	Fossil plant remains	10,490 ± 900	Diatomite with Folsom artifacts	Clovis, New Mexico
5	A-481	Carbonized plants	11,170 ± 360	Level of Clovis artifacts	"
6	Y-460	Spruce wood	11,410 ± 410	Associated with a late mastodon	Kings Ferry, New York
7A	Y-574a	Carbonate	11,810 ± 140	Parting Mud, top 8 inches	Searles Lake, California
7B	Y-574b	Organic carbon	10,700 ± 130	" "	"
8A	Y-425	Wood, 7–12 inch depth	10,120 ± 120	Gulf of Mexico silt, 120-foot terrace	Off Mississippi delta
8B	Y-426	Wood, 18–20 "	11,690 ± 170	" "	"
9	O-126	Wood	13,650 ± 300	Sand substratum, 210–240 feet subsea	Bayou Pigeon, Iberia Parish, La.
10A	Y-355B	Rooted tree, tar-free	13,890 ± 280	Tar pit with Upper Pleistocene mammals	Los Angeles, California
10B	Y-354B	Same tree, tar-free	15,390 ± 230	" "	"
10C	L-155		14,400 ± 200		

No.	Lab no.	Material	Age (years)	Description	Location
		"	17,190 ± 3??	...to ?? Magdalenian	Laussel Cave, southwestern France
11B	GrN-1632	"	17,190 ± 140	Culture layer: Magdalenian	"
12	NZ-207	Charcoal from hearth	18,000 ± 500	5 feet below Keilor skull	Keilor, near Melbourne, Australia
13	UCLA-121	Tufa	19,300 ± 400	Lake Manix shoreline; crude artifacts	Mojave Desert, California
14	W-92	Log	19,980 ± 500	Mid-Wisconsin; in late Wisconsin till	Butler County, Ohio
15	GrN-1888	Bone charcoal	20,890 ± 300	Lower Solutrean	Laugerie-Haute Est, Les Eyzies
16	GrN-1876	"	21,980 ± 250	Protomagdalenian	"
17A	GrN-1857	Charred bone	20,960 ± 220	"	Pataud shelter, Les Eyzies, France
17B	GrN-1862	Uncharred bone	21,940 ± 250		"
18	NZ-116	Wood	22,300 ± 350	Kumara glacial sand and silt	Greymouth, South Island, New Zealand
19	W-71	"	24,600 ± 800	Late Wisconsin varved silt	Cleveland, Ohio
20	Pi-7A	Marine shells	26,364 ± 1,405	Mid-Würm, bore hole	Cathedral square, Pisa, Italy
21A	L-217B	Wood	24,600 ± 1,600	Mid-Wisconsin	Port Talbot, Ontario
21B	W-177	"	27,500 ± 1,200		"
21C	L-185B	"	28,200 ± 1,500		"
22A	GrN-1363	Charcoal	27,860 ± 300	Level D (Aurignacian)	Gorham's Cave, Gibraltar
22B	GrN-1455	"	28,700 ± 200		"
23	GrN-1491	Charcoal from bone	29,100 ± 300	Aurignacian I, Caminade shelter	Near Sarlat, France
24	GrN-1493	Charred bone	31,400 ± 350	Aurignacian I	La Quina, Charente, France
25	Y-451	Tamarack log	32,000 ± 2,800	Wisconsin till	Meriden, Connecticut
26	GrN-2526	Charred bone	35,250 ± 530	Late Mousterian	La Quina, Charente, France
27	NZ-121	Peat from well	43,000	105 feet below sea level	Christchurch, South Island, N.Z.
28A	GrN-2580	Wood	44,420 ± 1,500	Rather low in the Wisconsin	Port Talbot, Ontario
28B	GrN-2597	Gyttja (pollen mud)	47,720 ± 250	"	"
28C	GrN-2570	"	47,220 ± 2,500	"	"
29	GrN-2649	Black ashes	47,000 ± 1,500	Late Acheulian, cold fauna	Jersey, Channel Islands
30A	GrN-1473	Charcoal	47,700 ± 1,500	Uppermost Mousterian—Level G	Gorham's Cave, Gibraltar
30B	GrN-1556	"	49,200 ± 3,200		"
31	GrN-1495	Charcoal from hearth	50,600 ± 3,000	Mousterian; Neanderthal skeleton	Shanidar Cave, Iraq
32	GrN-1307	Wood	64,220 ± 1,100	Very near Würm initiation	Amersfoort, Netherlands

* Mostly from Ref. 8. Some items from 1957–1960 volumes of *Science*. Ages are based on a half-life of 5,570 years for C14 and therefore are probably about 3 percent low. The first eight samples are from the top of the Pleistocene. Other samples show that the last glaciation occurred at about the same time in Europe, North America, and New Zealand (Sample 18). Many samples are helpful in dating Old World culture levels. Sample 32 indicates that the Würm glaciation began about 60,000 or 70,000 years ago.

Fig. 16-20. *Deglaciation of Scandinavia, as recorded by varves. Ice margins shown by lines, dashed where uncertain, with the numbers of years before 2000 A.D. indicated. Two precise varve ages shown, one at Lübeck, the other in north-central Sweden, and, in the Scandinavian highlands, two areas of remanent post-Pleistocene glaciation. (Adapted from Ref. 13.)*

the rapid retreat across southern and central Sweden, which clearly marked the end of glaciation for northern Europe, began about 10,000 years ago. The radiocarbon end-glacial dates are between these two values and consistent with them; in particular, a late-glacial date in southernmost Sweden is 10,680 ± 280 years B.P. (Ref. 8, Vol. 5).

In North America, the few varve sections are incomplete and have been pieced out with estimates of the time required for glacial retreats, lake-terrace formation, and the like. Thus pieced out, the varve method has resulted in age estimates some 50 percent higher than those from radiocarbon. For example, the age of the very late-glacial Two Creeks Forest Bed in Wisconsin, eighty miles north of Milwaukee, is about 11,000 years B.P. by radiocarbon (Table 16-2, No. 10) but is 18,000 or 19,000 years by the estimate that involves varves. The radiocarbon date is preferred, not only because of the uncertainties involved in the other estimate, but also because the radiocarbon values are concordant and include determinations on wood in good condition.

A set of selected Würm-Wisconsin radiocarbon ages make up Table 16-3. These dates show that the Würm glaciation in Europe was at least approximately contemporaneous with the Wisconsin in North America. Date No. 32, the oldest radiocarbon date that has been reported, indicates that the Würm glaciation began about 60,000–70,000 years ago. Dates in the Wisconsin stage are not inconsistent with a similar beginning for it. Among the most interesting dates in Table 16-3 are those for archaeological culture stages; these will be discussed later.

b. Argon/Potassium Ratios

The development of the J. H. Reynolds gas mass spectrometer and of special techniques of sample preparation and analysis at the University of California, Berkeley, have made possible meaningful determinations of age by the Ar^{40}/K^{40} method on very young rocks, particularly lavas (Fig. 16-21). Determinations as small as 50,000 years may have

some meaning, as the probable reliability is ±50,000–100,000 years. Estimates of laboratory precision are corroborated by the consistency of the magnetic polarities shown in the figure and by relative stratigraphic positions of the lava flows in a single region, such as the Sierra Nevada or Hawaii. The Olduvai event (a brief interval of normal magnetic polarity in the Matuyama reversed epoch) is contemporaneous with an Upper Villafranchian fauna in Olduvai Gorge, Tanganyika, Africa. If the Upper Villafranchian fauna is lowest continental Pleistocene, as it is usually assumed to be, the continental Pleistocene record may have begun a little more than two million years ago.

The marine Pleistocene record may go back even farther. The marl at San Pedro, California, labeled 1 in Figure 16-4, is considered Pleistocene because it contains a large molluscan fauna in which more than 90 percent of the species are Recent. Glauconite samples from nine beds in the marl have yielded twelve Ar/K ages between 2,800,000 and 3,200,000 years, with a mean of three million years (J. D. Obradovich, letters, 1964–1965). The strata have not been heated either by deep burial or by igneous action, and the ages are as reliable as glauconite ages can be. The glauconite grains are travel-worn and may possibly have formed during the late Pliocene, though the similarly worn small fossils all appear to be Pleistocene. Now one wonders if part of the marine (and continental?) Pleistocene is preglacial. This question is raised especially by the extrapolation of the estimations of age in Figure 16-10F to cover four glaciations and three interglacial epochs. The question may be settled by new Ar/K ages for volcanic rocks in glacial terrains.

16-5. *Pluvioglacial Periods of the Pleistocene*

The last (Wisconsin) glaciation of North America was accompanied by an exceptionally moist climate outside the glaciated region. At

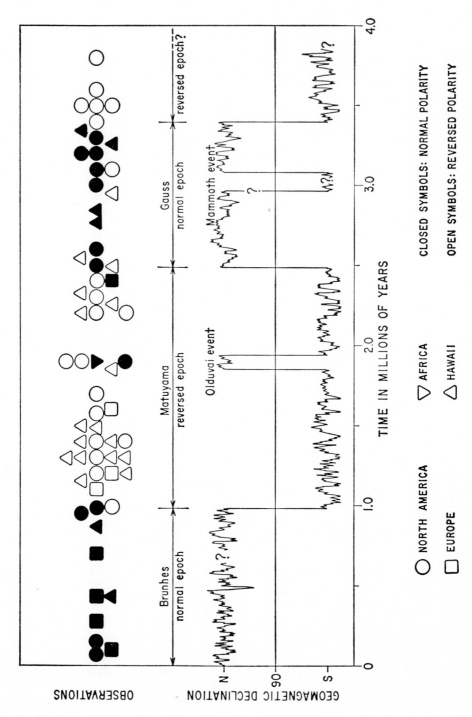

Fig. 16-21. *Argon/potassium ages and magnetic polarities of 64 young volcanic rocks. Geomagnetic declinations for moderate latitudes are indicated schematically. (From Ref. 16 by permission of the authors and the American Association for the Advancement of Science.)*

that time the rainy belt, extending southward in the Cordilleran region, included most of the now arid Great Basin area, between the Sierra Nevada of California and the Wasatch Mountains of Utah. The last wet period in this region was recorded by the high terraces of Lake Bonneville and other ancient lakes and also by muds, beneath the central salt pans, that contain pollen of moisture-requiring plants. The Lake Bonneville high terraces and the upper mud layer in the Searles Lake salts of eastern California have yielded radiocarbon dates ranging from 24,000 to 9,000 years B.P. —that is, from late-glacial to barely post-glacial times. Clearly the last pluvial period of the Great Basin was Wisconsin in age.

At least one earlier desiccation and a still earlier pluvial period are also represented by sediments and perhaps also by terraces in several parts of the Great Basin, notably Lake Bonneville in Utah and the ancestral Searles Lake in California. Sedimentation records in the Great Basin have thus far provided no data conclusively demonstrating more than two pluvial periods during the Pleistocene.

16-6. *Variations in Sea Level, and Deformation, Due to Pleistocene Ice Caps*

The ice caps of Antarctica and Greenland lock up water that otherwise would be a part of the ocean. Sea level is therefore lower, by perhaps 100–150 feet, than it would be in a non-glacial world. The ice caps have also depressed the land beneath them isostatically, so that part of it is below sea level. The great Pleistocene ice caps must have depressed the land in similar fashion, especially beneath their thick central portions, and must have lowered sea level, perhaps by 300–400 feet. The melting of the Pleistocene glaciers restored water to the sea and caused the glacially depressed lands to rise slowly to positions similar to but not exactly the same as those of preglacial time.

a. Eustatic Changes of Sea Level

The last great eustatic change of sea level, caused by the final melting of the Würm-Wisconsin glaciers, is shown everywhere, even in the mobile belt around the Pacific Ocean, by drowned valley mouths and by rather poorly defined submerged terraces on the continental shelves at 100–480 feet below the present sea level. One very large drowned area is at the southern end of the South China Sea, between Sumatra and Borneo and around the Malay Peninsula (Fig. 4-3). Here submerged river valleys with mouths about 300 feet below sea level and other topographic details can be made out; we cannot be sure, however, that all the features of the submerged topography originated during the last high-latitude glaciation and low-latitude emergence.

The records of earlier eustatic changes are harder to recognize and to interpret precisely. Most marine terraces are above sea level and so must indicate previous levels higher than the present one. Strangely enough, many horizontal, apparently undeformed terraces are farther above present sea level than the 100–150 feet the sea would be raised by the melting of the existing glaciers. We must leave out of consideration, of course, such mobile-belt terraces as those of the Palos Verdes Hills near Los Angeles (Fig. 16-4), the highest 1,300 feet above sea level, which were clearly made possible by local deformation of the land. But even in fairly stable regions high marine terraces are known, up to 250 feet in South Australia, up to 350 feet in Argentina, up to 600 feet in southern England, up to 950 feet in South Africa, and up to 1,100 feet near Algiers.

Along many coasts, including that of Algeria, a broad terrace at an elevation of about 325–350 feet extends for scores or even hundreds of miles. In the Mediterranean this terrace bears the Sicilian shell fauna, which is somewhat colder than the present Mediterranean fauna. The net change in sea level of more than 300 feet has therefore been opposite in direction to any change due to glacial

Fig. 16-22. *Late postglacial isostatic rise of Scandinavia: deformation of the initial sediments of the Littorina Sea (about 7000 B.P. on varve and pollen evidence), shown by contour lines on their present elevations, in meters (From Matti Sauramo,* BULL., *Com. geol. Finlande, 1939.)*

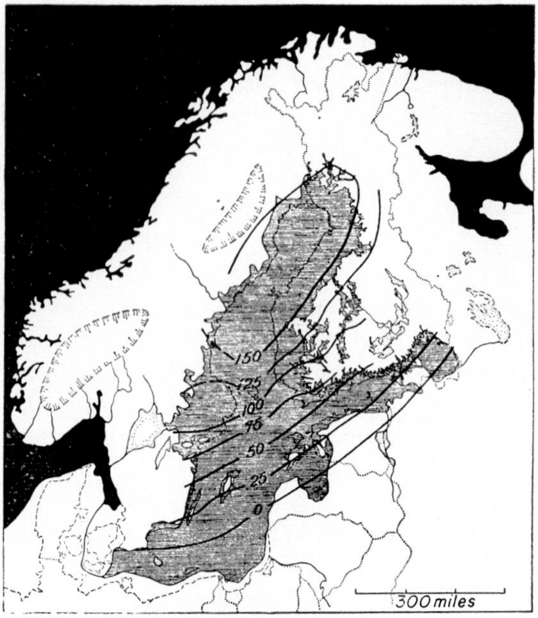

Fig. 16-23. *Deformation of the initial sediments of the Ancyclus Lake (about 8500 B.P.) in the Baltic region, shown by contour lines on their present elevations. (From Matti Sauramo, loc. cit.)*

control. The marine terraces of many regions, including much of the eastern United States, are more or less precisely matched by the extensive river terraces of the same regions. East-central North America, the Middle West of the United States, and large parts of the Cordilleran region seem to have risen hundreds, possibly thousands, of feet during the Pleistocene. Previously, eastern North America had been the site of persistent uplift since Triassic times. Africa has been more markedly and much longer emergent. As sediments accumulate in the sea near a continent, the sea floor sinks, and greater or lesser parts of the continent rise. It is a moot question whether the rise during the Pleistocene was exceptionally great. This question cannot be settled until more is known about the ages, in years, of the sediments on the elevated terraces.

b. Postglacial Deformation

Local rise of land in the last 10,000 years, reversing the isostatic depression caused by ice sheets, has been demonstrated in Scandinavia and in eastern Canada. The Scandinavian evidence is the dome-like deformation of the shore lines of successive water bodies in the Baltic area (Figs. 16-22, 16-23, and 16-24). The shore lines show that the total central uplift has been at least 900 feet; it was probably considerably more.

The postglacial rise of the land around Hudson Bay is rather clearly the isostatic rebound after the disappearance of the Wisconsin ice. It has been dated sufficiently well by radiocarbon so that its time and rate can be compared with those of the worldwide rise of sea level (Fig. 16-25). Some of the land

Fig. 16-24. *Map showing Scandinavia and its two relic glaciers at the end of the Pleistocene (Rhabdonema Sea stage). Contour lines indicate, in meters, the present elevations of the Rhabdonema shoreline. (From Matti Sauramo, loc. cit.)*

around Hudson Bay has risen at least 1,000 feet, but the dated part of this rise is somewhat less. The rebound within the solid earth has been a laggard one, as shown by a comparison of the sketched curves, which are roughly controlled by the data shown in the figure. Probably the land around Hudson Bay has not yet completed its isostatic rebound, for its time-rise curve has not yet flattened out completely.

16-7. *Are Historic Times Glacial, Postglacial, or Interglacial?*

When the evidence of Pleistocene glaciation of continental extent was discovered, about 1840, people naturally assumed that the Ice Age was over and done with. The later discovery of evidence of two or three warm interglacial intervals in the Pleistocene equally naturally led to speculation about the future. Will the glaciers return? Are we living in an interglacial interval now? Still more recently, since the large volumes of ice in Greenland and Antarctica have been measured with moderate accuracy, and comparisons of the existing climate with those of the past have become better and better grounded, on geochemical as well as paleontological evidence (§ 16-1.h), it has become apparent that the present temperatures of the oceans are intermediate between past highs and lows, just as the present high-latitude climates are intermediate between those of the last glacial epoch and the global warmth of the Carboniferous and the Jurassic-Cretaceous-Paleogene periods.

The all-important question of a possible renewal of the continental glaciers in a few thousands or tens of thousands of years is no doubt indeterminate. The discussion can, however, be carried a little farther after consideration of some possible causes of continental glaciation.

16-8. *Causes of Glaciation*

There is now abundant evidence, some of which has been given (Fig. 16-10), that at the time of the Würm-Wisconsin glaciation both sea and land temperatures were low in both low and high north latitudes. Less is known about the southern hemisphere, but the available radiocarbon determinations (for example, Table 16-3, No. 18) tend to show that the last glacial episode occurred at the same time in both hemispheres. We shall assume, for purposes of discussion, that each of the recognized glacial epochs of the Pleistocene was rather cool throughout the world.

The periodic coolness that brought on the Pleistocene glaciations may have been the result of one or more of the following conditions: (1) decrease in the amount of heat received from the sun, (2) increase in the amount of heat lost by the earth, (3) periodic variations in the earth's astronomic behavior,

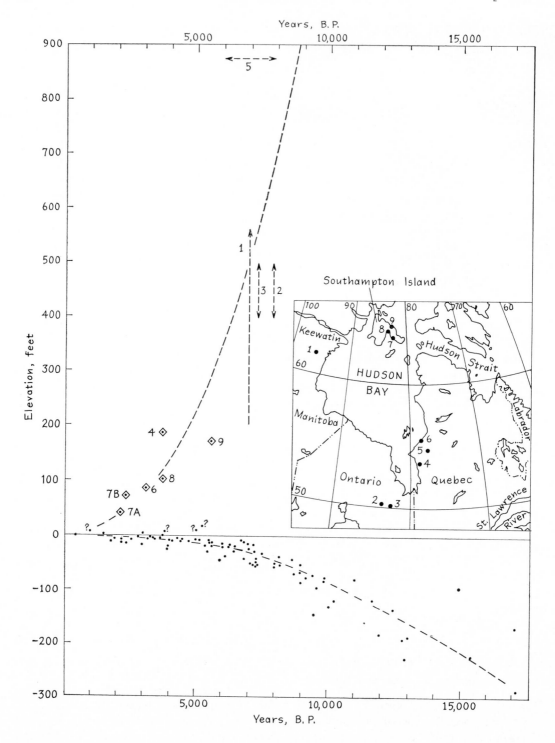

Fig. 16-25. *Postglacial changes of sea level in stable regions and around Hudson Bay. (After Refs. 14 and 15.)*

(4) variations in terrestrial conditions, particularly the sizes and elevations of the land areas.

The most obvious possible cause of glacial periods is a reduction in **insolation,** the amount of energy received from the sun. The amount reaching the earth might be less because the sun's output had been reduced or because the solar system was passing through a thin cloud of dust ("micrometeorites") in space. Thus far little direct astronomical support, theoretical or observational, has been found for either of these explanations, but they remain as possible causes of almost any conceivable sequence of warm and cold epochs on earth. The radiant energy from the sun received at the top of the earth's atmosphere has been measured more or less precisely since 1920, the slight fluctuations showing a net increase of 0.3 percent between 1925 and 1950.

The second general cause of glaciation, increase in the amount of heat lost by the earth, could be due either to reflection or to radiation. We consider *reflection* first. Ice and clouds are better reflectors than vegetation or dry earth; a moist, cloudy, icy earth might therefore be expected to get colder and colder through reflection. Conversely, an earth that had just lost ice and clouds might be expected to get warmer and warmer. That is, either glaciation or deglaciation, once started, would be self-accelerating. *Radiation* is decreased by any blanketing substance in the atmosphere. One such substance is carbon dioxide. In the Carboniferous and the Cretaceous exceptionally large amounts of carbon dioxide were removed from the air and locked up in coal. Perhaps the Pennsylvanian-Permian and Pleistocene glaciations were the results, though the Pleistocene ice caps were delayed suspiciously long. A more serious, in fact a fatal, flaw in the carbon dioxide theory is the complexity of Pleistocene climatic history, with two or three warm interglacial stages that cannot be explained by this theory alone.

The third cause, periodic variations in the earth's astronomical behavior, may help to explain the periodicity of Pleistocene glaciation.

These variations are changes in the position of perihelion (the earth's nearest approach to the sun), with a period of about 21,000 years, the slight wobble of the earth's axis of rotation, with a period of about 40,000 years, and the variation in the eccentricity of the earth's orbit, with a period of about 92,000 years. These changes do not affect the total amount of radiation received from the sun, but they do affect that at particular latitudes. The two shorter periods involve increases of intake in one hemisphere, with corresponding decreases in the other. The combined effects at latitude 65° N. for the last million years are shown in Figure 16-26. Seven notably cold periods of some 10,000 years each are shown, but these would not be matched in the southern hemisphere, and tropic seas would probably not be appreciably chilled. What is more, these astronomic periodicities presumably have affected the earth continuously ever since a very early stage in its history. They did not go into action just at particular times, such as the Pennsylvanian-Permian or the Pleistocene. They can only make a part, perhaps a small part, of any complete theory of glaciation.

As for the fourth possible cause of glaciation, the late-Pennsylvanian–early-Permian and the Pleistocene had one feature in common: both were times of expanded lands and restricted seas. In the Pleistocene, at least, the lands were also somewhat higher than just previously, as shown by the rejuvenation of streams in most, but not all, regions and by the formation of such canyons as those of the Colorado and the Zambesi. High lands favor snow and ice, which increase reflection and therefore loss of energy. But the high mountain areas glaciated during the Pleistocene were small. Reflection from their white surfaces could hardly have caused a general cooling sufficient to make possible the great continental glaciers that covered the lowlands of northern Europe and northeastern North America.

If one attempts to go beyond an orderly statement of the possible causes of continental glaciation, a distinction must be made between

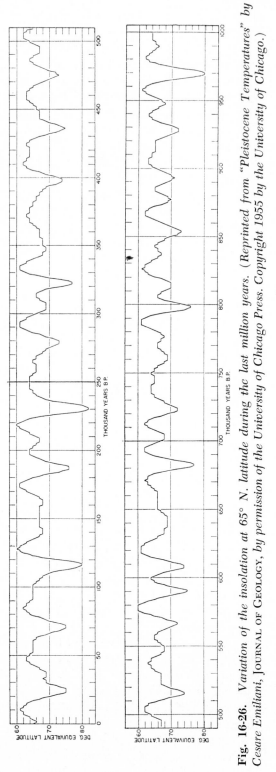

Fig. 16-26. *Variation of the insolation at 65° N. latitude during the last million years. (Reprinted from "Pleistocene Temperatures" by Cesare Emiliani, JOURNAL OF GEOLOGY, by permission of the University of Chicago Press. Copyright 1955 by the University of Chicago.)*

necessary and sufficient conditions. A continental or subcontinental expanse of land is implied in the term "continental glaciation." At first thought one would assume that the glaciated expanses must also be near the poles. This was true during the Pleistocene but may not have been true in the late Paleozoic. If continental drift is disproved, glacial theorists will face the formidable task of explaining subtropical Paleozoic glaciations of subcontinental extent. Even if the existence of continental areas in high latitudes is accepted as a necessary condition, it is not sufficient, as shown by the alternation of glacial and interglacial epochs in the Pleistocene.

The alternation of cold and warm Pleistocene epochs probably cannot be explained by periodic changes of the earth's astronomical relations during a time of continuous continental emergence, for all parts of the earth— tropic seas as well as northern and southern lands—seem to have changed climate simultaneously about 11,000 years ago.

It remains possible that the Pleistocene glaciations were the results of periodic decreases in insolation. Precise measurements of insolation, at the earth's surface and on satellites, are therefore of prime importance. After fifty or a hundred more years of such observations, a trend may become apparent, or even the existence of short cycles. In either case, forecasts for a few hundred years may then become possible.

Perhaps no single condition was sufficient to cause glaciation. Possibly each glacial epoch was the result of a combination of circumstances, beginning with the existence of broad continental areas, favored by the coincidence of periodic astronomic variations, and accentuated by changes in atmospheric circulation and by increased reflection from expanding snow fields.

16-9. *Pleistocene Life*

a. Mammals

Today large land mammals are especially abundant in southern Asia and in Africa south

of the Sahara. It is there that one would go to
find the elephant, rhinoceros, hippopotamus,
lion, and many another large herbivorous or
carnivorous mammal. The ancestors of these
animals ranged much more widely. In the
Tertiary, as we have seen, they were especially
common in North America. In the Pleistocene
they were widespread in Europe and northern
Asia, and most were also abundant in North
America. The Eurasian and North American
species that today have relatives in Africa
seem to have been mostly warmth-loving types
that ventured far north only during interglacial
epochs. But members of some lines, notably
the mastodon, the woolly mammoth, and the
woolly rhinoceros, became adapted to a much
cooler climate, where they were associated
with the musk ox and the reindeer. During the
later glacial epochs the cold fauna, including
the reindeer, moved as far south as southern
France and the Pyrenees. A typical member of
the warm fauna in Europe was *Rhinoceros*
(*Dicerorhinos*) *etruscus* (an Upper Villafranchian species, Fig. 16-27), with short-
crowned cheek teeth, and a typical cold form
was *Rhinoceros tichorhinus*, the woolly rhinoceros (Fig. 16-28).

In Europe three mammalian faunas, Lower,
Middle, and Upper, have been distinguished
in the Pleistocene. The Lower Pleistocene
fauna is the Villafranchian, especially the Upper Villafranchian. It is warm-temperate and
is characterized by the small horse (or zebra)
Equus stenonis, named in honor of Steno; an
elephant with rather simple teeth, *Elephas*
(*Archidiskodon*) *meridionalis* (Fig. 16-29);
Rhinoceros (*Dicerorhinus*) *etruscus*; and cattle, *Bos* (*Leptobos*) *etruscus*. As already suggested, in connection with Figure 16-9, this
fauna is probably pre-Mindel and perhaps pre-
Günz. The European Middle Pleistocene fauna
is mixed warm and cold, including the reindeer and the great cave bear (Fig. 16-30) as
well as the lion and a straight-tusked elephant
(*E. antiquus,* Fig. 16-29). This fauna appears
to begin in the Mindel glacial stage and persist
somewhat later. The Upper Pleistocene fauna
is cold and is characterized by the woolly

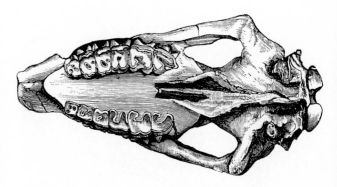

Fig. 16-27. *Skull of* Rhinoceros (Dicerorhinos)
etruscus, 22 inches long, viewed from below.
(*From Alleyne Nicholson and Richard Lydek-
ker, 1889.*)

mammoth, with curved tusks and complex
teeth (Fig. 16-31), the woolly rhinoceros, the
cave bear, and the reindeer. Where all these
forms are present, the fauna is no doubt always
glacial (periglacial, near an ice cap, during a
glacial epoch) and probably Würm, occurring
especially in many cave and alluvial deposits
that also contain human bones or artifacts.
Cattle, a bison, the modern horse, and the cave
hyena are other members of this fauna.

The three faunas are not sharply separated,
and this is not surprising with respect to either
evolution or facies. One example of mixing,
the occurrence of an elephant with teeth similar to those of the woolly mammoth in the

Fig. 16-28. Rhinoceros tichorhinus, *the woolly
rhinoceros.* (*From Max Hilzheimer,* NEUES
JAHRBUCH FÜR GEOLOGIE, *Beilageband 50,
1924.*)

Fig. 16-29. Elephas meridionalis (*above*) *and* Elephas antiquus (*below*). (*Reprinted with the permission of Charles Scribner's Sons from* Men of the Old Stone Age *by Henry Fairfield Osborn. Copyright 1915 Charles Scribner's Sons; renewal copyright 1943 A. Perry Osborn.*)

Fig. 16-30. *The cave bear,* Ursus spelaeus, *engraved in outline by cave man.* (*Reprinted with the permission of Charles Scribner's Sons from* Men of the Old Stone Age *by Henry Fairfield Osborn. Copyright 1915 Charles Scribner's Sons; renewal copyright 1943 A. Perry Osborn.*)

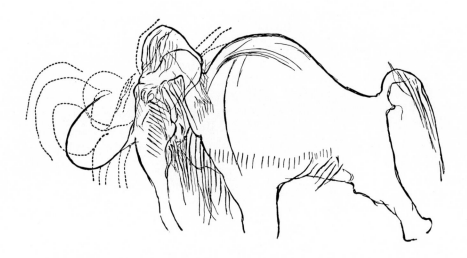

Fig. 16-31. *The woolly mammoth,* Elephas primigenius, *drawn on ivory by cave man; La Madeleine,* *France. (Reprinted with the permission of Charles Scribner's Sons from* Men of the Old Stone Age *by Henry Fairfield Osborn. Copyright 1915 Charles Scribner's Sons; renewal copyright 1943 A. Perry Osborn.)*

probably pre-Mindel Cromer Forest Bed of England, has been mentioned.

In America, a Lower Pleistocene fauna similar to the Upper Villafranchian is found in the High Plains from Texas north and may also be present in California. Two later Pleistocene faunas can probably be distinguished, especially in California. Bones are abundant in the uppermost Pleistocene beds at many places in the United States, notably in California, Texas, Florida, and other southern states; there is also a northern cold facies with the American mastodon (Fig. 15-14) and the woolly mammoth (Fig. 16-31). The southern facies is best known from the enormous fauna of Rancho La Brea, on Wilshire Boulevard, Los Angeles, which has been dated by radiocarbon as about 15,000 years B.P., in the main (Table 16-3). This fauna, as it may have appeared in life, is shown in Figure 16-32. It included the great imperial elephant, the saber-tooth "tiger" (Fig. 16-33), wolves, lions, horses, bison, camels, and also several kinds of giant ground sloths

(one shown in Fig. 16-34). The sloths were immigrants from South America, members of a peculiar mammalian fauna that had developed there during the Tertiary.

Notable features of the Upper Pleistocene warm faunas of the northern continents, developed especially in the southwestern United States, were the large number of species, the enormous number of individuals, and the large size of many specimens. Some elephants were fourteen feet high at the shoulder; some ground sloths, when standing on their hind legs, could reach even higher; and the saber-tooth tigers were fully capable of dealing with both these giants. The abundance of individuals is illustrated by the 2,000 saber-tooth skulls in the Los Angeles Museum, all from the Rancho La Brea tar pits. Equally notable is the suddenness with which most of these species disappeared. Fifteen thousand years ago they existed in great numbers; ten thousand years ago they were widespread; and then they were gone from America—mastodon,

Fig. 16-32.   *Panorama of the Late Pleistocene fauna and flora of Rancho La Brea, Los Angeles, California. (Painting by Charles R. Knight; courtesy of the Los Angeles County Museum.)*

Fig. 16-33.   *The Pleistocene saber-tooth,* Smilodon californicus, *from Rancho La Brea, Los Angeles,* California. *(Courtesy of the Los Angeles County Museum.)*

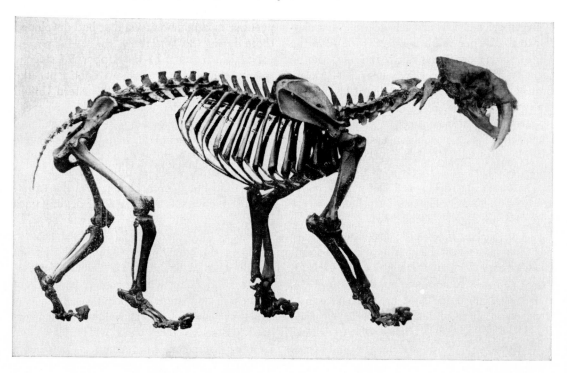

elephant, sloth, camel, tiger, lion, and even horse. Only the bison was left, in great herds on the western plains. The reasons for some disappearances are extremely hard to imagine. The horse, for example, flourished immediately upon reintroduction by the Spaniards, and was soon running wild everywhere.

One of the most interesting things about the distribution of Pleistocene mammals is the continued isolation of Australia. Just as in the Tertiary, the Australian Pleistocene mammals were all marsupials. But, paralleling northern development, some of the marsupials were of giant size. And then the giants and some of the

Fig. 16-34. *The Pleistocene ground sloth,* Paramylodon harlani, *from Rancho La Brea, Los Angeles, California. (Courtesy of the Los Angeles County Museum.)*

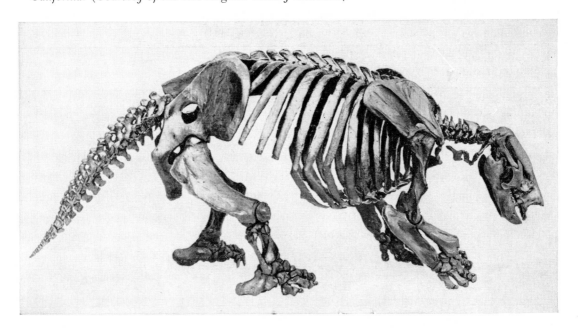

lesser marsupials disappeared suddenly, leaving, however, numerous surviving species, including the kangaroos.

b. Man

Jaws, skulls, and other bones of hominids, the subdivision of the primates to which man belongs, are rare as fossils. In the last hundred years, nevertheless, an impressive array of Pleistocene and earlier remains of human and prehuman hominids has been uncovered, mostly in the Old World. The first finds were of prehuman men in Europe: at Gibraltar, near Heidelberg, on the Italian border near Monaco, in the Neander Valley near Düsseldorf, and at many French localities. Then, in 1891, the definitely subhuman *Pithecanthropus* was found in Java. In 1923 a similar form was found near Peking. Still more recently find after find has been made in southern, eastern, and northern Africa. At most places the hominid fossils are accompanied by other mammalian bones, which commonly are very numerous. At most localities, especially the younger ones, shaped tools and weapons, called **artifacts,** are abundant. In the Pleistocene and early Recent deposits, the artifacts are mostly made from flint or other hard, fine-grained stone. As the Upper Pleistocene artifacts were merely shaped by chipping and the early Recent ones were polished, the late Pleistocene is also called the Paleolithic, or Old Stone, Age and the early Recent the Neolithic, or New Stone, Age. Sometimes an intermediate Mesolithic is also distinguished.

The human remains and artifacts occur in gravels and other alluvial deposits along rivers, in the loess that formed many times during the Pleistocene and now tends to mantle the whole land surface in such regions as northern France and western Germany, and especially beneath the floors of caves, in layers of rubble, clay, and travertine. The cave deposits, in particular, are isolated from other strata of anything like the same age. A special stratigraphy is therefore necessary to determine the relative ages of the various upland, river terrace, and cave deposits. First, the associated non-primate mammals may be used to place a stratum or other occurrence in the Lower, Middle, or Upper Pleistocene and perhaps also in a cold or warm interval. In Europe, in North Africa, in southwestern Asia, and less certainly elsewhere, **culture stages** based on artifacts make

TABLE 16-4

Culture Stages of the Old World

SYSTEM OR SUBSYSTEM	CULTURE STAGE	TYPE REGION	NOTABLE OCCURRENCE OUTSIDE THE TYPE REGION
Recent	Neolithic		
	Mesolithic		
Upper Pleistocene	Paleolithic		
	Azilian	Southwestern France	
	Magdalenian	Southwestern France	Northwestern Spain
	Solutrean	East-central France	Southwestern France
	Protomagdalenian	Southwestern France	
	Aurignacian	Southwestern France	Spain
	Mousterian	Southwestern France	Southwestern Asia
	Acheulian	Northeastern France	Eastern Africa
Middle Pleistocene	Abbevillian (Chellean)	Northeastern France	Rhine Valley; Thames Valley; possibly Peking, China
Lower Pleistocene	Pre-Paleolithic	(No type region)	Ain Hanech, Algeria; Olduvai Gorge, Tanganyika; Sterkfontein, South Africa

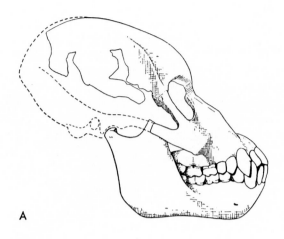

A

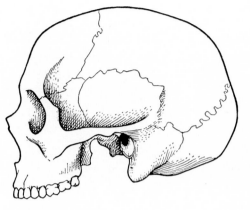

D

Fig. 16-35. *Hominid skulls.* (A, *from W. E. Le Gros Clark*, QUARTERLY JOURNAL, *Geol. Soc. London, 1949. B, C, D, reprinted from Ref. 5 by permission of the University of Chicago Press; copyright 1955 by the University of Chicago.*)

A. Proconsul africanus, *Miocene of eastern Africa.*

B. Homo (Pithecanthropus) pekinensis, *Middle Pleistocene of China.*

C. Homo neanderthalensis, *Monte Circeo, Italy.*

D. Homo sapiens.

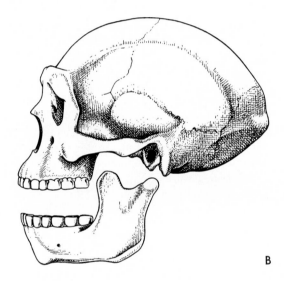

B

possible a more precise stratigraphy (Table 16-4). By radiocarbon dating (Table 16-3), much greater precision is now possible for late Paleolithic and subsequent stages. Some culture stages are so crude that they may be called pre-Paleolithic; in the Old World such stages are likely to be early Pleistocene. No pre-Pleistocene shaped tools or weapons are definitely known.

1. PRE-PLEISTOCENE AND EARLY PLEISTO-CENE HOMINIDS. Semi-erect pre-Pleistocene ancestors of man may have included *Proconsul africanus* (Fig. 16-35A) and other Miocene primates of east-central Africa. Forms intermediate between these early hominids and Pleistocene man have been found in Africa and in India.

The great finds of recent years in human prehistory have been early Pleistocene artifacts and bones discovered at many sites in Africa. At one place in South Africa, Lime-

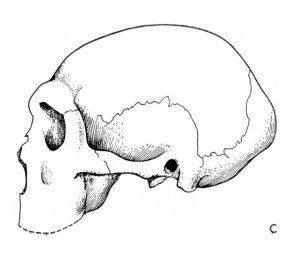

C

TABLE 16-5

Hominid Fossils of the Old World

SUBSYSTEM	HOMINID	ASSOCIATED CULTURE STAGE	REGION
Upper Pleistocene (Würm glacial)	*Homo sapiens*	Magdalenian Aurignacian	Europe Europe
	Homo neanderthalensis	Mousterian	Europe, southwestern Asia
	Homo sapiens?	Mousterian; Acheulian	Europe
Middle Pleistocene	*Homo heidelbergensis*	Abbevillian	Germany
	Homo (Pithecanthropus) erectus		Java
	Homo (Pithecanthropus) pekinensis	Abbevillian or Pre-Paleolithic	China
Lower Pleistocene	Australopithecinae		
	Australopithecus	Pre-Paleolithic	South Africa
	Paranthropus	Pre-Paleolithic	South Africa
	Zinjanthropus	Pre-Paleolithic?	East Africa
Pliocene	*Oreopithecus*		Tuscany, Italy
Miocene	*Proconsul*, etc.		East Africa, etc.

works Cave north of Kimberley, bones belonging to five individuals made up 0.26 percent of a collection of 7,000 bones and bone fragments. Most of the rest (92 percent of the total) belonged to 293 individual antelopes, mostly of species still living in Africa. The other kinds of animals represented are also mostly common in Africa today—zebras, rhinoceroses, hyenas, and the like—though the rather abundant baboons belong to an extinct species. Correlation with the Villafranchian faunas of eastern and northern Africa is fairly good, though for a short time all the South African occurrences were considered Pliocene and one site is now thought to be perhaps Middle Pleistocene. The South African hominids have been named australopithecines (southern "apes"). Most belong to two genera (Table 16-5), whose distinctions included the live weight of the individuals, that of one genus being 75–85 pounds, that of the other half again as much. These creatures stood erect and walked on two feet, as shown by the pelvic and upper leg structures of at least four individuals. Their teeth were much closer to those of men than to those of the great apes such as

the gorilla and the chimpanzee. Apparently they were hunters. At Limeworks Cave baboon skulls are bashed in and antelope bones are split, as by an animal that could hold stones in its hands rather than by one armed only with teeth. At another cave site (Sterkfontein), shaped stone tools have been found (Fig. 16-36).

Recent discoveries in eastern Africa have been equally significant. At Olduvai Gorge in Tanganyika, southeast of Lake Victoria, Dr. L. S. B. Leakey and his associates have found artifacts at several levels. At the lowest two, an Upper Villafranchian mammalian fauna is present; at the second level a skull and other bones of *Zinjanthropus*, a new australopithecine, were discovered in 1959 (Ref. 19) and later years. The cranial capacity of *Zinjanthropus* and other australopithecines (Fig. 16-37) is close to those of the great apes and far below the 1,350-milliliter average of modern man (*Homo sapiens*, Fig. 16-35D). The *Zinjanthropus* horizon has been dated at about 1,700,000 years B.P. by Ar40/K40 and the lowest Olduvai artifacts at about 2,300,000 years B.P.

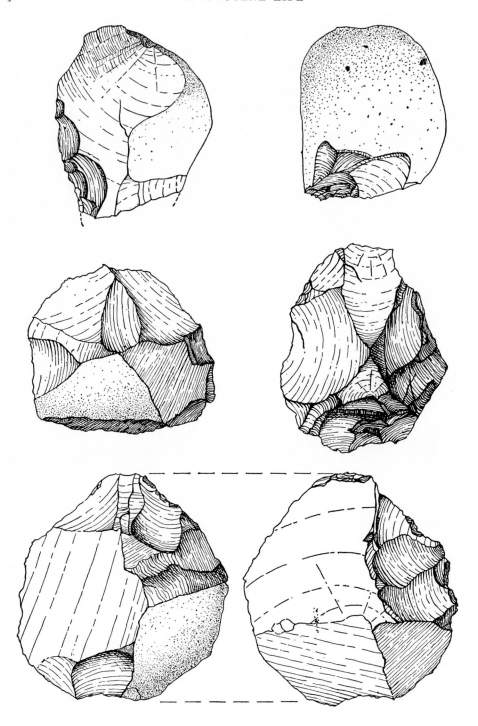

Fig. 16-36. *Pre-Paleolithic tools from Sterkfontein, South Africa. The lower four are partially shaped flakes, the upper two residual cores. The specimens are about four inches in diameter. (From Ref. 18 by permission of the author and the American Association for the Advancement of Science.)*

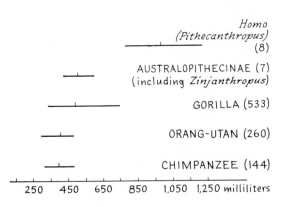

Fig. 16-37. *Cranial capacities of apes and men.* (*After Ref. 20.*)

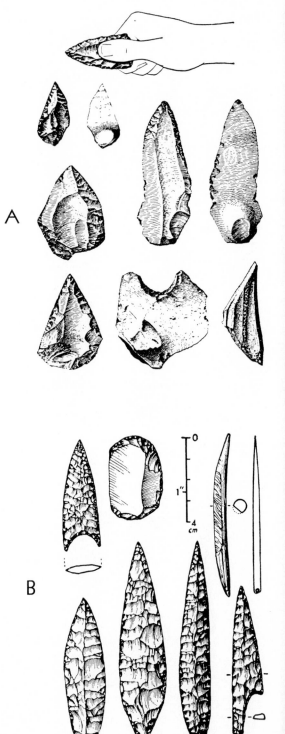

2. MIDDLE PLEISTOCENE HOMINIDS. Several hominids occur in association with mammals that are probably Middle Pleistocene; they are so man-like that they should probably be considered members of the genus *Homo*. Perhaps they should be assigned to two subgenera. One subgenus (*Pithecanthropus*) has been found at two widely separated places in Asia: *Homo* (*Pithecanthropus*) *erectus* in Java, *Homo* (*Pithecanthropus*) *pekinensis* (Fig. 16-35B) near Peking in northern China. The other type, Heidelberg man (*Homo heidelbergensis*), is known from a single jaw found in Germany. Java man comes from a tropical site near sea level, where no difference between glacial and interglacial stages has been made out; indeed, little difference

Fig. 16-38. *Tools of the Old Stone Age.* (A, reprinted with the permission of Charles Scribner's Sons from Men of the Old Stone Age *by Henry Fairfield Osborn. Copyright 1915 Charles Scribner's Sons; renewal copyright 1943 A. Perry Osborn. B, C, D, from Ref. 21 by permission of the American Association for the Advancement of Science.*)

A. *Mousterian lithic tools, with a suggestion of one way in which the points may have been used.*

B. *Solutrean lithic tools.*

C. *Magdalenian lithic tools.*

D. *Magdalenian bone tools.*

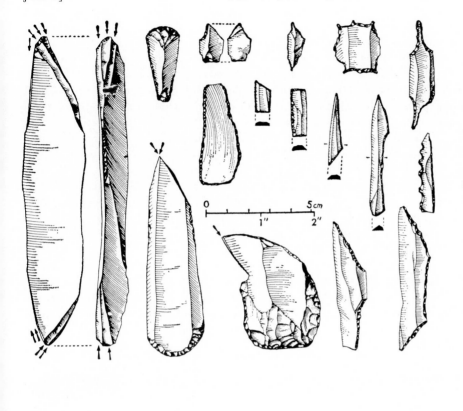

C

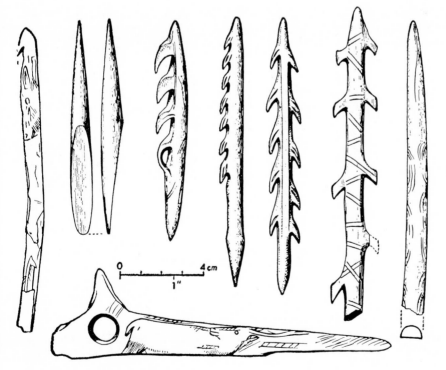

D

would be likely. The Peking human remains, which were numerous and excellent (though now lost in the wars), were found in a cave-fissure deposit that was excavated mostly between 1923 and 1932. The associated mammalian bones and plant pollen indicate Middle Pleistocene age and a glacial climate. The percentage of extinct mammals points to an age similar to that of the upper Mindel (upper Elster) glacial stage of Europe. The Heidelberg jaw, a very massive one, was found eighty feet below the ground surface, beneath two loess layers, and in sands that carry the Middle Pleistocene mammalian fauna, with *Elephas antiquus*. The occurrence may be Elster glacial in age. The hand axes of this time are of the crudest Paleolithic (Abbevillian). Their type locality is at Abbeville in the Somme Valley (or at Chelles-sur-Marne) in northeastern France.

Abbevillian-Acheulian artifacts have been found at several horizons in the volcanic-sedimentary sequence of Olduvai Gorge, Tanganyika, all above the *Zinjanthropus* horizon. Their Ar40/K40 ages range from about one million to about one-half million years. Probably this whole sequence should be considered Middle Pleistocene.

3. LATE PLEISTOCENE HOMINIDS. The Late Pleistocene in Europe is the time of the cold, chiefly Würm-glacial mammalian fauna that includes the woolly elephant and the reindeer. Most of the Paleolithic cultures are probably Late Pleistocene; no doubt they represent at least part of the Riss-Würm Interglacial as well as the Würm glaciation. Knowledge of Late Pleistocene man is now enormous. Whole books, full of fascinating details, have been written about the Paleolithic of Europe alone. Human bones are rather few, but artifacts are enormously abundant, especially in caves. Some cave walls are covered with Old Stone Age art.

Among the Late Pleistocene (post-Riss) tools and weapons, the flint hand axes are the oldest (Acheulian; Table 16-4). These were much improved over the Abbevillian type, but they were still crude tools or weapons. They were succeeded by arrow points, spear heads, stone knives, and varied implements, which culminated in the Solutrean and Magdalenian industries of the latest Paleolithic (Fig. 16-38), which flourished in southwestern France while the last Pleistocene glaciation prevailed farther northeast.

Several dozen more or less complete Upper

Fig. 16-39. *Reindeer and landscape engraved round fragment of reindeer antler, from Kesslerloch, Switzerland. (Reprinted with the permission of Charles Scribner's Sons from* Men of the Old Stone Age *by Henry Fairfield Osborn. Copyright 1915 Charles Scribner's Sons; renewal copyright 1943 A. Perry Osborn.)*

Pleistocene skeletons and numerous fragmentary human remains have been found in Europe. These have been supplemented by almost as much more material from the Near (Middle) East. The men are of at least two types, the low-browed, stooped Neanderthal man, *Homo neanderthalensis* (Fig. 16-35C), and the tall, straight, high-browed Cro-Magnon man, who definitely belongs to the species *Homo sapiens*, along with all existing human races, and whose bones are associated especially with the Solutrean and Magdalenian artifacts. Neanderthal man is known definitely from the last interglacial, but the unmistakable and well-dated remains of *Homo sapiens* are from the succeeding glacial epoch.

An especially primitive Neanderthal jaw was found in 1949 near Toulouse in southern France, associated with the warm facies of the Middle Pleistocene mammalian fauna. It is therefore interglacial, probably of the last interglacial interval, but possibly pre-Riss. Much more numerous Neanderthal remains, but no complete skeletons, have come from a locality near Weimar (Germany), one near Rome, and one in Yugoslavia, all associated with the Middle Pleistocene fauna and hence pre-Würm, probably from the Riss-Würm Interglacial. Other Neanderthal skeletons are associated with the Upper Pleistocene (Würm) cold fauna. At many places, including the cave of Le Moustier in southwestern France, bones of Neanderthal man are associated with Mousterian artifacts (Fig. 16-38A and Table 16-4).

Possibly *Homo sapiens* existed before the last glaciation. A fragmentary skull found in Thames terrace gravels at Swanscombe, below London, lay in a bed that also contained the *Elephas antiquus* fauna and Acheulian hand axes. The known part of the skull is made up of three fragments, found in 1935, 1936, and 1955, and still lacks the forehead. The shape and volume suggest *Homo sapiens;* but, lacking the brow, who can say that this was not a delicate Neanderthaler?

Several very late Pleistocene caves in western Europe, mostly in southwestern France and northwestern Spain, contain mural paintings and have yielded sculptures and en-

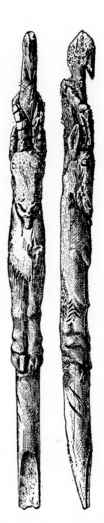

Fig. 16-40. *Front and side views of a saiga antelope carved on a bone dart-thrower; Magdalenian of Mas d'Azil, southern France. (Reprinted with the permission of Charles Scribner's Sons from* Men of the Old Stone Age *by Henry Fairfield Osborn. Copyright 1915 Charles Scribner's Sons; renewal copyright 1943 A. Perry Osborn.)*

gravings on bone and ivory that mark a climax in the history of art. The engraving of Figure 16-39 and the sculpture of Figure 16-40 give some idea of the moving qualities of these masterpieces. The greatest achievements, however, are the paintings in color, which can only be appreciated from colored reproductions (Ref. 6) or, best of all, from a visit to Lascaux and other caves of southwestern France. In

Fig. 16-41. *The original Folsom point, between the ribs of a bison, from Folsom, New Mexico, 1927; about 1/5 natural size. (Courtesy of H. M. Wormington, Denver Museum of Natural History. See Ref. 22.)*

the great hall of Lascaux one looks up at a breaking wave of overwhelmingly imminent cattle, whose smooth resistless curves are as fascinating as they are terrifying. If one turns away, one sees the graceful antlers of swimming reindeer, depicted with an economy of strokes that bespeaks a long tradition. Has man progressed much since Lascaux? Even if we take Praxiteles and Michelangelo into account, we realize the debatable nature of the advances made since the Pleistocene, compared with the development from traditionless beast to cave artist. The earlier advances, especially from nothing at all to a Cambrian *Olenellus* with movable legs and central management, were of course vastly greater. If all the more complicated forms of life should now be destroyed in a radioactive holocaust, a new evolutionary development might bring forth new forms of life with capacities beyond our imagination. The present cycle, however, is not likely to surpass Lascaux in imaginative emotional achievement.

It appears that man did not reach America

until about the end of the Pleistocene. Then he came from Siberia, across the Bering land bridge, as shown by similarities between Siberian and North American cultures. Topographic and geologic evidence at Bering Strait shows that the land bridge existed at each glacial stage, when sea level was low, and was broken when the rise of ocean waters filled the strait during each interglacial interval. Man, however, rather certainly did not cross until rather late in Wisconsin time. The going must have been rough, as the bridge and its approaches were all tundra and glacial ice. Despite all difficulties, by 11,000 years B.P. men were present in Alaska and had also reached Arizona and New Mexico (Table 16-3, Nos. 4 and 5), where they were killing bison with weapons tipped with beautiful projectile points, such as the one shown in Figure 16-41. Points beveled in this way are unknown in the Old World. Possibly men were living in the southwestern United States a little earlier (Table 16-3, No. 13), though the artifacts found at the edge of ancient Lake Manix in the Mojave Desert (southeastern California) may be younger than the 19,000 years indicated by radiocarbon for the tufa of the shoreline.

Conclusion

In the three hundred years since Steno, stratigraphy has become a worldwide ordered structure. Steno stated the fundamental laws and set up a local sequence (§ 1-3). William Smith and other Europeans discovered the usefulness of guide fossils and geologic maps (Chap. 3). The development of methods of stratigraphic study and their application in all parts of the world (§§ 4-3, 4-5, 4-7, 4-9; Chaps. 5 and 6; §§ 9-3, 10-1, 16-1) led to the completion of the stratigraphic structure and evaluations of its precision (Chaps. 7 and 8). Stratigraphy has paid its debt to biology by establishing the sequence and the successive changes in the evolving floras and faunas (§§ 2-1, 10-6; Chaps. 11, 12, 14, and 15; § 16-9). The physical history and the history of life, taken together, have shown that climaxes of change occurred at the beginning and end of the Paleozoic (Chaps. 10 and 13) and, somewhat less markedly, at the end of the Mesozoic (Chap. 14) and in the Pleistocene (Chap. 16). The time scale has been calibrated by radiometric data that are sensitive to millions or billions of years (Chaps. 8 and 9) or, just where needed, to thousands of years (Chap. 16).

The methods of stratigraphic study have been ingenious; they are enough to make any naturalist proud. Philosophers and mathematicians, however, are somewhat critical of the results. Correlations are vague and approximate, partly because statistical or rigorously logical treatments of the evidence have been rare. Now study of the rocks and even of some kinds of fossils is becoming quantitative. The interplay between radiometric age-determinations, paleomagnetic reversals, and fossil-based correlations is forcing the stratigrapher to take a critical attitude toward his own work and to adopt formally logical procedures. For these and other reasons, most of stratigraphy is likely to be reworked in the next few decades. Methods of gathering and handling evidence will become more precise and effective, full use will be made of computer programming, and the conclusions reached will be more definite and more satisfying. There is even some hope for the rational solution of obscure and complicated problems, such as Gondwanaland (Chap. 13), that have long been pending.

The fundamental problems, however, are likely to persist indefinitely. The nature of things may be beyond human understanding. In this book the course of organic evolution on our little planet has been described, from the simple to the complex. Large and efficient organisms, in water, on land, and in the air, were slow to develop; the earlier crude developments were abruptly eliminated, and in time more effective ones appeared as ecologic replacements. Since Darwin it has been customary to consider that evolution has occurred through natural selection. We have not found space in this book for a critical study of Darwin's hypothesis, which is considered by biologists the most helpful statement, mnemonically at least, that has been made. Even the most expert specialists in the laws of heredity, however, would hardly claim the ability to imagine the actual course that evolution has taken, given only a single stage in its development, such as the present faunas and floras. Accurate prediction of the long future is even less likely. Men can describe organisms and other things, and show the relations between organisms, between the chemical elements, and between matter and energy, but they have not discovered how matter and energy happen to exist. They may be on the verge of formulating a reasonable hypothesis for the origin of life on earth, but they are not likely to be able to say that evolution would, on another planet, take the course that has been followed here, or even that, with a new start, a closely similar development would occur on the earth's surface. Vertebrates, mammals, and man are obviously not inevitable.

REFERENCES

General

1. F. E. Zeuner: *The Pleistocene Period*, 2nd ed., 447 pages (Hutchinson, London, 1959)
2. R. F. Flint: *Glacial and Pleistocene Geology*, 553 pages (Wiley, New York, 1957)
3. J. K. Charlesworth: *The Quaternary Era*, 2 vols., 1,700 pages (Arnold, London, 1957)
4. Marcellin Boule and H. V. Vallois: *Fossil Men*, 535 pages (Dryden Press, New York, 1957)
5. W. E. Le Gros Clark: *The Fossil Evidence for Human Evolution*, 181 pages (University of Chicago Press, 1955)
6. Georges Bataille: *Lascaux or the Birth of Art* (Skira, Lausanne and New York, 1955)
7. W. F. Libby: *Radiocarbon Dating*, 2nd ed., 175 pages (University of Chicago Press, 1955)

Background Material

8. RADIOCARBON, vol. 1 and succeeding annual volumes (Yale University Press, New Haven, 1959–   )

9. D. B. Ericson and Goesta Wollin: "Micropaleontology, "SCIENTIFIC AMERICAN, July 1962, pp. 97–106

10. Cesare Emiliani, T. Mayeda, and Raimondo Selli: "Paleotemperature Analysis of the Plio-Pleistocene Section at Le Castella, Calabria, Southern Italy," BULLETIN, Geol. Soc. Am., vol. 72, pp. 679–688 (1961)

11. W. R. Riedel, M. N. Bramlette, and F. L. Parker: "'Pliocene-Pleistocene' Boundary in Deep-sea Sediments," SCIENCE, vol. 140, pp. 1238–1240 (1963)

12. Cesare Emiliani: "Paleotemperature Analysis of the Caribbean Cores A254-BR-C and CP-28," BULLETIN, Geol. Soc. Am., vol. 75, pp. 129–144 (1964)

13. E. H. de Geer: "La Déglaciation Scandinave selon la chronologie de Geer," BULLETIN, Soc. géol. française (6), vol. 5, pp. 169–192 (1955)

14. H. A. Lee: "Late Glacial and Postglacial Hudson Bay Sea Episode," SCIENCE, vol. 131, pp. 1609–1611 (1960)

15. F. P. Shepard: "Sea Level Changes in the Past 6,000 Years: Possible Archeological Significance," SCIENCE, vol. 143, pp. 574–576 (1964)

16. Allan Cox, R. R. Doell, and G. B. Dalrymple: "Reversals of the Earth's Magnetic Field," SCIENCE, vol. 144, pp. 1537–1543 (26 June 1964)

17. Björn Kurtén: "Villafranchian Faunal Evolution," COMMENTATIONES BIOLOGICAE, Soc. Sci. Fennica, vol. 26, No. 3, 18 pages (1963)

18. F. C. Howell: "The Villafranchian and Human Origins," SCIENCE, vol. 130, pp. 831–844 (2 October 1959)

19. L. S. B. Leakey: "A New Fossil Skull from Olduvai," NATURE, vol. 184, pp. 491–493 (1959)

20. P. V. Tobias: "Cranial Capacity of *Zinjanthropus* and Other Australopithecines," NATURE, vol. 197, pp. 743–746 (1963)

21. Denise de Sonneville-Bordes: "Upper Paleolithic Cultures in Western Europe," SCIENCE, vol. 142, pp. 347–355 (18 October 1963)

22. H. M. Wormington: *Ancient Man in North America*, Popular Series, Denver Museum of Natural History, No. 4, 4th ed., 322 pages (Denver, 1957)

APPENDIX A

*Classification of Animals**

Phylum Protozoa
       Class Sarcodina
            Order Foraminifera (Foraminiferida); Cambrian–Recent
            Order Radiolaria (Radiolariida); Cambrian–Recent
Phylum Archaeocyatha—sponge-like fossils; Cambrian
Phylum Porifera—sponges; Precambrian(?), Cambrian–Recent
Phylum Coelenterata
       Class Hydrozoa—*Hydra,* Portuguese man-of-war, etc.; Cambrian–Recent
       Class Scyphozoa—jellyfish; Precambrian(?), Cambrian–Recent
       Class Anthozoa—corals; Ordovician–Recent
Several phyla of rather simple worms; almost no fossils
Phylum Bryozoa—moss-animals
       Class Endoprocta—no fossils
       Class Ectoprocta; Ordovician–Recent
Phylum Brachiopoda—lampshells, etc.
       Class Inarticulata (with hingeless shells); Cambrian–Recent
       Class Articulata (with hinged shells); Cambrian–Recent
Phylum Mollusca
       Class Monoplacophora—chiton-like, with single valve (§ 10-6.a); Lower
          Cambrian–Recent
       Class Polyplacophora—chitons; Upper Cambrian–Recent
       Class Scaphopoda—tuskshells; Ordovician–Recent
       Class Pelecypoda—oysters, clams, etc.; Ordovician–Recent
       Class Gastropoda—snails; Lower Cambrian–Recent
       Class Cephalopoda
          Subclass Tetrabranchiata
             Order Nautiloidea—*Nautilus,* etc.; Upper Cambrian–Recent
             Order Ammonoidea; Devonian–Cretaceous
          Subclass Dibranchiata—squids, octopus, etc.; Mississippian–Recent
             Order Belemnitida—belemnites; Mississippian–Paleocene
Phylum Annelida—segmented worms; Cambrian–Recent
Phylum Onychophora—worm-like organisms (§ 10-6.b); Middle Cambrian, Recent

---

* This selective list includes most groups represented by numerous fossils.

Phylum Arthropoda

        Class Crustacea—crabs, barnacles, ostracodes (Camb.–Rec.); Middle Cambrian–Recent

        Class Arachnida—spiders, etc.; Silurian–Recent

        Class Trilobita—trilobites; Lower Cambrian–Permian

        Class Myriapoda—millipedes, centipedes; Devonian–Recent

        Class Insecta—insects; Devonian–Recent

Phylum Echinodermata

        Class Helicoplacoidea—*Helicoplacus* (§ 10-6.a); Lower Cambrian

        Class Cystoidea—cystids; Lower Cambrian–Devonian

        Class Blastoidea—sea-buds; Middle Ordovician–Permian

        Class Crinoidea—sea-lilies; Ordovician–Recent

        Class Edrioasteroidea; Cambrian–Mississippian

        Class Stelleroidea—starfish; Ordovician–Recent

        Class Echinoidea—sea-urchins; Ordovician–Recent

        Class Holothuroidea—sea-cucumbers; Ordovician–Recent

Phylum Chordata

    Subphylum Hemichordata—acorn-worms, etc.

        Class Graptolithina—graptolites; Upper Cambrian–Mississippian

    Subphylum Tunicata—tunicates (no fossils)

    Subphylum Cephalochordata—amphioxus (no fossils)

    Subphylum Vertebrata

      Superclass Pisces—fish (Chap. 11); Ordovician–Recent

      Superclass Tetrapoda—four-limbed vertebrates

        Class Amphibia; Upper Devonian–Recent

        Class Reptilia (Chap. 14); Carboniferous–Recent

        Class Aves—birds; Upper Jurassic–Recent

        Class Mammalia (Chap. 15); Jurassic–Recent

Recognition of Fossil Invertebrates and Simple Plants

THE COMMONEST fossils are remains of invertebrate animals and simple plants, most of them marine. These pages are intended as aids in making distinctions between major groups; they will be most useful if labeled specimens and microscopic preparations are also available.* Some invertebrate groups are discussed more generally in Chapter 2; vertebrates are considered in Chapters 11, 14, and 15; plants, especially the higher plants, in Chapter 12.

B-1. Simple Plants

a. Calcareous Algae

The pigmented—commonly green, blue-green, or brown—simple plants called algae mostly lack hard parts. A few, however, secrete rods, sheets, and concentric layers of calcium carbonate. Most such forms are marine; they contribute notably to tropical reefs. Examples are shown in Figures B-1 and 10-12. Note the large size of the Cambrian form represented in Figure 10-12. Calcareous algae are the principal Precambrian fossils; they are also abundant in later reef deposits.

* Obtainable from supply houses. Ward's Natural Science Establishment, Rochester, N.Y., has large stocks, including examples of *Kosmoceras* and other European ammonites discussed in Chap. 7.

b. Coccolithophorids and Discoasters

The minute stars, whorled plates, and other structures represented in Figure B-2 are called coccoliths and discoasters. All were probably parts of planktonic marine algae. The coccolithophorids (coccolith-bearers) have existed from the Jurassic to the present; the discoasters were chiefly Tertiary, especially early Tertiary. The tiny fossils make up large parts of some chalks and are abundant in some shales. They are barely visible under ordinary microscopes, but distinctive details can be made out if phase-contrast or electron microscopes are used. The discoasters, in particular, are becoming valuable guide fossils.

c. Diatoms

Diatoms are microscopic aquatic plants; they use chlorophyll in the manufacture of carbohydrates. They secrete a porous skeleton of amorphous silica (opal) composed of two parts, like a pill box and its cover. The marine diatoms are very important elements of the plankton; they are the grass of the sea. Many kinds are round—from spherical to disk-shaped (Fig. B-3A)—but other shapes (Figs. B-3B and 2-7) are common. Fresh-water forms are also abundant; some are rectangular in-

Fig. B-1. *Calcareous alga: Coralline alga* (Litho-phyllum molluccense), *Saipan, Mariana Islands,* × 4/5, *and* (right) *section through branch, showing the alternating layers of long and short cells characteristic of the species.* (*From J. Harlan Johnson, U.S. Geological Survey, 1957.*)

dividuals that are attached in chains (Fig. B-3C), and others are canoe-shaped (D) or round (E). Diatoms are known from the Jurassic to the present.

Individual diatom skeletons are gossamer trifles, but they occur in such abundance that their remains constitute formations thousands of feet thick in California and elsewhere. Some diatomites are rocks so porous that they float on water, but others are consolidated or are transformed into opaline chert. Diatomite and chert make up whole mountains in the California Coast Ranges; they are almost equally extensive in Algeria and Morocco.

B-2. *Phylum Protozoa: Foraminifers, etc.*

The Protozoa are the one-celled animals.

Most are either microscopic or barely visible to the naked eye, but a few grow as large as silver dollars. Structurally, protozoans seem simple, without the specialized tissues and organs of higher animals. Nevertheless, they successfully perform most of the operations that make higher animals effective. A protozoan grows, envelops food particles, digests and absorbs the food material, excretes unused residues, and finally reproduces in one of three ways: (1) simple division (one individual becoming two); (2) one individual making itself into a sac from which many young emerge; (3) sexual union of two newly formed cells. Reproduction is commonly asexual for several generations, then sexual once, then again asexual for several generations. A few groups of protozoans secrete or assemble skeletons of calcium carbonate, silica, or other material; uncountable numbers of these skeletons have been preserved in the rocks.

Fig. B-2. *Very small plankton. (From M. N. Bramlette, Scripps Institution.)*

A. *Coccolith 3.3 microns across, from Middle Eocene, beneath 6,500 feet of water, Tuamotu Ridge, central Pacific, 17° S. (Electron photomicrograph by R. E. F. Reimann, Scripps Institution of Oceanography, La Jolla, California.)*

B. Braarudosphaera bigelowi, *a coccolith-like form from the Paleocene of California;* × 1,500.

C. Discoaster septemradiatus, *from the Middle Eocene of California;* × 1,500.

D. Discoaster helianthus, *from the Paleocene of California;* × 1,500.

E. Discoaster limbatus, *from the Paleocene of California;* × 1,500.

F. *Discoasters and coccoliths from the Middle Eocene, 6 feet below the sea floor, beneath 15,000 feet of water, in the Pacific Ocean off southern Mexico (16° N., 114° W.);* × 460.

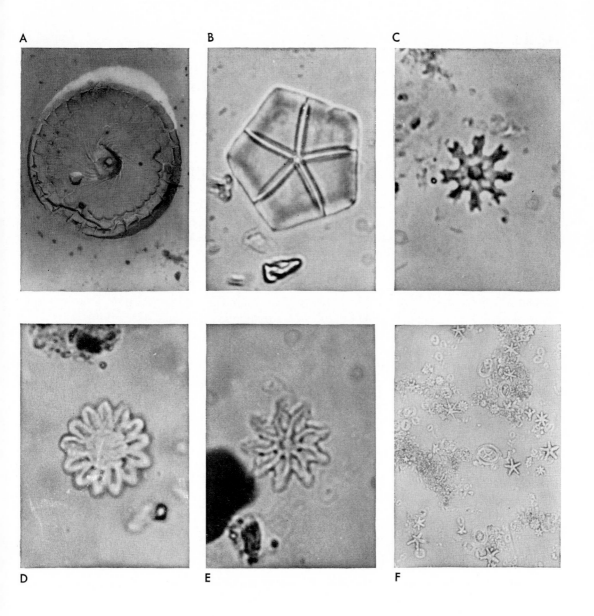

A B C

D E F

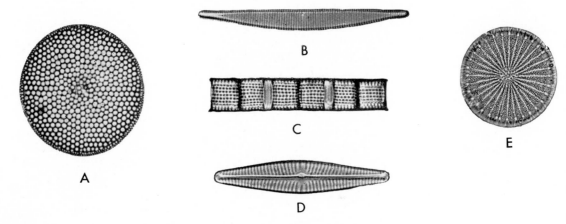

Fig. B-3. *Diatoms. (From K. E. Lohman, U.S. Geological Survey.)*
   A. Coscinodiscus salisburyanus (*marine*), *Miocene;* × 800.
   B. Pseudoeunotia doliolus (*marine*), *Pleistocene, North Atlantic;* × 775.
   C. Melosira granulata (*fresh-water*), *Miocene, Nevada;* × 530.
   D. Navicula peregrina (*fresh-water*), *Pleistocene, Idaho;* × 640.
   E. Stephanodiscus carconensis (*fresh-water*), *Plio-Pleistocene, California;* × 435.

a. Radiolaria

Radiolaria (Fig. 2-2E) are protozoans that secrete microscopic, porous skeletons, usually of opaline silica, in which long, pointed rays are likely to be prominent features. They are all marine, and most are planktonic. Accumulations of their siliceous skeletons make up oozes that cover moderately large areas of the present sea floor. Radiolaria are abundant in many shales—for example, in the Eocene of the California Coast Ranges. Some early Cenozoic siliceous formations are almost pure radiolarites, as on Barbados Island in the West Indies (Fig. 2-2E).

b. Foraminifera (*Foraminiferida, Foraminifers*)

By far the most numerous and important protozoans in the fossil record are the foraminifers (commonly called forams). They have skeletons of calcium carbonate or other materials, are considerably larger than radiolarians, and are very much larger than coccoliths or discoasters. Most foraminifers are exclusively marine; a few Recent forms live in fresh water. Fossil foraminifers are very rare in the Lower Cambrian and higher in that system, slightly commoner in the Ordovician, and moderately common from the Silurian on, with one great development in the late Paleozoic (fusulines, Fig. 7-18) and another that began in the Cretaceous and has continued to this day. The last expansion was marked by the abundance of several groups of very large foraminifers (nummulites, orbitoids, etc.) in the Paleogene, a system that is called the Nummulitic by the French. Great masses of Paleogene limestone in the Tethyan region are composed of these large foraminifers; blocks of this kind of limestone were used in building the Egyptian pyramids.

Though most foraminifers secrete chambered shells of calcium carbonate (Fig. B-4A), some genera cement together grains of quartz and other substances (Fig. B-4B), and a few have unpreservable horny skeletons or none at all. The shells are mostly less than a millimeter long, barely visible to the naked eye, but fusulines, orbitoids, and nummulites are from five to fifty times larger.

The variation of external ornamentation in a single foraminiferal species is shown in Figure B-5. In one specimen (AB, side and terminal views) the walls of the chambers are apparent, and also the terminal aperture or foramen that gives the group its name, but almost no other surface irregularities. Another specimen (CD) is ornamented by parallel ridges. An entirely different kind of variation, also characteristic of foraminifers, was discovered in this same species in 1883. The variation shows up in sections (E and F) that cut the walls of early-formed chambers, completely hidden in A–D. In E the first chamber is large and the complete shell rather small; in F the first chamber is very small and the complete shell rather large, though the outermost chambers are not shown in the figure. The E form is called *megalospheric*, the F form *microspheric*. Studies of the life cycles of living foraminifers show that the megalospheric and microspheric forms are features of the alternation of generations common among organisms (Fig. B-6). Megalospheric individuals grow from asexual bodies produced by a microspheric individual, whose organic matter is usually used up in the process. A megalospheric adult may then produce many gametes, sometimes in a cyst. The gametes conjugate to form new individuals of microspheric type.

Fig. B-4. *Foraminifers. (From Patsy Smith, U.S. Geological Survey, 1963, 1964.)*

    A. Bolivina pseudobeyrichi, *a Recent calcareous foraminifer,* × 112, *cut open to show internal walls of chambers.*

    B. Reophax dentalinaformis, × 45, *a Recent agglutinated (arenaceous) foraminifer from the floor of the Pacific off El Salvador.*

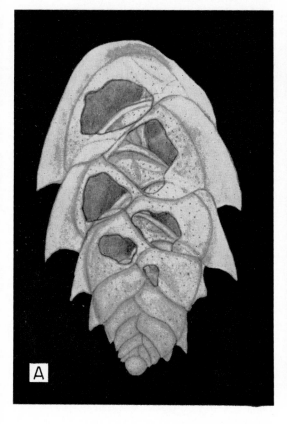
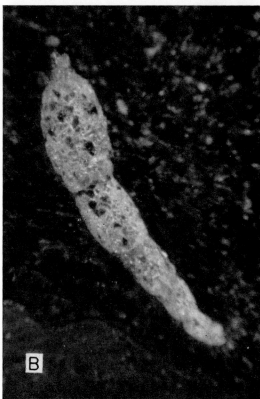

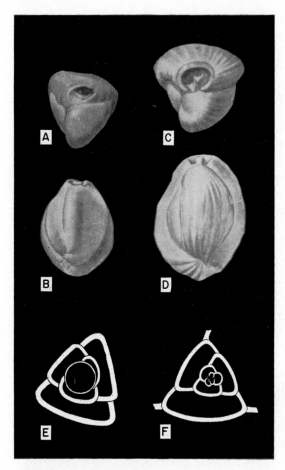

worldwide correlations, exhibiting the requisite qualities of wide horizontal distribution and short vertical range. The three *Globigerina* species are especially instructive. *G. bulloides* is the common species in the present oceans and goes back at least to the Oligocene; *G. eximia*, in 1956, was known only from the Lower Miocene of Saipan, in the western Pacific; and *G. nepenthes* was proving to be a useful guide fossil for correlations between widely separated regions, having been found in Saipan, Java, Morocco, Trinidad, the Dominican Republic, and Cuba, probably in the Lower Miocene only.

B-3. *Phyla Porifera* (*Sponges*) *and Archaeocyatha*

The sponges, living or dead, are so full of holes that they are properly called Porifera (pore-bearers). They are much the simplest multicelled animals living today. They are distinguished from protozoans not only by the association of many cells in a single mass (many protozoans stick together in colonies of identical cells) but also by the differentiation in form and function among the cells of a single mass. The associated cells are so necessary to one another that the masses must be

Fig. B-5. *Variations in* Triloculina trigonula, *a calcareous foraminifer.*

A, B, C, D. *Two types of sculpture, in side (B, D) and apertural (A, C) views; Recent, Saipan lagoon, Mariana Islands; × 47. (From Ruth Todd, U.S. Geological Survey, 1957.)*

E, F. *Megalospheric (E) and microspheric (F) forms, in section; Eocene. (From E. Munier-Chalmas and Charles Schlumberger, 1883.)*

Fig. B-6. *Alternation of generations in the Foraminifera. (After Léon Moret, 1958.)*

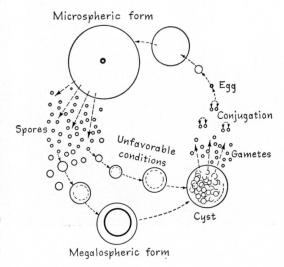

Most living foraminiferal species are bottom dwellers, and apparently most extinct forms were also benthonic. From the late Mesozoic on, however, small planktonic foraminifers swarmed in the upper layers of the oceans and on death sank to the bottom. Some of the planktonic genera, such as the Upper Cretaceous *Globotruncana* (Fig. B-7ABC) and the Cenozoic *Globigerina* (D–K), include species that are exceptionally good guide fossils for

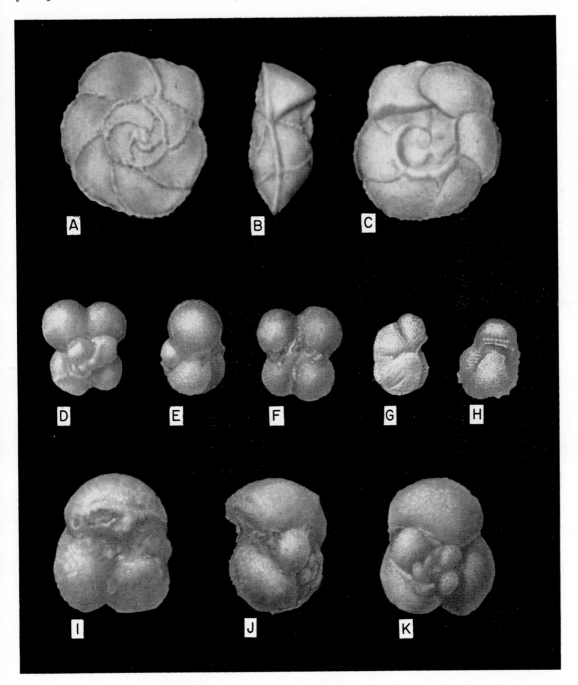

Fig. B-7. *The planktonic genera* Globotruncana *and* Globigerina. (*From J. A. Cushman and Ruth Todd, U.S. Geological Survey, 1946 and 1956.*)

ABC. *Three views of a specimen of* Globotruncana arca, *Upper Cretaceous of Texas;* × 60.

DEF. *Three views of* Globigerina bulloides, *Oligocene–Recent, worldwide.*

GH. *Two views of* Globigerina nepenthes, *Saipan; also found in Java, Morocco, and the Caribbean region, perhaps everywhere in the Lower Miocene.*

IJK. *Three views of* Globigerina eximia, *Lower Miocene of Saipan;* × 55.

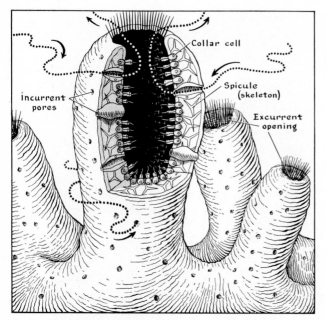

Fig. B-8. *Diagrammatic sketch of a colonial sponge.* (*From Garrett Hardin,* Biology: Its Principles and Implications, *W. H. Freeman & Co., 1961.*)

bonate. Skeletons of sponges, or disjointed spicules, mostly siliceous, are minor elements of marine faunas from the Cambrian on. Fresh-water sponges also exist but are almost unknown as fossils.

The archaeocyathids of the Cambrian (Fig. B-9) are porous, double-walled calcareous cups. They appear to be reliable guide fossils, mostly Lower Cambrian and especially abundant in South Australia.

B-4. *Phylum Coelenterata: Corals, etc.*

The coelenterates are a large group of marine and fresh-water animals considerably more complex than sponges. They are characterized by a simple, double-walled digestive cavity, the coelenteron, and by stinging capsules on the coelenteron walls and other surfaces. The life cycle in most classes of the phylum includes two contrasted stages, a

called complex animals instead of colonies of individual cells. Some sponge animals are of pinhead size, others a foot across. Sponge individuals of some kinds are also aggregated into connected colonies (Fig. B-8).

The individual sponge is a cup whose walls are pierced by pores lined by specialized cells bearing tiny whips (flagella) that set up currents flowing inward toward the central cup. Bits of food are captured from the current and digested by cells specialized for that function. Still other groups of cells carry on reproduction. Though the cells are specialized, no membranes or other tissues are distinguishable. This feature separates the sponges from the coelenterates and other higher animals.

Sponges secrete skeletons of rod-like or rayed spicules, more or less closely connected to form lattices. The living bath sponge has spicules of flexible spongin, a horny substance. Many other sponges, living and extinct, are characterized by skeletons of similar form but composed of opaline silica or calcium car-

Fig. B-9. *Diagrammatic sketch of a typical archaeocyathid,* Ajacicyathus. (*From Bernhard Kummel,* History of the Earth, *W. H. Freeman & Co., 1961.*)

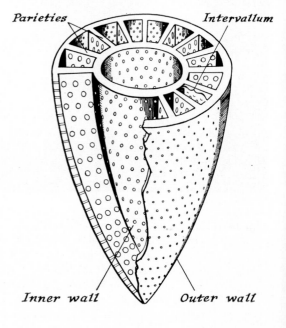

floating *medusa* stage and an attached *polyp* stage (Fig. B-10). The medusa has the shape of a tentacled umbrella, and the polyp is a sessile, tentacled cup. Coelenterates that go through both stages reproduce asexually in the polyp stage, sexually in the medusa stage.

Corals and sea-anemones (the latter are corals without hard parts) are members of the class Anthozoa, polyps that lack the medusa stage. The body cavity is divided into compartments by walls called mesenteries (Fig. B-11) and is commonly connected with the mouth by a gullet-like tube. The tentacles around the mouth carry numerous stinging cells. After a small fish or other prey has been stung into paralysis, it is brought into the cup by the tentacles, which are moved by muscles, tissues more complicated than anything in a sponge. Digestive juices from specialized cells in the mesenteries then prepare the food for absorption. The muscles are brought into action by the simplest of nervous systems. The animal is sensitive to touch and can bring its tentacles inside and close up tight, so that no aperture is seen.

Coral reproduction is either asexual, by budding, or sexual. In asexual reproduction the new individual usually remains connected with the old (Fig. B-10). Budding may go on and on, forming an extensive colony, commonly with a definite pattern. The sea-anemone and many other forms, however, are solitary. All corals, including the colonial ones, have the power of sexual reproduction, on occasion. The sexual elements are discharged into the sea water, where they unite to form very small polyps that soon settle on the sea floor.

A typical solitary coral secretes a calcareous cup, the *calyx*, in which it sits and from which it grows upward and outward, the calyx increasing in diameter along with the animal. The calyx is composed of a basal plate, an outer wall, vertical *septa* (Fig. B-11) within the mesenteries, horizontal plates or *tabulae*, and other (inclined) skeletal elements. Colonial corals secrete similar hard parts, with connected calyces.

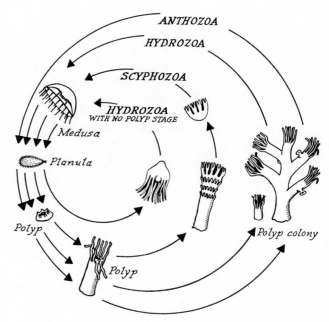

Fig. B-10. *Life cycles of the main groups of coelenterates.* (After Dorothy Hill and J. W. Wells, in Treatise on Invertebrate Paleontology, Geol. Soc. Am. and Univ. of Kansas Press.)

Fig. B-11. *Diagram showing polyp and skeleton of a modern coral.* (Adapted, for Kummel, op. cit., from Treatise on Invertebrate Paleontology, Geol. Soc. Am. and Univ. of Kansas Press.)

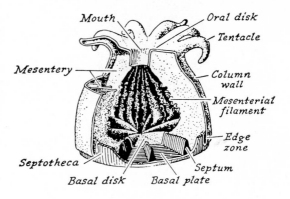

Corals are exclusively marine and grow best in warm water. Their remains, together with those of calcareous algae and other organisms, make up the limestone reefs of tropic seas, commonly called coral reefs even if algal remains predominate.

The three principal groups of fossil Anthozoa are the rugose, tabulate, and scleractinian corals. *Rugose corals* (Fig. B-12) have heavy, rough calyx walls, four initial septa, of which one is *cardinal,* and a characteristic insertion of successive intermediate septa higher and higher on the cardinal septum. Some rugose corals were solitary, others colonial. The group is exclusively Paleozoic.

Tabulate corals are all colonial, with the septa very faint and the horizontal tabulae very prominent. The commonest kinds are the honeycomb coral (Fig. B-13) and the chain coral (Fig. 7-16G). Most genera of tabulate corals are Paleozoic (Ordovician–Permian), but a few persisted to the Cretaceous.

No corals of any sort are known from the Lower Triassic; but, after this short interval without a record, corals of a new type appeared—ancestors of most later forms, including the modern reef corals. The new forms, the *scleractinians,* include both solitary and colonial types. The delicate septa appear more or less definitely in multiples of six, and the calyx walls are thin, vague, or missing.

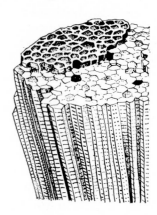

Fig. B-13. Favosites, *the honeycomb coral of the mid-Paleozoic; 50 mm high. (From Bernhard Kummel,* op. cit.)

Note that the two great Paleozoic groups are set off sharply from the modern reef-builders, but that there are small and great reefs, in part composed of coralline material, in the Paleozoic rocks.

B-5. *Phylum Bryozoa* (**Moss-animals**)

The tiny bryozoan individuals are aquatic animals, usually less than a millimeter long, that live joined together in colonies. A colony is composed of hundreds or even thousands of individuals. Most kinds of bryozoans are marine, a few fresh-water. The living marine forms are distributed through all latitudes and down to 18,000 feet. The colonies grow on the sea floor, mostly in clear water, attached to rocks or to other organisms. They secrete skeletal masses or crusts of calcium carbonate or organic material.

The individual animal is considerably more complex than a coral. It resembles a coral in having a sac-like body and tentacles (Fig. B-14). The body cavity, however, contains a separate U-shaped digestive tract, with mouth and anus, and also male and female reproductive organs. A separate ovicell develops, and encloses the growing embryo. Some living bryozoans bear processes that look like birds' heads (avicularia), with movable jaws that catch food.

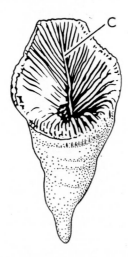

Fig. B-12. *A Paleozoic rugose coral,* Hallia, *55 mm long: C, cardinal septum. (From* Treatise on Invertebrate Paleontology, *courtesy Geological Society of America and University of Kansas Press.)*

The fossil bryozoans belong to five orders (Fig. B-15), two of which are exclusively Paleozoic. The Ctenostomata (Ordovician–Recent) secrete simple tubular networks that are only rarely calcified (A). The colonies of the Cyclostomata (Ordovician–Recent) have more complex tubular skeletons of calcium carbonate (B). The Paleozoic Trepostomata secreted closely packed masses of calcium carbonate (C). The Paleozoic Cryptostomata produced coral-like arborescent carbonate masses that are particularly abundant in Devonian and Mississippian limestones and other rocks (D). The rim-mouthed Cheilostomata (E) produce carbonate incrustations and masses with complex ornamentation and patterns.

B-6. *Phylum Brachiopoda (Brachiopods)*

A brachiopod is a sedentary marine animal that protects itself in a way quite different from that of the coral or bryozoan. It secretes a two-part shell somewhat like that of a clam

Fig. B-14. *Anatomy of a pair of Recent bryozoans*, Bugula; *highly magnified. (Adapted from* Treatise on Invertebrate Paleontology, *Geol. Soc. Am. and Univ. of Kansas Press.)*

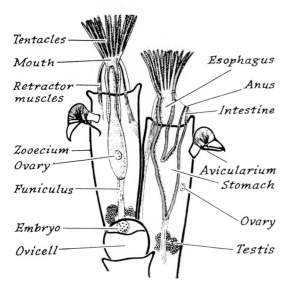

Tentacles

Mouth

Retractor muscles

Zooecium

Ovary

Funiculus

Embryo

Ovicell

Esophagus

Anus

Intestine

Avicularium

Stomach

Ovary

Testis

or oyster, inside which it lives. The brachiopod is considerably simpler than a clam and perhaps slightly more complex than a bryozoan.

A typical modern brachiopod (Fig. B-16) has a shell shaped like a Greek lamp, which is called a lampshell by collectors. The closely fitting upper and lower halves (valves) can gape open a little way, with movement on two tiny ball-and-socket joints at the ends of a short *hinge line*. The small animal inside the shell controls the movements of opening and closing the valves with two sets of muscles, the *diductors* that contract to open the shell and the *adductors* that contract to close it. In addition to the slender muscles, extending from one valve to the other, the soft parts include a small central mass at the hinge end of the shell, made up of alimentary canal, liver, etc., and a long, coiled, tentacled pair of fleshy grooves, the *lophophore*, which fills most of the shell and brings food to the mouth in currents set up by the movements of the tentacles. At the hinge end a fleshy stem, the *pedicle*, projects through a hole in the larger or *pedicle valve* and anchors the animal to a solid substratum. The smaller or *brachial valve* supports the arms (brachia) of the lophophore. A calcareous support for the lophophore, called the *brachidium*, is shown in A. This support is an advanced feature, not possessed by all brachiopods. In this, as in most brachiopods, only the minute, newly hatched young can move about, before settling down at a life site.

Note that the brachiopod shell differs from that of the clam in symmetry. In the brachiopod the plane of symmetry (separating halves that are mirror images of each other) passes through the middle of each valve perpendicular to the hinge line (Fig. B-17). The two valves of the brachiopod are unlike each other, but the two valves of most clams are exact or nearly exact mirror images.

Thousands of species of brachiopods occur as fossils, and many differ markedly from the typical lampshell. All, however, can be classified in two groups, the Articulata and the Inarticulata.

Articulate brachiopods, including the lamp-

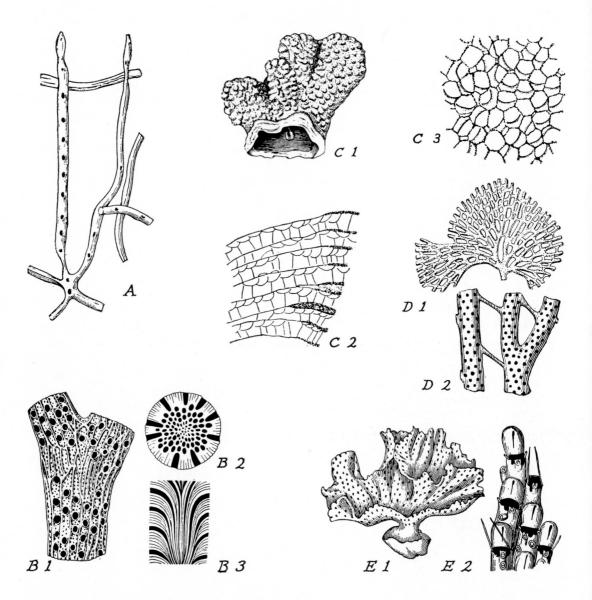

Fig. B-15. *Representative bryozoans. (Adapted from* Treatise on Invertebrate Paleontology, *Geol. Soc. Am. and Univ. of Kansas Press.)*

A. *Class Ctenostomata:* Vinella, *Ordovician, 25/1.*

B. *Class Cyclostomata:* Petalopora, *Cretaceous, 25/1 (1, surface; 2, transverse section; 3, longitudinal section).*

C. *Class Trepostomata:* Monticulipora, *Ordovician (1, a colony, 1/1; 2, longitudinal section, 25/1; 3, transverse section, 25/1).*

D. *Class Cryptostomata:* Polypora, *Lower Carboniferous of Ireland (1, a colony, 1/1; 2, part of colony, 5/1).*

E. *Class Cheilostomata:* Sertella, *Recent (1, a massive colony, 1/1; 2, individuals, 25/1).*

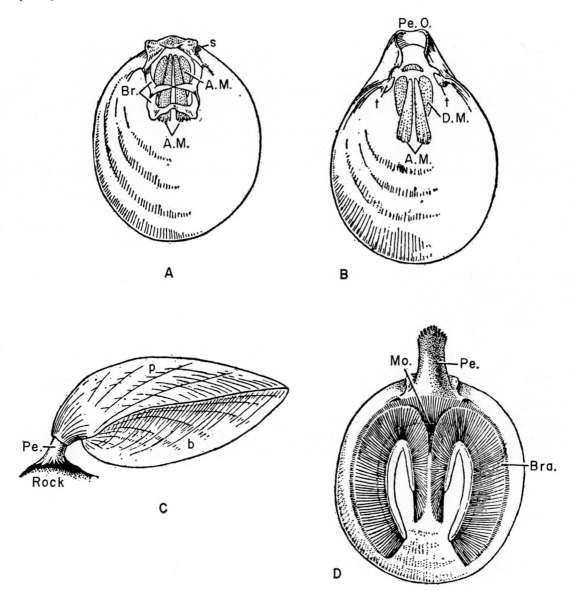

Fig. B-16. *A terebratuloid brachiopod (lampshell) from the coast of Maine:* A.M., *adductor muscle scar;* B, *brachial valve;* Br., *brachidium;* Bra., *lophophore;* D.M., *diductor muscle scar;* Mo., *mouth;* p, *pedicle valve;* Pe., *pedicle;* Pe. O., *pedicle opening;* s, *socket, into which fits the tooth,* t. 2/1. (*Adapted from* An Introduction to the Study of Fossils *by H. W. Shimer; reprinted with permission of The Macmillan Co. Copyright 1914 by The Macmillan Co, renewed 1942 by H. W. Shimer.*)

A. *Interior of brachial valve.*
B. *Interior of pedicle valve.*
C. *Side view of animal fastened to rock by pedicle.*
D. *Animal lying in brachial valve with pedicle valve removed.*

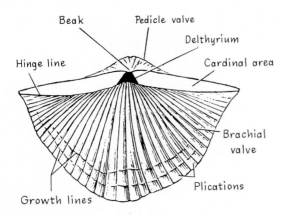

Fig. B-17. *External features of a brachiopod shell. (After H. W. Shimer, 1914.)*

shells, have hinged valves, with ball-and-socket joints. Inarticulate brachiopods lack hinges and so cannot gape open. In some living inarticulate forms, including those that live in mud unattached to any object or substratum, the shells open by sliding slightly on each other. Articulate brachiopods have calcium carbonate shells, but most inarticulates have shells of calcium phosphate, the same substance that makes up the bones of vertebrates.

Both articulate and inarticulate brachiopods are known from the earliest Paleozoic to the present. Articulate brachiopods were enormously abundant in the shallower parts of Paleozoic seas, where they were the commonest shellfish and perhaps the commonest

animals. In post-Paleozoic times the brachiopods declined; they became rare by the beginning of the Cretaceous and were restricted to special habitats, in foul mud or in deep water, their place in clear and shallow waters being taken by the more highly organized pelecypods (clams, oysters, etc.) of the Phylum Mollusca.

B-7. *Phylum Mollusca* (*Mollusks*)

A snail is a typical mollusk; it has head, eyes, and fairly complicated internal structures, including alimentary canal, simple nervous system, and either gills for getting oxygen from water or lungs for getting it from air.

The three principal molluscan classes are (1) the Pelecypoda (pelecypods), or the clams, oysters, etc., which are both marine and fresh-water; (2) the Gastropoda (gastropods), or the snails, which are marine, fresh-water, and land-living; (3) the Cephalopoda (cephalopods), or the nautilus, squid, octopus, etc., which are exclusively marine. All three groups have notable geologic records.

a. *Class Pelecypoda* (*Pelecypods*)

The pelecypods are headless mollusks that secrete bivalve shells of calcium carbonate. The soft parts, which in general are similar to those of a snail, include a muscular, hatchet-shaped foot, which gives the class its name.

Fig. B-18. *Interior (left), exterior, and transverse section (right) of a pelecypod shell, showing its relation to some of the soft parts. (From Bernhard Kummel, op. cit.)*

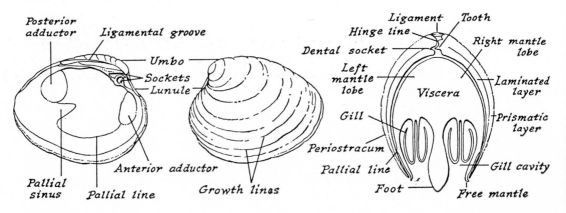

The foot is used by many clams to dig a hole in sand or mud, into which the animal disappears. The two valves of the shell (Fig. B-18), which are approximate mirror images of each other, can be closed tightly by the adductor muscles or allowed to gape by relaxation of the muscles, the opening being on a *hinge* that is usually toothed and the gape caused by the spontaneous contraction of the elastic *ligament*. The animal produces a large brood of young that float for a brief time and then settle on the bottom and begin to secrete minute bivalve shells. These shells grow chiefly by accretion on the side opposite the hinge, with growth lines marking successive interruptions of the growth process.

Pelecypods use as food small floating organic particles, notably plankton. Clams that dig into sand or mud and the specialized pelecypods that bore into wood or rock maintain connections with the general water body through a cylindrical *siphon* made up of two tubes, one for water wafted slowly in, the other for waste water moving out.

Fig. B-19. *A pecten from the Neogene of the Imperial Valley, southern California, 1/1. (Photograph by R. A. Bramkamp.)*

The soft parts of a clam are enveloped in a membrane, or mantle, that secretes the shell but is attached to it only part way out to the growing edge. When the shell is separated from the soft parts, the margin of attachment, the *pallial line*, shows clearly. In closing the shell, the animal withdraws the siphon into an embayment, or *pallial sinus*, in the line of attachment, at the rear of the shell. This sinus

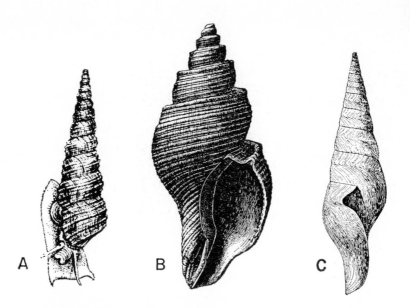

Fig. B-20. *Three Recent marine gastropods.*
A. Turritella communis *(from Arthur Adams, 1858).*
B. Neptunea tabulata, *Pacific coast of North America (from W. H. Dall, 1902);* × 3/4.
C. Antiplanes perversa, *off Baja California (from W. H. Dall, 1902);* × 3/2.

makes the interior of a single valve unsymmetrical. The exterior is usually also unsymmetrical, with the point of initial growth, or *umbo*, twisted toward the front end, the end opposite the pallial sinus. Thus the valves of a pelecypod, though symmetrical with respect to the plane of contact, are unsymmetrical to any plane perpendicular to the plane of contact. Almost the opposite rule prevails for brachiopod valves. Both rules of symmetry fail for the fairly numerous shellfish that are cemented by one valve to a substratum, in oyster fashion.

Pelecypods are mostly shallow-water animals, especially characteristic of sandy or muddy bottoms between the high-water line and a depth of a few tens of feet, though some species are found only at greater depths, even down to several thousand feet. Fresh-water forms, many with pearly shells, are found in lakes and rivers. A few genera, including the oysters, can endure both salt water and the brackish water of bays and estuaries.

Pelecypods were few and primitive in the Paleozoic but have become more numerous and more varied in later times. They have been notable elements of shallow-water marine faunas since the late Mesozoic. Many thick-shelled oyster-like forms flourished in the Cretaceous. For the subdivisions of the later Cenozoic, good local guide fossils are furnished by species of scallops (pectens, Fig. B-19), pelecypods that look more or less like the Shell Oil Company's symbol.

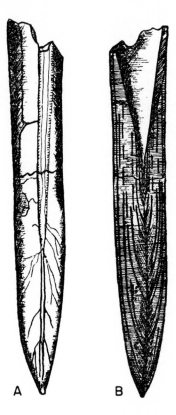

A   B

Fig. B-21. *The belemnite* Belemnitella praecursor, *from the Upper Cretaceous, Desna River, Russia; specimen 100 mm long. (Adapted from J. A. Jeletzky, 1948.)*

A. *Side view.*

B. *Vertical section, showing growth lines and, at top, the conical cavity.*

b. Class Gastropoda (Gastropods)

The large flat foot of the snail not only contains muscles that enable it to creep slowly about but also includes the alimentary canal and other organs, justifying the name Gastropoda, stomach-footed, for the class. The snail shell is a single valve, usually extended in an elongated spiral coil (Fig. B-20), but in some genera planospiral and in the "cap" gastropods a simple cone. If coiled, the shell is a continuous tube without partitions, from aperture to apex. The aperture is anterior (A) and in many genera (BC) prolonged into an *anterior canal*. (A posterior canal on the opposite side

of the aperture is also sometimes present.) Coiling is almost always dextral (right-handed), as in A and B, rarely sinistral, as in C. The last and largest whorl is called the *body whorl*, the remainder of the coil the *spire*.

Paleozoic gastropods, which are somewhat rare, are mostly low-spired without canals, or planospiral, or cap-shaped. In later rocks, gastropods are commoner and more varied; from the mid-Mesozoic on they are abundant in the shallow marine facies. One warm-water marine genus, *Turritella* (Fig. B-20A), which is common in the lower and middle Cenozoic rocks as far north as Paris and Seattle, has furnished many guide fossils useful in regional correlations, especially on the Pacific coast of North America. Many other gastropod genera also contain species that are regional guides to Cenozoic horizons.

c. Cephalopoda (Cephalopods)

The living cephalopods are rather few. They are marine, predatory animals with well-equipped biting mouths, large tentacles, and big eyes; they can move quickly by expelling water from a pouch. The Dibranchiata, or double-gilled forms, include the octopus, squid, and some other animals that either lack hard parts or secrete simple structures such as the cuttle bone of the squid. The Tetrabranchiata, or four-gilled forms, have but one living representative, the nautilus.

1. BELEMNITES. The belemnites are extinct forms, represented by abundant cigar-shaped structures in Jurassic and Cretaceous rocks. Rare impressions of the soft parts show that the animals were squid-like, with big eyes and large, hooked tentacles; no doubt they were dibranchiate. The hard part most commonly preserved is a dense, elongated cylinder of calcium carbonate, tapering to a point at one end; it is called the *guard* (Fig. B-21). At its large end the guard contains a slender conical cavity, shown in section (B), which sometimes contains a conical chambered shell, the *phragmacone*, which was internal in the belemnite but may be a relic of an external protective shell.

2. TETRABRANCHIATES. The tetrabranchiate cephalopods are divided into two groups, nautiloids (Cambrian–Recent) and ammonoids (Devonian–Cretaceous).

The nautiloids are typified by the living *Nautilus*, which lives in eastern seas, from Fiji to Java and the Philippines. The tentacled animal carries a chambered shell coiled in one plane (Fig. B-22). The shell is a continuously expanding tube, with between-chamber parti-

Fig. B-22.   Nautilus pompilius, *6 inches in diameter. (Adapted from H. B. Stenzel,* Treatise on Invertebrate Paleontology, Geol. Soc. Am. and Univ. of Kansas Press.)
    A. *Withdrawn into shell.*
    B. *Partially withdrawn.*
    C. *In normal resting position.*
    D. *Shell, mostly cut in half, showing septa and the last suture.*

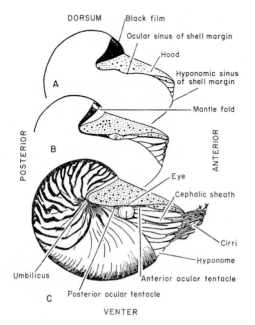

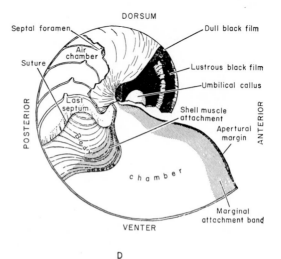

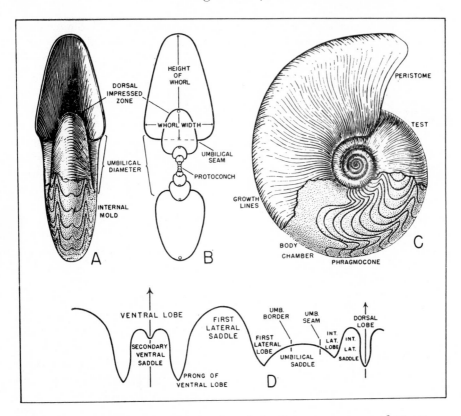

Fig. B-23. *Diagrammatic representation of the Devonian ammonoid* Manticoc-
eras. *(From A. K. Miller and W. M. Furnish via Bernhard Kummel,*
op. cit.)
   A. *Ventral view of aperture.*
   B. *Cross-section.*
   C. *Side view, with shell cut away to show sutures.*
   D. *Enlarged trace of one-half of a suture line.*

tions (*septa*, D) that are separate structures, each perforated by a central opening for a fleshy *siphuncle* that passes through all the chambers. The contact between a septum and the outer shell wall is a *suture*. The shell is made of aragonite, the unstable form of calcium carbonate. The animal lives in the last, open chamber of the shell, though the siphuncle extends back through the other chambers.

Fossil shells similar to that of the nautilus and therefore probably also representing closely related tetrabranchiate cephalopods are abundant in the Paleozoic. They are called nautiloids. Some of the Ordovician forms are coiled, but others are straight or slightly curved, chambered tubes (Fig. 7-16C). All resemble *Nautilus* in their simple sutures, but some have complicated siphuncular supports and may not have been very close to *Nautilus* anatomically. These varied animals reached their maximum in the Ordovician.

By mid-Paleozoic time the nautiloids were greatly reduced, and their place was gradually taken by the closely related ammonoid stock. The ammonoid shell has a more complex suture (Fig. B-23). Ammonoid shells retained the primitive *Nautilus* coil, in the main, but gradually became thinner and flatter-sided, ornamented by ribs and tubercles, and marked internally by increasing complications of the

Fig. B-24. *The Ordovician trilobite* Triarthrus becki (ABCD, *specimen 35 mm long; EF, greatly enlarged*): A., *anus;* Ant., *antennules, or feelers;* Ax., *axial lobe;* Ceph., *cephalon;* Dig.t., *digestive tube;* Fa.S., *facial suture;* L.L., *lower lip;* Mo., *mouth;* Pg., *pygidium;* Pl., *pleurae;* U.L., *upper lip. (Reprinted with permission of The Macmillan Co from An Introduction to the Study of Fossils by H. W. Shimer. Copyright 1914 by The Macmillan Co, renewed 1942 by H. W. Shimer.)*

A. *Upper side.*
B. *Lower side.*
C. *Transverse section at second thoracic segment.*
D. *Median longitudinal vertical section.*
E, F. *Larval molts.*

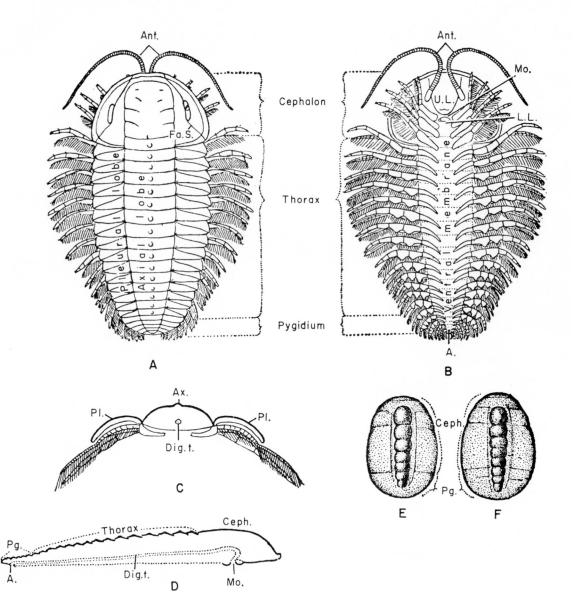

sutures. The central siphuncle moved out to the external margin at the very beginning of ammonoid differentiation. There was one climax of variation late in the Triassic: the extinction of all but one or two genera at the end of the period was followed by the maximum development of the group in the Jurassic and Cretaceous.

A late Paleozoic goniatitic ammonoid, with an angulated suture, is shown in Figure 7-17F, and typical Mesozoic forms, true ammonites with complex sutures, in Figure 7-2. Goniatites and ammonites are among the best of guide fossils. Species are distinguished chiefly by external features, but at some levels gross differences between sutures are useful; those of Figure 7-12C, for example, are exceptionally simple for a Jurassic horizon.

B-8. Class Trilobita (*Trilobites*)

The fossils called trilobites, found only in Paleozoic rocks, have external skeletons and jointed legs that place them in the phylum Arthropoda. Their closest living relatives appear to be in the classes Crustacea (crabs, lobsters, etc.) and Arachnida (spiders, etc.).

A typical trilobite (Fig. B-24) is made up of a head, or *cephalon*, a mid-section, or *thorax*, that is a series of similar body segments, and a more or less well-marked set of tail segments called the *pygidium*. Longitudinally, three lobes can be distinguished, a central *axial* ridge and *pleural* lobes at the sides that bear the legs and other appendages. The longitudinal lobes give the class its name. In some genera, head and tail are sharply set off (Fig. 10-3DH). The head is made up of seven segments fused together. On the upper side are compound eyes like those of an insect (Fig. 7-17C). Specialized appendages on the lower side of the head include long tentacles (Fig. B-24B). The thoracic appendages are forked. The upper branches apparently were used in crawling or swimming. The feathery lower branches seem to have been gill-like breathing organs. All the evidence indicates that the trilobites lived in water, and the associations with other animals indicate

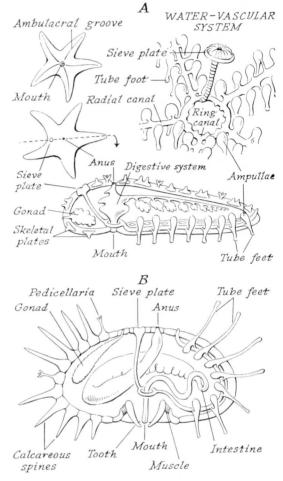

Fig. B-25. *Diagrams showing anatomical features of a starfish (A) and a sea urchin (B). (Adapted from Simpson, Pittendrigh, and Tiffany, Life, 1957, for Bernhard Kummel, op. cit.)*

rather conclusively that they lived in the sea.

As the trilobites had external skeletons, growth was by molting. Molted immature carapaces are fairly common, though adult or nearly adult cephala, pygidia, and complete carapaces are much more common. At a few places, as in some early Paleozoic limestones of western Virginia, great numbers of tiny early molts have been obtained by dissolving most of the rock with acid. These discoveries have demonstrated considerable changes during growth.

The trilobites were leading constituents of early Paleozoic faunas (Chap. 10) and were still abundant in the Silurian and Devonian. Then they became rare, and they finally disappeared in the Permian.

B-9. *Phylum Echinodermata* (*Echinoderms*)

The echinoderms (spiny-skinned ones), of which the starfish is a good example, are marine animals as unlike the trilobites as the latter are unlike the mollusks. They are set off from all other animals by their five-fold symmetry and by a water-vascular system made up of tubes and reservoirs freely connected with one another and less freely with the circumambient sea water through a sieve plate (Fig. B-25).

Two groups, the crinoids, or sea-lilies, and the echinoids, or sea-urchins, have left notable geologic records. They have skeletons of calcite plates. Some other groups, such as the asteroids, to which the starfish belongs, may have been moderately common members of ancient faunas but have not left extensive records because the hard parts do not hang together after death.

a. Crinoids and Their Allies

The present-day crinoids form rather dense groups of individuals here and there in all seas, from the equator to the Arctic, floating at depths from a few feet to thousands of feet below the surface. They are very rare in shallow water. In the Paleozoic and early Mesozoic, crinoids were much more abundant. Almost all were attached to the sea floor or other objects by short or long stalks (Figs. B-26, 2-18, and 2-19). The body of a typical crinoid is complex, but small compared with the spread of the arms and short compared

Fig. B-26. *Representative stalked echinoderms of the Paleozoic. (After F. A. Bather, 1900 and 1902, via Bernhard Kummel, op. cit.)*

A. *An eocrinoid,* Macrocystella.
B. *A carpoid,* Mitrocystites.
C. *A camerate crinoid,* Botryocrinus.

D. *An edrioasteroid,* Carneyella.
E. *A blastoid,* Orophocrinus.
F. *A cystoid,* Pleurocystites; *its plates have rows of pores.*

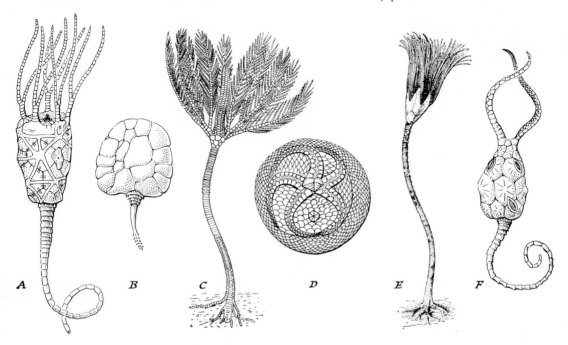

A   B   C   D   E   F

with the length of the stem. Some Paleozoic crinoids seem to have had fewer and shorter arms, and the closely related Paleozoic *cystoids* (Fig. B-26F) and *blastoids* (E) had few or rudimentary arms.

The blastoid body, or calyx, is so regular that it can be described easily. It is made up

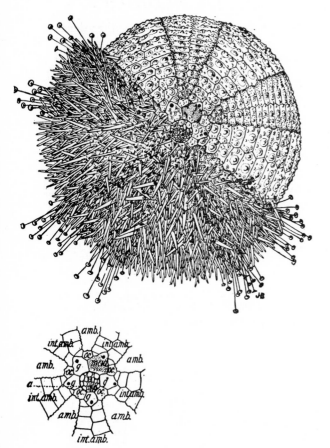

Fig. B-27. *A regular sea urchin,* Strongylocentrotus, *from the coast of Maine, with spines etc. removed from half of the skeleton. Below, the central dorsal area with ornamentation omitted:* a, *anus;* amb., *ambulacrum;* g, *genital plate, perforated by genital opening;* int. amb., *interambulacrum;* mad, *madreporite, or sieve plate;* oc., *ocular plate at tip of each ambulacrum.* (*Reprinted with permission of The Macmillan Co from* An Introduction to the Study of Fossils *by H. W. Shimer. Copyright 1914 by The Macmillan Co, renewed 1942 by H. W. Shimer.*)

chiefly of thirteen plates in three rows (Figs. B-26E and 7-17D). Each of the five principal plates of the skeleton embraces one of the five complex *ambulacral areas*, each made up of many plates and containing pores for the water-vascular system. Five smaller plates surround an *apical system* of minute plates and pores, and three basal plates complete the roster. The blastoids appeared rather early in the Ordovician, reached their maximum in the late Paleozoic, and became extinct in the Permian.

The crinoids have somewhat less obvious five-fold symmetry, slightly complicated by unique features that determine an obscure bilateral symmetry (Fig. B-26C). The calyx is usually made up of many rows of external plates and many complicated internal structures. The arms may be five in number at their bases, but they are likely to divide and subdivide. The upper or inner sides of the arms have ambulacral grooves along which food is wafted toward a central mouth. The crinoids reached their maximum development during the late Paleozoic. The major Paleozoic groups, including the Camerata, or box crinoids (Fig. B-26C), became extinct or almost extinct at the end of the era. The single post-Paleozoic group, the Articulata, flourished in shallow water in the early Mesozoic and then withdrew to obscure and sheltered spots in the sea. The great colonies of Mississippian crinoids found at a few spots in Iowa and elsewhere have given specialists material for lifetimes of study of these beautiful and complicated animals.

b. Echinoids

Echinoids (Fig. B-27) have globular or flattened subcutaneous skeletons of calcite plates. Most of them can move slowly about, chiefly by moving large or small spines. They live on rocky shores or sandy surfaces or partially buried in sand. The tube feet of the water-vascular system (Fig. B-25B) are extruded through pores in five porous (ambulacral) areas, two of which are shown, denuded of spines and feet, in Figure B-27. The feet, as

Fig. B-28. *An irregular echinoid,* Dendraster ex-centricus, *Recent, San Pedro, California, 1/1: A, upper side; B, lower side. Roman numerals mark the ambulacra, Arabic the interambulacra. (From U. S. Grant and L. G. Hertlein, 1938.)*

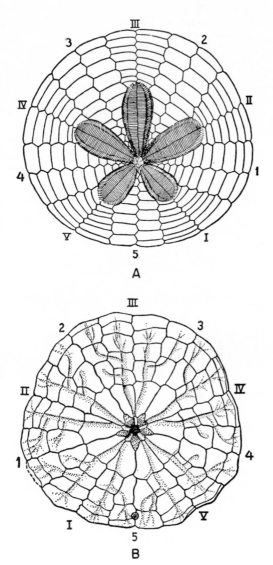

A

B

able parts, is in the center of the lower surface (not shown in the figure). Echinoids eat mud or small animals. They are known from the Ordovician to the present.

Echinoids can be divided into two groups: regular and irregular. The regular echinoids are symmetrical, with alternating pairs of am-bulacral and interambulacral plates extending from mouth to apical system, as in *Strongylo-centrotus* (Fig. B-27). Irregular echinoids (Fig. B-28), which are mostly Jurassic or younger, have lost much of their radial sym-metry, though bilateral symmetry has been preserved and accentuated. The pores for the tube feet commonly appear to be limited to the upper surface and are often concen-trated in petal-like areas, as in the figure. Flat, irregular echinoids, or sand-dollars, live today in large colonies just below the low-water line. Equally large colonies occur in Cenozoic, es-pecially Neogene, sandstones. Many species are good regional guide fossils. The figured genus (*Dendraster*, Pliocene–Recent) is un-usual in having an excentric apical system and very short ambulacral petals.

In a way, echinoids have taken the place of crinoids in the shallow waters of late Meso-zoic and Cenozoic seas. Echinoid fragments

Fig. B-29. *Reconstruction of the dendroid grap-tolite* Dictyonema. *(From L. Størmer, 1933, via Bernhard Kummel, op. cit.)*

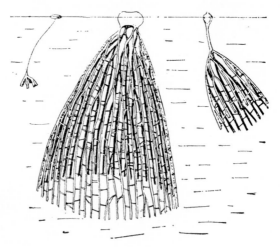

shown in the undenuded portion of the figure, terminate in suction disks that enable the ani-mal to cling to rocks. A central apical system, enlarged in the lower drawing of the figure, includes five small plates with genital pores and the porous sieve plate (compare Fig. B-25B). The mouth, with complicated mov-

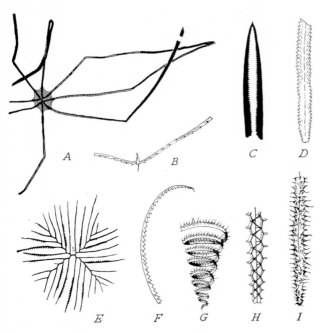

Fig. B-30. *Representative graptoloids.* (*From* Treatise on Invertebrate Paleontology, *courtesy Geological Society of America and University of Kansas Press.*)

A. Dichograptus, *Lower Ordovician; about 200 mm across.*

B. Leptograptus, *Middle and Upper Ordovician; 20 mm long.*

C. Didymograptus, *Lower Ordovician; 60 mm long.*

D. Diplograptus, *Middle Ordovician and Lower Silurian; 30 mm long.*

E. Goniograptus, *Lower Ordovician; about 50 mm across.*

F. Monograptus, *Silurian; 30 mm long.*

G. Monograptus, *Silurian; 22 mm long.*

H. Paraplectograptus, *Middle Silurian; 12 mm long.*

I. Hallograptus, *Ordovician; 33 mm long.*

Fig. B-31. *Variations in the forms of conodonts; approximately* × 20. (*From F. H. T. Rhodes,* Biological Reviews, *1954.*)

are also abundant in some late Paleozoic lime-stones, and good specimens are known from a few favored localities, one near St. Louis. Complete specimens, however, first become widespread at higher levels, where crinoids have become rare. The echinoids did not liter-ally take the place of crinoids. The two groups of animals have dissimilar modes of life; for one thing, the crinoids are either sessile or floating animals and the echinoids are self-propelled.

B-10. *Graptolithina* (*Graptolites*)

Shiny black carbonaceous streaks in early Paleozoic shales and other sedimentary rocks look so much like pencil marks that they were long ago called *graptolites* (from the Greek words for writing and rock). Careful study especially since 1870, has shown that the black streaks are the remains of organic rods, made up of or bordered by minute tubes and cups of great complexity and variety. Two main groups are distinguished: (1) *Dendroidea* (dendroids), colonies composed of numerous, commonly connected branches (Fig. B-29) and extremely minute cups, with a range from the Upper Cambrian to the Carboniferous, and (2) *Graptoloidea* (graptoloids), with more uniform and somewhat larger cups, distributed along fewer and less tangled branches (Fig. B-30), chiefly in the Ordovician and Silurian. Graptolites are most easily seen in shales, but their structures are best preserved in chert or limestone. Rather recently a Pole (Roman Kozlowski, 1938, 1949) has discovered well-preserved specimens of the chitinous fossils in chert and has demonstrated their probable re-lationship to hemichordates—minute modern marine animals that are somewhat like verte-brates. From the fossils with which the grapto-lites are associated it is apparent that they were marine. The dendroid *Dictyonema* and at least some graptoloid colonies seem to have floated about in the sea, supported by small bladders.

Typical Ordovician guide graptoloids are shown in Figure B-30CD, the Silurian genus *Monograptus* in F and G. Graptoloids are the best Ordovician and Silurian guide fossils for long-distance correlations. Graptoloid species have short ranges, usually a third of a system or less.

B-11. *Conodonts*

The conodonts are microscopic tooth-like fossils (Fig. B-31), composed of calcium phos-phate, which are abundant in rocks ranging in stratigraphic position from Lower Ordovician to Triassic. The specimens are unworn and cannot have been functional teeth used for seizing, cutting, or grinding food. Occasionally they lie in shale in pairs (Fig. B-32), making symmetrical patterns that suggest the pres-

Fig. B-32. *Five natural assemblages of cono-donts, from the Carboniferous of the eastern United States: 1, × 14; 2–5, × 7. (From F. H. T. Rhodes,* loc. cit.)

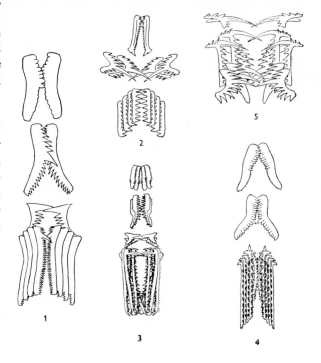

ence of conodonts of more than one type in a single animal body of which now not even an impression remains. The zoological affinities of the conodonts are unknown. Their phosphatic composition, shapes, and structures are consistent with the hypothesis that the animals were small, simple relatives of the vertebrates.

Snails and some worms have tooth-like structures of similar shape but of organic nitrogenous, non-phosphatic composition.

Some conodonts, notably in the Upper Devonian, are characteristic of thin zones and are so widespread that they may be of some value in intercontinental correlations (§ 7-6.d).

APPENDIX C

Jurassic Zones and Stages

THE LOWER and Middle Jurassic zones and stages are listed in Table C-1, and their distribution in thirteen selected columns is shown in Table C-2. Regional European Upper Jurassic zones and stages are listed in Table C-3.

1. NORTHWEST EUROPEAN PROVINCE. Columns 1–5 of Table C-2 are fair samples of the Lower and Middle Jurassic zonal stratigraphy of the Northwest European Province. All forty-one zones are present in England (column 1). Almost all are present in France, especially on the eastern side of the Paris Basin (column 2), and in or near the plateaus of the Swabian and Franconian Alb in southwestern Germany (column 3 and also Fig. 7-1). Almost all the zones are probably present in the northwest German basin, between the North Sea and the Harz Mountains (column 4) and in the Jura Mountains (column 5). [Jurassic rocks also extend into the Alps, but that region is excluded because of its geosynclinal character, complex structure, and somewhat different (Tethyan or Mediterranean) ammonite faunas.]

2. CHANGES IN ZONATION. The ammonite zones listed in the three tables are designed to represent prevalent current opinion. Changes in usage may occur in the future, either in the direction that has predominated in the past— increase in the number of zones—or in the opposite direction. Oppel, the originator of the zonal system used today, and his predecessor d'Orbigny gave twenty-three of the forty-one Lower and Middle Jurassic zone names now current (Table C-1). Oppel recognized more than twenty-three Lower and Middle Jurassic zones, but he did not stick exclusively to ammonite names for them. Later workers have replaced all non-ammonite names and have split up some of Oppel's zones. Many of the zones have acquired their present status rather recently. Obviously, the zonal numbers used in the accompanying tables are designed for temporary convenience.

3. SUBZONES. The European Jurassic zones have been divided into subzones characterized by ammonite species or assemblages. The number of subzones varies with the zone and the locality, depending on the abundance of fossils, the quality of their preservation, and the completeness of exposure of the beds. Subzones provide a convenient mode of representation for local details and show the minuteness of stratigraphic subdivision possible where ammonites are abundant. In Great Britain the twenty zones of the Lias can be divided into forty-nine subzones recognizable over the whole country.

Some of the British subzones have been recognized in the Jura Mountains of Switzerland and also in much more distant places. The Planicerclus Subzone of the Calloviense Zone (No. 37 of Table C-1) has been identified in the Paris Basin, in the Swiss and German parts of the Jura Mountains, in northwestern Germany, in Russia east of Moscow, and in the Mangyshlak Peninsula on the eastern side of the Caspian Sea. From the type locality of the subzone in Yorkshire to the

Mangyshlak Peninsula is 2,300 miles. In contrast, the adjacent Calloviense Subzone of the Calloviense Zone has so far been recognized only for the 300 miles between north-central England (Yorkshire) and the Paris Basin (J. H. Callomon, written communication).

Some subzones being only a few inches thick in some places, some of the guide fossils are too thick to squeeze into their own subzones. One large British ammonite specimen was actually worn down to the thickness of its subzone, the thinness of which at this spot must have been the result of inter-subzonal erosion.

4. BOTTOM AND TOP OF THE JURASSIC. In England the normal marine Jurassic formations, with guide ammonites, form a natural unit, bounded below and above by beds transitional to non-marine formations. The basal transition beds are called the Rhaetian (or Rhaetic) and are made up largely of shales and sandstones containing pectens and other shallow marine mollusks, but also include the Rhaetic bone bed, an inch or two thick, crowded with the remains of fish, amphibians, and reptiles, some of which lived on land. The Rhaetian has its type area in South Germany and North Tyrol; there, in the northeastern Alps, it contains a few ammonites of Triassic aspect that justify its incorporation in that system. In both England and Germany the Rhaetian is overlain conformably by Zone 1 of the Jurassic.

At the top of the English Jurassic the Purbeckian (Table C-3) is brackish and freshwater, without ammonites, and is overlain by the continental Wealden beds of the Weald anticline southeast of London. The Wealden beds are considered Cretaceous.

TABLE C-1

Stages and Zones of the Middle and Lower Jurassic[*]

STAGE	ZONE	PROPOSED BY	DATE
	MIDDLE JURASSIC		
Callovian	41. Quenstedtoceras lamberti	Hebert	1857
	40. Peltoceras athleta	d'Orbigny	1852
	39. Erymnoceras coronatum	d'Orbigny	1852
	38. Kosmoceras jason	d'Orbigny	1852
	37. Sigaloceras calloviense	Oppel (as subzone)	1857
	36. Macrocephalites macrocephalus	Oppel	1857
Bathonian	35. Clydoniceras discus	Buckman	1898
	34. Oppelia aspidoides	Oppel	1862
	33. Tulites subcontractus	Buckman	1898
	32. Gracilisphinctes progracilis	Buckman	1913
	31. Zigzagiceras zigzag	Oppel	1865
Bajocian	30. Parkinsonia parkinsoni	Oppel	1856
	29. Garantiana garantiana	Brasil	1895 [a]
	28. Strenoceras subfurcatum	Quenstedt(?)	1885(?)
	27. Stephanoceras humphriesianum	Oppel	1856
	26. Otoites sauzei	Oppel	1856
	25. Sonninia sowerbyi	Oppel	1863
	24. Graphoceras concavum	Buckman	1889
	23. Ludwigia murchisonae	Oppel	1856
	22. Tmetoceras scissum	Buckman	1910
	21. Leioceras opalinum	Quenstedt	1843
	LOWER JURASSIC (LIAS)		
Toarcian	20. Dumortieria levesquei	Benecke	1901
	19. Grammoceras thouarsense	Brasil	1896
	18. Haugia variabilis	Buckman	1888
	17. Hildoceras bifrons	Reynes	1868
	16. Harpoceras falcifer	Buckman	1898
	15. Dactylioceras tenuicostatum	Buckman	1910
Pliensbachian	14. Pleuroceras spinatum	Oppel	1856
	13. Amaltheus margaritatus	Oppel	1856
	12. Prodactylioceras davoei	Oppel	1856
	11. Tragophylloceras ibex	Oppel	1856
	10. Uptonia jamesoni	Oppel	1856
Sinemurian	9. Echioceras raricostatum	Oppel	1856
	8. Oxynoticeras oxynotum	Oppel	1856
	7. Asteroceras obtusum	Oppel	1856
	6. Caenisites turneri	Wright	1860
	5. Arnioceras semicostatum	Judd	1878
	4. Arietites bucklandi	Oppel	1856
Hettangian	3. Schlotheimia angulata	Oppel	1856
	2. Alsatites liasicus	Collenot	1869
	1. Psiloceras planorbis	Oppel	1856

[a] Mascke, 1907.

[*] S. S. Buckman of England and his contemporaries proposed and shuffled so many names, at so many dates, that for some zones the dates (and authors) given here may not be the best choices.

TABLE C-2

Correlation of Marine Lower and Middle Jurassic*

STAGE	ZONE	1 ENGLAND	2 EAST FRANCE	3 S.W. GERMANY	4 N.W. GERMANY	5 JURA MTS.	6 CAUCASUS	7 ARABIA	8 CUTCH, INDIA	9 EAST GREENLAND	10 WEST CANADA	11 WYOMING	12 EAST MEXICO	13 ANDES
MIDDLE JURASSIC														
Callovian U	41. Quenstedtoceras lamberti	z	z	z	z	z			z			z		
	40. Peltoceras athleta	z	z	z	z	z	ss		z				z	
Callovian M	39. Erymnoceras coronatum	z	z	z	z	ss	ss	ss	?		ss			S
	38. Kosmoceras jason	z	z	z	z	ss			?			+		
Callovian L	37. Sigaloceras calloviense	z	z	?	z	ss	z	ss	?	z	ss	++	x	
	36. Macrocephalites macrocephalus	z	z	z	z	z	z		z	z		++		
Bathonian U	35. Clydoniceras discus	z	z	?	?	z		?	ss?	1	ss?		S	
	34. Oppelia aspidoides	z	?		?	z			?	1				
Bathonian M	33. Tulites subcontractus	z	z	z	z	z	S	ss		1				
Bathonian L	32. Gracilisphinctes progracilis	z	z	z	z	z				1				
	31. Zigzagiceras zigzag	z	z	z	z	z	z	?				?	z	
Bajocian U	30. Parkinsonia parkinsoni	z	z	z	z	z	z	ss	?	ss?			z	
	29. Garantiana garantiana	z	z	z	z	z	z		?					
	28. Strenoceras subfurcatum	z	z	z	z	z	z		z					
Bajocian M	27. Stephanoceras humphriesianum	z	z	z	z	z	z	ss			z	ss	S	z
	26. Otoites sauzei	z	z	z	z	z	z				z	ss		?
	25. Sonninia sowerbyi	z	z	z	z	z	?							z
Bajocian L	24. Graphoceras concavum	z	z	z	z	z	?							
	23. Ludwigia murchisonae	z	z	z	z	z	z							
	22. Tmetoceras scissum	z	z	z	z	z	z		z	z	z			z
	21. Leioceras opalinum	z	z	z	z	z	z							
LOWER JURASSIC (LIAS)														
Toarcian U	20. Dumortieria levesquei	**z**	z	z	z	z?				ss	ss			ss
	19. Grammoceras thouarsense	z	z	z	z	?	S			ss				ss
	18. Haugia variabilis	z	z	z	z	⊛				z				
Toarcian L	17. Hildoceras bifrons	z	z	z	z	†								
	16. Harpoceras falcifer	z	z	z	z	†		ss			ss			ss
	15. Dactylioceras tenuicostatum	z	z	z	z	†								
Pliensbachian U	14. Pleuroceras spinatum	z	z	z	z	z								
	13. Amaltheus margaritatus	z	z	z	z	z								
Pliensbachian L	12. Prodactylioceras davoei	z	z	z	z	?	S			z	S		z	z
	11. Tragophylloceras ibex	z	z	z	z	z				z			?	z
	10. Uptonia jamesoni	z	z	z	z	z				z			?	z
Sinemurian U	9. Echioceras raricostatum	z	z	z	z	z						?	?	z
	8. Oxynoticeras oxynotum	z	z	z	z	z							?	
	7. Asteroceras obtusum	z	z	z	z	?	S?						?	
Sinemurian L	6. Caenisites turneri	z	z	z	z	z								
	5. Arnioceras semicostatum	z	z	z	z	z					z		z	?
	4. Arietites bucklandi	z	z	z	z	z	S?				z		z	?
Hettangian	3. Schlotheimia angulata	z	z	z	z	z					z		z	z
	2. Alsatites liasicus	z	z	z	z	z							z	
	1. Psiloceras planorbis	z	z	z	z	z					z		z	z

*Compiled from W. J. Arkell, *Jurassic Geology of the World* (1956), with modifications from Dean, Donovan, and Howarth (1961), J. H. Callomon (1955, 1961), and H. K. Erben (1956).

S = stage present; z = zone present; x = fauna bridging Middle and Lower Callovian; ? = zone perhaps present; 1 = six local Bathonian zones; + = five local zones; ss = substage present; ss? = substage perhaps present; † = perhaps all zones, condensed; U = Upper, M = Middle, L = Lower.

TABLE C-3

Upper Jurassic Stages and Zones in European Faunal Provinces

Northwestern Europe		*Western Tethys*		*Russia and the Arctic*	
STAGE	ZONE	STAGE	ZONE	STAGE	ZONE
Purbeckian	(No ammonites)	Upper Tithonian	Virgatosphinctes transitorius	Upper Volgian	Riasanites riasanensis Craspedites nodiger Craspedites subditus Craspedites fulgens
Portlandian	62. Titanites giganteus 61. Glaucolithes gorei 60. Zaraiskites albani	Middle Tithonian Lower Tithonian	Semiformiceras semiforme { Berriasella ciliata and Anavirgatites palmatus	Lower Volgian	{ Lomonossovella blakei and Epivirgatites nikitini Virgatites virgatus Zaraiskites scythicus Dorsoplanites dorsoplanus
Kimeridgian	59. Pavlovia pallasioides 58. Pavlovia rotunda 57. Pectinatites pectinatus 56. Subplanites wheatleyensis 55. Subplanites spp. 54. Gravesia gigas 53. Gravesia gravesiana 52. Aulacostephanus autissodorensis 51. Aulacostephanus eudoxus 50. Rasenia mutabilis 49. Rasenia cymodoce 48. Pictonia baylei	Lower (& Middle?) Kimeridgian	Subplanites vimineus { Taramelliceras lithographicum & Hybonoticeras hybonotum Hybonoticeras beckeri Aulacostephanus pseudomutabilis	Middle & Lower Kimeridgian	Subplanites etc.
Oxfordian	47. Ringsteadia pseudocordata 46. Decipia decipiens 45. Perisphinctes cautisnigrae 44. Perisphinctes plicatilis 43. Cardioceras cordatum 42. Quenstedtoceras mariae	} Oxfordian	Epipeltoceras bimammatum Gregoryceras transversarium 43. Cardioceras cordatum 42. Quenstedtoceras mariae	Oxfordian	Approximately the Tethyan zones

D-1. *Cretaceous Stages*

	NAME	TYPE LOCALITY	LITHOLOGY AT TYPE LOCALITY
Upper	Maestrichtian*	Maastricht, Holland	White chalk
	Campanian*	La Champagne, France	White chalk
	Santonian*	La Saintonge, France	Chalk
	Coniacian*	Cognac, France	Chalk
	Turonian	Touraine, France	Siliceous chalk
	Cenomanian	Le Mans, France	Glauconitic chalk
Lower	Albian	Aube, France	Greensand and Clay
	Aptian	Apt, France	Limestone
	Barremian	Barrème, France	Limestone
	Hauterivian†	Hauterive, Switzerland	Limestone
	Valanginian†	Valangin, Switzerland	Limestone
	Berriasian†	Berrias, France	Limestone

D-2. *Triassic Stages, All with Type Localities in the Eastern Alps*

UPPER TRIASSIC
  Rhaetian
  Norian
  Carnian

MIDDLE TRIASSIC
  Ladinian
  Anisian

LOWER TRIASSIC
  Scythian

* Formerly considered part of the Senonian Stage (white Chalk; Sens, France).

† Formerly considered part of the Neocomian Stage (Neuchâtel, Switzerland).

INDEX

References are to pages and conform to the following scheme:

245	text of both columns
245.1	text of column 1
245.2	text of column 2
245.il	illustration(s)
245&il	text of both columns and illustration(s)
245.1&il	text of column 1 and illustration(s)
245.m	map
245.t	table
245	term in boldface, accompanied by definition or other explanation

The following abbreviations are used:

def	defined
ref	reference publication by, in a list at the end of a chapter